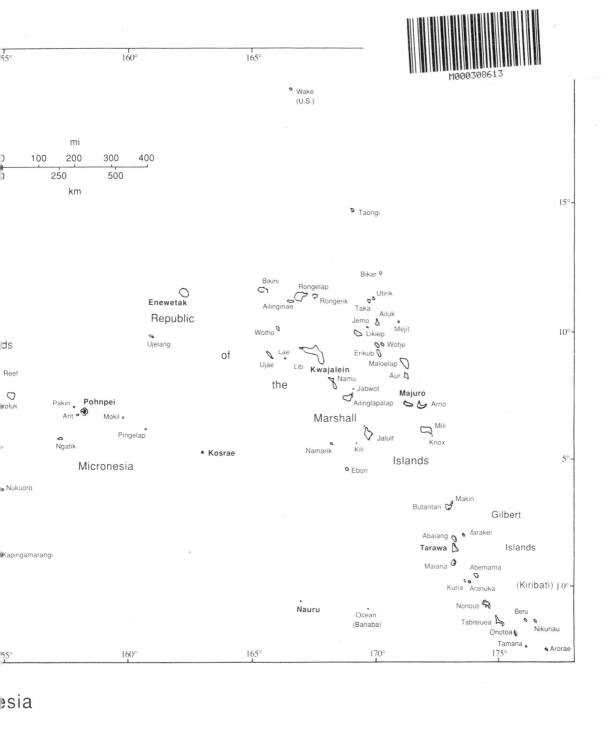

55°   160°   165°

Wake
(U.S.)

mi
100   200   300   400
   250   500
km

15°

Taongi

Bikar

Bikini
Rongelap
Utirik
Enewetak   Ailinginae   Rongerik
Republic   Taka   Ailuk
              Wotho   Jemo
of   Likiep   Mejit
ds   Lae   Erikub   Wotje
              Ujelang   Ujae   Lib   Maloelap
Reef   Kwajalein   Aur
                                   Namu
                              the   Jabwot
roluk   Pakin Pohnpei   Ailinglapalap Majuro
        Ant   Mokil   Marshall   Arno
        Pingelap
Ngatik   Mili
Micronesia   Kosrae   Namarik Kili   Knox
                              Namu
Nukuoro   Ebon   Islands

                                   Makin
                         Butaritari   Gilbert
Kapingamarangi   Abaiang   Marakei
                         Tarawa   Islands
                         Maiana   Abemama
                         Kuria Aranuka   (Kiribati)

                              Nonouti
Nauru   Ocean   Beru
        (Banaba)   Tabiteuea   Nikunau
                         Onotoa
                         Tamana
55°   160°   165°   170°   175°   Arorae

esia

Micronesian Reef Fishes

A Practical Guide to the Identification of the Coral Reef Fishes of the
Tropical Central and Western Pacific

Second Edition

by Robert F. Myers

A Coral Graphics Production

DEDICATION

This book is dedicated to John E. Randall, pioneer of the diving ichthyologists, who has tirelessly catalogued and described several lifetimes worth of tropical marine fishes with the highest scientific and educational standards and an unparalleled insight into their evolution and relationships. His work has made it possible for the scientist and layman alike to identify marine fishes and to better understand their place on this planet, and his encouragement, guidance, and inspiration have made it possible for me to make a small contribution to the knowledge of Indo-Pacific fishes.

And

to Kathleen J. Dummitt, whose love, compassion, encouragement, and patience have made it possible for me to complete this task.

Published by Coral Graphics,
P.O. Box 21153
Guam Main Facility,
Barrigada,
Territory of Guam 96921
United States of America

ISBN 0-9621564-2-6 (paperback)
ISBN 0-9621564-3-4 (hardbound)
Library of Congress Cataloging in Publication Data
Myers, Robert F., 1953-
Micronesian Reef Fishes: A Practical Guide to the Identification of the Inshore Marine Fishes of the Tropical Central and Western Pacific   Second Edition
Includes Index

Typesetting and pre-press production by Coral Graphics, Territory of Guam

Printed in the Republic of China

Publisher's note: This second edition differs little from the first with changes generally limited to correcting a few misidentifications and typographical errors, providing the names of species undescribed at the time of original publication, and adding a few range extensions. The color photographs, checklist, and zoogeographic and ecological analyses remain unchanged.

CONTENTS

Bold numerals indicate color plates, plain numerals indicate text pages

Front Cover:
Upper left: Orange-fin anemonefish (*Amphiprion chrysopterus*), 9 cm, 16 m, Saipan (p. 164).
Upper right: Clown triggerfish (*Balistoides conspicillum*), 20 cm, 4 m, Belau (p. 257).
Middle left: Reef whitetip shark (*Triaenodon obesus*), 120 cm, 18 m, Guam (p. 32).
Middle right: Bluefin trevally (*Caranx melampygus*), 50 cm, 15 m, Belau (p. 131).
Lower left: Blue-girdled angelfish (*Pomacanthus navarchus*), 15 cm, 12 m, Belau (p. 163).
Lower right: Lionfish (*Pterois volitans*), 12 cm, 1 m, Indonesia (p. 98).

Rear cover:
Top: Coral grouper (*Cephalopholis miniata*), 25 cm, 7 m, Belau (p. 104).
Bottom: Tassled scorpionfish (*Scorpaenopsis oxycephalus*),16 cm, 12 m, Guam (p. 97).

PREFACE

Shortly after making my first few dives in Micronesia 14 years ago, it became apparent that the region's fish fauna was much larger than previously thought, that it included many undescribed species, and that it was not adequately covered in any publication. In order to identify many of the species encountered, one had to have access to a large and costly library of scientific papers and faunal works as well as popular books covering other areas of the Indo-Pacific. This situation made it extremely difficult for the professional to acquire a working knowledge of the region's fishes, and nearly impossible for the interested layman to identify more than a handful of the more common and widespread species.

Although enormous strides in our knowledge of Micronesia's fishes have been made since then, we are still in the process of discovering just what species occur there and how they are related to one another. Many key groups need to be reviewed on an Indo-Pacific or worldwide basis, a number of species have not yet been described or named, many habitats remain inadequately collected, and important collections already made have not yet been systematically studied. It is estimated that over 95% of the fish species expected in the Mariana and Marshall Islands are known, but that less than 66% of those expected from Belau and less than 50% of those expected from most of the island groups in the Federated States of Micronesia are known. It would be reasonable to estimate that about 90% of the species that actually occur somewhere in Micronesia are known. Despite our incomplete knowledge of Micronesian fishes, the need for a comprehensive treatment of the subject as currently understood is long overdue.

The intent of this book is to provide the easiest and most affordable means possible of identifying any species of coral reef fish in Micronesia that is likely to be observed or collected from the shoreline to the limits of safe scuba diving. Nearly all species likely to be observed alive in the field are illustrated in color. Most of the remaining species remain hidden from view by living deep within the reef or beneath the sand, or by virtue of cryptic coloration or minute size. A few of these are shown in color and most are illustrated by diagnostic drawings or featured in keys.

It is hoped that this book will not only provide a useful and inexpensive means of identifying Micronesian reef fishes, but that it will also stimulate interest in and appreciation for the region's natural beauty and resources - resources that are suffering under the onslaught of increased fishing pressure and rapid development that is far outpacing progress in conservation. By covering most of the widespread tropical Pacific fishes, this book should also prove highly useful in other areas of the tropical Pacific.

Regrettably, it was not feasible to include the local names of the fishes since at least seven languages would be needed, many species share the same name, and many species have different names for each color or growth phase. This problem is best addressed in separate publications.

You can help too!

My primary purpose for producing this book is to increase public awareness and knowledge of Micronesia's reef fishes. With so much that remains to be discovered, you, the reader, can help by providing myself or other researchers with your observations on anything that seems to be new. Observations or photographs of species not yet reported from a particular area are of special interest. Specimens of species that are rare or new to Micronesia should be saved (kept frozen if possible) and taken to the local Fish and Wildlife Office, the University of Guam Marine Laboratory, or the author. Please send any new information, comments, or corrections to the author at CORAL GRAPHICS, P. O. Box 21153, GMF, Barrigada, Guam 96921.

ACKNOWLEDGEMENTS

This book would not have been possible without the generous assistance of colleagues, friends, and family as well as numerous taxonomists who have labored over the years to bring stability to the field of ichthyology.

John E. Randall deserves very special thanks for his assistance over the years with innumerable taxonomic problems, for sharing indispensable unpublished information, and providing reprints and advice at times when I produced little in exchange. He is also credited with giving me my first opportunity to visit a western Pacific coral reef - Enewetak Atoll. Richard E. Brock gave me the opportunity to visit Johnston Atoll and Steven S. Amesbury and Lucius G. Eldredge of the Universtiy of Guam Marine Laboratory provided the opportunities to visit Saipan, Truk, Pohnpei, Kosrae, and Pagan. Special thanks are due Terry J. Donaldson for reviewing much of the manuscript and providing considerable advice and encouragement.

Gerald R. Allen, Steven S. Amesbury, William N. Eschmeyer, Charles E. Dawson, Anthony C. Gill, and Jeffrey T. Williams kindly reviewed sections of the manuscript and offered their advice.

The following individuals provided literature, specimens, advice, or encouragement: Gerald R. Allen, Warren E. Burgess, Bruce Carlson, Kent E. Carpenter, Patrick L. Colin, Roger Cressey, Charles E. Dawson, William N. Eschmeyer, John Ford, Ronald Fricke, J. A. F. Garrick, Anthony C. Gill, Patricia Hadley-Hansen, Susan L. Jewett, Patricia Kailola, Helen K. Larson, Keichi Matsuura, John E. McCosker, Jack T. Moyer, Tetsuji Nakabo, Theodore W. Pietsch, Helen A. Randall, John W. Shepard and the late Catherine E. Shepard, William F. Smith-Vaniz, Victor G. Springer, Arnold Suzumoto, James C. Tyler, Robin S. Waples, Richard C. Wass, Richard Winterbottom, Jeffrey T. Williams, and David J. Woodland.

Robert S. Jones, Helen A. Larson, Harry T. Kami, and Michael Gawel collected and curated most of the fishes now housed in the University of Guam Marine Laboratory fish collection. Donald E. Baker, William Boyle, Thomas Campion, Harry Conally, Mark Eberl, Joseph Deville, John Eads, Tommy Perez, Edward Poppe, Donald Scaife, Barry Smith, Masao Tenbata, numerous unnamed fishermen and the following current and former faculty, staff, and students of the University of Guam Marine Laboratory provided specimens of Guam fishes or assisted in some way in this project: Steven S. Amesbury, Bruce Best, Charles E. Birkeland, Russell N. Clayshulte, Frank Cushing, R. Logan Kock, Roy Kropp, Paul Gates, Gerald E. Davis, Dennis R. Lassuy, Steven G. Nelson, Richard H. Randall, Richard "Kuni" Sakamoto, and Vaughan E. Tyndzik. Al Williams of the Micronesian Area Research Center and Bill Wursch of the Robert F. Kennedy Library were helpful beyond the call of duty.

Much of the early research that led to this book could not have been done had I concentrated more on conventional studies or employment. I owe a special debt of gratitude to my parents, James and Phoebe Myers, and my Aunt, Mary Lintner for helping me through some financially rough times.

Finally, without the love, encouragement, and patience of Kathleen Dummitt, I would not have been able to complete this task.

Photographic credits

Unless otherwise credited all photographs were taken by the author. Special thanks are due John E. Randall who generously provided most of the photographs of species the author has either not encountered or otherwise has not been able to photograph. Gerald R. Allen, Kathleen Dummitt, Jeff LaDouce, Anne F. Maben, Michael Neubauer, Richard Pyle, Tim Rock, Ronald E. Thresher, Mark Vanderlinden, and Mitchell Warner also kindly provided a number of photographs. Several black-and-white photographs and drawings were reproduced from the plates and figures in Trawled Fishes of Southern Indonesia and Northwestern Australia by Thomas Gloerfelt-Tarp and Patricia Kailola (included here are drawings of sharks published concurrently in Compagno, 1984).

Artwork

The bulk of the artwork was borrowed from the scientific literature where much of it lies hidden from the layman. I am indebted to the following institutions for generously allowing me to reprint their copyrighted work: American Society of Ichthyologists and Herpetologists, Biological Society of Washington, Gulf Coast Research Laboratory, J.L.B. Smith Institute of Ichthyology, and the Food and Agriculture Organization of the United Nations (FAO). Uncredited artwork was prepared by the author.

Typesetting

The entire book was typeset by the author on a Macintosh personal computer with commercially available software. The text was printed on a Linotronic 100. I am indebted to Frank and Lilly Yu and the typesetting staff of United Printing for their assistance and advice as well as the use of their printing facilities.

INTRODUCTION

Scope of the Book

With few exceptions, this guide covers all fishes known to inhabit Micronesian coral reefs at depths of 60 m (200 ft) or less. Omissions are limited to a few species of fishes that spend virtually all of their adult lives deep within the infrastructure of the reef or buried in sand and to a few newly discovered or unidentified species, most of which are small, inconspicuous, rare, or known only by collecting with poisons. The term "coral reef" is used in the broad sense to mean any place where corals occur: from turbid harbors, mangrove-fringed bays, and rocky tidepools to clear seaward reefs and all associated habitats such as seagrass beds, sandy plains, and barren wave-swept cliffs. As defined in this book, Micronesia includes the Territory of Guam; Commonwealth of the Northern Marianas; the Republic of Belau; Federated States of Micronesia (FSM); Republic of the Marshalls; and Wake Island (administered by the U. S. Navy). The metric system is used throughout, however maximum sizes and weights of fishes in the heading of each species account are also indicated in their English equivalents (Conversions are as follows: 1 cm = 0.394 in; 1 m = 3.281 ft or 39.37 in; 1 km = 0.6214 miles; 1 kg = 2.205 lbs; °C = 5/9[°F-32]).

Geography

Micronesia encompasses an area of the tropical western Pacific approximately the size of the continental United States (4,300 by 2,070 km or 2,672 by 1,286 mi.). It can be divided into three major island chains: the Caroline, Mariana, and Marshall Islands (inside front cover). Some works include the nearby islands of Nauru, Banaba (Ocean Is.), and the Gilbert Islands (part of Kiribati) within Micronesia. The Caroline Islands consist of five fringing or barrier reef-enclosed high islands, 43 atolls or low coral islands, and numerous shallow sunken atolls and approximately eight banks spanning some 3,260 km (2,026 mi.) from the Belau Archipelago in the west to Kosrae in the east. The islands consist of two political entities: the Republic of Belau stretching from Tobi to Kayangel, and the Federated States of Micronesia (FSM) encompassing all the islands to the east. Faunistically the Carolines can be conveniently divided into three regions: the western Carolines from Tobi to Fais (Republic of Belau and western Yap State of the FSM); the eastern Carolines from Eauripik to Kosrae (eastern Yap, Truk, Pohnpei and Kosrae States of the FSM); and the isolated outpost of Kapingamarangi (Pohnpei State).

The Marshall Islands, or the Republic of the Marshalls, consist of 32 atolls in two parallel chains stretching some 1,330 km (826 mi.) in a northwest-southeast direction east of the Carolines. Although there is no clear break, for the purposes of this book the atolls of Enewetak, Bikini, Rongelap, and Rongerik form the northern Marshalls, and the atolls from Kwajalein to the south form the southern Marshalls. The isolated atoll of Wake lies some 770 km (478 mi.) to the north of Bikini.

The Mariana Islands consist of a chain of 15 high islands and numerous small banks, seamounts, and pinnacles stretching some 800 km (497 mi.) in a north-south direction north of the central Carolines. Politically, the Marianas consist of the Territory of Guam and the Commonwealth of the Northern Marianas which includes all islands north of Guam. Geologically, the Marianas can be divided into two distinct arcs. The southern- and easternmost outer arc consists of the older, primarily limestone islands of Guam, Rota, Aguijan, Tinian, Saipan, and Farallon de Medinilla. The northern, inner arc consists of nine younger volcanic islands extending from Anatahan to Farallon de Pajaros. At least four of these contain active volcanos, and one, Mt. Pagan, has erupted violently since 1982. Several small shallow (7 to 100 m deep) banks topped with coral reefs lie to the southwest of Guam, between Guam and Saipan, and in a parallel arc 240 to 320 km (150 to 200 mi.) to the west of the Marianas.

Oceanography and Climate

Micronesia consists entirely of tropical oceanic islands that rise steeply from the deep ocean floor with their upper slopes constantly bathed in warm, clear water far from the influence of continental coasts. Oceanographic conditions within Micronesia are generally quite uniform with minor seasonal shifts in currents and minor changes in surface temperature. For most of the year much of Micronesia lies within the slow westward flow of the North Equatorial Current (Fig. 1). South of about 6 to 10°S, the Equatorial Counter Current flows from west to east through the southern Caroline and southern Marshall islands. A meandering southerly branch of the Kuroshio Current, the Subtropical Counter Current, occasionally transports water eastward from the Luzon Strait to the vicinity of the northernmost islands of the Marianas, particularly during the winter and spring.

Sea surface temperatures range from a monthly mean of 27 to 28°C in February to 30°C in August at Guam and throughout the Caroline and Marshall

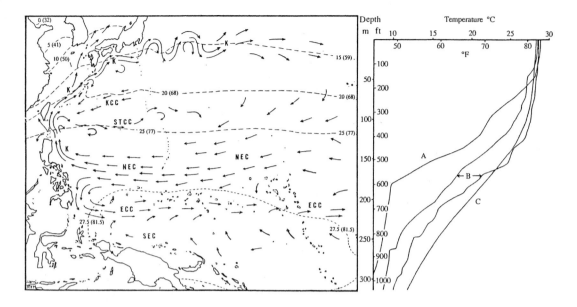

Figure 1 (left). Prevailing surface currents in Micronesia. Dashed lines represent mean monthly sea surface temperatures for the coolest month of the year. EEC = Equatorial Countercurrent; NEC = North Equatorial Current; K = Kuroshio Current; KCC = Kuroshio Countercurrent; SEC = South Equatorial Current; STCC = Subtropical Countercurrent. (°F in parentheses)

Figure 2 (right). Representative temperature profiles along steep seaward reef slopes (A = Augulpelu Reef, Belau (June); B = range during four submersible dives at Enewetak Atoll (summer); C = Cabras Island, Guam (February).

Islands to between 25°C in February and 29°C in August in the vicinity of Farallon de Pajaros, the northernmost of the Marianas. Subsurface temperatures (based on data taken at Guam, Enewetak, and Belau) generally remain above 26°C in the upper 100 m, then rapidly drop to 6 to 10°C at depths of 250 to 450 m (Fig. 2). Generally the temperature remains above 25°C in the upper 70 to 140 m, but periodic upwelling along the steep leeward walls of some islands may result in sudden drops in temperature of 2°C or more in as little as 40 m. The 20°C contour remains fairly stable between 130 and 220 m, and the 15°C contour fluctuates between 200 and 300 m. The latter probably represents the lower boundary of the distributions of most inshore fishes, although most "reef fishes" probably range no deeper than the upper limit of the 20°C contour.

Prevailing winds and both near and distant storms generate the ocean swells that pound against Micronesia's reefs and shorelines. Although wind and rainfall differ greatly from north to south, there are two main seasons, the rainy and the dry. Typhoons are possible throughout the year, but are rare in the southern Carolines and southern Marshalls, and occur seasonally in the Marianas and

northern Marshalls, with a peak in November. Over the open sea and atolls, annual rainfall ranges from a low of less than 80 cm (31 in) at Wake to well over 250 cm (100 in) in a band running through the Carolines and southern Marshalls. Heating of land and shallow lagoon surfaces can produce localized areas of higher rainfall. Orographic effects of high islands produce the highest annual rainfalls which may exceed 500 cm (197 in) over parts of Pohnpei and Kosrae.

The rainy season is characterized by high humidity, alternating periods of sunshine and rain, and light and variable winds punctuated by occasional squalls and tropical cyclones. For most of the region the seas are calm much of the time, but periodic typhoons can generate devastating surf (4 to 9 m) on the reefs in their path and large swells on distant reefs. In the western Carolines and the Marianas, periods of strong southwesterly winds feeding into storms moving to the north and west can cause high seas (2 to 4 m) to affect southwesterly exposures for days at a time. In the Marianas and Marshalls the rainy season generally runs from July to November. In the Carolines, the rainy season lasts longer but storms are less frequent the further one moves south. The dry season is dominated by moderate to strong northeasterly trade winds, lower humidities, and sunny weather occasionally punctuated by light showers. A nearly constant northeasterly sea and swell of 1 to 2 m pounds against all north- to easterly-facing("windward") exposures. The southern Marianas, Marshalls, and northern Carolines are frequently affected by typhoons well into December. Occasionally typhoons affect the Carolines and the Marianas during the months of April and May. From October to April, mid-latitude storms moving off the coasts of China and Japan generate a northwesterly swell of up to 3 m that affects the entire region.

Tidal range in Micronesia is relatively narrow, ranging from less than 1 m in the Marianas and central Carolines and increasing as one moves east or west to about 2 m in the eastern Marshalls and Belau. Water clarity depends to a large extent on coastal influences and degree of circulation with the open sea. Inner coastal bays influenced by rivers are typically murky with visibility ranging from three to 10 m, but dropping to near zero when rivers flood. Visibility is highest on seaward reef slopes, typically ranging from 25 to 40 m, occasionally reaching 60 m. Visibility in lagoons and channels can be quite variable and depends largely on tidal influences. Areas of atoll lagoons with poor circulation can be quite murky with visibilties of as little as 6 to 20 m whereas areas adjacent to deep channels can experience visibilities of 40 to 60 m at the peak of incoming tides. Time of day also influences visibility with the early morning often the clearest. As the day progresses, tradewinds increase in strength, creating a chop that stirs shallow lagoon waters, and particulate matter from the foraging activities and feces of fishes begins to cloud the water.

Types of Reefs

Coral reefs have traditionally been divided into three basic types: fringing reefs, barrier reefs, and atolls (Fig. 3; inside back cover). These correspond with stages of development, with fringing reefs representing the earliest stage and barrier reefs and atolls representing the mature stage. Fringing reefs are relatively young, generally narrow platforms that extend a short distance from shore and do not contain a substantial lagoon. As the reef grows outward, or upward if the seafloor sinks or the sea level rises, the innermost corals cannot keep pace and a lagoon develops. The reef has now become a barrier reef. Atolls start from fringing reefs surrounding volcanic islands. As the island erodes and subsides due to its own weight pressing on the sea floor, the fringing reef keeps pace with the sea surface along its seaward margin, leaving a lagoon along the shore. An atoll results when the island has completely disappeared beneath the surface. Other factors that affect reef development such as changing sea levels, uplift, subsidence, temperature, and freshwater intrusion shape reefs into a wide variety of forms. At all stages of development the seaward slope is steep, usually reaching depths of 200 m or more within 1.5 km of shore.

Habitats and Zonation

The terms *habitat* and *zone* have rather broad and often overlapping definitions. For the purposes of this book, the term habitat describes the kind of place where an animal lives in either physical or bi-

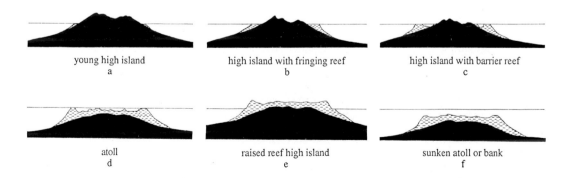

Figure 3. Basic types of tropical oceanic islands and reefs, showing the stages of development of an atoll: a) island with narrow fringing reef; b) island subsiding with growing fringing and incipient barrier reefs, c) remnants of a high island enclosed by a barrier reef, d) atoll, e) re-emerged high island formed by uplifting of an atoll or reef or by a drop in sea level, e) table-top bank or guyote formed when coral growth is unable to keep up with subsidence or a rise in sea level. Shaded area indicates reef development; black indicates the underlying surface of the earth.

ological terms. Generally the name of the dominant or most easily recognizable character of a given place is used as the name of a habitat. The terms tide pool, mangrove, seagrass bed, sand flat, rubble, pavement, patch reef, lagoon pinnacle, *Acropora* thicket, coral-rich area, surge channel, cave, crevice, and ledge are frequently used to describe habitats. Habitats can be further subdivided into specific microhabitats such as a *Pocillopora* coral head. A zone describes a place in terms of its overall physiographic structure and location. A reef zone refers to a part of a reef in relation to the physical parameters of land, sea surface, and depth. A variety of habitats characterize a zone. Some habitats may be present in several zones while others are restricted to one or two. Characteristic reef zones are shown in figure 4.

High islands contain the greatest number of reef zones and habitats. They are the only islands that contain significant fresh and brackish water habitats. Nutient-rich rivers may carry large quantities of silt as well as fresh water which result in highly productive, but turbid, muddy habitats that inhibit the growth of corals and in some areas, may extend deep down the island slope. Mangrove forests thrive along the intertidal shorelines of estuaries and river mouths and seagrasses thrive on silty inner reef flats and shallow lagoon floors. Mangrove and seagrass habitats are required by the young of a large variety of marine fishes, some of which migrate to coral reefs as adults. Consequently high island reefs tend to support a greater diversity of inshore fishes than atolls. The high islands of Belau, Yap, Truk, Pohnpei, and Kosrae are surrounded by barrier reefs or wide fringing reefs and have a wide range of habitats. Belau is particularly rich in habitats including numerous marine lakes with differing degrees of isolation from the sea, and coral reefs growing through leaf litter at the bases of heavily forested cliffs.

Some high islands or sections of high islands originated as uplifted coral reefs and thus consist of highly porous limestone. They lack rivers, and have flat tops and steep sides which may plunge directly into the sea, be undercut, or be fringed by benches or reef flats. They generally lack mangroves and do not support many of the species associated with mangroves or river mouths. With the exception of southern Guam, the southern Marianas are typical uplifted coral reefs. The young volcanic islands of the northern Marianas are relatively depauperate in coastal habitats. With the exception of two small limestone reef flats on Pagan, the coastal habitats are limited to black sand beaches, cliffs, and boulder-strewn slopes, of which much of the hard substrate is overlain with well-developed coral communities.

Atolls lack rocky cliffs and benches as well as the rivers and well-developed mangrove communities of high islands. They thus lack many of the species associated with these habitats. However, the sheer size of the lagoons of large atolls may provide better opportunities for colonization by dispersing fishes, so that the number of species on large atolls may exceed that on smaller high islands.

Reef Zones

Coastal bays: The convoluted shorelines and steep slopes of many high islands form relatively sheltered coastal bays, often with a river emptying at the head. Coastal bays generally have sheltered, somewhat turbid waters and silty bottoms. Mangroves often line the shore, particularly where the slope is gentle and along the banks of rivers to the upper limits of tidal influence. By extending roots laterally beneath the mud, mangroves consolidate sediments, spread seaward, and may eventually transform mud flats into dry land. The shelter provided by their extensive root systems and nutrient-laden waters make them among the richest of nursery grounds for a wide variety of marine life. The young of many species of coral reef fishes occur among mangroves. It is along the outer fringes of mangroves where some species of corals may grow that the coverage of this book begins. Coastal bays may be bordered by narrow reef flats which drop off steeply and are often riddled with caves and holes along their seaward edges. Several species of fishes not commonly found on offshore reefs occur here, among them: *Lutjanus argentimaculatus*, leiognathids, *Scarus rivulatus*, numerous species of apogonids and gobiids, *Siganus lineatus*, and *S. vermiculatus*.

Lagoons: The term lagoon refers to the area enclosed by the low tide line of the inner edge of the barrier or atoll reef flat. The depth may vary from less than a meter (3 ft) at low tide to 90 m (300 ft) or more. Lagoons often contain numerous patch reefs ranging in size from a few small pieces of coral to massive pinnacles which may be topped with reef flats and islands. Some lagoons contain a maze of elongate or interconnected reefs that may enclose isolated pools. Water clarity depends on the degree of water circulation, input of terrestrial runoff, and proximity to channels. High island lagoons are often relatively turbid with muddy bottoms. Deep channels often lie opposite river mouths and follow the river's prehistoric course that was formed during periods of lowered sea level. Atoll lagoons may be clear in some areas and turbid in others. Incoming tides, particularly in the vicinity of major channels, flood the lagoon with clear oceanic waters, and outgoing tides dump turbid lagoon waters out to sea. Surf generates currents that flow over the reef crest and into the la-

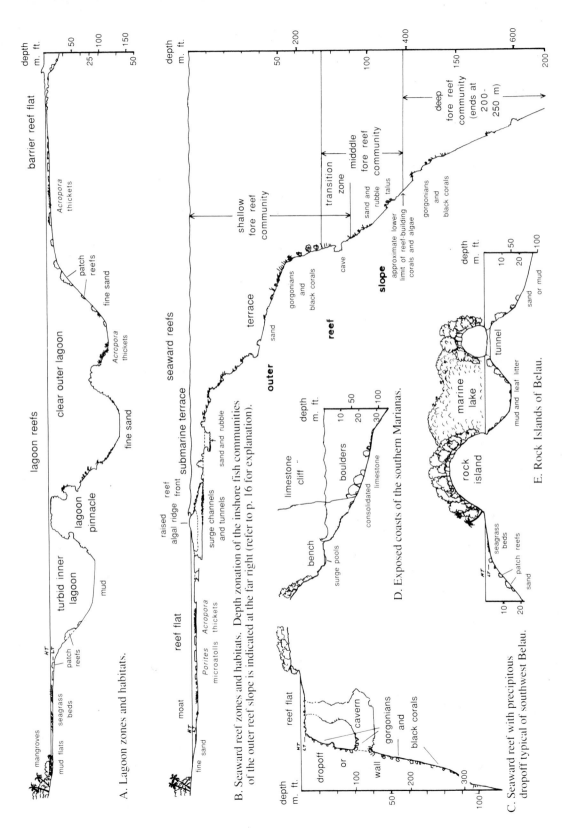

Figure 4. Zonation and associated habitats of Micronesian coral reefs. (HT=high tide; LT=low tide)

A. Lagoon zones and habitats.

B. Seaward reef zones and habitats. Depth zonation of the inshore fish communities of the outer reef slope is indicated at the far right (refer to p. 16 for explanation).

C. Seaward reef with precipitous dropoff typical of southwest Belau.

D. Exposed coasts of the southern Marianas.

E. Rock Islands of Belau.

goon, carrying the sand that accumulates on the lagoon slope. The finer sediments accumulate on the lagoon floor. Protected from wave action, delicate branching corals thrive where they can find a stable surface to settle and grow. Meadows of seagrass may grow on shallow sand or mud flats and may be particularly well developed in high island lagoons. Many species of fishes are characteristic of lagoons and various lagoon habitats.

Channels: Channels connect the lagoon to the outer reef slope. Tidal currents provide ideal conditions for plankton-feeding animals. Filter-feeding invertebrates thrive wherever they can maintain a foothold. Channel walls are frequently densely overgrown with both soft and hard corals. Gorgonians are an important inhabitant of channels in the Carolines. Deep channels entering large lagoons may have such strong tidal currents that the channel floor is a barren wasteland of shifting sand and rubble. In channels with less severe currents, hard-bottomed portions of the channel floor may be as overgrown with corals as are the walls. Here one may find a diversity of fishes rivaling the richest areas of outer lagoons and outer reef slopes. Sharks and other large predators such as groupers, snappers, and sweetlips are often abundant.

Reef flats: The reef flat is the intertidal and extreme upper subtidal portion of the reef. Reef flats can range in width from a few meters to a few kilometers. The surface can range from a featureless, pavement-smooth platform to a complex maze of sand patches and coral-choked tidepools. Coral growth is limited to the areas low enough to avoid dessication during the lowest tides. Coral growth is relatively poor in areas regularly subjected to overheated stagnant water during low tide and is luxuriant in areas nearly constantly washed by clear water such as many interisland atoll reefs. Reef flats can often be subdivided into several zones.

The inner reef flat frequently retains some water during the lowest tides. Flat-topped heads of massive *Porites* corals, called microatolls, are common. Subtidal areas of inner fringing reefs not quite deep enough to qualify as lagoons but deep enough to retain enough water to avoid overheating (0.5 to 1 m at the lowest tides) are known as moats. Meadows of seagrasses are a common feature of inner reef flats of high islands. Luxuriant growths of branching and massive species of *Porites* and thickets of branching *Acropora* corals may be present. *Dascyllus aruanus*, *Chromis viridis*, *Stegastes lividus*, and *Halichoeres trimaculatus* are among the most characteristic fishes.

The outer reef flat is generally a barren, pavement-smooth expanse dotted with blocks of dead coral rock wrenched from the reef margin during storms. This "barren" zone is generally covered with a thin film to thick mat of filamentous algae which at high tide becomes the grazing ground for roving schools of herbivorous fishes. Away from heavily fished areas, small blacktip sharks, *Carcharhinus melanopterus*, may be common.

The seaward margin of reef flats are frequently quite porous and dissected by deep undercut channels running perpendicular to the reef edge and extending well down the outer reef slope. Low profile *Pocillopora* and small corymbose *Acropora* corals are common here. Where the seaward margin of a reef flat is subject to a nearly constant surf, a raised ridge of encrusting coralline algae, appropriately named the "algal ridge," may form. *Chrysiptera leucopoma*, *Halichoeres margaritaceus*, *Thalassoma fuscum*, *T. purpureum*, numerous species of blenniids, tripterygiids, *Acanthurus guttatus*, and numerous other acanthurids are among the most characteristic fishes.

Reef front and spur and groove zone: The area from the seaward edge of the reef flat to the submarine terrace is known as the reef front. Where there is frequent wave assault, the reef front is dissected by the deep channels originating beneath the reef margin. This zone of alternating ridges and vertical sided sand, rubble, or boulder-floored channels is known as the "spur and groove zone." The lower channel walls are kept smoothed by the constant abrasion of sand and even boulders during storms. The tops of the ridges are covered with stout-branched *Pocillopora* and small corybose *Acropora* corals. Where wave assault is severe, the corals tend to be stout-branched or low and stubby, and the channel floors consist of boulders; where wave assault is moderate, the corals may be more delicate, and the channel floors are sandy. Some characteristic fishes are *Cirrhitus pinnulatus*, the pomacentrids *Chrysiptera leucopoma*, *Plectroglyphididon leucozona*, *P. dicki*, and *Stegastes fasciolatus*, *Thalassoma quinquevittata*, *Acanthurus lineatus*, *Naso unicornis*, other acanthurids, *Istiblennius chrysospilos*, *Cirripectes* spp., other blenniids, and *Rhinecanthus rectangulus*. In sheltered areas, the reef front may lack deep channels and instead consist of a gentle slope covered with large stands of branching and tabular *Acropora* corals. Here other species of fishes less characteristic of the surge zone dominate.

Submarine terrace: The submarine terrace begins where the ridges of the reef front flatten out. Here the channels become shallower and have sand rather than rubble floors. On reefs exposed to constant surge, the corals are mostly low-profile encrusting, crymbose, or massive species. Scattered pinnacles, often topped with fire corals, *Millepora* spp., may be present. In relatively sheltered areas, large branching and tabular *Acropora* corals are generally common. Many of the species characteristic of the reef front also occur on shallow exposed reef terraces. *Cephalopholis urodelus*, *Centropyge flavissimus*, and *Dascyllus reticulatus* reach their peak abundances on submarine terraces, and roving mixed-species schools of scarids and acanthurids are common.

Outer reef slope: The outer reef slope is the portion of the seaward reef that slopes into deep water. It is generally fairly steep (30° or more) with moderate to high coral cover. The slope may be dissected by sand- and rubble-bottomed channels. The nature of the coral cover is dependant upon the degree of exposure, with branching and tabular species more common where there is less frequent exposure to storm swells. The diversity and abundance of corals as well as fishes is greatest along promontories and other areas exposed to tidal currents. In clear Micronesian waters coral cover and diversity often remain high to depths of 40 to 60 m (131 to 197 ft). Below these depths, coral cover decreases rapidly and branching corals are replaced by platelike forms which have been observed as deep as 112 m (368 ft). The dominant calcareous algae, *Halimeda*, occurs to beyond 100 m (328 ft.), and some small macroalgae and algal films have been observed as deep as 140 m (460 ft). Gorgonians and soft corals are the dominant growth forms below 100 m (328 ft). Many of the species found in deep lagoons also occur here. As one goes further down the slope, a number of common shallow water species are replaced by deeper water analogues. *Cirritichthys falco*, *Macolor niger*, *Chromis amboinensis*, *Naso hexacanthus*, and *Odonus niger* are some of the distinctive elements.

Dropoffs: Dropoffs (often known to divers as walls) are outer reef slopes that are nearly vertical (≥70°) to slightly undercut. Sand and rubble occur only where there is sufficient shelving or in less steeply sloping channels or chutes that may dissect the reef face. Like less steeply sloping reef faces, the diversity and abundance of corals and fishes is highest in areas exposed to currents. Heavy surge inhibits the development of vertical reef faces, hence dropoffs occur in shallower water on leeward exposures, and are best developed in the southern parts of Micronesia where there are few destructive storms. At Enewetak, the windward outer reef slope is nearly vertical below 60 m, but portions of the leeward slope may be nearly vertical within a few meters of the surface. The southwestern barrier reef of Belau has some of the world's most spectacular dropoffs where one can literally step into water hundreds of meters deep from a coral head in knee-deep water! Here, deep-dwelling organisms come closest to the surface. Gorgonians and black corals compete for space with stony

corals to within a few meters of the surface, and some species of fishes normally found below 30 m (100 ft) may occur in 10 to 20 m 33 to 66 ft). *Anthias pleurotaenia*, *Cephalopholis analis*, *Centropyge multifasciatus*, *Amblyglyphidodon aurea*, *Chysiptera caeruleolineata*, and *Xanthichthys auromarginatus* are typical examples.

Benches: Benches are narrow reef flat-like structures occurring at the bases of steep high-island slopes. They are best developed where there is constant wave action and are formed primarily by the outward growth of coralline red algae. Where there is enough wave action to keep the surface awash, benches may be raised a few meters above sea level. The top may consist of a series of shallow pools at different levels. The surface is generally covered with a thick mat of fleshy and filamentous algae. Small corals may be present in the deeper pools. Blennids, tripterygiids, and juveniles of many surge zone fishes are common.

Cliffs: In the southern Marianas, limestone cliffs may plunge directly into the sea. There is generally a certain degree of shelving at depths of 12 to 20 m (40 to 65 ft). Boulders fallen from the cliff face may be piled on this shelf. Coral cover is generally low, but where there is enough shelter in the form of corals, holes, or boulders, there is an abundance of fishes. Roving schools of scarids and acanthurids roam the shelf grazing on algae. Planktivores are abundant where there are moderate to strong currents.

History of Ichthyology in Micronesia

The modern system of classification of plants and animals began in 1758 with the tenth edition of Carolus Linnaeus' *Systema Naturae*. A few of the fishes in this guide were named by him, although it remains unknown if any of them were collected in Micronesia. The first known collections of fishes from Micronesia were made in the early 19th century and described in the works of Quoy and Gaimard from 1824 to 1834, Cuvier and Valenciennes from 1830 to 1837, and Guichenot in 1847. Systematic studies of fishes from various islands began in 1901 with Seale's "Report of a Mission to Guam" which listed 142 species. In 1911 Kendall and Goldsborough reported 58 species of fishes from the Marshall Islands, and in 1925 Fowler listed 160 species from Guam. These fishes and many others now known from Micronesia were included in Fowler's subsequent works on the fishes of Oceania (1928 to 1949) and the Philippines (1928 to1949; with Bean in 1929). Collections of fishes from Belau were reported in Herre in 1935 and Abe in 1939, the latter listing 376 species. In

1943 Hiyama published a book on poisonous fishes of the Marshall Islands for the Japanese military in which 71 species were illustrated in color. In 1945, Fowler reported on a small collection of 30 species from Saipan.

The most important collections of Micronesian fishes to date were made during the 15 years following the Second World War. The largest of these were obtained at the northern Marshall atolls of Bikini, Enewetak, Rongelap, and Rongerik during 1946 and 1947 in connection with the atomic bomb tests of Operation Crossroads. These as well as smaller collections from the southern Marianas, Kwajalein, and other areas of the Indo-Pacific were reported in great detail in the three-volume work "Fishes of the Marshall and Mariana Islands" by Leonard P. Schultz and collaborators (1953-1966). That work contains the descriptions and illustrations of 543 species from the Marshall Islands, 218 species from the southern Mariana Islands, and a small number from outside Micronesia. Many of the species were described as new, and most remain valid. However, the most speciose family, the Gobiidae, was not included and is still under study. Most of the 65,000 specimens are housed in the vast collection of the Smithsonian Institution in Washington D.C. Schultz's work has remained an essential reference for anyone seriously interested in identifying western Pacific fishes. In an unpublished 1953 report, Strasburg listed 345 species of fishes collected in the southern Marshalls (primarily from Arno), including 26 species not reported by Schultz and collaborators. In another unpublished report, Rofen (1961) listed 423 species collected from Ifaluk Atoll and 450 from Kapingamaringi Atoll, both in the Caroline Islands. Both of these reports are of limited use because they lack illustrations or descriptions and thus require a thorough knowledge of contemporary ichthyology. Rofen's collections are housed at the California Academy of Sciences. The real value of fish collections lies not in the checklists that often result, but in their availability to ichthyologists around the world for region-wide comparisons. Only when one is able to study a species or group of species on an Indo-Pacific-wide basis is one able to determine the true identity of a species and its relationships to its closest relatives.

Until the recent closure of the Mid-Pacific Marine Laboratory, Enewetak Atoll was the center of ichthyological activity in the region. Much of our contemporary knowledge of the biology and ecology of Indo-Pacific fishes has resulted from studies conducted there by visiting scientists from throughout the world. During the late 1960's and 1970's the University of Guam Marine Laboratory emerged as an important center of coral reef studies. During the last 25 years, the emphasis has been on experimental rather than descriptive research, and fish collecting has generally been on a small scale and scattered throughout Micronesia.

In 1986 Randall recorded an additional 60 species from the recent literature and 106 new records from the Marshall Islands based on collections made at Enewetak, Bikini, and Kwajalein. Randall and Randall (1987) include nearly 40 additional undescribed species in an annotated checklist of the fishes of the Marshall Islands. During the late 1960's and 1970's a number of fish collections were made at Guam by the University of Guam Marine Laboratory and the Guam Division of Aquatic and Wildlife Resources. These resulted in a series of checklists (Kami et al., 1968; Kami, 1971, 1975; Myers and Shepard, 1980; Shepard and Myers, 1981). In 1982, Amesbury and Myers produced the book "Guide to the Coastal Resources of Guam, Vol. 1: The Fishes" which featured 225 species figured in color. Myers (1988) has recently prepared an annotated checklist of the fishes of the Marianas. Minor collections have also been made by the University of Guam Marine Laboratory in the northern Marianas and at Saipan, Kosrae, Pohnpei, Truk, Yap, and Belau. The results of a number of these as well as ecological studies are included in several University of Guam Marine Laboratory technical reports. Amesbury (1979) lists 208 species observed at Yap, and Myers (1979) lists 337 species observed at Kosrae, by habitat. Small collections of fishes from Belau and Yap, and Truk, Pohnpei, and Majuro, were reported by Matsuura in 1982 and 1984, respectively. Numerous small fish collections have been made in Belau by visiting scientists during the past 20 years, but with the exception of 312 species listed in a paper on Belauan fish names by Helfman and Randall (1973), no recent checklist of any of the Caroline Islands has been attempted. Recent records of fishes from several of the islands lie scattered throughout the literature. In 1980 Springer led a major collecting expedition to Pohnpei and nearby atolls for the Smithsonian Institution. A very preliminary list (pers. com.) indicates about 550 species, or somewhat less than half of the likely fauna. A checklist of inshore fishes, including all published records known to the author by island or island group is given at the end of this book.

Very few deepwater fishes have been reported from Micronesia. Only some 35 species in 25 families are known from deep slope (> 200 m) or mesopelagic habitats in the Marianas, the best collected area in the region.

SPECIES COMPOSITION and ZOOGEOGRAPHY

Species Composition

The fish fauna of Micronesia consists primarily of coral reef associated species. The ten largest families comprise over half the fauna and the twenty largest families comprise nearly 70% of it (Table 1). These families typically comprise the bulk of the fish faunas throughout most of the Indo-Pacific. Half of the ten most speciose families consist of the colorful and conspicuous species (wrasses, damselfishes, fairy basslets and grou-

pers, butterflyfishes, and surgeonfishes) that make coral reefs such delightful and fascinating places to visit. The other half consists of somewhat less conspicuous or cryptic species (eels, cardinalfishes, blennies, and gobies). Many of these are seldom noticed without careful observation and some are never seen unless driven from hiding with poisons (it should be noted that the only legitimate use for poisons is to collect for scientific purposes and that scientific collections usually require a government permit.)

Table 1. Twenty most speciose families of Micronesian fishes.

Family	Number of genera	Number of species	% of total fish fauna
Gobiidae (Gobies)	38	159	11.3
Labridae (Wrasses)	32	100	7.1
Pomacentridae (Damselfishes)	16	90	6.4
Serranidae (Fairy basslets and Groupers)	15	79	5.6
Blennidae (Blennies)	23	61	4.3
Apogonidae (Cardinalfishes)	12	58	4.1
Muraenidae (Moray eels)	13	54	3.8
Chaetodontidae (Butterflyfishes)	5	40	2.8
Acanthuridae (Surgeonfishes)	5	39	2.8
Syngnathidae (Pipefishes)	15	37	2.6
Scaridae (Parrotfishes)	6	33	2.3
Scorpaenidae (Scorpionfishes)	11	31	2.2
Carangidae (Jacks)	14	31	2.2
Lutjanidae (Snappers)	9	29	2.1
Holocentridae (Soldierfishes and Squirrelfishes)	5	29	2.1
Pomacanthidae (Angelfishes)	6	27	1.9
Ophichthiidae (Snake eels)	17	26	1.8
Lethrinidae (Emperors)	5	21	1.5
Microdesmidae (Wormfishes and Dartfishes)	5	21	1.5
Balistidae (Triggerfishes)	11	20	1.4
Total		984	69.9

Zoogeography

The reasons for the present-day distribution of inshore fishes are complex and is the subject of fascinating research, much of which is fairly recent and ongoing. The primary factors that determine the distribution of inshore fishes are: 1) the prehistoric distributions of the world's tectonic (crustal) plates and their movements (plate tectonics), 2) the evolutionary history of fishes (see classification and morphology), 3) the relative ability of each species of fish to disperse, 4) the availability of suitable

habitats for colonization and suitable oceanographic conditions for survival and reproduction, and 5) the affects of lowered sea levels on the distribution and availability of habitats and island types due to the recent ice ages (Pleistocene glaciation). A detailed discussion of each of these is beyond the scope of this book, but a few brief comments are offered in the following discussion of the zoogeography of Micronesian fishes.

The surface of the earth consists of some 14 crustal plates (Fig. 5). These plates are constantly moving and changing shape by grinding against

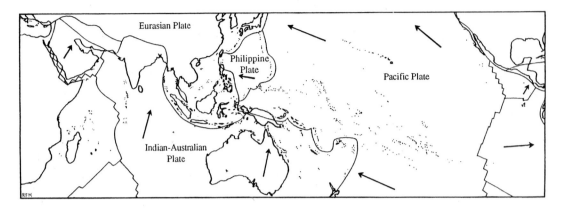

Figure 5. Present day distribution and movement of tectonic plates in the Indo-Pacific region.

one another, sliding beneath one another, or expanding. The continents, islands, and ocean floor with the plants and animals that inhabit them are thus carried with the plates over the course of time. This movement can cause faunas and floras to separate, to come together, or to be carried into new climatic regions. The resulting isolation, mixing, colonization and extinction are some of the forces that have shaped the course of evolution of fishes as well as all other life on earth.

The vast area of tropical ocean stretching more than halfway around the world from the Red Sea to the islands of Polynesia is known as the Indo-Pacific Region (Fig. 6). This region contains the world's largest shorefish fauna, estimated at over 4,000 species in 179 families. Most of the families (111 or 62%) and perhaps 25% of the species have broad distributions that extend from the western Indian Ocean to the central Pacific. The Indo-Pacific can be divided into subregions (sometimes known as provinces) characterized by a number of endemic taxa, that is, organisms that occur nowhere else. The three primary subregions of the Indo-Pacific are the Indian Ocean, West Pacific, and Pacific Plate subregions. Each of these subregions may contain smaller areas of high endemism such as the Red Sea and Hawaiian Islands.

The West Pacific subregion is the richest, closely followed by the Indian Ocean. Each contains nearly all the families (162 to 175 or 91 to 98%) and probably at least half of the species of Indo-Pacific shorefishes. The term Indo-west Pacific is thus applied to both subregions collectively. Since the boundary between the continental shelf fauna of the Indo-west Pacific and insular fauna of the central Pacific islands closely follows the boundary of the Pacific Plate, that term is applied to the fauna as well as the crustal surface.

All of the families and at least 3,700 species of Indo-Pacific inshore fishes occur in the Indo-west Pacific, but only 111 (62%) families, containing some 1,312 species, occur nonmarginally on the Pacific Plate. Only 10 genera and less than 300 species are endemic to the Pacific Plate or some portion thereof. The southern Philippines and western Indonesia at the center of the Indo-Australian Archipelago have the richest inshore fish fauna of the world with over 2,500 species in 165 families. The decrease in families and species as one moves from west to east onto the Pacific Plate is rather abrupt (Fig. 7). Micronesia, on the westernmost fringe of the Pacific Plate is an area of transition between the Indo-west Pacific and Pacific Plate faunas.

A direct comparison of the numbers of inshore fishes between various Indo-Pacific localities is difficult due to differences in collecting effort from one area to the next. Presently, the only Pacific Plate localities with ichthyofaunas sufficiently known to permit a direct comparison are the Mariana Islands, Marshall Islands, Samoa, Society Islands, Hawaiian Islands, Johnston Island, and Easter Island. The Marianas (872 species), Marshalls (827[*]spp.; Randall and Randall, 1987), and Samoa (915 spp.; following Randall and Randall, 1987), all near the western margin of the Pacific Plate, are comparable in diversity. There is a gradual decrease in diversity within the Pacific Plate as one moves east, or north and south of an axis running from Samoa to the Tuamotus.

There are a number of reasons for the abrupt drop in species richness as one moves onto the Pacific plate. A large number of families absent from the Pacific Plate nonmarginally, have short larval stages and are unable to disperse over the greater distances of open water between oceanic island

*See also Thresher and Colin, 1986.

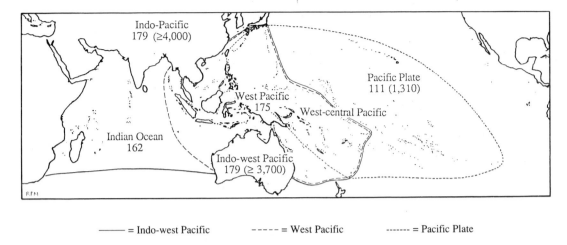

———— = Indo-west Pacific   ----- = West Pacific   ------ = Pacific Plate

Figure 6. Map of the Indo-Pacific region showing major zoogeographic subdivisions and estimated numbers of inshore fish species and families. The major subdivisions are separated by transition zones rather than fixed boundaries. The Indian Ocean and West Pacific collectively comprise the Indo-west Pacific subregion. The West-central Pacific is a descriptive term applied to distributions that extend both east and west of the West Pacific/Pacific Plate region of overlap. It does not have the same status as the Indo-west Pacific since relatively few species have such distributions, but most of them occur in Micronesia and form a significant element of the Micronesian fish fauna (see also Table 2).

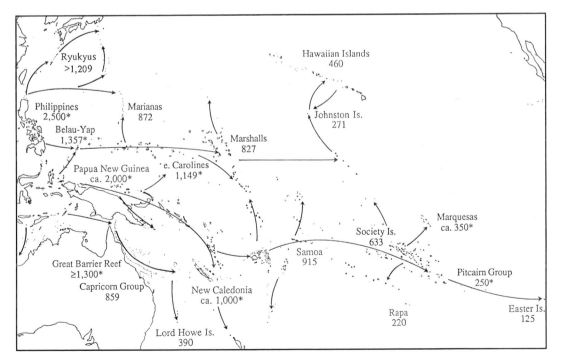

Figure 7. Map of the Pacific showing most recent estimates of numbers of inshore fish species by area and likely routes of colonization. An asterisk indicates an estimate.

groups. Others are characteristic of estuarine or freshwater habitats, or have juvenile stages better suited to develop in those habitats but may spread to adjacent coral reefs as they grow. Estuarine and freshwater habitats are limited to high islands which, with the exception of the eastern Caroline Islands, occur on the Pacific Plate nonmarginally only in southeastern Polynesia and Hawaii, areas well isolated from the Indo-West Pacific. With two exceptions, all 56 species of Micronesian estuarine or freshwater fishes that are typically not associated with coral reefs are confined to high islands. At least 54 of these occur or are expected at Belau-Yap, 34 in the eastern Carolines and 21 in the southern Marianas. A few of these also occur in the distant islands of Polynesia. The close proximity of Belau to the southern Philippines and Moluccas, short inter-island distances in the Carolines and eastward flow of the Equatorial Counter Current combine to enhance dispersal of Indo-Australian fishes onto the Pacific Plate. Yet there remain a number of families and a very large number of species that seem to have no ecological or ontogenetic basis for their absence from nonmarginal areas of the Pacific Plate. This sharp difference in the number of species on either side of the western boundary of the Pacific Plate and rate of endemism for the Pacific Plate of over 20% justify its

consideration as a major subunit of the Indo-Pacific region.

One may ask what the ice ages have to do with the distribution of tropical marine fishes. The answer lies in the effect of ice ages on sea level and the effect sea level has on changing the shapes of oceans and the sizes of areas suitable for coral reef development and the colonization and dispersal of reef fishes. During most of the past two million years, the earth has been locked in periods of glaciation lasting up to 100,000 years alternating with short warm intervals of about 10,000 years. We are currently in the last thousand years of a warm interval. During periods of glaciation, a significant portion of the earth's water is tied up in massive polar ice caps, reducing the sea level by as much as 150 m. The result is that most of the world's continental shelves become dry land and all of the present-day coral atolls are left high and dry (Fig. 8). The draining of the continental shelves results in the near separation of the tropical Indian and Pacific Oceans and the isolation of certain Indo-Australian seas. This isolates populations of widespread species into two or more groups, enabling some to differentiate into distinct species. Remixing and recolonization occur during interglacial periods, sometimes blurring the faunal boundaries established during periods of glaciation. Some

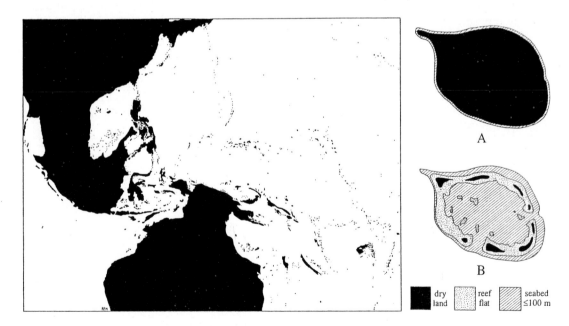

dry land | reef flat | seabed ≤100 m

Figure 8 (left). Distribution of land in the tropical west Pacific approximately 20,000 years ago when the sea level was more than 130 m lower than today.

Figure 9 (right). Comparison of dry land and shallow (≤ 100 m) seabed associated with a typical atoll 20,000 years ago (A) and today (B).

Table 2. Zoogeographic analysis of Micronesian inshore and epipelagic fishes*.

Distribution	Number of species	% of species with known distributions	Remarks of zoogeographic significance
Widespread Indo-Pacific	674	49.4	No. species on
Indo-west Pacific	160	11.7	continental plate: 1,281(93.9%)
West Pacific	199	14.6	
West-central Pacific	189	13.9	No. species limited
Pacific Plate	57	4.2	to continental plate
Circumtropical	52	3.8	and its margin: 359(26.3%)
Philippine Plate	7	0.5	
Endemic	26	1.9	No. species on
Uncertain	43	-	Pacific plate: 972(71.3%)
Total	1,407	100%	

* Zoogeographic categories are defined as follows:

Indo-Pacific: widespread species with western limit west of the Andamans and eastern limit east of non-marginal areas of the Pacific Plate.

Indo-west Pacific: widespread species with northeastern limit on the Pacific Plate marginally in the Carolines, but not reaching the Marshalls.

West Pacific: limited to the area bound by the Andamans and Cocos-Keeling in the west to the margin of the Pacific Plate in the east, north to s. Japan, south to w. and e. Australia.

Indo-Australian: a subset of the W. Pacific, n. to s. Taiwan, e. to the Solomons, s. to the Great Barrier Reef.

West-central Pacific: west Pacific and Pacific Plate distributions; may include e. Pacific.

Pacific Plate: may include east margin of the continental plates and eastern Pacific.

Philippine Plate: includes southeast Asian islands adjacent to w. margin of the Philippine Plate.

Endemic: known only from Micronesian localities.

species that evolved in small areas may eventually become extinct, but ecological factors that tend to reduce competion could allow many species to remain. This is one of the processes that resulted in the enormous diversity of Indo-Australian fishes found today with many endemic species of limited distribution.

The effect of a lower sea level on steeply-sloping coral atolls and high islands on the Pacific Plate was equally profound if not considerably different. It is well known that the size of an area suitable for settlement and the distance between suitable areas have direct effects on the rates of colonization and extinction of species. As a result, habitat size and inter-island distances both affect the ability of organisms to disperse across a series of suitable islands or "stepping stones". Larger areas and shorter distances between areas allow greater opportunities for colonization and reduce the chances of extinction. A larger island is a bigger target for a drifting colonizer to stumble upon and a shorter distance increases the chance of survival during the journey. A chain of large islands close together thus enables more species to dis-

perse over a greater distance. During periods of reduced sea level, atolls become high islands with steep slopes. Since reef-building corals live only in the upper 50 to 100 m, the elimination of present-day lagoons reduces the size of the coral reef habitat to a narrow ring around what has become a high island. For present-day high islands, the area circumscribed by the sea surface and lower limit of coral reef development would increase with a lowering of sea level, resulting in an increase in the area of coral reef habitat.

The vast bulk of Pacific Plate islands are atolls. A glance at a detailed bathymetric map of the tropical Pacific will give an indication of the enormous loss in the area of potential coral reef habitat that would result with a reduction in sea level of 50 to 150 m (Fig. 9). Since most present-day high islands of any size are in the eastern portion of the Pacific Plate (Hawaiian Islands, Marquesan Islands, Society islands), the ability of most species of fishes to disperse within the plate, or of Western Pacific (Indo-Australian) species to disperse onto the plate, was greatly curtailed during recent episodes of glaciation. With the loss of atoll lagoons,

Table 3. Micronesian and Philippine Plate endemic inshore fishes.

Philippine Plate and its margins	Widespread Micronesian	Marianas
Gymnothorax neglectus (dp)	*Gymnothorax marshallensis*	*Pseudanthias* sp.
Corythoichthys polynotatus	*Stolephorus pacificcus*	*Chaetodon flavocoronatus*
Holanthias katayamai (dp)	*Liobranchia stria*	*Centropyge shepardi*
Plectranthias kamii (dp)	*Pseudoplesiops revellei*	*Pomachromis guamensis*
Chaetodon burgessi	*Chrysiptera traceyi*	*Synchiropus circularis*
Eviota saipanensis	*Pomachromis exilis*	*Synchiropus* sp.
Sicyopus leprurus (fw)	*Labropsis micronesica*	*Awaous guamensis* (fw)
Xyrichtys sp.	*Enneapterygius nanus*	*Xenobalistes tumidipectoris* (dp)

Belau	Eastern Carolines	Marshalls
Evipes percinctus	*Parioglossus verticalis*	*Cirricaecula johnsoni*
Epibulus n. sp.	*Acanthurus chronixis*	*Amphiprion tricinctus*
Parioglossus lineatus	?*Parioconger*	*Callogobius bauchotae*
Redigobius horiae (fw)	*kapingamarangiensis*	
Sicyopus n. sp.(fw)		

dp = deep, > 60 m; fw = fresh water or estuarine as adults.

Table 4. Number of species of Micronesian fishes by island group*.

Island group	Number of species known to date	Island chain	Number of species known to date	Number of species expected†
Belau	892 (837)	Belau-		
Yap	385 (370)	Yap	920 (859)	1,357 (1,223)
Ifaluk**	416 (413)			
Truk	208 (205)	eastern ††		
Pohnpei	471 (445)	Caroline	766 (739)	1,149 (1,040)
Kosrae	363 (351)			
Kapingamarangi	437 (434)			
Southern Marianas	862 (756)	Mariana	872 (763)	904 (817)
Northern Marianas	315 (287)			
no. Marshalls	773 (762)	Marshall	827 (799)	875 (824)

* Parentheses indicates reef fishes (≤ 60 m) only.

** Includes Ulithi. Totals for Ifaluk and Kapingamarangi do not match the totals given by Rofen (1960) due to subsequent synonymizations as well as uncertain numbers of unidentified species.

†Based on interpolation of gaps in the known distribution of each species. These include species with "uncertain" distributions at island groups to the south and west of where they are known to occur by assuming they are not Pacific Plate endemics. The estimates do not consider species not yet known from Micronesia and are therefore conservative.

††Ifaluk east to Kosrae.

most lagoon-dependent species would become extinct on the plate or become isolated to whatever small lagoonal areas that remain on contemporary banks or slopes. The combination of distance between high island groups and their faunal source regions, and slightly increased coral reef areas among them, would increase the chances of speciation there. And that is precisely where one finds the highest rates of endemism on the Pacific Plate. Widespread Pacific Plate endemics may be better suited to survive periods of lower sea level on the Pacific Plate than many other Indo-west Pacific species. These endemics, as well as many Pacific Plate species with disjunct populations in the extreme eastern Indian Ocean, tend to be characteristic of clearwater seaward reefs; none are dependent on lagoon or reef flat environments.

Half of Micronesia's inshore fishes are widespread Indo-Pacific species (Table 2). Ninety-four percent of them occur among the continental islands of the tropical western Pacific and 72% of them occur non-marginally on the Pacific Plate. Twenty six percent of Micronesia's inshore fish species are continental forms that extend no further onto the Pacific Plate than the eastern Carolines and 4% are widespread Pacific Plate endemics that do not range further west than the eastern margin of the Asian Plate. Micronesia therefore contains as much as 35% of the the Indo-Pacific inshore fish fauna, 37% of the species inhabiting the Indo-west Pacific, and 74% of the species occuring non-marginally on the Pacific Plate. With the exception of a few undescribed species which could be expected to turn up elsewhere, only 32 species (2.4% are endemic to Micronesia or Micronesia and the eastern margin of the Asian Plate (Table 3). Four of these are rare deepwater forms (an additional two occur in moderately deep water), ten are tiny cryptic forms, and two are burrowing eels; it is quite conceivable that they could show up elsewhere, leaving only 17 likely true endemics. Fifteen of the 24 Micronesian endemics are known from single island groups : 5 from Belau, 2 from the eastern Carolines, 7 from the Marianas, and 3 from the Marshalls. The somewhat higher rate of endemism in the Marianas may be due to their relative isolation from the Belau-eastern Carolines-southern Marshalls route of dispersal.

Within Micronesia, it is clear that Belau has the richest fish fauna and that there is a gradual decrease in diversity as one moves eastward through the Carolines to Marshalls, and north through the Marianas (Table 4). Although there are presently fewer species known from Belau than from the Marshalls, careful interpolation of the known distributions of fishes clearly indicates that Belau, Yap, and the eastern Carolines have considerably more species than the Marshalls and Marianas.

Over 96% of the Micronesian fish fauna may be expected at Belau, followed by 82% in the eastern Carolines and slightly less than 66% in the Marianas and Marshalls. The transitional nature of the Micronesian fish fauna is also evident. The decrease in diversity as one moves eastward through Micronesia is due almost entirely to the large number of West Pacific species that drop out: 167 (151) reef species) do not occur beyond Belau or Yap and 269 (231 reef species) do not occur north or east of the eastern Carolines. Most of the widespread Pacific Plate endemics (slightly more than 57) occur in the Marshalls and Marianas, but only about 30 out of 57 reach the eastern Carolines and only 16 reach Belau. A number of widespread Indo-Pacific species occur non-marginally on the Pacific Plate only in the Marshalls. Some of these fail to reach the Marianas. It is clear that there is active dispersal of Indo-west Pacific fishes onto the Pacific Plate along a Belau-Carolines-Marshalls conduit.

ECOLOGY and BEHAVIOR

Ecological Theory

There are more species of fishes on a coral reef than there are vertebrates in any land habitat. By living on the sea floor as well as among and above the corals, and feeding on both plants and animals, reef fishes may be likened to the birds of a tropical rainforest, but they far surpass them in diversity of size, shape, and number. In terms of numbers, reproductive potential, and color they are more comparable to the butterflies. Why have so many varieties evolved and how do they coexist?

One of the cornerstones of ecology, the competetive exclusion principle, predicts that no two species with the same ecological requirements can coexist indefinitely on the same limiting resource: One will eventually outcompete the other. In other words, every species has its own unique niche. Coral reefs provide a wide variety of habitats, each with its own set of characteristic species. Differences in the degree of exposure to wave action, currents, light levels, the amount of algae, plankton and other food, and the abundance, shape, and varieties of coral and other shelter combine to create a large variety of possible niches. Not only is each conceivable niche occupied by a species of fish, but some niches appear to be occupied by a random assemblage of a number of species of fishes. This apparent violation of the competetive exclusion principle may be the result a number of factors that prevent competetive exclusion. Differential recruitment of juveniles, occasional disturbances such as storms that wipe out whole groups of fishes from a coral head, and heavy predation may keep any one species from realizing an advantage over another.

One way ecologists classify animals is by their place in the food chain. In the simplest form, a food chain consists of producers (plants), comsumers (animals), and decomposers (bacteria). Each tier from the producer to the terminal carnivore is called a trophic level. Most food chains are complex with numerous levels, subdivisions, and alternate pathways, so the term food web is also used. Among consumers, there are three basic trophic levels: herbivores for those that feed on plants, omnivores for those that feed on plants and animals, and carnivores for those that feed on animals. For fishes, the term planktivore is used to identify the carnivores that feed on zooplankton. (Very few fishes, primarily mullet, feed on phytoplankton). The term corallivore is used for the omnivores that feed on corals, since corals contain both plant and animal tissue. The term detritivore is used for those omnivores that feed on decomposing plant and animal particles. The term piscivore refers to carnivores that feed primarily on fishes.

Community Structure and Distribution

The tropical marine inshore fish fauna generally occurs to a depth of 200 to 250 m (656 to 820 ft). Since light level decreases with increasing depth, coral cover decreases dramatically below 40 to 60 m (131 to 197 ft), and coral and algae dissappear entirely between 110 and 140 m (360 to 460 ft). Consequently, the relative proportions of trophic categories of fishes also changes with depth. The inshore fish fauna of the upper 250 m of seaward reefs can therefore be divided into three communities: the shallow forereef community (upper 75-90 m or 246-295 ft); the middle forereef community (75-90 to 120 m); and the deep forereef community (below 120 m or 393 ft). Overall diversity is highest in the shallow forereef community where there is complete representation of trophic levels. As herbivores and corallivores decrease in abundance below 30 m (100 ft) and dissappear below about 110 m (361 ft), they are replaced by additional planktivores. The middle forereef community is dominated by a few species of planktivores and contains a high percentage of species that do not normally occur closer to the surface. A greater proportion of the relatively large roving carnivores occur in the shallow and deep forereef communities than do the planktivores. Diversity is lower but density remains relatively high. At depths below 120 m, the temperature also begins to drop significantly, further limiting the depth limits of most remaining reef fishes. The amount of available shelter is also greatly reduced. The deep forereef community is therefore characterized by low levels of diversity and abundance. Since only the shallow forereef community is available to exploration by scuba divers, the fish fauna of that community is the subject of this book.

A simplified breakdown of the Micronesian fish fauna relative to major habitat and behavioral groupings is summarized in Table 5. This analysis is at best very generalized and does not take into consideration zonation and depth, both of which have a profound impact on the localised distributions of inshore fishes. Examples of common species characteristic of various reef zones are given in the section on reef structure and zonation.

At least 70% of Micronesia's fish fauna consists of diurnal species, that is, those that are active by day. A few of these may be active by night as well. The largest category is composed of diurnal reef species that spend the daylight hours on the surface of the reef or a short distance above it. These are the colorful and conspicuous fishes most often associated with coral reefs. Included in this category are most wrasses, damselfishes, fairy basslets, groupers, butterflyfishes, surgeonfishes, parrotfishes, snappers, angelfishes, triggerfishes, hawkfishes, and some goatfishes. Thirty-six percent of this category are carnivores, followed by omnivores, herbivores, and planktivores. The larger groupers and snappers tend to be predators of fishes while most of the carnivores - primarily smaller groupers and snappers, emperors, wrasses, goatfishes, and hawkfishes - may be specialized or generalized predators of a wide variety of motile invertebrates and fishes. The larger angelfishes tend to feed on sponges and tunicates. The omnivores include butterflyfishes that feed primarily on small invertebrates or coral polyps, damselfishes that feed on filamentous algae and small invertebrates, and triggerfishes and puffers and their relatives that specialize on well-armored invertebrates, corals, sponges, or calcareous algae. Most of the planktivores including the fairy basslets, damselfishes, and a few wrasses feed on the smaller zooplankton such as copepods, fish eggs, and the earliest larval stages of fishes and invertebrates.

Twenty-nine percent of the shorefish fauna consists of cryptic reef species that are seldom noticed by the casual observer. Most are generally small and well camouflaged or spend most of their time hidden within the structure of the reef. Many are rarely seen unless they are flushed from hiding with chemical ichthyocides. Morays, most gobies, blennies, pipefishes, and most scorpionfishes fit this category. Some scorpionfishes that lie completely exposed are so well camouflaged that they are extremely difficult to detect. The bulk of these are carnivores. Some such as the morays feed on relatively large prey by night as well as day while most, primarily syngnathids and gobies, are diurnal predators of minute invertebrates. The herbi-

vores of the group are comprised primarily of blennies, and the omnivores of detritus-feeding gobies. The planktivores consist chiefly of hole-dwelling dartfishes and gobies that spend much of their time a short distance above the reef but rapidly disappear when approached. The herbivores, omnivores, and planktivores are diurnal.

Many species of fishes remain hidden in caves and in crevices during the day but emerge to feed on the surface of the reef or in the water close above it during the night. Squirrelfishes, soldierfishes, many cardinalfishes, and bigeyes typically feed on larger elements of the zooplankton in the water above the reef, while soldierfishes and many cardinalfishes feed on motile invertebrates on the reef's surface. Many cryptic species such as morays and scorpionfishes as well as some goatfishes become more active and spend more time in the open at night. Notably absent from this nocturnal assemblage are herbivores, omnivores, and planktivores of the smaller elements of the zooplankton.

Another major shorefish component consists of species that live on or beneath sand, mud, or rubble. Although these underwater "deserts" are not as richly or abundantly inhabited as coral-rich areas, like their terrestrial counterparts, they may contain a surprising diversity of life. Snake eels, lizardfishes, flatfishes, sandperches, flatheads, and many gobies live on or just beneath the surface, while sandivers, wormfishes, and certain wrasses spend a good portion of their waking hours in the water immediately above the sand. Most of these are carnivores of small invertebrates. Many fishes that shelter on the reef venture well out over large expanses of sand or rubble. These include some of the larger herbivorous surgeonfishes and several species of carnivorous groupers, snappers, emper-

Table 5. Composition of Micronesian inshore fishes relative to habitat/behavioral and trophic groups.

Habitat/behavioral group	Number of species by trophic category				No. species	% of total fish fauna
	herbivore	omnivore	planktivore	carnivore		
Diurnal reef	109	141	94	198	542	40.4
Cryptic reef	48	6	15	319	388	29.0
Nocturnal reef	0	0	73	51	124	9.3
Sand, mud, and rubble	11	6	4	105	126	9.4
Mid-water reef	0	9	37	65	111	8.3
Pelagic	0	0	17	32	49	3.7
Total no. species	168	162	240	770	1340	100.1
% of total fish fauna	12.5	12.1	17.9	57.5	100.0	100.0

ors, and breams. A large variety of smaller reef fishes tied more closely to the shelter of the reef may forage on small sand patches.

A relatively small portion of the shorefish fauna is composed of transient mid-water species that roam relatively large areas. This group includes the fusiliers, jacks, barracudas, and most sharks. Most are carnivores, but a few, primarily the fusiliers, are planktivores. The largest reef-associated species of all, the manta ray, feeds on zooplankton. Carnivorous needlefishes and omnivorous halfbeaks typically occur immediately beneath the water's surface. Occasionally pelagic species - those adapted for life in the open ocean such as tunas and flying fishes - visit seaward reef dropoffs or enter deep lagoons. Most are carnivores. Although they rarely feed on adults of reef fishes, many of them feed on the late larval and early juvenile stages of reef fishes.

Feeding

At the base of the reef's food web are marine plants, including diatoms (benthic unicellular algae with a silica exoskeleton), dinoflagellates (unicellular benthic or floating algae), phytoplankton (unicellular floating algae), zooxanthellae (unicellular algae that live within the tissue of corals and certain invertebrates), benthic algae (seaweeds), and seagrasses. There are fishes that feed on each of these. Few fishes feed on phytoplankton; mullets and milkfish feed on the algal diatomaceous and detrital scum of soft bottoms; a number of butterflyfishes and other corallivores feed on zooxanthellae contained within the tissue of corals; a few species of parrotfishes and surgeonfishes feed on seagrasses; and a very large number of herbivorous fishes feed on filamentous and fleshy benthic algae. Grazers scrape the thin filamentous algal film that grows on all bare surfaces, while browsers nip fronds of leafy algae. Parrotfishes, surgeonfishes, and rabbitfishes are the primary roving grazers, the marine equivalent of cattle. Smaller grazers such as blennies and many damselfishes are generally territorial around small areas affording sufficient shelter. Some parrotfishes, surgeonfishes, rabbitfishes, and rudderfishes browse on the fronds of leafy macroalgae.

Butterflyfishes as well as triggerfishes and puffers and their allies are the primary omnivores. Many species of butterflyfishes feed on a variety of small invertebrates and coral polyps, taking a little of each over a large home range. Some butterflyfishes and the filefish *Oxymonacanthus longirostris* feed exclusively on coral polyps which are snipped from the coral skeleton by specialized snouts and teeth. The large humphead parrotfish, *Bolbometa-pon muricatum*, and several triggerfishes, filefishes, and puffers feed on pieces of corals, skeleton and all. A number of triggerfishes, filefishes, and puffers feed on a variety of well-armored invertebrates such as sea urchins, crustaceans, and starfishes as well as hard calcareous algae. Detritus enters the fish food chain primarily through benthic invertebrates that are preyed upon by carnivores. Only a few fishes such as mullet and some gobies feed directly on detritus.

A large number of reef fishes feed on zooplankton. The largest of all fishes, the pelagic whaleshark and manta rays, feed on zooplankton strained from the water, as do anchovies, herrings, and silversides. Damselfishes and fairy basslets feed on individual zooplankters, chiefly copepods, picked from the water one by one. Some triggerfishes and snappers, particularly deep-dwelling species, feed on large, gelatinous zooplankton such as salps and ctenophores. Nocturnal planktivores such as squirrelfishes, cardinalfishes, and bigeyes feed primarily on large zooplankton such as crustacean larvae.

The bulk of the reef fishes are carnivores, ranging from tiny gobies that feed upon minute benthic crustaceans to large sharks that feed on large fishes, turtles, and other sharks. A variety of strategies are used to capture prey. Eels are specialized for slithering through narrow crevices, or through sand and rubble, locating prey through the sense of smell, and seizing prey with long, needle-like or stout, crushing teeth. Well camouflaged scorpionfishes, lizardfishes, and flatheads sit on the reef's surface, or partially buried in the sand, waiting to ambush unwary fishes or crustaceans. Groupers and snappers cruise about the reef in a nonthreatening manner, all the time prepared for an unwary fish to drop its guard, then lunge, more often than not unsuccessfully. Jacks rush into a school of small fusiliers or silversides, attempting to separate an individual from the safety of the school so it can be captured with relative ease. Many of the piscivores become more active at dusk and dawn during the day-night changeover when they become less visible to potential prey. Goatfishes probe the sand or crevices of the reef with long barbels to detect buried crustaceans or small fishes. They may be accompanied by opportunistic wrasses or small jacks that grab prey that are flushed out. Emperors scan the surface of the sand for any sign of movement that betrays the presence of buried prey. Rays excavate craters in the sand for buried molluscs which they crush with their pavement-like teeth. Some species such as the cleaner wrasses are specialized feeders of parasites and damaged tissue of other fishes while others pose as cleaners in order to aggressively tear out scales or pieces of fins.

Social Interactions

Fishes exhibit a diverse array of life styles to cope with living together in the crowded and competitive world of the reef. Some species are always found in groups while others occur in pairs or are solitary. Schooling is a strategy adopted by many species that live or travel in open water away from the protection of the reef. The sheer numbers of fishes in many schools insure that all but an unlucky few survive each attack by a predator. An individual among large numbers of closely spaced, constantly moving, and identical looking fishes is much more difficult for a predator to single out than if that individual were alone. If the predator blindly lunges at the school it will usually come up empty. Some aggregating as well as schooling species rely on disruptive coloration, such as a pattern of contrasting vertical bars, to make it even more difficult for a predator to single out an individual. Many roving herbivores occur in large mixed-species schools. Not only does this increase an individual's safety in numbers but it also enables the schooling fishes to overwhelm the defenses of territorial species guarding an algal food source. Many species of parrotfishes, surgeonfishes, and some rabbitfishes adopt this strategy. Species that depend on a small isolated area, such as a single coral patch for shelter tend to occur together in groups or colonies. This is particularly true for small planktivores that must feed in a vulnerable postion above their shelter. By occurring in groups they eliminate the need for leaving the vicinity of their "home" coral for reproduction. When danger threatens they quickly retreat to the safety of the coral. Fairy basslets, many damselfishes, and some wrasses are common examples.

A large number of reef fishes are territorial. Territorial species typically guard an area enclosing one or more resources of food, shelter, or potential mates or nesting sites. They are typically most aggressive towards outsiders of their own kind. The dominant territory holder will generally drive away rivals such as another adult of the same sex but share the territory with smaller subordinates of the opposite sex. Some species are aggressive towards almost any intruder while others are aggressive primarily towards their closest competitors - similar species with similar needs. Some species may have quite large territories or separate feeding and sleeping territories. Species that roam the same large area of reef on a routine basis are known as home-ranging species. They may carry with them a "portable" territory within which competitors are not allowed. Many home-ranging species may be relatively sociable during times of abundant resources, but become aggressive during lean times. Most medium to large species are home-ranging. They frequently have a favorite sleeping site to which they return and aggressively defend at the end of each day. Many species maintain a territory for reproduction. It may have the same boundary as a feeding territory or be a small portion of a home range (see reproduction).

Many small herbivores maintain a territory enclosing a patch of rock coated with a thin veneer of algae. Several damselfishes, blennies, and some surgeonfishes are common examples. Some species share territories with others. The aggressive surgeonfish *Acanthurus lineatus* may share its feeding territory with a much smaller damselfish *Stegastes fasciolatus*. The value of the pugnacious damselfish at driving away other competitors outweigh its cost as a competitor or the cost that would be required to drive it away, so its presence is tolerated. One or more species of blennies may also occupy the territory as parasitic freeloaders since they do not contribute to the territory's defense. Their small size, speed, and ability to hide in very small holes enable them to remain in the territory. This ability of the damselfish and the blenny to take advantage of progressively smaller shelter holes is one way in which coexistence is achieved by different species that utilize the same limited resource, the algae. Perhaps the most pugnacious of the territorial fishes are the so-called "farmer fishes" of the damselfish genera *Stegastes* and *Hemiglyphidodon*. They typically live in colonies among staghorn corals whose dead bases are covered with a mat of filamentous algae. They encourage the growth of the favored filamentous species of algae by "weeding" out the undesirable species - literally snipping and removing them from the territory.

Vision and color are of paramount importance in the social lives of most species of reef fishes. Distinctive color patterns enable each species to recognize its own kind as well as the rank of an individual within a social system. Behaviorally controlled changes in coloration and posturing convey messages among fishes just as facial expressions do among humans. In some species sounds and scents may also play a role in social interactions. Flared operculae and fins are commonly used to convey aggression. Males of many species flash brilliantly intense colors during courtship. At night, most species exhibit a subdued color pattern, often with contrasting blotches or bars that may help them match their background.

Reproduction and Development

Reproduction among fishes is highly varied and often quite complex (Fig. 10). The vast majority of fishes lay eggs. The birth of fully developed young is extremely rare among bony fishes and common only among cartilagenous fishes (see p.

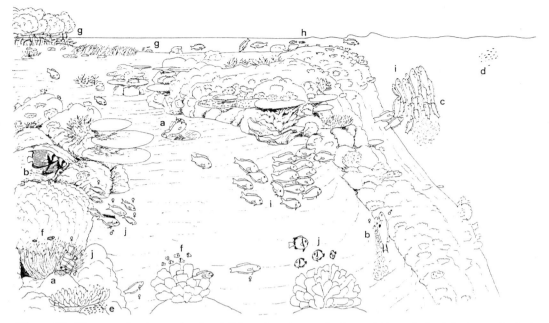

Figure 10. The reproductive cycle of reef fishes: Spawning may be demersal (a) or pelagic. Pelagic spawning is either by pairs (b) or en masse (c). After a pelagic larval phase (d), larvae settle back to the reef (e) where they quickly develop into pigmented juveniles (f). Settlement sites vary among species. Some species live among mangroves or on flats as juveniles (g), then migrate to outer reef areas as subadults (h). Many species that normally live on coastal or inner reefs, migrate to specific spawning sites (i) while others live in or near permanent spawning territories (j).

29). Eggs of fishes are typically small (about 1 mm in diameter) and generally take about a week to hatch. The eggs hatch into larvae which bear little resemblance to the fishes familiar to most poeple. Larvae start out as tadpole-like creatures with large eyes, without pigment or scales, and often with an external yolk sack to nourish them until their gut develops. Larvae are adapted to a pelagic life, drifting with the currents and feeding on phytoplankton to progressively larger zooplankton as they grow. Some larvae actively swim, guided by environmental cues that may help them find a suitable settling site. In many species the larvae develop enlarged bony plates or spines that help protect them from predation. In some species larvae settle and transform into juveniles within days of hatching while in others they may go through a prolonged late larval stage that may last up to two months or more. Once they locate a suitable place to settle, larvae become bottom-oriented and rapidly acquire the pigments, scales, and full compliment of fin rays characteristic of juveniles. Juveniles usually resemble adults in form, but in reef species, may often have a color pattern entirely different from that of adults. Growth rate and life span vary among species. Some species grow at a steady rate until they die while others grow more slowly after reaching a certain size. Small species

may reach maturity within six months and live to an age of one to two years while large species may take several years to mature and live as long as 80 years or more.

Most species of fishes have the familiar male and female sexes, but only a minority of them go through adult life as monogamous pairs. In fact, the majority of reef fish species so far studied are not only polygamous but undergo sex reversal as a normal part of their sexual development. This is called sequential hermaphroditism. Species in which individuals begin their life as females before changing to males are known as protogynous hermaphrodites whereas those that change from male to female are known as protandrous hermaphrodites. No species exhibit both protogyny and protandry but a few species are simultaneous hermaphrodites, and a very few of these (none known from Micronesia) are occasionally self-fertilizing.

Most wrasses and parrotfishes are typical examples of sequential hermaphrodites. In most species individuals begin their adult life as either males or females and each has a similar, relatively dull color pattern. This is known as the primary or initial phase. Primary males are usually incapable of changing sex, but females have the capacity to change sex into brilliantly colored males, known as secondary or terminal phase males. Secondary males are larger than, and dominant over all primary phase individuals. The change of sex is socially controlled - the presence of terminal males inhibits females from changing sex. If the ratio of terminal males to females falls below a certain threshold, the dominant female will change sex. Terminal males generally pair spawn with numerous females of their choice, while primary males often band together and spawn in large groups with the females which on occasion may be "raided" from a courting terminal male. In simpler systems, typified by the fairy basslets (genus *Pseudanthias*), primary males are absent, and all males are terminal, usually with a distinctive, gaudier coloration. These are known as haremic systems. In most haremic systems there is one male dominant over a group of females, but in some large colonies of *Pseudanthias* there may be more than one male. If the male is removed, the dominant female changes sex, insuring the constant reproductive capacity of a group of fishes that may spend their entire postlarval lives confined to the safety of a small area of suitable shelter.

In protandrous hermaphrodites such as the anemonefishes, the social hiearchy of the sexes is reversed. In a typical large anemone there is usually a single pair of reproductively active anemonefishes and often one or more immature individuals. The female is the largest and most dominant. Should she be removed, the male will change sex and the largest of the juvelines will rapidly grow and mature into a male. The presence of the female inhibits the male from changing sex and the presence of the male stunts the growth and development of the juveniles. This is another example of a strategy that insures the reproductive capacity of a small colony of animals confined to a very limited space.

Some species, particularly large roving carnivores, may normally be solitary in their day-to-day lives but migrate to favorite spawning sites at certain times of the year or throughout the year on a lunar rhythm. Some locations, usually current-swept promontories or channel entrances, are the sites of mass spawning aggregations of hundreds or thousands of individuals of some species. Some species may spawn as pairs that break off from the main aggregation while others may spawn *en mass*.

Most species of reef fishes are pelagic or broadcast spawners, that is they spew their gametes into the water usually at the apex of an ascent well above the bottom. Most species also spawn at a favorable time, usually on an outgoing tide, more often than not near or during dusk. Many species spawn on a lunar rhythm, around full moon, new moon, or both which is when the tidal range is greatest and tide-induced currents the strongest. These strategies increase the chances of the eggs escaping the hungry mouths of the innumerable small diurnal planktivorous fishes and filter feeding invertebrates that populate every reef. The favored sites of migrating spawners may also be near gyres in ocean currents that return the larvae to natal or nearby reefs after they have had two to three weeks to develop and are ready to settle.

There is a rough correlation between adult size and reproductive behavior. Since most fishes have eggs that ripen at a diameter of about a millimeter, large species have a much greater reproductive capacity than smaller ones. A 100 cm grouper may carry a million or more eggs whereas a small goby may only have a few dozen. Since an average of only two progeny per adult pair per generation need to survive to adulthood and spawn to insure the continued survival of the species, the larger species can better afford to spew their gametes into the vastness of the sea than can smaller ones. Many of the smaller species such as the gobies, blennies, and damselfishes therefore spawn in nests that are usually guarded by one or more of the parents. Hatching generally occurs after about a week, usually at night and on an outgoing tide. Cardinalfishes take parental care a step further by brooding the eggs in the mouth of the male until hatching. By providing a measure of protection for their eggs, nesting species greatly reduce egg predation, thereby evening the odds with the more fecund broadcast spawners.

Protective Resemblance and Mimicry

Among the multitude of lifestyles of reef fishes are those that depend on the color of other plants and animals. Protective resemblance and mimicry are ploys utilized by a number of species to capture prey or escape predators. Many species rely on camouflage to blend in with their surroundings. Scorpionfishes and frogfishes have fleshy tassles or warts that resemble fronds of algae and some even *have* algae growing on them. Many groupers have color patterns that do not resemble any particular background, but when overlain with a series of darker diagonal bands that break up their outline, they become virtually invisible. Some fishes do not match their background at all but closely resemble something else of no interest to a potential predator or prey. The juvenile of the wrasse *Novaculichthys taeniourus* looks like, and swims as if it is a clump of seaweed swaying back and forth in the surge.

Protective resemblance is known as mimicry when an organism resembles another that is protected from predation by virtue of distastefulness, toxicity, or some other characteristic. Mimicry occurs in two basic forms: Batesian mimicry when an otherwise unprotected animal resembles a protected one, and Müllerian mimicry when two or more protected animals closely resemble one another. Among reef fishes Batesian mimicry is the more common of the two. The protected species, or model, generally has a distinctive, often gaudy color pattern (termed aposematic coloration) that potential predators learn to avoid after one or more bad experiences. The similar looking mimic is also avoided.

In Batesian mimicry, the protected species is usually more common than the mimic. This decreases the chances of the mimic encountering an inexperienced predator that may attempt to eat it. A typical example of Batesian mimicry involves the noxious puffer *Canthigaster valentini* (p. 268) and the edible filefish *Paraluteres prionurus* (p. 263). The puffer is distasteful and quite likely toxic; it is a relatively slow swimmer that makes little attempt to hide. The edible filefish not only looks like the puffer, but swims like it as well. In aggressive mimicry, the mimic takes its charade a step further in order to gain an advantage other than protection at the expense of another animal. Aggressive mimicry is perhaps best developed among the sabre-toothed blennies (p. 214). In a classic example, the cleaner mimic *Aspidontus taeniatus* has evolved a color pattern identical to that of the cleaner wrasse *Labroides dimidiatus*. The wrasse makes a living grooming other fishes by removing parasites and pieces of damaged tissue. Large piscivorous fishes will pose with their mouths agape as the cleaner swims inside looking for a meal. The piscivores recognize the cleaner's service and will not attempt to eat it. The blenny uses its disguise to closely approach other fishes expecting to be groomed. But instead of grooming, the blenny darts in to make a meal of a piece of fin or scale! The blenny's disguise is not perfect though; older, more experienced fishes usually learn to distinguish the two and avoid the mimic.

Many juvenile sweetlips, *Plectorhinchus* spp., are possible Müllerian mimics, but it has not yet been demostrated that they are noxious. They typically have a similar color pattern of highly contrasting light and dark blotches, and swim or hover in the open with distinctive, greatly exaggerated movements of the body and fins. By resembling one another, the effectiveness of their aposematic coloration is reinforced since a predator can learn to avoid them collectively through a bad experience with just one. In Müllerian mimicry each participant therefore acts as both model and mimic.

Symbiosis

The lives of some of the reef's animals are closely associated with, and often dependent upon the life of another species. This is known as symbiosis.

There are three basic forms of symbiosis: mutualism when both organisms depend upon each other, commensalism when one organism depends upon the other without harming it, and parasitism when one benefits to the detriment of the other. All three are found among Micronesia's reef fishes.

The prawn-associated gobies (p. 226) are a classic example of mutualism. The goby lives only in a burrow excavated by a prawn which is blind or nearly so. The prawn spends much of its time maintaining the burrow, and each time it dumps a load of sand out the entrance it is exposed to predation. The goby stands guard at the entrance to the burrow and is quite alert and difficult to approach closely. When at the entrance, the prawn usually maintains contact with the goby by touching it with one of its antennae. If the goby detects danger, it signals the prawn with a flick of its tail before following the prawn into the burrow. The goby also benefits by feeding on small invertebrates exposed by the prawn's digging.

Perhaps the best known example of commensalism is that of the anemonefishes (p. 164). Anemonefishes occur only in the vicinity of certain large sea anemones. The surface of the sea anemones are covered with venomous stinging cells capable of killing most fishes. But the anemonefishes are not stung and utilize the anemone as a predator-free home. The key is a substance acquired from the anemone itself, through a careful process of acclimation, that is present in the anemonefishes mucus. The stinging cells recognize the anemonefish as a part of the anemone and will not sting it. Although anemonefishes have been observed to carry food to their host, the anemone is not dependent upon the anemonefish. Perfectly healthy anemones occur without anemonefish, but the anemonefishes are invariably found with an anemone.

Parasitism on the part of coral reef fishes seems to be limited to the pearlfishes (p. 65) which live within the body cavities of certain invertebrates. The most common species occur within certain sea cucumbers and starfish. While some species occasionally feed on the respiratory tree of their host, others may be harmless.

REEF FISHES and MAN

Reef Fishes as a Resource and Its Conservation

The native peoples of Micronesia have traditionally depended on fishes as their primary source of protein. With the exception of a few toxic species, nearly all reef fishes are edible, and a wide variety are used as food. A wide variety of methods are employed, including, nets, traps, hook and line, and spears. The book Words of the Lagoon gives an excellent review of traditional fishing in Micronesia, and Fishing on Guam describes both traditional and modern fishing in the Marianas. In the recent past, most islanders learned to swim by the time they could walk and were adept spearfishermen using the most primitive equipment. Until recently, reef fishes were exploited only on a subsistence basis for day to day needs. With the exception of the Marianas, the large areas of reef surrounding most islands could easily sustain native populations without being overtaxed, and there was little impact on the structure of reef fish communities.

With the advent of cash economies as well as modern diving and fishing equipment, outboard motors, and refrigeration, virtually all of the islands connected by regular air service are now exploiting fishes commercially. Much of the reef fish catch is exported to markets on Guam where the resource is stretched to the limit. A vicious cycle is set up where the demand for money to pay for consumer goods is satisfied only by selling more fish. As nearby stocks become depleted, the fishermen must go further away to get their catch and the depleted area gets larger. It is only a matter of time before the incoming flow of money drops to match whatever sustained level of harvest can be maintained. Many large and vulnerable species are being heavily impacted, particularly by spearfishing at night. Certain large species such as the giant humphead parrotfish (p. 193) that were once common are now rarely seen on Guam and becoming scarce in Belau. Groupers over 25 kg (55 lb) are rarely seen anywhere.

Destructive methods of fishing such as the use of explosives or poisons such as chlorine or natural root extracts are widespread in Micronesia. These methods are particularly reprehensible because they kill most if not all marine life in the area and may render it unsuitable for normal recolonization. Although these methods are illegal, enforcement is difficult and often lax.

Land-uses that have nothing to do with fisheries management may have an indirect impact on reef fishes. Recent prolonged and continuous infestations of the crown-of-thorns starfish in the southern Marianas are most likely the result of increased nutrient flow into the waters of Guam due to erosion caused by widespread brush fires (mostly the result of arson), construction, and agriculture. The sustained widespread destruction of most species of corals has a direct impact on the structure of reef fish communities. Certain herbivorous species such as parrotfishes and surgeonfishes may benefit from the increased area of dead reef available for algal growth, while others that feed on corals or live within them, particularly many species of butterflyfishes, may disappear. The decrease in the available shelter may limit populations of many species.

Since traditional concepts of conservation and ownership are often applied only to traditional methods, they are being lost as traditional methods give way to modern. Unfortunately, traditional conservation practices are not being replaced by modern ones. Many of the methods used to manage single- or few-species stocks in temperate regions are impractical on coral reefs where dozens of species are caught by each method, where there is little seasonal variation, and where distinct size classes are absent. Even the most abundant species on coral reefs only comprise a small portion of the harvestable catch. When the cost of learning the population dynamics of an individual species may exceed its annual value, and policymakers and special interest groups demand answers before action, the resource is bound to suffer. Other less species-specific approaches are needed to maximize the sustainable harvest and preserve species for traditional uses. Bag limits, protection for certain vulnerable species, banning the use of scuba diving while spearfishing, limiting the sale of speared fish, and limited entry into a fishery may offer some hope, but the real answer lies in economic diversification and in maximizing the non-consumptive uses of the resource.

Small colorful species suitable for home aquariums also form an important, largely untapped resource. Unlike many of the larger species exploited for food, most popular aquarium species are small and have a high turnover rate which makes them much less susceptable to overfishing. As long as fish-collecting chemicals are banned or strictly controlled, and catches are monitored, there is little danger of overexploitation. Generally only certain sizes are in demand and only certain habitats are practical for collecting, so most individuals are left to grow and reproduce. Only one firm, located on Majuro, currently exports aquarium fishes on a regular basis. Recent ventures on Guam and Belau have more-or-less collapsed due primarily to unreliable cargo service and partially to other factors such as competition from lower priced Philippine fishes and restrictions on foreign owned businesses in the new island nations.

For some places, the value of a reef fish resource for non-consumptive activities such as tourism, photography, and education far outweighs its value as a food resource. Unfortunately the potential for using reef fishes for non-consumptive activities remains unrealized in Micronesia. Scuba diving is one of the fastest growing sports of the last two decades. Millions of Americans and Japanese are certified divers. Most of them visit a coral reef at some time in their lives and many return to favorite locations year after year. Partly as a result of lessons learned in the early days of diving, spearfishing has given way to underwater photography and "fish-watching" as the most popular recreational activities of divers. Most divers want to see or photograph large fishes at close range. A place that offers exciting encounters with large tame fish or simply a chance to view a reef in pristine condition is likely to be visited time and time again. A place where large fishes are uncommon or flee at the first sight of a diver is seldom visited twice.

In many parts of the world there are underwater parks where marine life is protected and fish feeding is a popular activity. Unfortunately, there are none in Micronesia. In the Caribbean, the economic prosperity of whole islands depends on their underwater parks and the tourism they attract. It is difficult to understand why this concept has not caught on in Micronesia. Each of Micronesia's island·groups has more species of reef fishes and many times the species of corals than does the entire Caribbean. Ten years ago, Belau easily equalled the world's best dive spots. It is still one of the very finest dive destinations, but in the three years between my first and last visits, there was a perceptible decline in the numbers of certain large species of fishes. I was also disappointed in not being able to closely approach many of the larger fishes - the same species I have seen being hand fed in photographs taken in other parts of the world. It is clear that spearfishing is the reason. Consequently, photographs of a number of the species in this book had to be taken in Indonesia or Hawaii at locations where marine life is protected. As I was preparing this chapter, I was pleased to learn that the groundwork is being laid for Belau's first national park which will include the underwater area around the Seventy Islands.

Underwater parks and marine conservation areas also benefit the fishermen by offering a refuge for heavily exploited species to grow and reproduce so that the species' continued presence outside the conservation area is ensured. The key to the future well-being of Micronesia's reef fish resource is clear. The establishment of underwater parks is a necessity if the maximum and well-balanced benefits of food, recreation, education, and economic development of the region's marine resources are to be realized.

Dangerous Marine Fishes

Although some of Micronesia's reef fishes are potentially harmful, there is rarely any danger to a person that uses common sense and leaves unfamiliar fishes alone. With the possible exception of the tiger shark, there are no animals on Micronesian reefs that would consider a human as potential prey. Most bad encounters with marine life are the result of the victim's lack of knowledge of an animal's anatomy, behavior, and defenses, and are almost always avoidable. One stands a much greater risk of being killed or maimed on the way to the dive site than as a result of an encounter with a potentially dangerous species of fish. There are three basic types of potentially dangerous fishes: those that bite, those that sting, and those that are poisonous to eat.

When one thinks of fishes that bite, the word shark immediately comes to mind. All three of the world's most dangerous species of shark occur in Micronesia, but only one, the tiger shark (p. 36), enters diveable coral reef waters. The tiger shark is the only Micronesian coral reef-inhabiting shark that is large enough to consider a human as a potential meal. Fortunately, it generally avoids shallow water during the day when most divers are in the water. It is most likely to be encountered in relatively deep water along steep outer reef slopes. The few sightings made in lagoons have usually been in the vicinity of deep channels leading to the seaward reef. Occasionally tiger sharks forage in shallow reef front waters, primarily at night. Even if one does encounter a tiger shark, it more than likely will not attack unless it is stimulated by the presence of speared fish. The best thing to do if one is encountered is to get out of the water. The only Micronesian record of a great white shark is based on the teeth of a specimen caught 6 miles at sea of Bikini Atoll. The great white shark is a cool water species that occurs in Micronesia only as a rare wanderer in deeper waters within the thermocline. The world's third most dangerous species of shark is the oceanic whitetip (p. 34) which occurs in all offshore tropical waters. It very rarely occurs on the edges of deep offshore banks, areas generally not visited by divers.

The grey reef shark (p. 34) is the most dangerous species commonly encountered by divers. It is aggressive and territorial and may view man as a competitor. Although it won't hesitate to take a fish off the end of a spear, attacks on people are territorial in nature and are invariably preceded by a distinctive swimming behavior known as threat-posturing. In most popular dive areas, grey reef sharks have become accustomed to divers and generally ignore them. As with most sharks, it is advisable for the diver to be aware of the shark's behavior and to get out of the water if the shark becomes persistently curious. Several other species of reef sharks are potentially dangerous, particularly when stimulated by fish being speared or hooked.

The other "biters" most feared by humans are barracudas and moray eels. There are no records of attacks by barracudas in Micronesia, although at least one species, the great barracuda, has been implicated in attacks elsewhere. These attacks are invariably the result of mistaken identity or provocation. In murky water, a shiny object such as bracelet may be mistaken for a small fish, resulting in the limb to which it is attached being bitten, or a speared barracuda could attack in self defense. Bites from moray eels are invariably the result of some form of provocation or stimuli. They have been attributed to thrusting a hand into a hole occupied by an eel, spearing an eel, and holding speared fish in the hand. The latter two were the causes of two well-documented crippling attacks by very large *Gymnothorax javanicus* (p. 44) at Johnston Atoll. Although temperament varies between species and individuals, certain large morays have become popular "pets" among dive tour operators who feed them and pet them. The eels appear to enjoy the stimulation of being scratched or stroked. Tragically, a popular *Gymnothorax javanicus* named Homer from a reef off Guam no longer trusts people after surviving being speared in the head.

There are a number of reef fishes that possess venomous spines. The most dangerous of these are the scorpionfishes and rabbitfishes. One species of scorpionfish, the stonefish (p. 97), has caused fatalities among humans. Most scorpionfishes are extremely well-camouflaged. Several species, including the stonefish are common on shallow reef flats, but they usually station themselves against rocks and are rarely stepped on. Although the dorsal spines of the stonefish are capable of penetrating tennis shoes, sturdy footware greatly reduces the chances of them penetrating the skin. One group of scorpionfishes, the lionfishes (p. 97) are quite conspicuous and make little effort to avoid the diver. Rabbitfishes (p. 251) also have highly venomous dorsal and anal spines. Although they have not been implicated in fatalities, the sting of some species is feared as much as that of the stonefish. Surgeonfishes (p. 244) have either a pair of razor-sharp, moveable, sheathed spines or two pairs of sharp, fixed bucklers on their sides near the base of the tail. Squirrelfishes have prominent preopercular (cheek) spines. Stingrays have one or more sharp detachable spines on the basal portion of their whiplike tails that are capable of severely wounding a wader who inadvertently steps on one. Although less hazardous than the fishes listed above, most other species of reef fishes have some form of defense in the form of sharp spines,

beaks, or teeth, and should be handled cautiously.

A number of reef fishes are poisonous by possessing toxins that make them unpalatable. Toxicity may be due to either substances made by the fish itself, or to substance ingested with other organisms. Puffers and boxfishes have highly toxic skin, vicera, or flesh which protects them from predation. The toxin, tetraodontotoxin, is among the most powerful poisons known and is responsible for many fatalities throughout the world. Soapfishes and possibly juvenile sweetlips also possess toxic or bitter skin secretions that discourage predation.

Perhaps the most dangerous form of fish poisoning from the standpoint of public health is ciguatera. Ciguatera is a toxin that may be present in a wide variety of fishes, but reaches its highest concentrations in the piscivorous fishes at the top of the food chain. It does not affect the fishes themselves but can cause extreme illness and even death in humans and land animals. Symptoms vary from a tingling of the lips and extremities in the mildest cases to reversal of the sensations of hot and cold, muscular weakness, vomiting, diarrhoea, shortness of breath, and cardiac arrest. There is no known cure, and until very recently, no practical means of detecting the toxin in fishes. Its greatest danger is its unpredictability of occurrence in some of the most valuable food fishes.

The toxin is produced by a small dinoflagellate, *Gambierdiscus toxicus*, that colonizes the bare surfaces of rock, piers, shipwrecks, or even blades of algae. It is eaten along with filamentous algae by herbivorous fishes which are in turn eaten by predatory fishes. Since the toxin is not metabolized, it accumulates in the flesh and particularly the liver and reproductive organs. Each time a predator eats a smaller fish, it accumulates its victim's lifetime supply of ciguatera. Consequently, the highest concentrations occur in large predatory fishes. The occurrence of ciguatera varies from place to place and through time. In Micronesia, large red snapper, *Lutjanus bohar*, and the moray eel, *Gymnothorax javanicus*, are the most frequently implicated species and should never be eaten. Large groupers, particularly *Plectropomus laevis* and *Epinephelus lanceolatus*, other large snappers, large emperors, large jacks, large barracuda, and large triggerfishes should always be treated with caution. It is wise not to eat any predatory reef fish larger than those that are commonly caught and consumed locally. Fortunately, ciguatera is not present in the offshore pelagic and deep reef food chains that form the basis of the regions largest commercial fisheries.

CLASSIFICATION and MORPHOLOGY

The System of Classification

In order to efficiently catalogue and understand how the world's two million or more varieties of animals relate to one another, scientists classify them in a hierarchial scheme based on kinship, that is, on their common ancestry and evolutionary development. In order to standardize such a scheme, all levels of classification use latinized names. Without such a universal language, any attempt at a conceivable scheme would result in chaos. In order to distinguish between levels of classification, many levels use standardized endings. The names of orders, families, and subfamilies end in "iformes", "idae", and "inae", respectively, as shown in boldface in the following example (Table 6). The levels pertinent to the classification of Micronesian fishes using the emperor angelfish as an example are as follows:

Table 6. System of classification of fishes.

Level of classification	Example	Common name
class	Osteichthyes	Bony fishes
subclass	Actinopterygii	Ray-finned fishes
superorder	Teleostei	"Modern" ray-finned fishes
order	Perc**iformes**	Perch-like fishes
family	Pomacanth**idae**	Angelfishes
subfamily	Pomacanthi**inae**	(no available common name)
genus	*Pomacanthus*	genus and species together =
species	*imperator*	emperor angelfish

In addition to the levels shown, there are intermediate subdivisions (e.g. division, suborder, "tribe", subgenus) that are useful primarily to the specialist. Some of these are not well standardized, and the proper position of many groups of fishes within them still has not been worked out. The levels of interest to the non-specialist are the family and species. A family consists of a group of species with a common ancestry. Each species in a family is more closely related to one another than to any other species. The species is a group of "the same kind" of organisms, that is, organisms that are capable of breeding with one another and producing fertile offspring which in turn are capable of producing future generations. The species name always consists of two parts, the genus and the "specific epithet". Both parts are always italicized (or underlined if italic type is not available); the genus is always capitalized, and the specific epithet is never capitalized. The genus name is used for one or more species and denotes a group of very closely related species distinguishable from one another by minor differences in morphology. The specific epithet denotes a single species within a genus; it cannot be used for another member of that genus, but can be used for species in other genera. Together the two parts form a unique name that distinguishes a species from all others. Thus *Pomacanthus imperator* is a member of the genus *Pomacanthus* (with four other species in Micronesia), in the family Pomacanthidae, and so on. For some species, populations in different geographic regions have become sufficiently isolated from one another to maintain minor differences in coloration or morphology. These are indicated as subspecies by a third part added to the species name which is also latinized and italicized.

Living fishes fall into four major classes: the lampreys (Cephalaspidomorphi), the hagfishes (Pteraspidomorphi), the cartilagenous fishes (Chondrichthyes), and the bony fishes (Osteichthyes). The primitive lampreys and hagfishes, which lack jaws, consist of a few dozen species confined to cold waters. Hagfishes occur in the tropics only on soft bottoms in deep, cold water and are represented in Micronesia by at least one species. Cartilagenous and bony fishes are well represented in all seas. Nearly 1,400 species of inshore fishes are known from Micronesia. Twenty five of these are cartilagenous fishes; the remainder are bony fishes.

Morphology

Class Chondrichthyes (Cartilagenous fishes)

All of Micronesia's shallow-water cartilagenous fishes are members of the subclass Elasmobranchii which can be conveniently divided into two major groups: the Squalimorphea (sharks) and the Batoidea (sawfishes, guitarfishes, skates, and rays). All possess a skeleton consisting of cartilage rather

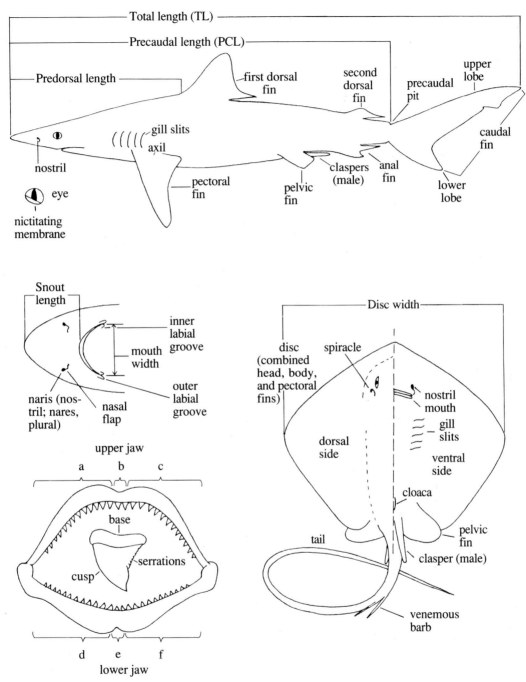

Dental formula, expressed as no. of teeth per region of
jaw (a-f) shown above is:
a-b-c / d-e-f (= 13-1-13 / 12-1-12 in example shown).

Figure 11. External features of cartilagenous fishes.

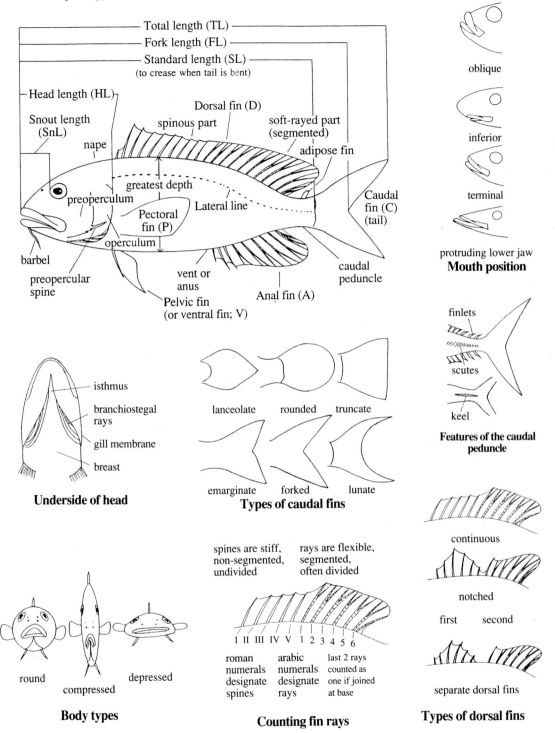

Figure 12. External features of a bony fish and methods of measuring and counting.

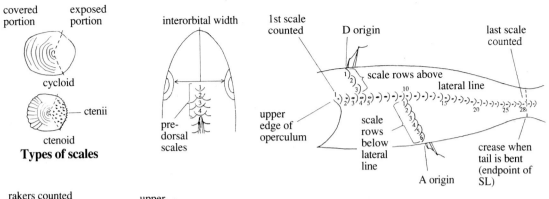

Types of scales

covered portion | exposed portion
cycloid
ctenii
ctenoid

interorbital width
pre-dorsal scales

1st scale counted
D origin
last scale counted
scale rows above lateral line
upper edge of operculum
scale rows below lateral line
A origin
crease when tail is bent (endpoint of SL)

Counting scales

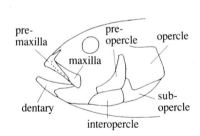

rakers counted from top to bottom
raker at angle included in lower limb count

developed rakers (length > width)

rudiments (length ≤ length)

upper limb
lower limb
gill filaments

Counting gill rakers

LL = no. of lateral line scales
LP = no. of lateral line pores (= LL if 1 pore per scale and none in series without a pore)
LR = no. of lateral scale rows (LSS or LS in some works)
preD = no. of predorsal scales, i.e. scales on midline in front of dorsal fin
TR = no. of transverse scale rows (= TRa+TRb+1)
TRa = no. of scale rows above lateral line
TRb = no. of scale rows below lateral line

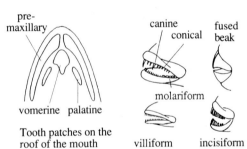

pre-maxilla
pre-opercle
opercle
maxilla
dentary
sub-opercle
interopercle

Outermost principle bones of the head

pre-maxillary
vomerine   palatine
Tooth patches on the roof of the mouth

canine
conical
fused beak
molariform
villiform   incisiform

Types of teeth

Meristic formula: an example of a typical case shown below:

dorsal fin   anal fin   pectoral fin   lateral line   gill rakers   body depth

D VII+I, 9-10; A III, 7-8; P 15-16; LL 29-33; GR 4-6+18-21=23-26; depth 3.2-3.4.

no. spines | no. rays | no. spines | no. rays | no. rays | no. of pored scales | range for upper limb | range for lower limb | total | expressed as SL ÷ greatest body depth

first (D₁)   second (D₂)

( ) indicates the usual count or range; + indicates two or more of D, LL, or GR; - indicates a range; < "means less than"; ≤ means "less than or equal to"; > means "greater than"; ≥ means "greater than or equal to"; depth, HL, and SnL are expressed as the number of times these measurements fit into SL.

than true bone, have five to seven gill slits, a spiral-valve intestine, and lack a gas bladder. In sharks, the pectoral fins are not attached to the head, and the gill slits are located on the sides behind the jaws and usually in front of the pectoral fins. In the batoids, the pectoral axis is expanded and fused to the sides of the head, and the gill slits are located on the flattened underside. Elasmobranch scales consist of small tubercles, known as dermal denticles or placoid scales, rather than overlapping plates. These are structurally similar to teeth and give the skin a rough, sand paper-like texture, particularly when stroked towards the head. The teeth are modified dermal denticles that are continually being formed on the inner surface of the jaws. When an outer tooth is lost, it is quickly replaced by the next available inner one. There is a great deal of variability in the shape and size of denticles and teeth. Triangular, serrated, blade-like teeth occur in species that feed on pieces cut from relatively large prey; multicuspid teeth occur in species that catch and hold "bite-sized" prey; and pavement-like nodular teeth occur in multiple functional rows in species that feed on hard-shelled molluscs and crustaceans. A few species have minute, functionless teeth and feed on plankton strained from the water through highly modified gill arches. Most sharks use the large, oil-filled liver in lieu of a gas bladder and continuous swimming to achieve neutral buoyancy.

Elasmobranches possess a number of acute sensory abilities. These include extremely well-developed auditory (vibration reception akin to hearing), olfactory (smell), and electroreceptory systems, as well as taste and vision sensitive to movement and low-light levels. The auditory system consists of lateral-line pores on the head and sides, pit organs on the back, and an inner ear. Together these enable a shark to perceive the vibrations or sounds produced by feeding or wounded fish, or other stimuli from great distances. At closer range, olfaction, and finally vision become important. Sensory pits inside the mouth enable sharks to discriminate between items and reject those that are distasteful. Recent studies have shown that elasmobranchs possess an acute ability to detect the weak electrical fields emitted by the muscular action of living organisms. This is particularly useful for species that prey on sand- or crevice-dwelling organisms.

Fertilization of elasmobranchs is internal and achieved by the insertion of one of a pair of male organs known as claspers. Although resembling a penis, each clasper is actually a modification of the pelvic fin which has an internal hook that anchors inside the female's cloaca. In sharks, the male grasps the female behind the head and twists his body around the female's to copulate. Unlike bony fishes, elasmobranchs produce relatively few offspring that require a lengthy period of gestation. Most sharks and rays give birth to fully-developed young that strike out on their own immediately after birth. In ovoviviparous species, the embryos develop inside an egg case and hatch internally. In viviparous species, there is no egg case and the embryos obtain nutrition from a yolk as well as an umbilical cord. A few species are oviparous, that is they lay eggs which, in sharks and rays, are encased in a leathery case.

Only a small number of the worlds 700-800 species of elasmobranches dwell on coral reefs. Approximately 13 species of sharks, one guitarfish, and 5 rays occur on Micronesian reefs. A few primarily pelagic species that are transient visitors to offshore reefs and banks are also included.

Class Osteichthyes (Bony Fishes)

This class includes the vast bulk of the world's approximately 23,000 species of fishes. Although there is an enormous range in morphology within the group, most bony fishes are characterized by distinct upper and lower jaws, a single gill opening on each side of the head, overlapping scales covering the body, a bony skeleton, and bony rays supporting the fins. With the exception of four families of lobefin fishes (the coelacanth and three families of lungfishes) that contain less than a half-dozen species, all living species are members of the subclass Actinopterygii, popularly known as ray-fin fishes. The ray-fin fishes further consist of a few primitive families of freshwater fishes and the more recently evolved teleostean or "advanced bony fishes". The teleosts comprise about 22,000 species of fishes that have invaded virtually every aquatic niche of the planet from high mountain streams to the deepest ocean depths, from deep caves and thermal springs to beneath the polar ice caps. About 10,000 species live in fresh water, the remainder in marine or brackish waters. Teleosts range in size from minute gobies less than 10 mm (0.4 in) in length to the giant blue marlin which reaches a length of 5 m (16 ft) and a weight of over 1,000 kg (2,200 lbs).

Approximately 1,243 of the 1,382 species of bony inshore fishes known from Micronesia inhabit or regularly visit coral reefs at depths of less than 60 m. All are featured in individual accounts, and nearly all of the species conspicuous enough to be seen by even the most careful observer are illustrated in color.

SYSTEMATIC SECTION

How to use this book

This book is written primarily as an identification guide to fishes as they are seen living in their natural habitat. As such, the color photographs are the primary means of identification. Unfortunately, not all species can be easily distinguished by photographs alone, some are rarely seen and virtually impossible to photograph in their natural state, and colors usually alter after death and are lost after a few weeks of preservation. For these reasons, the basic morphological characters that can be counted or measured (termed meristics) are given for each species. For difficult groups, keys or other aids to identification are provided. The color plates are located between pp. 154 and 155. Text figures are numbered consecutively within families (except small families may be lumped). A representative species account and explanation is provided below:

scientific name, describer, and year —

common name ——————

incorrect recently used scientific names

maximum size and meristics

notes on ecology, behavior, and life history

geographic distribution ————

Chromis viridis (Cuvier, 1830)   Pl. 77B,C —— location of illustrations

Blue-green chromis

(*C. caerulea*)

SL: to 68 mm (2.7 in); D XII, (9)-11; A II, 9-11; P 17-18; LP 15-17; GR 8-10+20-24=28-30.

Huge aggregations of this brilliant little chromis often occur above thickets of branching corals in sheltered areas such as subtidal reef flats and lagoons to a depth of 12 m. Swarms of juveniles occur above smaller isolated coral heads. Courting males develop blackish dorsal fin and upper pectoral rays and in some areas (e.g. Kosrae) may become mostly yellow posteriorly.

Indo-Pacific: Red Sea to Line, Marquesan , and Tuamotu Is., n. to the Ryukyus, s. to New Caledonia; throughout Micronesia.

Scientific and common names: both are given (see p. 26). Since there are six or more native languages in Micronesia, it is unfeasable to give the native names of the fishes. Those interested in Micronesian names are advised to use an appropriate reference together with this book (see Amesbury and Myers, 1982; Helfman and Randall, 1973; Johannes, 1982).

Describer and year: the person who first described this species and the year in which it was described. Parentheses indicate that the species was originally described in a different genus. In this case, *Chromis viridis* was originally named as a member of the genus *Heliases* by Cuvier in 1830. *Heliases* is now regarded as a synonym of the earlier named genus, *Chromis*.

Incorrect recently used scientific names: synonyms and misidentifications. In this case, *Chromis caerulea* is a different species. Recent (1953 or later) misidentifications of Micronesian fishes are followed by the author and date of the work containing the misidentification (not to be confused with the describer and date of the species named in the misidentification). That work can be found in the bibliography. A synonym is a name given to what was originally thought to be an undescribed or a different species. Unlike a synonym, a name used in a misidentification is either a valid name of a different species or a synonym of a different species.

Maximim size: the maximum reliable known size for this species, usually given as standard length.

Meristics: counts and measurements useful for identifying the species. Consult pp. 28 -30 for standard methods and the family introduction for methods specific to the family in question.

Notes on ecology, behavior, and life history: the heart of the text. Here the habitat, diet, behavior, and other anecdotal information on the species are given.

Geographic distribution: the approximate limits of the species' distribution, followed by its known distribution within Micronesia. "Throughout Micronesia" indicates that the species has been reliably recorded from at least one island in each of the major island groups: the Carolines (Belau to Kosrae), Marianas, and Marshalls.(but not necessarily the outlying atolls of Kapingamarangi and Wake.)   More specific Micronesian localities are given in the checklist (pp. 271-281).

Class CHONDRICHTHYES

Order LAMNIFORMES (SHARKS)

RHINCODONTIDAE (WHALE SHARK)

Rhincodon typus (Smith, 1825)   Fig. 7a
Whale shark
TL: to at least 12 m (39 ft), possibly 18 m (59 ft); Wt: to
41,000 kg (45 tons).
The whale shark is the world's largest fish. Although exclusively pelagic, it has been known to enter atoll lagoons or
swim above outer reef slopes. Despite its enormous size, it
is harmless and on rare occasions has given divers the thrill
of hitching a ride on its fins. Whale sharks feed on plankton, pelagic crustaceans, baitfish, squid and even unwary
tuna that are sieved from the water by spongy tissue between
the gill arches. The recent discoveries of free-swimming
juveniles as small as 550 cm as well as an internal yolk sac
in the only known embryo, suggest that whale sharks are
ovoviviparous, that is they give birth to fully developed
young that are hatched inside the mother. (Lit.: Compagno,
1984; Johnson, 1978)
Circumtropical: rare throughout most of its range; recently
photographed at Belau.

ORECTOLOBIDAE
(NURSE, ZEBRA, and CARPET SHARKS)

Sharks of this family possess distinctive nasal barbels, a
groove that joins each nostril to the mouth, relatively small
mouths with upper and lower lip grooves and small multicuspid teeth, and elongate tails that lack a distinct lower
lobe. They are relatively sluggish and harmless, spending
most of the time resting on the bottom. Two species occur
in Micronesia. (Lit.: Compagno, 1984; Johnson, 1978)

Nebrius concolor (Rüppell, 1837)   Pl. 7A; Fig.1b
Nurse shark
(*N. ferruginius* Lesson, 1830: a *nomen nudum*)
TL: to 320 cm (10.5 ft).
This large sluggish shark is typically found resting on sand
near coral heads, particularly where currents flow. It occurs
on both lagoon and seaward reefs at depths of 1 to at least 70
m. It is most active at night and feeds on a variety of animals including cephalopods, crustaceans, fishes, and even
sea urchins. It has been observed to literally suck prey from
a crevice or root it from shelter by breaking coral. Males
mature at 250 cm TL and females mature at 230 cm. Four
or more fully developed young are born per litter.
Indo-Pacific: Red Sea to the Tuamotus, n. to s. Japan, s. to
New Caledonia; throughout Micronesia.

Stegastoma varium (Seba, 1758)   Pl. 7B; Fig.1c
Zebra shark (juv.); **Leopard shark** (adult)
(*S. fasciatum*)
TL: to 233 cm (7.7 ft).
The juvenile color pattern of white bars on a black back-
ground gradually breaks up into a pattern of leopard-like
spots with growth. The leopard shark inhabits sand, rubble,
or coral bottoms at depths of 5 to at least 30 m. It generally
rests on the bottom during the day and forages at night for
molluscs or an occasional small fish. In the western Indian
Ocean females mature at 170 cm and bear fully developed
young as small as 20 cm.
Indo-Pacific: Red Sea to Samoa, n. to s. Japan, s. to New
South Wales; Belau and Yap in Micronesia.

HEMIGALEIDAE

Triaenodon obesus (Rüppell,1835)
Reef whitetip shark   Pl. 7C; Fig. 1d
TL: to 170 cm (5.6 ft); spiracles usually present; teeth 47-
50/44-46, in at least 2 functional rows; no interdorsal ridge.
The white tips on the dorsal fins and tail fin, blunt snout,
and nasal flaps are distinctive. This is one of the most common sharks of lagoon and seaward reefs at depths below 3 m
and has been observed as deep as 122 m from a submersible.
Like the nurse sharks, it often rests on the bottom, usually
on a sand patch, or in a channel, or "resident" cave. It is
more active at night or during slack tide in areas of strong
currents. Reef whitetips feed on fishes, octopuses and crustaceans. They are especially adept at wrenching prey from
the shelter of the reef. In turn they occasionally fall prey to
larger sharks or giant groupers. They are relatively inoffen-
sive unless provoked or attracted by speared fish. Males
mature at 100 cm, females at 125 cm. One to five 60 cm
young are born per litter. (Lit.: Compagno, 1984; Johnson,
1978; Randall, 1977)
Indo-pan-Pacific: Red Sea to Panama, n. to the Ryukyus and
Bonins, s. to New South Wales, New Caledonia, and the
Australs; throughout Micronesia.

CARCHARHINIDAE (REQUIEM SHARKS)

This appropriately named family includes some of the most
dangerous of sharks. Its members are typically sleek, active
swimmers characterized by the first dorsal fin base located in
front of the pelvic fins, single cusped teeth in one functional
row in each jaw, a tail fin with a distinct lower lobe, and an
absence of nasal barbels. (Lit.: Compagno, 1984; Garrick,
1982; Johnson, 1978)

Carcharhinus albimarginatus (Rüppell, 1835)
Silvertip shark   Pl. 7D; Fig. 1e
TL: to 275 cm (9 ft); teeth 13-1 or-2-13/12-1 or 2-12; inter-
dorsal ridge present.

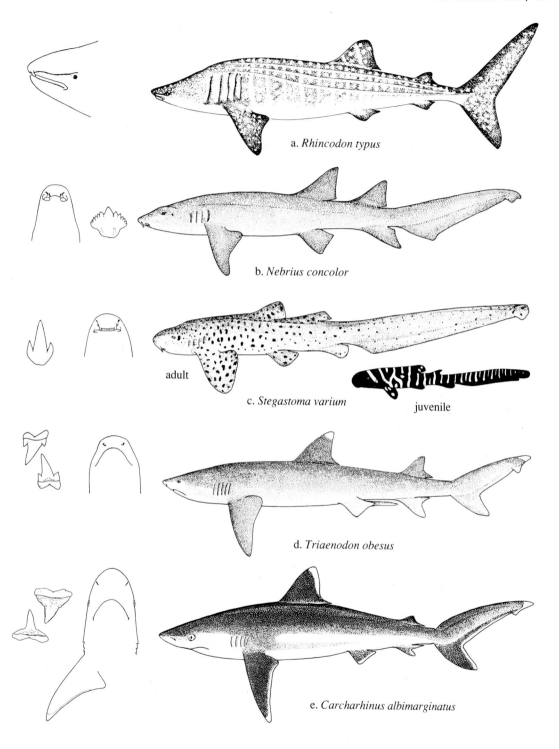

a. *Rhincodon typus*

b. *Nebrius concolor*

adult

c. *Stegastoma varium*

juvenile

d. *Triaenodon obesus*

e. *Carcharhinus albimarginatus*

Fig. 1. Micronesian sharks (all except juv. *Stegastoma* after Gloerfelt-Tarp and Kailola, 1984).

The white tips and trailing margins of the dorsal, pectoral, and tail fins are distinctive. This species typically inhabits dropoffs and offshore banks at depths of 30 to 400 m, but occasionally enters lagoons and deep channels or approaches the surface. It feeds primarily on both bottom oriented and pelagic fishes including eagle rays and small sharks, and occasionally on cephalopods. It is generally cautious, but when attracted by a stimulant such as speared fish, may be quite persistent and potentially dangerous. In the southern hemisphere both breeding and pupping occur in summer. Up to 11 pups ranging in size from 50 to 80 cm are born after a gestation period of 12 months. Males mature at a length of 165 cm or more, females at over 170 cm.

Indo-pan-Pacific: Red Sea to Central America and the Galapagos Is., n. to s. Japan, s. to New Caledonia and the Tuamotus; throughout Micronesia; absent from Australia and the Hawaiian Is.; primarily insular.

Carcharhinus amblyrhynchos (Bleeker,1856)
Grey reef shark   Pl. 7E; Fig. 2a
(*C. menisirrah*; *C. wheeleri*)
TL: to 233 cm (7.1 ft); teeth 13-1 or 2-13/12 or 13-1-12 or 13; no interdorsal ridge.

The grey reef shark closely resembles a number of other species, but can be distinguished by a broad dark band along the trailing edge of its tail. This is the species of shark most likely to be encountered in open water above the reef, particularly along steep outer reef slopes or dropoffs, and is known from the depth range of 1 to 274 m. It is not common on the heavily fished, most accessible reefs of Guam but is abundant on many of the offshore banks, the islands of the northern Marianas and Micronesian atolls where it frequents lagoons and channels as well as seaward reefs. Although usually merely curious, the grey reef shark has gained a reputation for aggressive behavior which may be manifested in the form of a distinctive display termed "threat posturing" which may be followed by an attack. Aggression towards humans appears to be territorial in nature rather than hunger-motivated and attacks generally result in one nasty, usually non-fatal, bite. It is fortunate that this shark remains relatively small. When present in large numbers and stimulated by speared fish, a feeding frenzy may ensue. Occasionally grey reef sharks, particularly juveniles, occur in roving packs. They feed primarily on small fishes under 30 cm in length and to a lesser extent on larger fishes, cephalopods, and crustaceans such as lobsters and crabs. The grey reef shark is viviparous, that is, it gives birth to fully developed young. Gestation takes about a year and litter sizes range from 1 to 6. Newborn pups are 45 to 60 cm and maturation occurs at a size of 130-140 cm and age of 7 years. Maximum lifespan is probably on the order of 25 years.

Indo-Pacific: Red Sea to the Marquesas and Easter Is., n. to the Hawaiian Is., s. to Lord Howe Is; throughout Micronesia.

Carcharhinus falciformis (Bibron, 1841)
Silky shark   Fig. 2b
TL: to 305 cm (10 ft); teeth 16-2-16/16-1-16; interdorsal ridge present.

The short dorsal fin, general lack of distinctive markings, and occasional brownish tint are useful identifying characteristics. Although pelagic, the silky shark occasionally visits offshore banks or outer reef slopes adjacent to deep water. Its usual habitat is the upper 400 to 500m of open sea. It feeds on fishes, including tuna and baitfishes, cephalopods, and even crabs. Maturation occurs at roughly 210 cm TL, and two to fourteen 73 to 87 cm pups are born per litter.
Circumtropical: throughout Micronesia.

Carcharhinus galapagensis
(Snodgrass & Heller, 1905)   Fig. 2c
Galapagos shark
TL: to 370 cm (12.1 ft); teeth 14-1-14/14-1-14; interdorsal ridge present.

This species closely resembles the grey reef shark but differs by lacking a dusky margin on the trailing edge of its tail and attaining a larger size. It is one of the most abundant sharks of steep outer reef slopes and offshore banks at depths from below 30 to at least 180 m. Juveniles have been observed in 2 to 25 m. Adults may be lured to the surface by hooked or speared fish and can be quite aggressive. This species feeds primarily on fishes, including other sharks and rays, and to a lesser extent on cephalopods and crustaceans. In the Hawaiian Islands, 6 to 16 young of 57 to 80 cm are born per litter.
Circumtropical: throughout Micronesia.

Carcharhinus limbatus (Valenciennes, 1841)
Blackfin shark   Fig. 2d
TL: o to 247 cm (8.1 ft); o to 226 cm (7.4 ft); teeth 15-2 or 3-15/15-1-15; no interdorsal ridge.

This uncommon shark has a distinctively pointed snout and black tips (sometimes indistinct) on all of its fins except the upper lobe of its tail. It prefers turbid lagoons, inshore waters, or estuaries at depths of less than 30 m but is occasionally encountered in passes or on outer reef slopes. It is a rapid swimmer that feeds primarily on fishes, including fast-swimming pelagic species, and occasionally on cephalopods or crustaceans. Breeding and pupping take place during the warmer half of the year. Off East Africa, maturation occurs at under 180 cm and females bear from 1 to 10 young per litter, each at a size of 60 cm.
Circumtropical: Marshalls in Micronesia.

Carcharhinus longimanus (Poey, 1861)   Fig. 2e
Oceanic whitetip shark
TL: to 270 cm (12.1 ft); teeth 14-2-14/14-2-14; interdorsal ridge usually present.

The unusually large, well-rounded fins with white tips are unmistakable. The oceanic whitetip is probably the most abundant shark of the surface layers of tropical seas above the 200 to 500m depth contours. On rare occasions it visits reefs or offshore banks as shallow as 17m. It feeds primarily on pelagic squids and fishes, including tuna and mahimahi. Males mature at <198 cm TL, females at 180 to190 cm. One to fifteen 60 to 65 cm pups are born per litter.

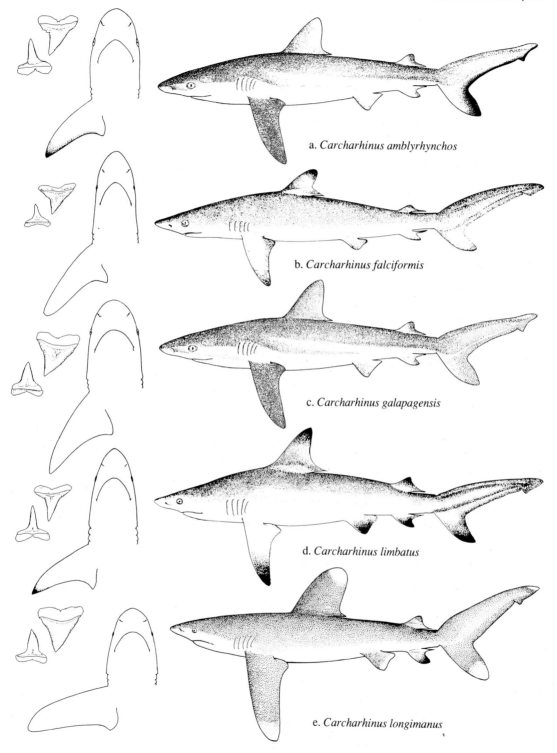

a. *Carcharhinus amblyrhynchos*

b. *Carcharhinus falciformis*

c. *Carcharhinus galapagensis*

d. *Carcharhinus limbatus*

e. *Carcharhinus longimanus*

Fig. 2. Micronesian sharks (all except c after Gloerfelt-Tarp and Kailola, 1984).

Circumtropical: usually in water over 20°C; rarely in water as cool as 15°C.

Carcharhinus melanopterus
(Quoy & Gaimard, 1824)   Pl. 7F; Fig. 3a
Reef blacktip shark

TL: to 180 cm (5.9 ft); teeth 12-1 or 2-12/11-1-11; no interdorsal ridge.

The black tips on the fins, white band on the dorsal fin, and light streak on each side are distinctive. The reef blacktip is the most frequently encountered shark of reef flats, shallow lagoons, and reef margins. It rarely occurs at depths of 20 to 75 m. When in pursuit of prey it may enter water so shallow that much of its back and fins are exposed. It feeds on small fishes and cephalopods. On rare occasions it has been known to bite waders but these are probably cases of mistaken identity since it is normally quite shy and easily frightened. Maturation occurs at a small size (109 cm for males; 112 cm for females) and in some areas there may be two breeding seasons. Two to four 46 to 52 cm pups are born per litter.

Indo-Pacific: Red Sea to Mangareva and the Marquesas, n. to s. Japan and the Hawaiian Is., s. to New Caledonia; throughout Micronesia.

Galeocerdo cuvier (Peron & Lesueur,1822)
Tiger shark   Fig. 3b

TL: to at least 550 cm (18 ft); teeth 10 or 11-1-10 or 11/11-1-11; spiracles and interdorsal ridge present.

In Micronesia, the tiger shark typically inhabits deep outer reef slopes and offshore banks. It occasionally enters shallow waters of channels and lagoons to forage, generally at night. It is an indiscriminate scavenger of almost anything of animal origin as well as occasional inanimate refuse. Dietary items reported include other sharks, rays, fishes (including toxic or armored species such as *Lactoria cornuta* or *Diodon hystrix*), porpoises, whales, sea turtles, sea birds, crustaceans, cephalopods, domestic animals, humans, tin cans, and plastic bags. Up to 80 or more pups ranging from 51 to 104 cm are born in each litter. Males mature at a size of 290 cm, females at 340 cm. There is little doubt that the tiger shark is the most dangerous animal inhabiting coral reefs and that it has been responsible for numerous fatal attacks on humans. Fortunately, it is rarely encountered by divers since it tends to frequent relatively deep waters by day or turbid inshore areas of large land masses.

Circumglobal in tropical and warm temperate seas; throughout Micronesia.

Negaprion acutidens (Rüppell, 1835)   Fig. 3c
Lemon Shark

(*Hemigaleops forsteri*)

TL: to 310 cm (10.2 ft); teeth 14-1 or 2-14/14-1 or 2-14; spiracles minute or absent; no interdorsal ridge.

The two nearly equally large dorsal fins and yellowish hue distinguish the lemon shark from other Micronesian carcharhinids. This rare species occurs in both lagoons and on seaward reefs but is reported to prefer turbid inshore lagoons un-der 30 m deep. It feeds on bottom-dwelling fishes and rays. It is reputed to be very shy yet easily enraged if disturbed. Where known, mating and pupping take place during the late spring and early summer. One to eleven 45 cm young are born per litter.

Indo-Pacific: Red Sea to the Tuamotus, s. to Queensland, n. to Belau and the Marshalls in Micronesia.

SPHYRNIDAE (HAMMERHEAD SHARKS)

Hammerhead sharks are easily identified by the bazaar laterally expanded blades extending from the sides of the head. The eyes are located at the tip of each blade. The blades presumably serve to increase the shark's sensory capabilities by allowing more space for a larger lateral line system, more Ampullae of Lorenzi, expanded nasal organs, and possibly enhanced electromagnetic senses and binocular vision. At least two of the world's nine or ten species occur in Micronesia. (Lit.: Compagno, 1984; Johnson, 1978)

Sphyrna lewini (Griffith & Smith, 1834)   Fig. 3d
Scalloped hammerhead shark

TL: to 330 cm (10.8 ft); teeth 15-2-15/15-1-15.

Adults of this hammerhead are primarily pelagic and inhabit depths in excess of 200 m. However, mating and pupping occur in shallow turbid backwaters such as Guam's inner Apra Harbor. Juveniles are particularly common there. Up to 30 pups, ranging in size from 43-55 cm, may be born per litter. Males mature at a size of over 140 cm, females at a size of over 200 cm. Young often occur in schools which forage near the bottom, then migrate to deeper outer reef waters as they grow. The scalloped hammerhead's diet consists primarily of fishes, including other sharks and rays, and to a lesser extent of cephalopods and crustaceans. It is generally non-aggressive unless stimulated by the presence of wounded or struggling fish.

Circumtropical: Carolines and Marianas in Micronesia.

Sphyrna mokorran (Rüppell, 1837)   Fig. 3e
Great hammerhead shark

TL: to 545 cm (17.9 ft); teeth 17-2-17/17-1-17.

This large hammerhead differs from *S. lewini* by having a nearly straight snout profile and a much longer and more sharply pointed dorsal fin. It has not previously been reported from Micronesia, but has been photographed at a depth of about 36 m near the Saies Cavern along the outer dropoff of leeward Belau. In French Polynesia, it occurs in atoll lagoons and passes. There it is not considered aggressive, but elsewhere it is known to attack man. This species feeds primarily on fishes, particularly rays, but will also eat crabs and squid. Maturation occurs at over 300 cm, and pupping takes place in the late spring or summer in the northern hemisphere. Up to 38 pups ranging in length from 56 to 70 cm are born per litter.

Circumtropical: Belau in Micronesia.

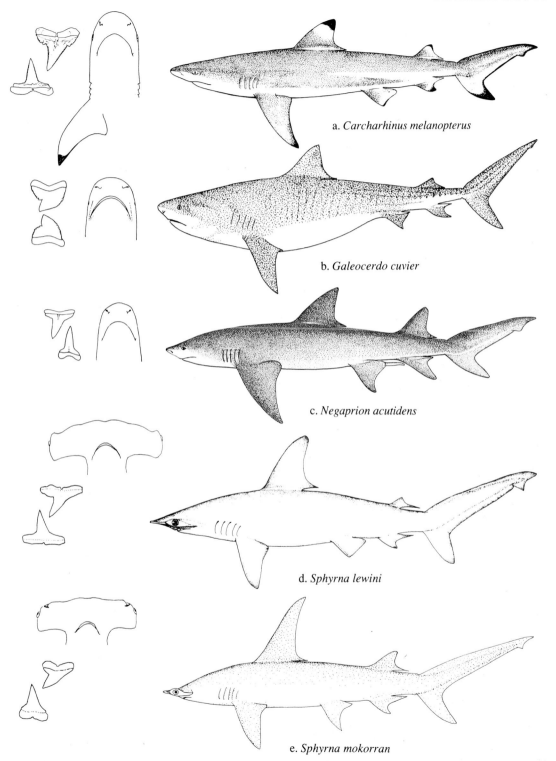

a. *Carcharhinus melanopterus*

b. *Galeocerdo cuvier*

c. *Negaprion acutidens*

d. *Sphyrna lewini*

e. *Sphyrna mokorran*

Fig. 3. Micronesian sharks (all except b after Gloerfelt-Tarp and Kailola, 1984).

ALOPIIDAE (THRESHER SHARKS)

Alopias pelagicus Nakamura, 1935
Smalltooth thresher shark
Fig. 4a.

TL: to 330 cm.

Thresher sharks are readily identified by the greatly elongate upper tailfin lobe which is nearly as long as the body. In the tropics they are usually mesopelagic, inhabiting relatively cool water below 300m. On rare occasions they may enter atoll lagoons and a juvenile specimen has been speared near a dropoff at Guam. Thresher sharks may use their tail to aggregate, then stun the small fishes on which they feed. (Lit.: Compagno, 1984; Johnson, 1978)

Circumglobal: generally mesopelagic in the tropics; to the surface in temperate seas.

Order RHINOBATIFORMES

RHINOBATIDAE (GUITARFISHES)

Rhynchobatus djiddensis (Forsskål, 1775)   Pl. 8B
White-spotted guitarfish

TL: to 305 cm (10.0 ft); Wt: to 227 kg (500 lb); teeth 31-41/37-48.

Guitarfishes are elongate, thick-bodied rays that resemble a cross between a shark and a ray. Like other rays their mouths are small and contain flattened, pavement-like teeth. The white-spotted guitarfish inhabits shallow sandy bottoms from the surfline to a depth of 30 m or more. It feeds on crabs, squid, and small fishes. Off East Africa, males mature at 156 cm and females mature at 177 cm. Fully developed young are born at a size of 55 to 67 cm. Guitarfishes are rare around oceanic islands but common along continental shorelines. (Lit.: Compagno *in* Smith and Heemstra, 1986)

Indo-west-Pacific: Red Sea to New Caledonia, n. to s. Japan, s. to New South Wales; Marianas in Micronesia.

Order MYLIOBATIDIFORMES (RAYS)

DASYATIDIDAE (STINGRAYS)

Stingrays have a greatly depressed disc, a distinct tail with one or more venemous barbs, a small mouth with close-set pavement-like teeth, and lack dorsal fins. They respire by drawing water through a small hole behind each eye known as a spiracle and expelling it through gill slits located under the disc. They give birth to fully developed young that are nourished from glands within the uterus as embryos. (Lit.: Compagno *in* Smith and Heemstra, 1986)

Dasyatis kuhlii (Müller & Henle, 1841)   Pl. 8C
Blue spotted stingray

Width: to 40 cm (1.3 ft); TL: to 80 cm (2.6 ft); tooth rows 25-30 in each jaw.

The blue spotted stingray inhabits sand flats of lagoon and seaward reefs from the shoreline to depths of 50 m. It occasionally covers itself with sand, leaving only its eyes and tail visible, and feeds on sand-dwelling invertebrates.

Indo-west-Pacific: Red Sea to Samoa, n. to s. Japan, s. to New Caledonia; Marianas and Carolines in Micronesia.

Himantura uarnak (Forsskål, 1775)   Fig. 4b
Leopard ray
(*Dasyatus gerrardi*)

Width: to 175 cm (5.7 ft); TL: to ca. 6 m (20 ft, but mostly tail); Wt: to 118 kg (260 lb); tooth rows 26-40/27-44.

The coloration of this ray is quite variable, ranging from a light brown with almost imperceptable darker spots to a light cream with black spots that turns into a reticulated pattern of dark squiggly lines with age. There may be more than one species involved. The leopard ray occurs in a wide range of sandy to muddy habitats from brackish water river mouths to clear lagoon or seaward atoll reefs at depths of 1 to at least 42 m.

Indo-west-Pacific: Red Sea to Kapingamarangi, n. to the Ryukyus, s. to Queensland; Carolines in Micronesia.

Taeniura melanospilos Bleeker, 1853   Pl. 8D
Black-spotted stingray, Giant reef ray
(*T. brocki*)

Width: to 164 cm (5.4 ft); TL: to ca. 300 cm (10 ft); Wt: to 153 kg (337 lb); tooth rows 37-46/39-45.

This is the largest of the bottom-dwelling rays known from Micronesia. It is relatively uncommon but occurs in a variety of habitats ranging from shallow lagoons to outer reef slopes and has been trawled from as deep as 430 m off East Africa. It feeds on both sand-dwelling and reef-dwelling fishes; the latter are probably taken at night as they sleep.

Indo-Pacific: Red Sea to the Marquesas, n. to s. Japan, s. to New Caledonia; throughout Micronesia.

Urogymnus asperrimus (Bloch &Schneider, 1801)
Porcupine ray
Fig. 4c
(*U. africanus* ?)

Width: to >100 cm (36 in); tooth rows ca. 48 in each jaw.

The porcupine ray lacks a venemous barb, but its upper surface is covered with thornlike tubercles. It is known from Micronesia on the basis of a specimen recently taken from the lagoon of Enewetak Atoll.

Indo-Pacific: E. Africa to the Great Barrier Reef and Marshall Is.

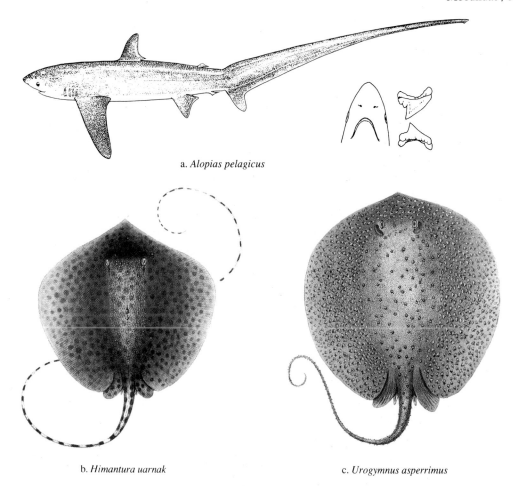

a. *Alopias pelagicus*

b. *Himantura uarnak*

c. *Urogymnus asperrimus*

Figure 4. Micronesian thresher sharks and rays (a, after Gloerfelt-Tarp and Kailola, 1984; b, c, after Bleeker).

MYLIOBATIDAE (EAGLE RAYS)

Aetobatis narinari (Euphrasen, 1790)   Pl. 8E
Spotted Eagle ray

Width: to 229 cm (7.5 ft); Wt: to 227 kg (500 lb).

The spotted eagle ray occurs from shallow sand flats to outer reef slopes at depths of 80 m or more in areas of clear water. It is usually solitary but occasionally occurs in groups of a dozen or more. It feeds on mollusks and crustaceans which it digs from the sand. Unlike most rays, it spends much of its time swimming well above the bottom. An average of four pups, ranging in size from 17 to 35 cm in width, are born per litter. (Lit.: Compagno *in* Smith and Heemstra, 1986)

Circumtropical: throughout Micronesia.

MOBULIDAE (MANTA RAYS)

Manta alfredi (Krefft, 1868)   Pl. 8A
Manta ray

Width: to >300 cm (10 ft).

Mantas are the largest of all rays: one species, *M. birostris*, which may be identical to, and a senior synonym of *M. alfredi*, attains a width of 6.7 m (23 ft) and weight of 1,400 kg (3,100 lb). Mantas occur singly or in small groups in surface or mid-waters of lagoons and seaward reefs, particularly near channels. They feed by straining zooplankton or baitfish from the water through a branchial sieve apparatus and are entirely harmless. (Lit.: Compagno *in* Smith and Heemstra, 1986)

Indo-Pacific: Red Sea to the Marquesas and Tuamotus, n. to the Hawaiian Is., s. to New South Wales; throughout Micronesia.

Class OSTEICHTHYES - BONY FISHES

Order ANGUILLIFORMES

MURAENIDAE (MORAY EELS)

The morays are a diverse group of eels characterized by large mouths with numerous teeth, small gill openings, and the absence of pectoral and pelvic fins. Most have stout muscular bodies but a few are extremely elongate and ribbon-like (*Rinomuraena, Strophiodon*). Most have long, sharp canine teeth (*Enchelycore, Gymnothorax*) and feed on fishes and cephalopods; some have rounded nodular teeth (*Gymnomuraena*) or short conical teeth (*Echidna, Sideria*) and feed on crustaceans. Like most eels, morays undergo a lengthy pelagic leptocephalus larval stage resulting in most species being widely distributed. Morays are much more abundant than one might suspect, but tend to be secretive, remaining in holes and crevices. Many are more active at night than during the day. Most species will bite if provoked, but are normally docile. Large individuals are capable of inflicting serious wounds. Morays are edible and hunted for food throughout much of the world but large individuals in the tropics are frequently ciguatoxic and should never be eaten. At least 53 species in 12 genera are known from Micronesia. Three species (*Gymnothorax berndti, G. elegans*, and *G. neglectus*) are deep-dwelling (ca. 100-300 m) and one (*G. amblyuranodon*) lives primarily in fresh and estuarine waters. They are not included below. (Lit.: McCosker et al., 1984; McCosker and Rosenblatt, 1975; McCosker and Randall, 1977, 1982; Randall and McCosker, 1975; Randall et al., 1981)

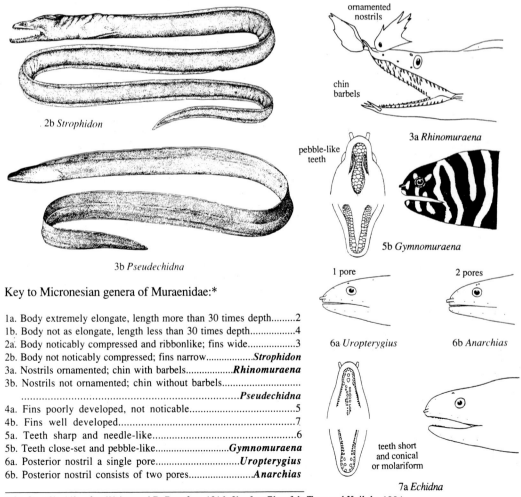

2b *Strophidon*

ornamented nostrils

chin barbels

3a *Rhinomuraena*

pebble-like teeth

3b *Pseudechidna*

5b *Gymnomuraena*

1 pore

2 pores

6a *Uropterygius*

6b *Anarchias*

teeth short and conical or molariform

7a *Echidna*

Key to Micronesian genera of Muraenidae:*

1a. Body extremely elongate, length more than 30 times depth.........2
1b. Body not as elongate, length less than 30 times depth.................4
2a. Body noticably compressed and ribbonlike; fins wide.................3
2b. Body not noticably compressed; fins narrow.................**Strophidon**
3a. Nostrils ornamented; chin with barbels.................**Rhinomuraena**
3b. Nostrils not ornamented; chin without barbels.............................
....**Pseudechidna**
4a. Fins poorly developed, not noticable.....................................5
4b. Fins well developed...7
5a. Teeth sharp and needle-like..6
5b. Teeth close-set and pebble-like.........................**Gymnomuraena**
6a. Posterior nostril a single pore.............................**Uropterygius**
6b. Posterior nostril consists of two pores.......................**Anarchias**

* 3a, 3b, 10b, 11b, after Weber and DeBeaufort, 1916; 2b after Gloerfelt-Tarp and Kailola, 1984.

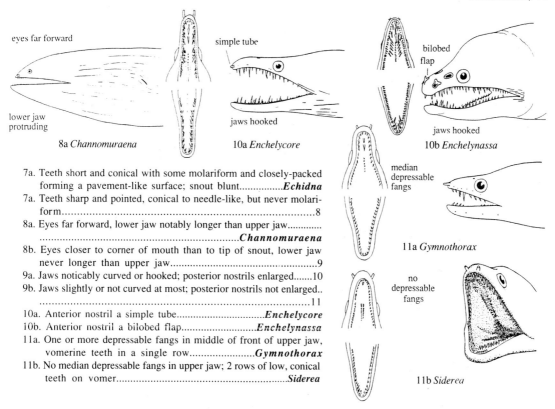

eyes far forward

lower jaw protruding

8a *Channomuraena*

simple tube

jaws hooked

10a *Enchelycore*

bilobed flap

jaws hooked

10b *Enchelynassa*

median depressable fangs

11a *Gymnothorax*

no depressable fangs

11b *Siderea*

7a. Teeth short and conical with some molariform and closely-packed forming a pavement-like surface; snout blunt................***Echidna***

7a. Teeth sharp and pointed, conical to needle-like, but never molariform...8

8a. Eyes far forward, lower jaw notably longer than upper jaw...***Channomuraena***

8b. Eyes closer to corner of mouth than to tip of snout, lower jaw never longer than upper jaw.......................................9

9a. Jaws noticably curved or hooked; posterior nostrils enlarged.......10

9b. Jaws slightly or not curved at most; posterior nostrils not enlarged..11

10a. Anterior nostril a simple tube................................***Enchelycore***

10b. Anterior nostril a bilobed flap.........................***Enchelynassa***

11a. One or more depressable fangs in middle of front of upper jaw, vomerine teeth in a single row.....................***Gymnothorax***

11b. No median depressable fangs in upper jaw; 2 rows of low, conical teeth on vomer...***Siderea***

Anarchias allardicei Jordan & Starks, 1906
Allardice's moray

TL: to 17 cm (6.7 in); Hl 7.5-7.8; depth 18-22.

Species of *Anarchias* are rarely seen unless driven from interstices of the reef by the application of an ichthyocide such as rotenone. This species is uniformly light brown.

Indo-Pacific: Chagos Is., to the Hawaiian and Society Is., s. to the s. Great Barrier Reef; throughout Micronesia.

Anarchias cantonensis (Schultz, 1943)   Fig. 1a
Canton Island moray

TL: to 20 cm (7.9 in); HL 7.2-8.0; depth 20-28.

This species is brown with light stellate spots.

Pacific Plate: Marianas and Marshalls to Johnston Is. and Rapa; throughout Micronesia.

Anarchias seychellensis Smith, 1962)
Seychelles moray

(*A. leucurus* Schultz, 1953)

TL: to 29 cm (11 in); HL 8.1-9.6; depth 20-25.

This species has rows of irregular or stellate pale spots which tend to be larger than those on *A. cantonensis*. It occurs common among rubble, coralline algal debris, and coral heads of shallow wave-washed reefs.

Indo-Pacific: E. Africa to Easter Is., n. to Marcus Is., s. to Lord Howe and Rapa Is., Marianas and Marshalls in Micronesia.

Channomuraena vittata Richardson, 1844
Long-jawed moray   key 8a

TL: to 120 cm (3 ft 11 in).

This rare eel is remarkable in both morphology and distribution. The small cranium, anterior position of the eyes, and enlarged lower jaw are unique. It is known from a few specimens taken from outer reef slopes to depths of 10 m or more.

Circumtropical: Christmas Is., Hawaiian Is., and Belau in the Indo-Pacific.

Echidna leucotaenia Schultz, 1943   Fig. 1b
Whiteface moray

TL: to 75 cm (30 in); HL 6.7-7.4; depth 13-19.

Species of *Echidna* have stout conical teeth that tend to become pebble-like, more numerous, and closely-packed with age. This species lives among rubble deposits on the lee side of shallow wave-washed reefs.

Indo-Pacific: E. Africa to the Line and Tuamotu Is., n. to Johnston Is.; throughout Micronesia.

Echidna nebulosa (Ahl, 1789)   Pl. 9A
Snowflake moray

TL: to 75 cm (30 in); HL ca. 7; depth 15-20.

The snowflake moray is among the most abundant and conspicuous morays of intertidal reef flats where it may on occasion leave the water to travel between tidal pools. It also occurs on shallow lagoon and seaward reefs to depths of 10 m or more. It is popular in the aquarium trade and is a relatively safe tankmate for other fishes since it feeds primarily on crustaceans.

Indo-pan-Pacific: Red Sea to Panama, n. to the Bonin, Ryukyu, and Hawaiian Is., s. to the Society and Lord Howe Is.; throughout Micronesia.

Echidna polyzona (Richardson, 1844)   Pl. 9B
Barred moray   Fig. 1c
TL: to 60 cm (24 in); HL 6.5; depth ca. 13.

Young individuals are characterized by wide black bands on a white or cream background; the bands become obscure with age. Like *E. nebulosa*, this species inhabits primarily reef flats and clear shallow lagoons. It feeds on small crustaceans during both day and night.

Indo-Pacific: Red Sea to the Hawaiian, Marquesan, and Tuamotu Is., n. to the Ryukyus, s. to the s. Great Barrier Reef; throughout Micronesia.

Echidna unicolor Schultz, 1943   Fig. 1d
Unicolor moray
TL: to 29 cm (11 in); HL 8.3-9.9; depth 18-25.

This uncommon species is uniformly tan to light brown with a dark ring around each eye. It has been collected from shallow lagoon reefs to dropoffs as deep as 25 m.

Indo-Pacific: E. Africa to the Line, Marquesan, and Society Is., n. to the Marshalls and Johnston Is.; throughout Micronesia.

Enchelycore bayeri (Schultz, 1953)   Fig. 1e
Bayer's moray
SL: to 55 cm (22 in); HL 6.9-7.8; depth 12-27.

Species of *Enchelycore* and *Enchelynassa* possess narrow, hooked jaws jammed full of long daggar-like teeth, giving them a truly fearsome appearance. They are quite secretive and rarely encountered by divers. This uniformly brown species occurs on benches and seaward reefs to depths of at least 20 m.

Indo-Pacific: Chagos Is. to the Line and Society Is., n. to the Marianas, s. to the Great Barrier Reef; throughout Micronesia.

Enchelycore bikiniensis (Schultz, 1953)   Fig. 1f
Bikini Atoll moray
TL: to 60 cm (24 in); HL 9.1-10.9; depth 17-24.

In this mottled species, each posterior nostril is greatly enlarged and surrounded by a crenulated rim, and the fins are white-edged. It inhabits crevices of surge channels and rugged wave-swept reefs.

Pacific Plate: Marianas, Marshalls, and Kapingamarangi to Samoa and the Marquesas.

Enchelycore schismatorhynchus(Bleeker, 1853)
White-margined moray
TL: to 120 cm (3 ft 11 in).

In this species, the longest canines of the lower jaw are confined to the anterior third of the toothed area. Its coloration

is a uniform tan with a conspicuous white margin on the fins. It inhabits seaward reefs.

Indo-Pacific: Chagos Is. to the Marquesan and Society Is., n. to the Ryukyus; Marianas and Kapingamarangi in Micronesia.

Enchelynassa canina (Quoy & Gaimard, 1824)
Viper moray   Pl. 9C; key 10b
TL: to 152 cm (5 ft); HL 7.4-8.1; depth 12-17.

In *Enchelynassa* each posterior nostril, located in front of and above the eye, is large and surrounded by a fleshy rim, and each anterior nostril bears a bilobed fleshy protuberance which is absent in species of *Enchelycore* (some ichthyologists place *Enchelynassa* in *Enchelycore*). *E. canina* occurs primarily in areas of strong surge such as benches, outer reef flats and reef fronts to depths of 10 m or more. It probably feeds on fishes and octopuses and appears to be nocturnal, remaining well-hidden during the day.

Indo-pan-Pacific: Chagos Is., to Panama, n. to Marcus and the Hawaiian Is., s. to Tonga and Mangareva; throughout Micronesia.

Gymnomuraena zebra (Shaw, 1797)
Zebra moray   Pl. 9D; key 5b
TL: to 150 cm (4 ft 11 in); HL 15; depth 20.

This species has close-set pebble-like teeth used for crushing hard shelled prey and a unique color pattern of narrow white bands on a black background. It is a secretive inhabitant of crevices and ledges of seaward reefs from the surge zone to depths of at least 39 m. It feeds primarily on xanthid crabs but also takes other crustaceans, mollusks, or even sea urchins. It is rare in Micronesia. It is amazingly docile and on several occasions in the Hawaiian Islands, the author forcibly pulled one by hand from a crevice without ever being bitten.

Indo-pan-Pacific: Red Sea to Panama, n. to the Ryukyu and Hawaiian Is., s. to the Society Is.; throughout Micronesia.

Gymnothorax buroensis (Bleeker, 1837)
Buro moray
TL: to 33 cm (13 in); HL ca. 6.7; depth 9-15.

This small moray is dark brown with irregular dark spots anteriorly, interspersed with lighter granulations that form diffuse crossbars on the tail. It inhabits shallow lagoon and seaward reefs among coral and algae to at least 25 m. It is common in the Marshalls but uncomon in the Marianas.

Indo-pan-Pacific: E. Africa to Panama, n. to the Ryukyu and Hawaiian Is., s. to the Tuamotus; throughout Micronesia.

Gymnothorax enigmaticus
McCosker & Randall, 1982   Fig. 2a
Enigmatic moray
(*G. rupelli*)
TL: to 58 cm 23 in); HL 8; depth 16-23.

This colorful moray closely resembles *G. rueppelliae* but differs in the anteriormost black bands which are complete on the underside rather than incomplete as in *G. rueppelliae*. It is a relatively uncommon inhabitant of intertidal reefs.

a. *Anarchias cantonensis*, Kiribati

b. *Echidna leucotaenia*, Kiribati

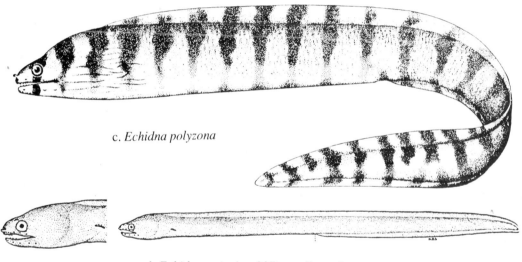

c. *Echidna polyzona*

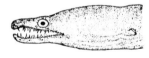

d. *Echidna unicolor*, 227 mm, Rongelap

e. *Enchelycore bayeri*, 398 mm, Rongelap

fimbriated
anterior nostril

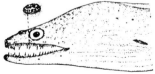

f. *Enchelycore bikiniensis*, mm, 555 mm, Bikini

Fig. 1. Micronesian moray eels (a, b, after Schultz, 1953; d, e, f, after D. B. Schultz *in* Schultz et al., 1953; c, after Jordan and Evermann, 1903).

Indo-Pacific: Gulf of Aden to the Tuamotus, n. to the Ryukyus, s. to Samoa; throughout Micronesia.

Gymnothorax fimbriatus (Bennett, 1831)   Pl. 9E
Fimbriated moray
TL: to 80 cm (32 in); HL 6.8-7.4; depth 15-18.
This small colorful moray inhabits lagoon and seaward reefs to depths of at least 26 m. It is rarely seen by divers and is probably nocturnal.
Indo-Pacific: Mauritius to the Society Is., n. to the Ryukyus, s. to Queensland; throughout Micronesia.

Gymnothorax flavimarginatus(Rüppell,1828)
Yellow-margined moray   Pl. 9F
TL: to > 123 cm (4 ft); HL 6.4-9.7; depth 11-18.
This species has been confused with *G. javanicus* in some recent books. Unlike *G. javanicus*, *G. flavimarginatus* lacks the leopard-like spots of *G. javanicus* and possesses a green fringe on its fins and has reddish eyes. It inhabits coral or rocky areas of a variety of zones ranging from reef flats and protected shorelines to seaward reefs to depths of 150 m. It feeds on fishes and crustaceans.
Indo-pan-Pacific: Red Sea to Panama, n. to the Ryukyu and Hawaiian Is., s. to New Caledonia, the Tuamotus, and the Australs; throughout Micronesia.

Gymnothorax fuscomaculatus (Schultz, 1953)
Brown spotted moray   Fig. 2b
TL: to 18 cm (7.1 in); HL 7.1-7.5; depth 16-19.
The dorsal fin of this species and *G. marshallensis* begins far behind the head, closer to the anus. Although their teeth are short and conical like those of *Siderea*, they possess a single row of vomerine teeth. This small species matures at under 13 cm. It inhabits coral and rubble of seaward reefs to 25 m.
Indo-Pacific: E. Africa to the Tuamotus, s. to Fiji; throughout Micronesia.

Gymnothorax gracilicaudus Jenkins, 1903   Fig. 2c
Graceful-tailed moray
TL: to 30 cm (12 in); HL 7.5-9.1; depth 18-23.
This small mottled moray occurs among corals or rocks of lagoon and seaward reefs.
Pacific Plate: Carolines and Marianas to the Hawaiian, Line and Tuamotu Is.; throughout Micronesia.

Gymnothorax hepaticus (Rüppell, 1828)
TL: to 100 cm (3 ft 4 in).
This species is known from Micronesia on the basis of three tiny juveniles (≤ 90 mm) identified with "considerable uncertainty". They are distinguished from other *Gymnothorax* by their high dorsal fin (≥ depth at anus) and plain brownish coloration with light margins on the fins.
Indo-Pacific: Red Sea to Samoa and the Hawaiian Is. (?), n. to s. Japan; Ifaluk and Guam in Micronesia.

Gymnothorax javanicus (Bleeker, 1859)   Pl. 9G
Giant moray
TL: to 239 cm (7.8 ft), possibly to 300 cm (10 ft); Wt: to

35 kg (77 lb), possibly to 70 kg (154 lb); depth 11-18.
The black specks that grade into leopard-like spots behind the head, black area surrounding the gill opening, and large size are distinctive. Juveniles are tan with numerous large black spots. This is probably the world's largest, but not the longest, species of moray. It occurs on both lagoon and seaward reefs to depths of at least 46 m. Juveniles are more secretive and occur as shallow as 0.2 m on reef flats. The leopard moray is relatively common throughout most of its range where it is among the species most likely to be encountered by divers. It is somewhat more active at night and feeds primarily on fishes and occasionally on crustaceans. Its position at the top of the reef's food chain make it one of the most frequently and severely ciguatoxic of fishes. Even individuals as small as 4 kg should not be eaten.
Indo-Pacific: Red Sea to the Marquesas and Oeno Atoll (Pitcairn group), n. to the Ryukyu and Hawaiian Is., s. to the Australs and New Caledonia; throughout Micronesia.

Gymnothorax margaritophorus Bleeker, 1865
Blotch-necked moray   Fig. 2d
TL: to 70 cm (28 in); HL 7.5-7.9; depth 18-20.
This dark brown moray is characterized by a row of 4 to 5 large, closely-spaced oval black blotches extending behind the eye, and lighter specks that become diffuse bars on the tail. It occurs on reef flats as well as outer reef slopes to a depth of at least 20 m and is unlikely to be encountered without the use of an ichthyocide.
Indo-Pacific: E. Africa to the Line and Society Is., n. to the Ryukyus, s. to the s. Great Barrier Reef; throughout Micronesia.

Gymnothorax marshallensis (Schultz, 1953)
Marshall Islands moray   Fig. 2e
TL: to 18 cm (7.1 in); HL 8.3-9.3; depth 21-26.
This species differs from the similar *G. fuscomaculatus* by its plain brown coloration. It inhabits coral and rubble of shallow wave-washed reefs.
Micronesia: Carolines, Marianas, and Marshalls.

Gymnothorax melatremus Schultz, 1953
Dirty yellow moray   Pl. 9H; Fig. 2f
TL: to 18 cm (7.1 in); HL 7.1-8.9; depth 15-20.
This small uncommon moray has short conical teeth like those of *G. fuscomaculata* and *G. marshallensis*. It is a dirty yellow when alive. It inhabits holes and crevices of seaward reefs from the surge zone to over 26 m.
Indo-Pacific: E. Africa to the Marquesas and Mangareva, n. to the Hawaiian Is., s. to the Australs; throughout Micronesia.

Gymnothorax meleagris (Shaw & Nodder, 1795)
Whitemouth moray   Pl. 10A; Fig. 2g
TL: to 120 cm (3.9 ft); HL 7-8; depth 12-19.
The inside of this colorful moray's mouth is completely white. The whitemouth moray inhabits coral-rich areas of lagoon and seaward reefs from depths of 1 to over 36 m. It feeds primarily on fishes and to a lesser extent on crusta-

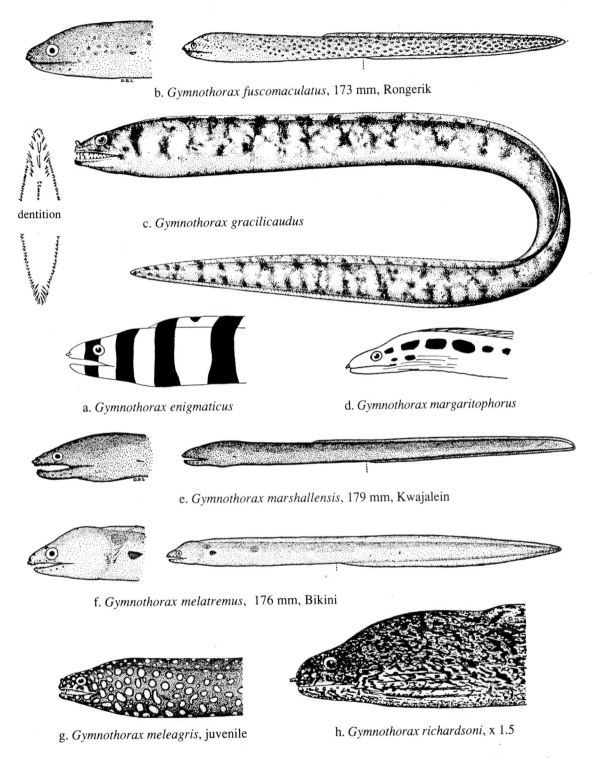

b. *Gymnothorax fuscomaculatus*, 173 mm, Rongerik

dentition

c. *Gymnothorax gracilicaudus*

a. *Gymnothorax enigmaticus*

d. *Gymnothorax margaritophorus*

e. *Gymnothorax marshallensis*, 179 mm, Kwajalein

f. *Gymnothorax melatremus*, 176 mm, Bikini

g. *Gymnothorax meleagris*, juvenile

h. *Gymnothorax richardsoni*, x 1.5

Fig. 2. Micronesian moray eels (b, e, f, after D. B. Schultz *in* Schultz et al., 1953; c, g, after Jordan and Evermann, 1903; h, after Weber and deBeaufort, 1916; dentition after Schultz, 1953).

ceans. Although common in the Hawaiian Islands, it is relatively uncommon in Micronesia.

Indo-Pacific: Red Sea to the Marquesas and Mangareva, n. to s. Japan and the Hawaiian Is., s. to Lord Howe Is.; throughout Micronesia.

Gymnothorax monochrous Bleeker, 1864
Monochrome moray

TL: to 80 cm (32 in); HL 8-9; depth 19-22.

This species is chestnut brown becoming darker posteriorly. It differs from the uniformly brown *G. pindae* by lacking fine serrations on the posterior edges of the lower jaw teeth and by having a mouth that may not quite close completely. It occurs in relatively turbid areas of sheltered lagoon reefs.

Indo-Pacific: E. Africa to the Marshalls, n. to the Ryukyus; Marshalls in Micronesia.

Gymnothorax monostigmus (Regan, 1909)
One-spot moray

TL: to 44 cm (17 in); HL 8.2-9.0; depth 16-20.

This plain brown moray has a distinctive dark ring around each eye that extends backwards as a rectangular blotch and white spots surrounding each mucus pore around the mouth. It occurs on surge-swept seaward reefs.

Pacific Plate: Carolines, Marianas, and Papua New Guinea to the Marquesas and Tuamotus; throughout Micronesia.

Gymnothorax nudivomer (Playfair, 1867)
Yellowmouth moray

TL: to 180 cm (5 ft 11 in); HL 8; depth 11.

Small individuals resemble *G. meleagris* but have conspicuously yellow rather than white mouths. On large individuals the white spots become very small and numerous anteriorly, but large and widely spaced posteriorly and the long median vomerine teeth may disappear. This species produces a toxic mucus of uncertain function. It is known from Micronesia on the basis of a single specimen fished from deep water off Guam. In the Red Sea, it occurs as shallow as 4 m, but in the Hawaiian Islands and elsewhere, it is known from the depth range of 30 to 165 m.

Indo-Pacific: Red Sea to the Hawaiian and Marquesan Is., n. to the Ryukyus, s. to New Caledonia.

Gymnothorax pindae Smith, 1962
Pinda moray

(*G. moluccensis*)

TL: to 39 cm (15 in); HL 6.4-7.3; depth 16-19.

This uniformly brown moray differs from *G. monochrous* by having lower jaw teeth that are finely serrated on their posterior margins. It occurs on reef flats as well as lagoon and seaward reefs to a depth of at least 43 m.

Indo-Pacific: E. Africa to the Society Is., n. to the Marshall and Hawaiian Is., s. to the s. Great Barrier Reef; throughout Micronesia.

Gymnothorax richardsoni (Bleeker, 1852)   Fig. 2h
Richardson's moray

TL: to 32 cm (13 in); HL 6-7; depth 14-16.

This species is dark brown with darker mottling, a lighter chin and throat, and white margins around the lip pores. It occurs on shallow seaward reefs.

Indo-Pacific: Red Sea to the Society Is., n. to the Ryukyus, s. to the Cooks; Marianas and Carolines in Micronesia.

Gymnothorax rueppelliae (McClelland, 1845)
Yellow-headed moray   Pl. 10B; Fig. 3a

(*G. petelli*)

TL: to 80 cm (32 in); HL 7-8; depth 15-20.

This species differs from the similarly banded *G. enigmaticus* by lacking complete bands on its yellowish head and having dark bands that are wider than the light interspaces. The yellow headed moray inhabits both lagoon and seaward reefs to depths of at least 30 m, generally in areas of clear water. It is primarily nocturnal and feeds on fishes and crustaceans.

Indo-Pacific: Red Sea to the Hawaiian, Tuamotu and Marquesan Is., n. to the Ryukyus, s. to the s. Great Barrier Reef; throughout Micronesia.

Gymnothorax undulatus (Lacepède, 1803)
Undulated moray   Pl. 10C

TL: to over 150 cm (4 ft 11 in), usually < 100 cm (3 ft 3 in) in Micronesia; HL 6.5-8; depth 10-20.

This moray is characterized by a distinctive pattern of light undulating lines and speckles on a dark green background. Its jaws are relatively elongate and may be slightly hooked. It is a common inhabitant of reef flats among rocks, rubble, or debris and also occurs on lagoon and seaward reefs to depths of 26 m or more. It is primarily nocturnal and feeds on fishes, octopuses, and probably crustaceans.

Indo-pan-Pacific: Red Sea to Panama, n. to s. Japan and the Hawaiian Is., s. to the s. Great Barrier Reef, Rapa, and the Australs; throughout Micronesia.

Gymnothorax zonipectis Seale, 1906   Fig. 3b
Zonipectis moray

TL: to 46 cm (18 in); HL 7-8; depth 18.5.

This distinctively patterned moray inhabits ledges and rubble of outer reef slopes to depths of 40 m or more. It does not seem to be particularly common in Micronesia.

Indo-Pacific: E. Africa to the Marquesan and Society Is., n. to the Philippines; throughout Micronesia.

Pseudechidna brummeri (Bleeker, 1859)
White ribbon eel   Pl. 10G; key 3b

(*Strophidon brummeri*)

TL: to 103 cm (3.4 ft); depth ca. 44.

This ribbon eel has a more typical muraenid head than does *R. quaesita*. At Guam, it is a rarely seen inhabitant of shallow lagoons and reef flats that spends most of its time buried in sand or rubble.

Indo-Pacific: E. Africa to the Cooks, n. to the Yaeyamas, s. to Fiji; Marianas in Micronesia.

Rhinomuraena quaesita Garman, 1888   Pl. 10D
Ribbon eel

(*R. ambonensis*)

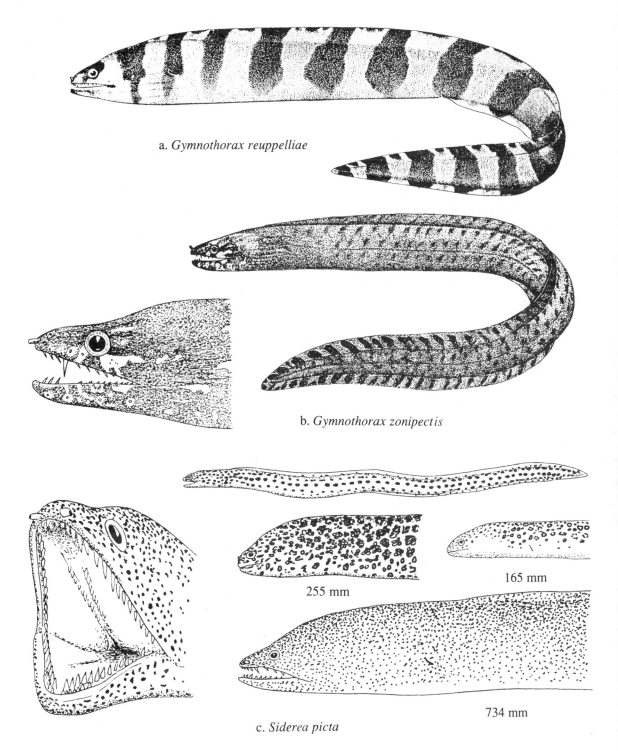

a. *Gymnothorax reuppelliae*

b. *Gymnothorax zonipectis*

255 mm

165 mm

734 mm

c. *Siderea picta*

Fig. 3. Micronesian moray eels (a, after Jordan and Evermann, 1903; b (right), after Schultz, 1953; b (left), c, after Weber and deBeaufort, 1916).

TL: to 120 cm (3.9 ft); HL ca. 18-20; depth ca. 70.

This extremely elongate and compressed moray has three fleshy tentacles on the tip of its lower. jaw, a single fleshy pointed projection at the tip of its snout, and tubular anterior nostrils ending in gaudy, fanlike expansions. The ribbon eel is also the only species of moray that undergoes abrupt changes in coloration and sex. It is a protandrous hermaphrodite, that is it matures first as a male, then reverses sex to become a female. The juvenile is black, then at a size of approximately 65 cm, it matures into a brilliant blue male with yellow fins which subsequently may develop into a yellow female at a length of 94 to 120 cm. The ribbon eel is a secretive species which remains hidden in rubble or sand, sometimes with only its head protruding. It occurs on both lagoon and seaward reefs in the depth range of 1 to at least 57 m and feeds on small fishes. It is rare in Micronesia and known from the Marianas only on the basis of reliable sightings. Its brilliant coloration, unusual appearance, and ready availability from the Philippines has made it a popular aquarium fish.

Indo-Pacific: E. Africa to the Tuamotus, n. to s. Japan and the Bonins, s. to New Caledonia and the Australs; Marianas and Marshalls in Micronesia.

Siderea picta (Ahl, 1789)   Pl. 10E; Figs. 3c; key 11b
Peppered moray
TL: to 120 cm (3.9 ft); HL 7-8; depth 15-20.

Species of *Siderea* have somewhat blunt rounded snouts similar to those of *Echidna*, but lack molariform teeth as well as the depressable vomerine fangs of most *Gymnothorax* and have two rather than three rows of vomerine teeth. *Siderea picta* is covered with small black dots (in the form of small circles in juveniles) and attains a larger size than the white snouted, light brown *S. prosopeion*.. It inhabits reef flats and rocky intertidal shorelines where it feeds on small-fishes and crustaceans such as the sally lightfoot crab, *Grapsus tenuicrustatus.*

Indo-pan-Pacific: S. Africa to the Galapagos, Cocos, and Clipperton Is., n. to the Hawaiian and Ryukyu Is., s. to Mangareva and s. Queensland; throughout Micronesia.

Siderea prosopeion (Bleeker, 1853)   Pl. 10F
White-eyed moray
(*Gymnothorax thyrsoideus* Schultz, 1953)
TL: to 65 cm (25 in); HL 9.0-9.6; depth 20-22.

The white-eyed moray is a fairly common inhabitant of reef flats where it is usually encountered in shallow tidal pools.

West-central Pacific: Christmas Is., to the Tuamotus, n. to the Ryukyus, s. to Tonga; throughout Micronesia.

Strophidon sathete (Hamilton, 1822)   key 2b
Giant estuarine moray
(*Thyrsoidea macrura*)
TL: to 394 cm (12.9 ft); HL 12; depth ca. 40.

Although its length is impressive, its narrow body does not give this eel much bulk. A 255 cm specimen from Guam weighed only 4.5 kg. By comparison, a *Gymnothorax* of similar length would be a monster of 10 times that weight! The giant estuarine eel inhabits muddy bottoms of tidal riv-

ers and inner bays to a depth of 15 m.

Indo-west-Pacific: E. Africa to Fiji, n. to the Ryukyus, s. to New Caledonia; Belau (?) and Guam in Micronesia.

Uropterygius concolor Rüppell, 1837
Unicolor snake moray
TL: to 32 cm (12.6 in); HL ca. 9; depth 25-30; teeth biserial.

Species of *Uropterygius* are long and snakelike with greatly reduced fins restricted to the end of the tail and mouths containing numerous needle-like teeth. This is the only Micronesian species that is uniformly brown to gray. It inhabits mangrove swamps, brackish rivers, and shallow coral reefs to depths of at least 8 m.

Indo-Pacific: Red Sea to the Marquesan and Society Is., n. to s. Japan, s. to New Caledonia; Carolines in Micronesia.

Uropterygius fuscoguttatus Schultz, 1953   Fig. 4a
Brown spotted snake moray
TL: to 30 cm (12 in); HL 9.1-10.0; depth 17-25.

This small eel is uniformly brown anteriorly becoming covered with darker brown spots on the tail. It is the most common species of *Uropterygius* on lagoon reefs in the Marshalls from depths of 6 to over 12 m. It occurs on seaward reefs to depths of at least 23 m in the Hawaiian Islands.

Pacific Plate: e. Carolines and Marshalls to the Society Is., n. to the Hawaiian Is., sw. to Samoa.

Uropterygius goslinei McCosker & Randall, 1977
Gosline's snake moray   Fig. 4b
TL: to 53 cm (21 in); HL 8.6; depth 18; teeth triserial.

This species has multiseral dentition. It inhabits shallow lagoon reefs in areas of sand, coralline algae, and coral heads.

Indo-Australian: New Guinea and the Solomons to Belau and Kapingamarangi in Micronesia.

Uropterygius kamar McCosker & Randall, 1977
Moon moray   Fig. 4c
TL: to 37 cm (14.6 in); HL ca. 10; depth 26; teeth triserial, except biserial on sides of lower jaw.

This species has multiseral dentition and occurs in two color morphs: both have white vertically elongate spots anteriorly, one with a uniformly dark background, the other mottled. It inhabits coral rubble botttoms at depths of 3 to 55 m.

Indo-Pacific: E. Africa to Oeno Atoll, n. to the Marshalls; Belau and the s. Marshalls in Micronesia.

Uropterygius macrocephalus (Bleeker, 1865).
Large-headed snake moray   Fig. 4e
(*U. reidi, U. knighti, U. necturus*)
TL: to 40 cm (16 in); HL 6.8-7.7; depth 16-27; teeth biserial.

This species inhabits exposed seaward reefs to a depth of 14 m or more.

Tropical-pan-Pacific: Christmas Is., Indian Ocean, to Panama, n. to s. Japan and the Hawaiian Is., s. to the Society Is.; throughout Micronesia.

a. *Uropterygius fuscoguttatus*, 176 mm, Bikini

dentition

b. *Uropterygius goslinei*, 483 mm

dentition

c. *Uropterygius kamar*

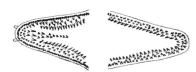

dentition

d. *Uropterygius marmoratus*, x 0.8

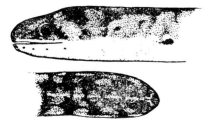

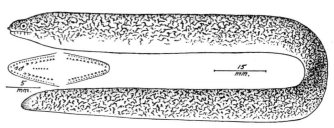

c. *Uropterygius macrocephalus*, Samoa

e. *Uropterygius micropterus*, Saipan

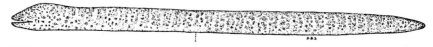

f. *Uropterygius supraforatus*, 373 mm, Johnston Is.

Fig. 4. **Micronesian moray eels** (a, f, after D. B. Schultz *in* Schultz et al., 1953; b, redrawn from McCosker and Randall, 1977; d, after Weber and deBeaufort, 1916; e after Fowler, 1945).

Uropterygius marmoratus (Lacepède, 1803)
Marbled snake moray   Fig. 4d

TL: to 50 cm (20 in); HL 9-11; depth 19-23; teeth triserial.
The marbled snake moray is an uncommon inhabitant of reef
flats and seaward reefs to a depth of 20 m.
Indo-Pacific: E. Africa to the Hawaiian, Marquesan and Tuamotu Is., n. to the Yaeyamas, s. to Tonga; throughout Micronesia.

Uropterygius micropterus (Bleeker, 1852)   Fig. 4f
Tidepool snake moray

TL: to 28 cm (11.0 in); females mature at <19 cm; HL 8.5-
10; depth 16-20; teeth biserial.
In the Marianas this small species is abundant among rubble
of intertidal reef flats. It feeds on small crustaceans and
probably on small fishes as well.
Indo-Pacific: E. Africa to the Phoenix and Samoa Is., n. to
s. Japan, s. to the s. Great Barrier Reef; Marianas in
Micronesia.

Uropterygius polyspilus (Regan, 1909)
Large-spotted snake moray

TL: to 72 cm (28 in); teeth biserial.
This rare snake moray is covered with large dark purplish-
brown spots arranged in 2 to 3 irregular series on a reddish-
tan background. It has been collected on reef flats.
Indo-Pacific: Red Sea to the Hawaiian, Line , and Society
Is.; e. Carolines in Micronesia.

Uropterygius supraforatus (Regan, 1909)   Fig. 4g
(*U. dentatus*)

TL: to 37 cm (15 in); HL 10-11; depth 20-21; jaw teeth
multiserial.
This eel inhabits lagoon and seaward reefs as deep as 37 m.
Indo-Pacific: Chagos Is. to the Hawaiian and Society Is.,
n. to the Marshalls; throughout Micronesia.

Uropterygius xanthopterus Bleeker, 1859

TL: to 35 cm (14 in); HL 7.5; depth 25-30; teeth biserial.
This species differs from other *Uropterygius* by the combination of prominent white specks on the head, a white edged
tail, and an unusually elongate body. It inhabits corals and
crevices of shallow reefs as well as dropoffs to 56 m.
Indo-Pacific: E. Africa to the Line, Marquesan, and Society
Is., n. to the Marshalls; throughout Micronesia.

Uropterygius (Scuticaria) tigrinus (Lesson, 1828)
Tiger snake moray   Pl. 10H

TL: to 120 cm (3.9 ft); HL 13; depth 30; teeth biserial.
This species resembles *U. polyspilus*, but its large dark
spots differ greatly in size from one another and its anus is
located about two-thirds rather than one-half of the way to
the tip of the tail. The tiger snake moray is an extremely
secretive uncommon inhabitant of both lagoon and seaward
reefs. When it is found, often only a small portion of its
body is visible through the recesses of the reef.
Indo-pan-Pacific: E. Africa to Panama, n. to the Philippine
and Hawaiian Is., s. to the Society Is.; Kapingamarangi in
Micronesia.

CHLOPSIDAE (FALSE MORAYS)

The false morays vaguely resemble morays, but most species possess pectoral fins and their posterior nostrils open to
the margin of the upper lip. Males are generally smaller
than females and possess slightly larger, more recurved teeth
which may be useful for grasping the female during courtship. They probably migrate off the reef to spawn. All species are extremely secretive indwellers only seen when
flushed from the reef with an ichthyocide.

Key to Micronesian species of *Kaupichthys*

1a. P longer than maximum eye diameter......................2
1b. P shorter than maximum eye diameter........*brachychirus*
2a. P 10-11..*atronasus*
2b. P 14..*hyoproroides*

Kaupichthys atronasus Schultz, 1953   Fig. 1a
Black-nostril false moray

TL: to 11 cm (4.3 in); P 10-11; HL 7.5-7.7; depth 27-31.
This small uncommon species inhabits coral heads to depths
of at least 14 m.
Indo-Pacific: Chagos Is. to Samoa, n. to the Ryukyus, s. to
the s. Great Barrier Reef; throughout Micronesia.

Kaupichthys brachychirus Schultz, 1953   Fig. 1b
Shortfin false moray

TL: to 13 cm (5.1 in); HL 7.3-7.9; depth 24-28.
This species has shorter pectoral fins than the other Micronesian species. It inhabits seaward and lagoon reefs to a
depth of at least 43 m in areas of mixed coral and sand that
are subject to strong currents.
West-central Pacific: Rowley Shoals to the Society Is.; Carolines and Marshalls in Micronesia.

Kaupichthys hyoproroides (Strömann, 1896)
Common false moray   Fig. 1c
(*K. diodontus*)

TL: to 30 cm (11.8 in); P 14; HL ca. 7; depth 22.
This common, widely distributed species occurs on seaward
reefs at depths of 0 to 56 m.
Indo-Pacific & w. Atlantic: E. Africa to the Marquesan and
Society Is., n. to the Ryukyu and Hawaiian Is.; throughout
Micronesia.

CONGRIDAE (CONGER EELS and GARDEN EELS)

This family is subdivided into three subfamilies: the Bathy-
myrinae (Short congers) and Congrinae (Conger eels) which
have well-developed pectoral fins and are typically eel-like in
behavior and appearance, and the Heterocongrinae (Garden

a. *K. atronasus*, 93 mm

a. *K. atronasus*, underside of head   b. *K. brachychirus*, underside of head

b. *K. brachychirus*, 128 mm

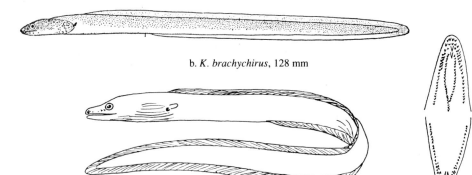

c. *K. hyoproroides*, ca. 125 mm with dentition at right

Fig. 1. Micronesian species of *Kaupichthys* (a, b, after D. B. Schultz, dentition after Schultz, *in* Schultz et al., 1953).

eels) which are smaller, extremely elongate burrowing forms with upturned mouths and reduced or absent pectoral fins. Most species of congrids inhabit cooler temperate or deep slope waters; at least five inhabit shallow Micronesian coral reefs. (Lit.: Böhlke & Randall, 1981; Randall, 1986)

Subfamily Bathymyrinae:

Ariosoma scheelei (Strömman, 1896)   Fig. 1a
Scheele's conger
(*A. obud* Schultz, 1953)
TL: to 20 cm (7.9 in); LP 38-42 before anus; D 146-178 (40-55 before anus); A 119-135; head 5.5-6.5; depth 15-22.
In short congers the anus is located about halfway down the body whereas in the Congrinae it is located about one-third of the way down. This uncommon species inhabits lagoon reefs to depths of at least 9 m.
Indo-Pacific: E. Africa to at least Samoa, s. to the s. Great Barrier Reef; Marshalls in Micronesia.

Subfamily Congrinae:

Conger cinereus cinereus Rüppell, 1828   Pl. 11A
Moustache conger
TL: to 130 cm (4.3 ft); LP 37-41 before anus; head 7.8-8.2; depth 17-23.
This is the only large conger eel that inhabits shallow

Micronesian coral reefs. It seems to be most common on reef flats and seagrass beds of shallow lagoons but ranges to depths of 80 m on outer reef slopes. It is a nocturnal predator of fishes and small crustaceans and is rarely seen during the day. At night it assumes a pattern of broad dark bands.
Indo-Pacific: Red Sea to the Marquesas and Easter Is., n. to s. Japan, s. to Lord Howe and Rapa Is.; throughout Micronesia; the subspecies *marginatus* in the Hawaiian Is.

Poeciloconger fasciatus Günther, 1871   Fig. 1b
Barred sand conger
SL: to 51 cm (20 in); P 13-14; LP 145-149 (+10 anterior to gill opening).
This colorful congrid lives beneath the sand of lagoon and seaward reefs at depths of 2.5 to at least 32 m. Only five specimens are known.
Indo-Pacific: Madagascar, Sulawesi, Society, Hawaiian, and Marshall Is.

Subfamily Heterocongrinae:

Gorgasia sp.   Fig. 1c
Garden eel
TL: ca. 60 cm (24 in); anterior nostrils on snout tip between restricted labial flanges; P moderately developed with ca. 10-14 rays (all *Gorgasia* spp.).
Garden eels occur in large colonies on certain current-swept

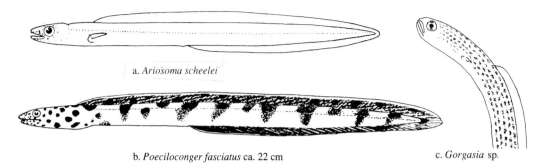

a. *Ariosoma scheelei*

b. *Poeciloconger fasciatus* ca. 22 cm

c. *Gorgasia* sp.

Fig. 1. Micronesian conger and garden eels (b, based on Randall, 1986).

sandy expanses or slopes. They live individually in burrows from which they protrude to feed on drifting plankton. From a distance they resemble a garden of shoots swaying in a breeze. A large green mottled *Gorgasia* has been observed at depths of 18 to 45 m in the vicinity of Double Reef and Facpi Point, Guam. A similar, if not identical species has been collected at Enewetak Atoll.

Heteroconger hassi
(Klausewitz & Eible-Eibesfeldt, 1959) Pl. 11B;
Spotted garden eel Fig. 1d

TL: to 35 cm (14 in); anterior nostrils included in continuous free labial flange; P minute; total vertebrae 163-177, anal origin below vertebra 59-66.

The spotted garden eel is known from a few colonies in the Agat Bay to Facpi Point area of Guam at depths of 18 to over 30 m. It occurs as shallow as 7 m at Belau and as deep as 45 m elsewhere.

Indo-Pacific: Red Sea to the Samoan and Line Is., n. to the Ryukyus, s. to New Caledonia and Tonga; throughout Micronesia.

MORINGUIDAE (SPAGHETTI EELS)

Spaghetti eels possess extremely elongate bodies with the anus located about two thirds of the way back. They undergo radical changes in morphology with maturation. Immature individuals are orange-brown and have small eyes and reduced fins. At maturity they develop large eyes and enlarged fins, including a distinct caudal fin. Mature males are longitudinally bicolored: orange-brown dorsally and white ventrally. Immature and female individuals are relatively common

in shallow sandy areas, but normally remain hidden beneath the surface of the sediment. They migrate to the surface to spawn with males that are pelagic. Three species in the genus *Moringua* occur in Micronesia.

Key to Micronesian species of ***Moringua***:

1a. P absent; head 16-19, depth 75-105 in TL; ca. 100 LL pores before anus; vertebrae 153-160..........*M. javanica*
1b. P present but reduced to a vestigial flap; head 10-15, depth 36-63 in TL...2
2a. Depth 36-51 in TL; ca. 63 LL pores before anus; vertebrae 105-113......................................*M. microchir*
2b. Depth 49-63 in TL; ca. 73 LL pores before anus; vertebrae 115-125......................................*M. ferruginea*

Moringua ferruginea Bliss, 1883 Fig. 1a
Rusty spaghetti eel ·

TL: to ca. 140 cm (4.6 ft); head 13-15; depth 49-53.
Indo-Pacific: E. Africa to Easter Is., n. to the Ryukyus; throughout Micronesia.

Moringua javanica (Kaup, 1856) Fig. 1b
Java spaghetti eel

TL: to 120 cm (3.9 ft); P absent; depth 75-105.
Indo-Pacific: E. Africa to the Tuamotus, n. to the Ryukyus; throughout Micronesia.

Moringua microchir Bleeker, 1853
Spaghetti eel
(*M. abbreviata*)

TL: to ca. 30 cm (12 in); head 10-15; depth 36-51.
Indo-Pacific: E. Africa to the Samoa, n. to the Ryukyus; throughout Micronesia.

a. *M. ferruginea* ca. 120 cm

b. *M. javanica* ca. 60 cm

dentition

Fig. 1 (Moringuidae). Micronesian species of *Moringua*.

OPHICHTHIDAE (SNAKE EELS)

Snake eels are named for their elongate, nearly cylindrical muscular bodies which give them a snakelike appearance. Unlike true snakes, they lack scales, have downward-pointing tubular nostrils, and in most species, have median fins and small pectoral fins. Those in the subfamily Myrophinae have a flexible tail with a caudal fin confluent with the dorsal and anal fins, and constricted mid-lateral gill openings; those in the subfamily Ophichthinae have a hard, pointed, finless tail tip and unconstricted mid-lateral to ventral gill openings. Most species of snake eels remain completely buried in sediment, but a few occasionally emerge to traverse sand, rubble, or seagrass habitats. They appear to be more active at night when some species may be attracted to a light. Some, if not all species, briefly come to the surface to spawn at night. At least 26 species in 17 genera are known from Micronesia, but it is likely that several more remain to be discovered. Since most are strictly indwellers known only from poison stations, only a few of the more conspicuous or noteworthy species are discussed. (Lit.: McCosker, 1970; 1977; 1979; McCosker and Castle *in* Smith, 1986)

Key to Micronesian genera and species of Ophichthidae*:

1a. C rays conspicuous, tail tip flexible; gill opening small, midlateral to ventrolateral (subfamily Myrophinae)..2

1b. Tail tip hard or fleshy finless point; gill openings often elongate, midlateral to entirely ventral (subfamily Ophichthinae)..10

2a. P present..*Myrophis uropterus*

2b. P absent..3

3a. Ventral side of snout with prominent median toothed groove, bordered by dermal folds, extending to anterior nostrils; anterior nostrils elongate tubes = eye in length.. ....*Schismorhynchus labialis*

3b. Ventral side of snout without prominent groove bordered by dermal folds; anterior nostrils ≤ eye in length..4

4a. Teeth absent on vomer, absent or embedded on intermaxillary, those on maxillary and dentary minute or villiform; D origin behind anus (genus *Schultzidia*)....................5

4b. Teeth present on intermaxillary, maxillary, dentary, and vomer; D origin either before or behind anus (genus *Muraenichthys*)..6

5a. Upper lip smooth; depth 24-30 in TL..*S. retropinnis*

5b. Upper lip with small dermal papillae on edge between anterior nostrils; depth 45-54 in TL..*S. johnstonensis*

6a. D origin notably before anus...7

6b. D origin above or behind anus...8

7a. D origin closer to anus than to gill opening.......................................*M. sibogae*

7b. D origin closer to gill opening than to anus, or nearly equidistant......*M. macropterus*

8a. Rear margin of eye over rictus of mouth..*M. laticaudata*

8b. Rear margin of eye in advance of rictus of mouth...9

9a. Snout bluntly rounded; greatest depth 20-30 in TL...............................*M. schultzei*

9b. Snout acute; greatest depth 30-50 in TL..*M. gymnotus*

10a. Body entirely finless; snout sharply conical; gill openings ventral, converging forward..11

10b. At least a low D present...13

11a. Cirri present on upper lip...*Cirricaecula johnsoni*

11b. Upper lip smooth...12

12a. Rear nostril opening outside mouth, with flap; front nostril tubular; eye moderately developed...*Apterichtus klazingai*

12b. Rear nostril opening inside mouth, with or without flap; front nostril not tubular; eye minute...*Ichthyapus vulturis*

13a. P absent..14

13b. P present (vestigial in *Evipes*)..17

14a. Gill opening entirely ventral..*Caecula polyophthalmus*

14b. Gill opening low-lateral, crescentic..15

1a
1b

Cirricaecula
11b

Apterichtus
12a

Ichthyapus
12b

*Excludes a possibly undescribed *Ophichthus* from Enewetak.

15a. Only fin a low D, extending from just behind occiput to < 3 head lengths behind gill opening..*Phaenamonas cooperi*

15b. D extending from head nearly to tip of tail; A present (genus *Callechelys*)...........16

16a. Coloration mostly marbled or spotted with black-and-white areas........*C. marmorata*

16b. A single wide band along middle of body with white above and below; D margin black becoming white near end of tail...*C. catostomus*

17a. P vestigial, ≤ eye; body longer than tail....................................*Evipes percinctus*

17b. P developed, > eye; body shorter than tail..18

18a. Upper lip noticeably fringed...19

18b. Upper lip entire, although nasal barbels may be present 20

19a. Both lips fringed; body as long as tail; canine teeth in jaws and on vomer..............
....*Brachysomophis sauropsis*

19b. Lower lip entire; tail much longer than body; no canine teeth...............................
....(*Cirrhimuraena playfairi*)†

20a. Teeth molariform or granular; P broad based (genus *Myrichthys*)......................21

20b. Teeth pointed; P base restricted, opposite upper half of gill opening..................23

21a. About 30 dark saddles approximately reaching LL; no spots or bands.....*M. bleekeri*

21b. Saddles absent; coloration consists of spots or bands.......................................22

22a. Distinctly banded in black on light background, circular spots may be present in interspaces..*M. colubrinus*

22b. Numerous dark brown spots on light background...........................*M. maculosus*

23a. Vomerine teeth absent, or at most 1-3 small teeth...25

23b. A series of teeth on vomer...24

24a. P developed, > 2 times gill opening length; D origin behind gill opening..............
....*Ophichthus cephalazona*

24b. P reduced, ca. = gill opening length; D roigin above or before gill opening............
....*Elapsopsis versicolor*

25a. Conpicuous leaf-like appendages on anterior nostrils; head and trunk length ≥ tail length; color uniform..*Phyllophichthus xenodontus*

25b. No leaf-like appendages on anterior nostrils; head and trunk length ≤ tail length; body with numerous saddles...*Leiuranus semicinctus*

Brachysomophis
19a

Cirrhimuraena
19b

Myrichthys
20a

20b

Phyllophichthus
25a

Subfamily Myrophinae: characterized by a flexible caudal fin with conspicuous rays.

Muraenichthys gymnotus Bleeker, 1864   Fig. 1a
TL: to 38 cm (15 in); P absent; PL 59; depth 30-50.
Members of the subfamily Myrophinae have a flexible caudal fin with conspicuous rays that are confluent with the dorsal and anal fin. This translucent to whitish species occurs in loose sand and fine gravel.
Indo-Pacific: Red Sea to the Line and Society Is., n. to s. Japan and Johnston Is., s. to Rapa and the s. Great Barrier Reef; Marshalls and Carolines in Micronesia.

Muraenichthys laticaudata (Ogilby, 1897)
TL: to 35 cm (13.8 in); P absent; depth 24-35.
This species has been collected from reef flats and lagoon and seaward reefs to a depth of 26 m.
Indo-Pacific: E. Africa to Ducie, s. to Lord Howe Is.; throughout Micronesia.

Muraenichthys macropterus Bleeker, 1857
TL: to ca. 20 cm (7.9 in); P absent; PL 45-51; depth 36-53.
Indo-Pacific: E. Africa to the Society Is., n. to the Ryukyus, s. to the s. Great Barrier Reef; throughout Micronesia.

Muraenichthys schultzei Bleeker, 1857
TL: to ca. 24 cm (9.4 in); P absent; PL 50; depth 20-42.
This species inhbaits reef flats and lagoons to at least 13 m.
Indo-Pacific: E. Africa to Samoa, n. to the Ryukyus; Carolines and Marshalls in Micronesia.

Muraenichthys sibogae Weber & deBeaufort, 1916
TL: to ≥7.4 cm (2.9 in); depth 53.
West-central Pacific: Timor, Arno, and Samoa.

Myrophis uropterus (Temminck & Schlegel, 1842)
TL: to 60 cm (23.6 in); P 14-16; PL 46-49; depth 35-52.
Indo-Pacific: E. Africa to the Society Is., n. to s. Japan; Carolines and Marshalls in Micronesia.

Schismorhynchus labialis (Seale, 1917)
(*Leptenchelys labialis*)
TL: to 20 cm (7.9 in); P absent; depth 30-55.
This species has been collected from shallow lagoon reefs.
Indo-Pacific: Chagos Is. to the Hawaiian, Society, and Easter Is.; Belau in Micronesia.

Schultzidia johnstonensis (Schultz & Woods,1949)
TL: to 30 cm (12 in); depth 24-30.   Fig. 1b
This species is finely peppered with pigment dorsally. It occurs on lagoon and seaward reefs to depths of 12 m or more.
Indo-Pacific: Chagos Is. to the Hawaiian, Marquesan, and Society Is.; Belau, Carolines, and Marshalls in Micronesia.

† Expected in region.

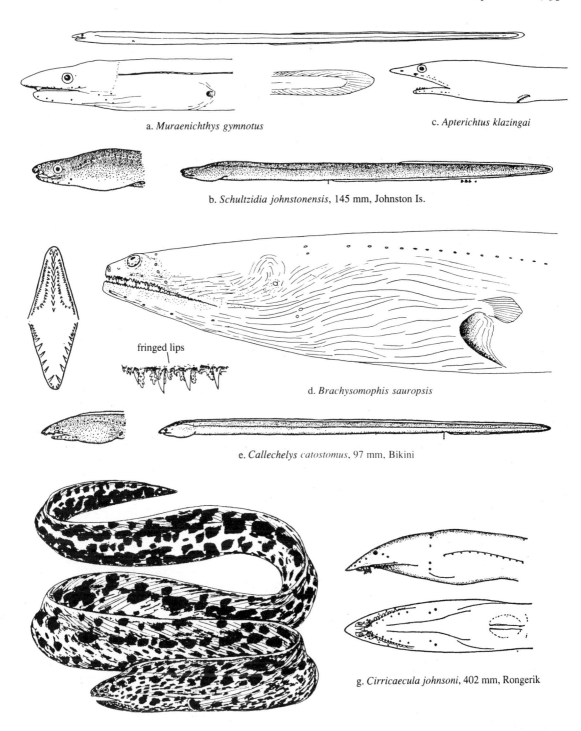

a. *Muraenichthys gymnotus*

c. *Apterichtus klazingai*

b. *Schultzidia johnstonensis*, 145 mm, Johnston Is.

fringed lips

d. *Brachysomophis sauropsis*

e. *Callechelys catostomus*, 97 mm, Bikini

g. *Cirricaecula johnsoni*, 402 mm, Rongerik

f. *Callechelys marmorata*

Fig. 1. **Micronesian snake eels** (a, after Schultz, 1953; b, f, after D. B. Schultz *in* Schultz et al., 1953; d, redrawn from Schultz, 1953; e, after Weber and deBeaufort. 1916).

Schultzidia retropinnis (Fowler, 1933)

TL: to ≥11.1 cm (4.4 in); depth 45-54.

West-central Pacific: Philippine, Solomon, Caroline, and Marshall Is.

Subfamily Ophichthinae: characterized by a tail tip consisting of a hard or fleshy finless point.

Apterichtus klazingai (Weber, 1913)   Fig. 1c

TL: to 39 cm (15.4 in); finless; depth 60-72; teeth small, sharp, uniseral on jaws and vomer.

The distinctive finless tail tip of members of the subfamily Ophichthinae is an adaptation for living buried in sand. Many species are able to burrow just as rapidly backwards as well as forwards. This species lacks fins altogether.

Indo-Pacific: E. Africa to ; Marshalls in Micronesia.

Brachysomophis sauropsis Schultz, 1943   Fig. 1d
Reptilian snake eel

TL: to 48 cm (19 in); PL 96-99; depth 16.6-32.

Species of *Brachysomophis* have long, sharp canine teeth, curiously fringed lips, and eyes located near the tip of the snout. They probably lie in wait just beneath the surface of the sand to ambush the small fishes and octopuses on which they feed. Further study is needed to determine whether or not this species and the Hawaiian species, *B. henshawi*, are conspecific with the widespread Indo-Pacific species, *B. crocodilinus*.

Pacific Plate: Marianas and Marshalls to Johnston Is. and the Tuamotus.

Caecula polyophthalma (Bleeker, 1853)

TL: to 32.5 cm (12.8 in); depth ca. 30.

Indo-Pacific: Mauritius to the Marquesan and Society Is.; Marianas in Micronesia.

Callechelys catostomus (Bloch & Schneider, 1801)
Dark band snake eel   Fig. 1e

(*C. melanotaenia*; *Leptenchelys pinnaceps* =juvenile)

TL: to 85 cm (33 in); depth 44-63.

Adults have a broad lateral black band along the middle of each side. This species occurs in shallow areas beneath loose sand and gravel.

West-central Pacific: Moluccas to the Society Is., n. to s. Japan, s. to Lord Howe Is.; throughout Micronesia.

Callechelys marmorata (Bleeker, 1853)   Fig. 1f
Marbled snake eel

TL: to 87 cm (34 in); PL 175-180; depth 40-44.

This species occurs in shallow areas beneath loose gravel and sand and is generally encountered only through the use of ichthyocides.

Indo-Pacific: E. Africa to the Society Is., s. to Lord Howe Is.; Marianas, Kapingamarangi, and Marshalls in Micronesia.

Cirricaecula johnsoni Schultz, 1953   Fig. 1g
Fringelip snake eel

TL: to 40 cm (16 in); depth 29-36.

This genus and species is known only from the type specimens collected from a surge-washed sand patch at Rongerik Atoll. It is unique among ophichthids by its combination of no fins, a long and pointed upper snout, and cirri on the upper lips.

Rongerik Atoll

Elapsopsis versicolor (Richardson, 1844)

Belau (also possibly Australia and Lord Howe Is.)

Evipes percinctus McCosker, 1972   Fig. 2a

TL: 126 mm (only one specimen known); depth 24 in TL.

This species has prominent dark saddles similar to those of *Leiuranus semicinctus*, but is easily distinguished by its thicker body and and large canine teeth. The only known specimen was collected in less than 10 cm of water.

Belau

Ichthyapus vulturis (Weber & deBeaufort, 1916)

SL: to 44.6 cm (17.6 in); depth 33-53.

Indo-Pacific: Mascarenes to the Hawaiian and Easter Is.; Belau in Micronesia.

Leiuranus semicinctus (Lay & Bennett, 1839)
Saddled snake eel   Fig. 2c

TL: to 66 cm (26 in); P 8-10; PL 70-74; depth 33-70.

This common snake eel inhabits sandy areas and seagrass beds of both lagoon and seaward reefs from the shoreline to a depth of 10 m or more. It is occasionally observed in the open, but like many snake eels, it uses its stiff pointed tail quite effectively to rapidly burrow backwards into the sand when threatened. It feeds on small sand-dwelling fishes and crustaceans which are sought out by its sense of smell. This species rises to the surface to spawn. There, one or more males may seize a female by the back of the neck and remain attached for hours before spawning occurs.

Indo-Pacific: E. Africa to the Hawaiian, Marquesan, and Mangareva Is., n. to s. Japan, s. to n. New South Wales; throughout Micronesia.

Myrichthys bleekeri Gosline, 1951

(*Ophisurus fasciatus* var. *semicinctus* Bleeker, 1864)

TL: to ≥39.5 cm (15.6 in); depth 53-68.

West-central Pacific: Indonesia to the Marshall, Phoenix, and Johnston Is.

Myrichthys colubrinus (Boddaert, 1781)   Pl. 11C
Banded snake eel

TL: to 88 cm (35 in); P 9; PL 85; depth 48-55.

This beautiful species superficially resembles the highly venemous sea snake *Laticauda colubrina*, but is entirely harmless. In Micronesian areas outside of Belau, the sea snake is absent or at best a rare straggler and reports of sea snakes are likely misidentifications of this eel. The banded snake eel is a common inhabitant of shallow sandy flats and seagrass beds. Its behavior is similar to that of *L. semicinctus*.

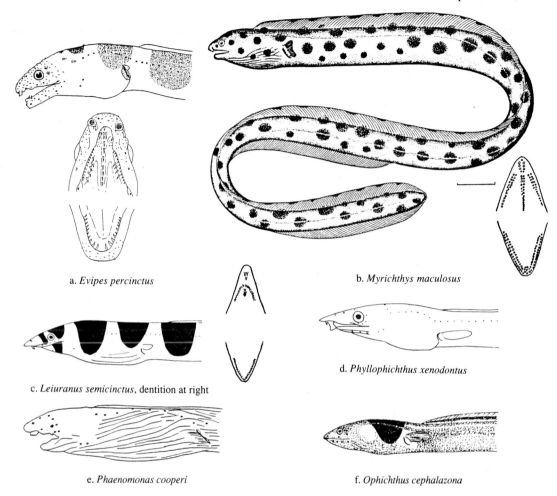

a. *Evipes percinctus*

b. *Myrichthys maculosus*

c. *Leiuranus semicinctus*, dentition at right

d. *Phyllophichthus xenodontus*

e. *Phaenomonas cooperi*

f. *Ophichthus cephalazona*

Fig. 2. Micronesian snake eels (a, redrawn from McCosker, 1970; c, d, and e, redrawn from McCosker in Smith and Heemstra, 1986; b, after Jordan and Evermann, 1903; f, after Weber and deBeaufort, 1916; dentition after Schultz, 1953.

Indo-Pacific: Red Sea to the Society Is.; n. to the Ryukyus, s. to Queensland; throughout Micronesia.

Myrichthys maculosus (Cuvier, 1817)
Spotted snake eel   Pl. 11D; Fig. 2c
TL: to 100 cm (3.3 ft); P 12-14; PL 73-77; depth 35-50.
The spotted snake eel is a common inhabitant of sandy areas of reef flats as well as lagoon and seaward reefs. It has even been observed from a submersible at a depth of 262 m off Johnston Island. In certain areas it aggregates in large numbers under lights at night. Its behavior is similar to that of *Myrichthys colubrinus* and *Leiuranus semicinctus*.
Indo-Pacific: Red Sea to the Hawaiian, Marquesan, and Society Is., n. to s. Japan, s. to Lord Howe and Rapa Is.; throughout Micronesia.

Ophichthus cephalozona (Bleeker, 1864)   Fig. 2f
Dark-shouldered snake eel

TL: to 100 cm (3.3 ft).
This distinctively marked species inhabits muddy to sandy inshore areas. It occasionally forages in the open at night.
West-central Pacific: E. Indies to the Society Is., n. to the Marianas, s. to Queensland; Marianas and Marshalls in Micronesia.

Phaenomonas cooperi Palmer, 1970   Fig. 2e
TL: to 59 cm (23.2 in); P, A absent; depth 117-150; pinkish in life; eye vestigial.
This species has been collected as deep as 60 m.
Indo-Pacific: Red Sea to the Hawaiian and Marquesan Is.; Belau in Micronesia.

Phyllophichthus xenodontus Gosline, 1951
TL: to 42 cm (16.5 cm); depth ca. 40.   Fig. 2d
Indo-Pacific: E. Africa to the Hawaiian, Marquesan, and Society Is.; Carolines and Marshalls in Micronesia.

a. *Megalops cyprinoides*, 133 mm, Guam. b. *Albula glossodonta*, 116 mm, Guam.

Fig. 1 (Elopiformes). Micronesian species of tarpon and bonefish.

Order ELOPIFORMES

MEGALOPIDAE (TARPONS)

Megalops cyprinoides (Broussonet, 1782)
Indo-Pacific tarpon   Fig. 1a
SL: to 90 cm (35 in); D 16-20; A 23-31; LL 36-40.
Elopiform fishes are among the most primitive of teleosts.
They are characterized by ventrally located pectoral fins, ab-
dominal pelvic fins with 9 or more rays, a bony gular plate
(between the jaw bones), numerous (>23) branchiostegals,
and a deeply forked tail. Like the eels, they have a transpar-
ent ribbon-like late larval stage called the "leptocephalus".
Tarpon occur in fresh or salt water and can tolerate oxygen
poor water by "breathing" air into a lung-like air bladder.
Megalops cyprinoides occurs primarily in river mouths, inner bays, or among mangroves.
Indo-Pacific: Red Sea to the Society Is., n. to s. Korea, s. to
New South Wales; restricted to high islands (Belau, Carolines, and Marianas) in Micronesia.

ALBULIDAE (BONEFISHES)

Albula glossodonta (Forsskål, 1775)
Indo-Pacific bonefish   Pl. 11E; Fig. 1b
SL: to 90 cm (35 in); D 15-19; A 8-9; LL 68-80.
Bonefishes differ from tarpons by having an underslung jaw

and smaller more numerous scales. They inhabit mudflats
of turbid inner reefs and mangroves as well as sandy stretches of clear lagoons. They feed on subsurface invertebrates
by nosing into the sediment. In Belau and the Gilberts, they
form large schools that migrate through channels to the outer reef slope to spawn during either full or new moons. An
additional species, *A. neoguinaica*, may occur in Micronesia.
Indo-Pacific: Red Sea to the Hawaiian and Tuamotu Is., n.
to s. Japan, s. to Lord Howe Is.; throughout Micronesia.

Order GONORHYNCHIFORMES

CHANIDAE (MILKFISH)

Chanos chanos (Forsskål, 1775)   Fig. 1
Milkfish
SL: to 180 cm (5.9 ft), but rarely >50 cm (20 in); D 14-16;
A 9-10; P 16-17; V 11-12; LL 75-91; GR 147-160+107-
165.
Milkfish superficially resemble bonefishes but are evolu-
tionarily more advanced by lacking the leptocephalus larval
stage and having few (4) branchiostegal rays. They occur in
a variety of habitats ranging from fresh to salt water ponds
and mangroves to coral reef lagoons and outer reef slopes.
They feed on benthic algae and sediment with its associated
invertebrate fauna and are more abundant in turbid rather than
clear water environments. Milkfish are the most important
food fish throughout much of S.E. Asia where they form the
basis of an aquaculture industry that depends upon the cap-

Fig. 1 (Gonorhynchiformes). The milkfish, *Chanos chanos* (after Jordan
and Evermann, 1903).

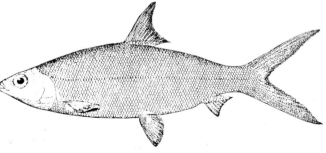

ture of millions of fry that seasonally enter rivers. In Belau milkfish spawn near the surface beyond the edge of the reef during a few days around both full and new moons. The fry subsequently return to brackish waters at an age of 10 to 14 days.

Indo-Pacific: Red Sea to the Hawaiian, Marquesan and Society Is., n. to s. Japan, s. to New Caledonia; throughout Micronesia.

Order SILURIFORMES (CATFISHES)

PLOTOSIDAE (EEL CATFISHES)

Plotosus lineatus (Thünberg, 1787)
Striped eel catfish   Pl. 11F; Fig. 1
TL: to 30 cm (12 in); D I,5-80-100; A 70-81; P I,11; V 12.
Most of the world's 2,000 or more species of catfishes occur in fresh water. Only two families with a small number of species occur in marine waters and only *Plotosus lineatus* is

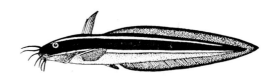

Fig. 1. *Plotosus lineatus.*

likely to be encountered on coral reefs. It possesses four pairs of mouth barbels and a single highly venemous serrate spine at the beginning of the first dorsal and each of the pectoral fins. Wounds from these spines may be dangerous, even fatal in rare cases. A 3 cm juvenile can cause a sting like that of a wasp. Juveniles occur in dense ball-shaped schools over reefs and seagrass beds; adults are solitary and hide under ledges during the day.

Indo-west-Pacific: Red Sea to Samoa, n. to s. Korea, s. to Lord Howe Is.; Belau and Yap in Micronesia.

Order CLUPEIFORMES

ENGRAULIDIDAE (ANCHOVIES)

This is one of the largest families of so-called "baitfishes", that is, small silvery schooling fishes commonly used as live bait for pole and line tuna fisheries. Anchovies are characterized by an underslung lower jaw, one dorsal fin, pelvic fins with 6-7 rays located far down the body, scutes along the belly, and scales that are easily shed. Most species have a brilliant silver mid-lateral band. Anchovies typically inhabit estuaries and turbid coastal waters but some occur over inner protected reefs and at least one, *Encrasicholina punctifer*, inhabits the open sea. All are planktivores. Identification in the water is nearly impossible and with the specimen in hand is often difficult. An illustrated key is provided to aid in the identification of Micronesian species. (Drawings after Lewis et al., 1983; Lit.: Baldwin, 1983; Lewis et al., 1983)

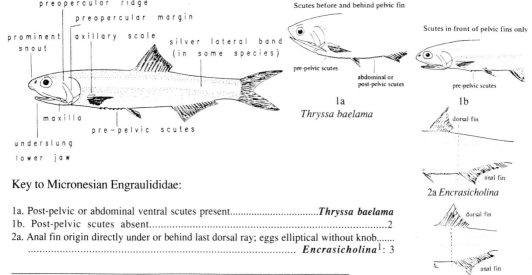

Key to Micronesian Engraulididae:

1a. Post-pelvic or abdominal ventral scutes present.................................***Thryssa baelama***
1b. Post-pelvic scutes absent...2
2a. Anal fin origin directly under or behind last dorsal ray; eggs elliptical without knob.......
.... ***Encrasicholina***[1]: 3

---

[1] New genus proposed by Whitehead and Nelson, 1983 (after Lewis et al., 1983).

3a *Encrasicholina punctifer*   3b

2b. Anal fin origin under dorsal fin base; eggs with distinct knob............................retained genus *Stolephorus*[2]: 5

3a. Maxilla short, truncated posteriorly, not reaching preopercular ridge...***punctifer***

3b. Maxilla pointed posteriorly, reaching beyond preopercular ridge and bearing prominent recurved teeth distally..4

4a. Maxilla length 5.7-6.2 in SL; silver lateral band usually with very clear dark blue line defining top edge; back blue...***heterolobus***

4b. Maxilla length 5.1-5.6 in SL; lateral band gold with a less distinct margin, especially near head; back golden....
....***devisi***

5a. Maxilla long, tip reaches to or beyond preopercular margin...***insularis***

5b. Maxilla short, tip reaches just beyond preopercular ridge.
....6

6a. Five or more prepelvic scutes; 20-26 lower-limb GR.....
....***indicus***

6b. Four or less prepelvic scutes; 33-38 lower-limb GR......
....***pacificus***

Thryssa baelama (Forsskål, 1775)
Little priest
SL: to 150 mm (5.9 in); D 14-16; A 27-30; LR 36-38; GR 20-26.

This species occurs in large schools in turbid water of river mouths and inner bays.

Indo-west-Pacific: Red Sea to Samoa, n. to the Philippine, Caroline, and Mariana Is., s. to New Caledonia.

Encrasicholina punctifer (Remove) Fig. 1a
Oceanic anchovy
SL: to 55 mm (2.2 in); D 12-15; A 14-17; P 13-17; LR 35-43; lower GR 21-27; scutes 2-7.

This anchovy is one of the most important forage organisms for tuna and other pelagic fishes. It occasionally enters large atoll lagoons or deep, clear water bays.

Indo-Pacific: Persian Gulf and E. Africa to the Hawaiian and Society Is., n. to s. Japan, s. to New Caledonia; throughout Micronesia.

Encrasicholina heterolobus (Rüppell, 1835) Fig. 1b
Blue anchovy
SL: to 65 mm (2.6 in); GR 24-27.

When alive, this species has a distinct blue upper edge to its lateral stripe. It occurs primarily in deep bays under oceanic influence.

Indo-west-Pacific: Red Sea to Fiji, n. to the Ryukyus, s. to New Caledonia; Carolines and Guam in Micronesia.

[2]Excludes *S. apiensis*, reported from Pohnpei (Baldwin,1983).

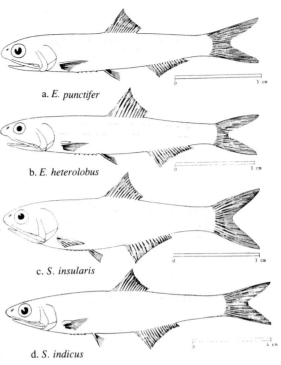

a. *E. punctifer*

b. *E. heterolobus*

c. *S. insularis*

d. *S. indicus*

Fig. 1. Micronesian anchovies.

Encrasicholina devisi (Whitley, 1940)
Gold anchovy
SL: to 55 mm (2.2 in); GR 19-21+21-26.

This species has a golden hue when alive. It occurs in coastal waters.

Indo-west-Pacific: Gulf of Aden to Samoa, n. to the Carolines.

Stolephorus insularis Hardenberg   Fig. 1c
Gold estuarine anchovy
SL: to 80 mm (3.1 in).

This species has a golden hue like *S. devisi*, but occurs in more estuarine situations, often with *S. indicus*.

Indo-west-Pacific: e. India to w. Samoa, n. to the Carolines, s. to New Caledonia.

Stolephorus indicus (Van Hasselt, 1823)   Fig. 1d
Indian anchovy
SL: to 120 mm (4.7 in); D 15-17; A 18-21; LR 37-42; lower GR 20-26; scutes ≥5.

This large anchovy inhabits estuaries and coastal bays.

Indo-Pacific: Red Sea to the Society Is., n. to the Ryukyus, s. to New Caledonia; Carolines and Marianas in Micronesia.

Stolephorus pacificus Baldwin, 1984
West Pacific anchovy
SL: to 78 mm (3.1 in); D 15-17; A 19-22; P 12-15; LR 36-38; lower GR 33-38; scutes ≤4.

This anchovy was recently discovered in estuaries of Guam and Kosrae.

Guam and Kosrae

CLUPEIDAE (HERRINGS, SPRATS, and SARDINES)

Clupeids are characterized by a single spineless dorsal fin, small terminal mouth, elongate body, pelvic fins with 8-9 rays located roughly halfway down the body, and silvery cycloid scales that are easily shed. Round herrings and sprats(subfamily Dussumierinae) are nearly round in cross section and lack scutes; herrings and sardines (subfamily Clupeinae) are compressed and possess scutes along the belly. The former contains several species that inhabit coral reefs as well as coastal waters; the latter contains species that inhabit coastal waters of large land masses or high islands., All species are planktivores. (Drawings mostly after Lewis et al., 1983; Lit.: Baldwin, 1984; Lewis et al., 1983; Whitehead, 1986)

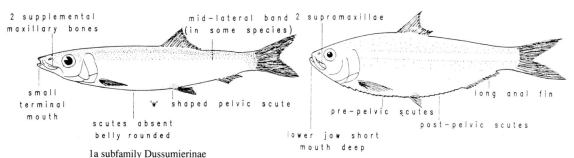

1a subfamily Dussumierinae

1b subfamily Clupeinae

Key to Micronesian Clupeidae:

1a. Belly rounded; scutes absent or hidden, never present behind V base......................subfamily Dussumierinae: 2

1b. Scutes present along whole belly, often forming a sharp keel.......................................subfamily Clupeinae: 6

2a. D origin nearer to tail base than to snout tip; branchiostegal rays 14-19.........................genus *Dussumieria*: 3

2b. D origin nearer to snout tip than to tail base; branchiostegal rays 4-8...4

3a. Body very elongate, its depth 6.7-8.2 in SL.................. ....***D. elopsoides***

3b. Body not as elongate, its depth 5.8-6.0 in SL.............. ....***Dussumieria***: sp. B

4a. V base under or behind last two D rays; upper jaw slender...***Eutremus teres*****

4b. V base under last half of D; upper jaw deep................. ....genus ***Spratelloides***: 5

5a. Silver mid-lateral band; no prominent markings on caudal base; A rays 11-13..............................***S. gracilis***

5b. No lateral band; 2 pairs of dark lines on caudal base; A rays 9-11...***S. delicatulus***

6a. Usually a black spot present at D origin; many (7-14) fronto-parietal striae; second supramaxilla symmetrical... ....genus ***Amblygaster***: 7

6b. No dark spot at D origin; few (3-6) fronto-parietal striae on top of head; second supramaxilla asymmetrical (lower portion of lobe longer than upper portion.................... ....***Herklotsichthys quadrimaculatus***

7a. Spots along flanks (gold, turning black); lower GR 31-43; D yellowish...***A. sirm***

7b. No spots on flanks; lower GR 27-31; D dusky............. ....***A. clupeoides***

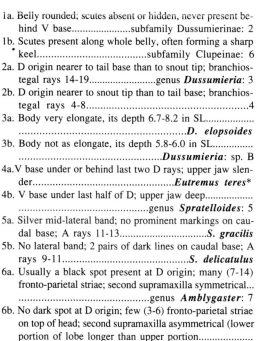

2a

branchiostegal rays
head from below

5b

6a *Amblygaster*:
7-14 lines

fronto-parietal striae on top of head

symmetrical shape

2nd supramaxilla

6b *Herklotsichthys*:
3-6 lines

asymmetrical shape

a. *Spratelloides gracilis*

b. *Amblygaster sirm*

Fig. 1. Micronesian sprats and sardines (b, after A. M. Awl *in* Schultz, 1953.

Subfamily Dussumierinae

Dussumieria elopsoides Bleeker, 1849
Hasselt's sprat

(*D. hasselti*)

SL: to > 62 mm (2.4 in); D 16-18; A 15; P 11-12; LR 61; GR 10+1+21; depth 6.7-8.2.

Known from Micronesia on the basis of two damaged specimens collected in Bikini Atoll lagoon nearly 40 years ago.

West-central Pacific: Indonesia and the Philippines to the Carolines and Marshalls.

Dussumieria sp. B
Sharp-nosed sprat

SL: to 190 mm (7.5 in); lower GR 19-22; depth 5.8-6.0.

This undescribed species occurs in deep lagoons and along outer reef slopes at depths of 1 to over 21m.

Tropical w. Pacific: New Guinea and Carolines to Fiji, n. to Guam.

Spratelloides delicatulus (Bennett, 1831)   Pl. 11G
Blue sprat

SL: to 61 mm (2.4 in); D 11-13; A 10-11; P 11-13; V 8; LR 41-42 (36-40SA); GR 9-11+26-32.

This species occurs in large schools in relatively clear coastal waters, lagoons, and along reef margins. It generally schools near the surface where it feeds on plankton. In the Marianas it is caught by butterfly (lift) nets and used as bait or food.

Indo-Pacific: Red Sea to the Society Is., n. to the Ryukyus, s. to New Caledonia; throughout Micronesia.

Spratelloides gracilis (Schlegel, 1846)   Fig. 1a
Silver sprat

(*S. atrofasciatus*)

SL: to 60 mm (2.4 in); D 12-13; A 12-13; P 13-15; LR 41-42; GR 7-9+27-37.

This species also occurs in large schools in relatively clear

coastal, lagoon, and seaward reef waters.

Indo-Pacific: Red Sea to the Tuamotus, n. to s. Japan, s. to Lord Howe Is.; Belau and the Marshalls in Micronesia.

Subfamily Clupeinae

Amblygaster clupeoides (Bleeker, 1849)
Blue pilchard

SL: to 170 mm (6.7 in).

This species occurs in coastal waters of large land masses and high islands.

Indo-Pacific: India to Irian Jaya and Fiji, n. to s. Japan; Belau and Pohnpei in Micronesia.

Amblygaster sirm (Walbaum, 1792)   Fig. 1b
Spotted pilchard

SL: to 200 mm (7.9 in); D 17-19; A 15-19; P 16-17; LR 40-43; GR 38-42; 30-32 abdominal scutes.

This species occurs in coastal waters and lagoons.

Indo-Pacific: Red Sea to Samoa, n. to the Ryukyus, s. to Queensland and Tonga; Belau, Carolines, and s. Marshalls in Micronesia.

Herklotsichthys quadrimaculatus (Rüppell, 1835)
Gold spot herring   Pl. 11H

SL: to 153 mm (6.0 in); D 19-20; A 16-19; P 14-17; GR 14-17+ 29-37; scutes 16-19+12-14.

The goldspot herring has a pair of gold spots on each operculum as well as a longitudinal blue stripe. It is an important food fish in many areas. It schools near mangroves and above sandy shallows of coastal bays and lagoons during the day, and moves into deeper water at night to feed. In Belau, it migrates to tidal creeks to spawn from November to April. Unlike some of its relatives, it avoids brackish water.

Indo-Pacific: Red Sea to Samoa, n. to s. Japan, s. to New Caledonia; Belau, Carolines, and s. Marshalls in Micronesia; recently introduced to the Hawaiian Is.

Order AULOPIFORMES

SYNODONTIDAE (LIZARDFISHES)

Lizardfishes are slender cylindrical fishes with spineless fins and a large mouth full of slender sharp teeth, including up to several dozen on the tongue. They have a short, high dorsal fin with 10 to 13 rays followed by a tiny adipose fin, and large pelvic fins with 8 or 9 rays. They are voracious, well-camouflaged, ambushing predators of small fishes. They are capable of capturing amazingly large prey with an equally amazing burst of speed. Some species typically lie on or almost entirely buried in sand while others sit on rock or coral. At least 7 species occur on shallow Micronesian coral reefs; undoubtedly more remain to be discovered, particularly in deeper reef waters. (Lit.: Cressey, 1981; Moyer and Sano, 1985; Waples, 1981)

Key to Micronesian species of Synodontidae:

1a. Several rows of villiform teeth present externally on lips; V rays 9..genus **Saurida**: 2
1b. No teeth present externally on lips; V rays 8...............
....genus **Synodus**: 3

1a *Saurida*

1b *Synodus*

2a. P usually 13 (rarely 12 or 14) and long, longest ray ≥12 % of SL, tip extending clearly past pelvic insertion to within 2-3 scale rows of D origin; upper jaw ≤ 16.2% of SL...................................***Sa. gracilis***

2b. P usually 12 (rarely 11 or 13) and short, longest ray ≤11.8 % of SL, tip of which just reaches pelvic insertion to within no closer than 4 scale rows of D origin; upper jaw ≤ 16.2% of SL..........***Sa. nebulosa***

3a. 3¹/2 scales above LL..***Sy. binotatus***

3b. 4¹/2 - 6¹/2 scales above LL...4

4a. Scales on cheek behind mouth; dermal flap of anterior nostril short.....
....***Sy. variegatus***

4b. No scales on cheek behind mouth; anterior nostril flap short or long...
....5

5a. C peduncle with conspicuous dark blotch; anterior nostril flap short....
....***Sy. jaculum***

5b. No dark blotch on C peduncle; anterior nostril flap extends well past nostril margin when depressed anteriorly.............***Sy. dermatogenys***

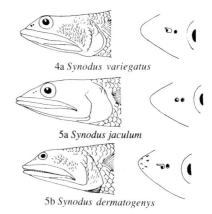

4a *Synodus variegatus*

5a *Synodus jaculum*

5b *Synodus dermatogenys*

Saurida gracilis (Quoy & Gaimard, 1824)
Graceful lizardfish   Pl. 12A

SL: to 31.5 cm(12.4 in); usually under 20 cm (7.9 in); D 11-12; A 9-10; P 12-14 (usually 13); LP 50-52.

Species of *Saurida* differ from all other lizardfishes by possessing several rows of villiform teeth extending outward onto the lips beyond the normal row of large canines, and 9 instead of 8 pelvic rays. This is the most common lizardfish of shallow lagoons, reef flats, and sheltered seaward reefs. Elsewhere it has been reported from as deep as 135 m. It prefers a substrate of sand or rubble adjacent to ledges or rocks sheltering small fishes and often conceals itself by partially burying in sand.

Indo-Pacific: Red Sea to the Marquesas, and Ducie Is., n. to the Ryukyu and Hawaiian Is., s. to Norfolk and Rapa Is.; throughout Micronesia.

Saurida nebulosa Valenciennes, 1849   Pl. 12B
Nebulous lizardfish

SL: to 16.5 cm (6.5 in); D 10-11; A 9-10; P 1-13 (usually 12); LP 50-52.

This species differs from *S. gracilis* by possessing shorter pectoral fins (longest ray <11.8% of SL vs. >12%) and a shorter upper jaw (<16.2% of SL vs. >16.7%). A dark brown *Saurida* which rests on hard substrates such as rock, coral, or even clumps of the calcareous green algae, *Halimeda* is provisionally identified as this species. Confirmation of the identity of this form is needed by the collection of specimens. However, published ecological information suggests that the nebulous lizardfish occurs primarily in inshore habitats such as mangroves and seagrass beds.

Indo-Pacific: Mauritius to the Society Is., n. to the Hawaiian Is., s. to Queensland; Belau, Yap, and the Marianas in Micronesia.

Synodus binotatus Schultz, 1953   Pl. 12C
Twospot lizardfish

SL: to 13 cm (5.1 in); D 12-14; A 8-10; P 12; LP 52-56; scale rows above LL, 3.5.

This species has larger scales (3.5 rows above LL) than all other Micronesian *Synodus*. This as well as a "striated" ap-

pearance of the back of some individuals are features that can often be distinguished in the field. Unfortunately, the twin black spots at the tip of the snout are present in other species. This lizardfish occurs on seaward reefs from depths of 1 to rarely as deep as 30 m. It is generally solitary and typically rests on hard surfaces, occasionally in a head down position on a steep slope.

Indo-Pacific: Gulf of Aden to Mangareva and the Hawaiian Is., n. to Taiwan, s. to Tonga and the Great Barrier Reef; throughout Micronesia.

Synodus variegatus (Lacepède, 1803)   Pl. 12D
Variegated lizardfish

SL: to 19.5 cm (7.7 in); D 11-13; A 8-10; P 13; LP 60-63; scale rows above LL, 5.5.

The reef lizardfish is usually, but not always, redder in coloration than other shallow water *Synodus*. On some individuals the hourglass-shaped markings along its side may be obliterated by an almost solid dark red band and large ones are often thick-bodied, giving a hump-backed appearance. This is the most common lizardfish of deep lagoon and seaward reefs from depths of 5 to well over 40 m. It prefers to rest on hard surfaces and frequently occurs in pairs.

Indo-Pacific: Red Sea to the Hawaiian, Line, Marquesan, and Ducie Is., n. to the Ryukyus, s. to Lord Howe, Kermadec, and Rapa Is.; throughout Micronesia.

Synodus jaculum Russell & Cressey, 1979
Blackblotch lizardfish   Pl. 12E

SL: to 13.6 cm (5.4 in); D 11-13; A 8-10; P12-13; LP 59-62; scale rows above LL, 5.5 (6.5 in Line Is.)

This uncommon lizardfish may be distinguished from all others by the prominent black blotch on its caudal peduncle. It occurs on sandy substrates of protected reefs at depths of 2 to 88 m.

Indo-Pacific: E. Africa to the Line, Marquesan, and Society Is., n. to the Izu Is., s. to New South Wales; Belau to Kosrae in Micronesia.

Synodus dermatogenys Fowler, 1912   Pl. 12F
Sand lizardfish

SL: to 18 cm (7.1 in); D 10-13; A 8-10; P 11-13; LP 56-61; scale rows above LL, 5.5.

The yellowish streaks between each ray (less intense in females) on otherwise unmarked pelvic fins are distinctive. This species occurs on sandy expanses of lagoon and seaward reefs at depths of 1 to over 20 m. It often buries itself leaving only its eyes and nostrils exposed. It is generally solitary, but up to four males have been observed courting a single larger female. A courting male may station itself atop a female and puff out its opercula and spread its fins in a display of aggresion towards other males.

Indo-Pacific: Red Sea to the Hawaiian, Line, Marquesan, and Tuamotu Is., n. to the Ryukyus, s. to Lord Howe Is.; throughout Micronesia.

Order OPHIDIIFORMES

OPHIDIIDAE (CUSK EELS)

Cusk eels are elongate tapered fishes with long dorsal and anal fins that may join with the caudal fin, numerous tiny scales, and thin pelvic fins located under the vicinity of the eye, if present at all. Most species inhabit deep slope waters; those that inhabit coral reefs remain hidden deep within crevices by day, but actively hunt small crustaceans and fishes by night. Only two species are currently known from Micronesian coral reefs.

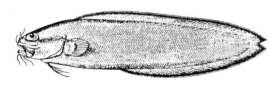

Fig. 1. *B. multibarbata*, 376 mm TL, Hawaii (after Jordan and Evermann, 1903).

Brotula multibarbata Temminck & Schlegel, 1846
Reef cusk eel   Fig. 1
SL: to 43 cm (16.9 in); D 109-139; A 80-106; C 10; P 22-26; V 2.

Micronesian species of *Brotula* possess three pairs of barbels on the snout and three pairs on the chin. In addition to meristic counts, *B. multibarbata* differs from *B. townsendi* by possessing a larger eye (width > interorbital space) and having a slightly different coloration (dark brown with a submarginal black band and narrow white border on the dorsal and anal fins vs. greenish to orange brown with orange-bordered dorsal and anal fins). This species is common on shallow lagoon and seaward reefs and occurs to depths of at least 220 m.

West-central Pacific: Christmas Is. to the Hawaiian Islands and Mangareva, n. to s. Japan; s. to Lord Howe Is; throughout Micronesia.

Brotula townsendi Fowler, 1900
Townsend's cusk eel
SL: to 18 cm (7.1 in); D 100-105; A 71-84; P 25; V 2.
This species occurs on shallow reefs where it seems to be less common than *B. multibarbata*.
Pacific Plate: Pohnpei (?) and the Marshalls to the Hawaiian Is., s. to Samoa.

BYTHITIDAE (LIVEBEARING BROTULAS)

Bythitids closely resemble brotulids, but lack barbels, are ovoviviparous (the eggs hatch inside the female before birth) and males possess a copulatory organ (penis). Some bythitids are even more secretive than brotulids, being known only from poison stations or dug from deep beneath rubble.

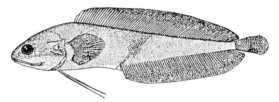

Fig. 1. *B. pautzkei*, 54 mm, Bikini (after A. M. Awl *in* Schultz et al., 1953).

Brosmophyciops pautzkei Schultz, 1960   Fig. 1
Free-tailed reef brotula
SL: to >6 cm (2.4 in); D 78-84; A 58-62; P 23-29; V 2 (looks like 1); LR ca. 100-106; GR 1(+3 platelets)+2(+8 platelets).

When alive this fish is brown with translucent orange fins and is covered in a thick granular mucus so adherent that it cannot be removed without tearing away the scales. It inhabits interstices of lagoon or seaward reefs at depths of 6 to 54 m. Its large eyes suggest that it is nocturnally active.

Indo-Pacific: Red Sea to Samoa and the Australs, n. to the Ryukyus, s. to Rowley Shoals; throughout Micronesia.

Dinematichthys iluocoeteoides Bleeker, 1855
Yellow pigmy brotula
SL: to >11 cm (4.3 in); D ca. 75-88; A 59-69; P 21-26; LR ca. 100; GR 2+1+7-12.

Dinematichthys differs from other shallow water Micronesian bythitids by the combination of tiny eyes and the presence of a distinct tailfin. In recent works, three or more species have been lumped under this name, but the holotype has been lost and it remains uncertain which species it actually represents. At least one yellow to orange species occurs in Micronesia. It is an extremely secretive indweller of deep interstices of lagoon and seaward reefs to a depth of at least 30 m. Some specimens have come from beneath nearly a meter of closely-packed rubble. Its minute eyes suggest that it is nearly blind and does not venture out even at night.

West-central Pacific: Christmas Is. to Ducie, n. to the Ryukyus, s. to Rapa; throughout Micronesia.

Microbrotula sp.
Pigmy brotula
SL: probably <6 cm (2.4 in).
Microbrotula differs from *Dinematichthys* by lacking a distinct tail. One unidentified species has recently been collected at Pohnpei.

CARAPODIDAE (PEARLFISHES)

These highly modified eel-like fishes lack scales, lack pelvic fins, and, in some species, even lack pectoral fins, and have a transparent body that tapers to a long pointed tail. Many live commensally in the body cavities of sea cucumbers, starfish, clams, sea urchins, or tunicates; some are free-living at great depths (to 600 m or more). All have two specialized free-living larval stages: the first, known as the *vexillifer* is an elongate pelagic stage characterized by a long filament called the *vexillum* that arises out of the dorsal fin; the second, known as the *tenuis* is a benthic stage in which the body becomes cylindrical and produces an extremely long tail, most of which disappears as it transforms into an adult. Six species in three genera are known from Micronesian coral reefs, all of which are commensals of invertebrates. (Lit.: Williams, 1984; Olney and Markle *in* Smith and Heemstra, 1986)

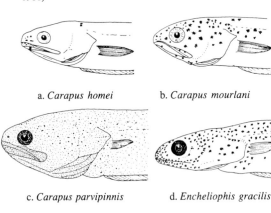

a. *Carapus homei*   b. *Carapus mourlani*

c. *Carapus parvipinnis*   d. *Encheliophis gracilis*

e. *Encheliophis vermicularis*   f. *Onuxodon margaritifer*

Fig. 1. Micronesian species of pearlfishes.

Carapus homei (Richardson, 1846)   Fig. 1a
Silver pearlfish
TL: to 14 cm (5.5 in), tenuis to 20 cm (7.9 in); head large, 6.6-7.1 in TL; P 17-21, 1.4-1.8 in head; preC vertebrae 17-19.

This pearlfish inhabits the body cavities of sea cucumbers which are entered tailfirst through the anus. Its usual host is the black *Stichopus chloronotus* but it will occasionally inhabit other species such as the ocellated *Bohadschia argus*. Both hosts are commonly found on shallow reef flats as well as lagoon and seaward reefs to depths of 30 m or more. *C. homei* leaves its host at night to feed on small fishes and shrimps. Inside its host it has been known to cannibalize recently settled tenuis larvae. Spawning probably occurs during the summer. . At Guam, the elongate tenuis larvae settle into their hosts from October to February when infection rates may approach 90%.
Indo-Pacific: Red Sea to the Hawaiian and Society Is., n. to the Ryukyus; s. to Queensland; throughout Micronesia.

Carapus mourlani (Petit, 1934)   Pl. 13G; Fig. 1b
Pincushion star pearlfish
TL: to 17 cm (6.7 in); P 19; preC vertebrae 15-17; vomer with 2 large canines.
This species differs from *C. homei* by possessing scattered melanophores over most of the body. It prefers the pincushion starfish *Culcita novaeguineae* for a host but has been known to occur in certain holothurians (e.g. *Bohadschia argus*, *Stichopus* sp.) on rare occasions.
Indo-Pacific: E. Africa to the Hawaiian Is.; throughout Micronesia.

Carapus parvipinnis (Kaup, 1856)   Fig. 1c
Pinhead pearlfish
TL: to 30 cm (11.8 in); head small, 10 in TL; P 15-21, 4 in head; eye small, 9 in head; preC vertebrae 15-16; 3-4 large, stout teeth on vomer.
This pearlfish lives within the holothurians *Thelenota ananas* and *Bohadschia argus*.
Indo-Pacific: Mauritius to the Society Is., n. to Taiwan and the Yaeyamas; Marianas and Carolines in Micronesia.

Encheliophis gracilis (Bleeker, 1856)   Fig. 1d
Graceful pearlfish
TL: to 30 cm (11.8 in); P 17-18; preC vertebrae 26-31; vomer with median row of ca. 3 teeth.
In *Encheliophis*, the maxillary is bound to the head for much of its length and the eye is covered by a layer of adipose tissue. This species is parasitic on the gonads and respiratory tree of its host (usually *Bohadschia argus* and rarely *Holuthuria atra*) and is known to form male-female pairs in *B. argus*.
Indo-Pacific: E. Africa to the Hawaiian, Line, and Tuamotu Is., n. to the Ryukyus, s. to Queensland; throughout Micronesia.

Encheliophis vermicularis Müller, 1843   Fig. 1e
Worm pearlfish
TL: to 12 cm (4.7 in).
This species lacks pectoral fins. It occurs within the holothurians *Holuthuria leucospilotus* and *H. scabra*.
West-central Pacific: Philippines to Society Is., n. to the Ryukyus; Belau in Micronesia.

Onuxodon margaritifer (Rendahl, 1921) Fig. 1f
Bivalve pearlfish

TL: to 10 cm (3.9 in); P length 28-54% head length; P 16; precaudal vertebrae 20-22.

In *Onuxodon*, the chest is keeled and the body is deeper than the preceeding genera (width 3 in depth vs. 2 in depth) and adults possess a pair of enormous fangs at the front of the lower jaw. *O. margaritifer* inhabits pearl oysters (*Pinctada* spp.) and other large bivalves (*Pycnodonta hyotis*, *Pteria* spp., *Pinna* spp.). It feeds on crustaceans and polychaetes and is reported to tend towards sexual pairing in the host.

Indo-Pacific: E. Africa to the Line, Marquesan, and Society Is., n. to the Hawaiian Is., s. to New Caledonia; Pohnpei in Micronesia

Order GOBIESOCIFORMES

GOBIESOCIDAE (CLINGFISHES)

The clingfishes are small, highly specialized fishes characterized by a large ventral sucking disc (Fig. 1a), depressed head, terminal mouth, single dorsal fin, scaleless body covered with a heavy coat of mucus, and absence of an air bladder. The sucking disc is formed by greatly modified pelvic fins and in most species contains flattened dermal papillae. It is used by most species for clinging to rocky surfaces of tidepools and shorelines subject to strong wave action. Some species are commensal with invertebrates such as crinoids. (Lit.: Allen and Starck, 1973)

Lepadichthys caritus Briggs, 1961 Fig. 1b
Crinoid clingfish (con't. at upper right)

SL: to 29 mm (1.2 in); D 10-11; A 8-9; P 25-29; C 12-14; GR 8. This clingfish lives in groups among the bases of the arms of certain comasteroid crinoids (e.g. *Himenometra robustipinna*), or feather stars, as well as in surge channels. It has been reported from depths of 4 to 20 m.

Indo-west-Pacific: E. Africa to New Guinea, n. to Belau, s. to Lord Howe Is.

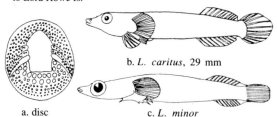

b. *L. caritus*, 29 mm

a. disc   c. *L. minor*

Fig. 1. Micronesian species of *Lepadichthys*.

Lepadichthys minor Briggs, 1957 Fig. 1c
Minor clingfish

SL: to 2.2 cm (0.9 in); D 9-10; A 8; P 27-28; disc length 5.1-5.3 in SL; GR-5, blunt knobs on 2nd arch; upper attachment of gill membrane opposite 12th-15th P ray. This small species inhabits tidepools of benches and outer reef flats.

West-central Pacific: Moluccas to Samoa and the Phoenix Is., n. to the Marianas, s. to New Caledonia; Marianas in Micronesia.

Liobranchia stria Briggs, 1955
Minute clingfish

SL: to 1.8 cm (0.7 in); D 7; A 7; P 21-24. This tiny intertidal dweller is light pink in life.
Marshalls and Marianas

Order BATRACHOIDIFORMES

ANTENNARIIDAE (FROGFISHES)

Frogfishes have bulbous bodies, jointed elbow-like pectoral fins that are used like arms, small holes behind the pectorals for gill openings, and large upturned mouths. The first dorsal spine is modified into a "fishing pole" tipped with a "lure" (called the *esca*; the entire unit is collectively termed the *illicium*). The esca is flicked enticingly above the mouth to attract other fishes that are swallowed in one lighting-fast motion. Their highly distensible bodies enable frogfishes to swallow prey longer than themselves and their cryptic coloration and habit of sitting motionless renders them all but invisible. Their loose prickly skin is often adorned with fleshy or filamentous appendages. At intervals of three to four days, reproductive females lay thousands of tiny eggs imbedded in a large, sometimes scroll-shaped gelatinous mass. At least 12 species occur in Micronesia, but all are rarely encountered. (Lit.: Pietsch *in* Smith and Heemstra, 1986; Pietsch and Grobecker, 1987).

Key to Micronesian Antennariidae:[*]

1a. Numerous fleshy seaweed-like tassles extending from otherwise smooth surface of body; two dermal cirri on mid-dorsal line of snout in front of base of first dorsal spine; no dermal flap at symphysis of premaxillaries...............***Histrio histrio***

1b. Skin prickly, other dermal protuberances, if present, limited to warts or filamentous tassles; no dermal cirri in front of base of first dorsal spine; a small flaplike cirrus at symphysis of premaxillaries between dentigerous parts....................2

*Excludes *Antennarius biocellatus*, a primarily estuarine or freshwater species recently reported from Belau.

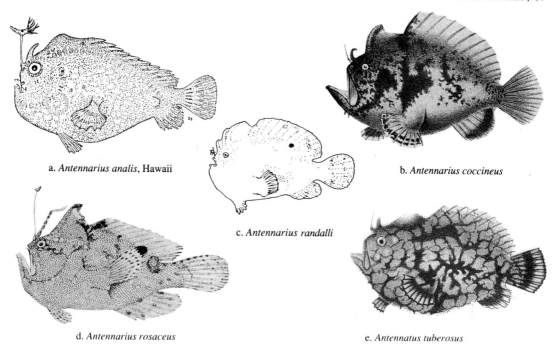

a. *Antennarius analis*, Hawaii

b. *Antennarius coccineus*

c. *Antennarius randalli*

d. *Antennarius rosaceus*

e. *Antennatus tuberosus*

Fig. 1. Micronesian frogfishes (a, after Schultz, 1957; b, d, after Schultz, 1966; e, after Bleeker, 1865).

2a. Esca absent; no groove between upper jaw and base of illicium; A rays nearly always undivided; A and C fins with dark margins and a broad dark band in the middle..***Antennatus tuberosus***

2b. Esca well developed, consists of a group of filaments or a ribbonlike tentacle with filaments or tentacles or a bulbous tip or combination of these; a groove between upper jaw and base of illicium; A rays all divided; A and C fins without a broad dark band in the middle..genus ***Antennarius***: 3

3a. Gill opening near anal fin origin, far behind pectoral fin "elbow"..*A. analis*

3b. Gill opening near pectoral fin "elbow"..4

4a. C peduncle nearly absent; dorsal and anal fins end at or near base of caudal fin rays..*A. coccineus*

4b. C peduncle distinct..5

5a. Second D spine slender and free with several spiny tufts along its length and a filamentous tip, and elongate, its length < 2.8 in length of soft D fin base..*A. rosaceus*

5b. Second D spine robust like the third, connected to the body posteriorly by a web of skin, and short, its length > 3 in length of soft D fin base..6

6a. Bony part of first D spine (i.e. the "rod") longer than second D spine..7

6b. Bony part of first D spine about as long as or shorter than second D spine..9

7a. A 8; D rays usually 13; P rays usally 10; membrane behind 2nd D as thick as spine itself........................*A. commersoni*

7b. A 6 or 7; D rays usually 12; P rays usually 10; membrane behind 2nd D thinner than spine..8

8a. Skin with numerous warty protuberances; 2nd D spine expanded from base; illicium resembles a small fish..*A. maculatus*

8b. Skin with few or no warty protuberances; 2nd D spine tapered from base; illicium doesn't resemble a small fish..*A. pictus*

9a. All D rays simple; no conspicuous dark spot or ocellus at base of soft D fin..*A. dorehensis*

9b. Last few D rays branched; a conspicuous dark spot or ocellus at base of soft D fin..10

10a. Bony part of illicium ca. 1/2 length of 2nd D spine; esca bulbous with ca. 8-10 club-shaped tentacles; dark basidorsal spot small, about = diameter of orbit; max. size ca. 20 mm SL..*A. randalli*

10b. Bony part of illicium nearly = length of 2nd D spine; esca bulbous with filamentous tentacles; dark basidorsal spot larger, ca. 1.5 x diameter of orbit; max. size ca. 10 mm SL..*A. nummifer*

Antennarius analis (Gosline, 1957)   Fig. 1a
Pigmy frogfish
SL: to 44 mm (1.7 in); D I+I+I, 12; A 7; P 10.
This is the only Micronesian antennariid with gill openings located far back near the anal fin origin. It has been collected from tidepools to outer reef slopes at depths of 3 to 20 m.
West-central Pacific: Christmas Is. to the Hawaiian and Society Is., n. to the Marshall and Mariana Is.

Antennarius coccineus (Lesson, 1831)   Fig. 1b
Freckled frogfish

SL: to 11.5 cm (4.5 in); D I+I+I, 12-13; A 7; P 10-12; illicium about equal to length of 2nd D spine; esca a spherical, whitish blob.

This is the only Micronesian antennariid that essentially lacks a caudal peduncle. It has been collected from tidepools as well as lagoon and seaward reefs.

Indo-pan-Pacific: Red Sea to Costa Rica and the Galapagos and San Felix Is., n. to the Ryukyu and Hawaiian Is., s. to Lord Howe and Easter Is.; throughout Micronesia.

Antennarius commersonii (Latreille, 1804)
Giant frogfish   Pl. 13D
(*A. moluccensis*)

SL: to 26.5 cm (10.4 in); D I+I+I, 12-(13), all rays unbranched; A 8; P 10-(11); bony part of illicium with about 15 dark crossbands and nearly as long as 2nd D spine; esca a small tuft of flattened appendages.

The giant frogfish comes in a variety of colors, including yellow, orange, green, brown, and black. Reports of "footlong" frogfishes at Guam are most certainly this species.

Indo-pan-Pacific: Red sea to Panama, n. to s. Japan and the Hawaiian Is., s. to Lord Howe and the Society Is.; observed at Guam.

Antennarius dorehensis Bleeker, 1859   Pl. 13A
Bandtail frogfish
(*A. altipinnis*)

SL: to 5 cm (2.0 in); D I+I+I, 11-13; A 7; P 8-10 (9); bony part of illicium shorter than 2nd D spine; esca oblong or tapering, usually directed ventrally.

This species ranges in color from an ashy grey or light yellow to dark brown or even pitch black. On dark individuals the median fins have pale edges. It has been collected from intertidal reef flats.

Indo-Pacific: E. Africa to the Line and Society Is., n. to the Ryukyus, s. to Fiji; Belau, Marianas, and Kapingamarangi in Micronesia.

Antennarius maculatus(Desjardins, 1840)   Pl. 13B
Warty frogfish

SL: to 85 mm (3.3 in); D I+I+I, 11-(12); A 6-(7); P (10)-11; esca large, resembles a small fish in life, bony part of illicium with numerous crossbands and ca. twice as long as 2nd D spine.

This distinctive frogfish is characterized by numerous prominent wartlike protuberances on its skin and a large esca that mimics a tiny fish. Its coloration is highly variable, ranging from cream to yellow, brown, or black with scattered dark circular spots and saddles or blotches ranging from white to pink, rust-red, or red. Most individuals resemble a piece of candy, but heavily spotted ones may reseme *A. pictus*. All specimens with accompanying depth data were collected in less than 11 m.

Indo-west Pacific: Mauritius to the Solomons, n. to the Ryukyus, s. to the Great Barrier Reef; Guam in Micronesia.

Antennarius nummifer (Cuvier, 1817)   Pl. 13E
Spotfin frogfish

SL: to 10 cm (3.9 in); D I+I+I, 12; A 7; P (10)-11; bony part of illicium shorter than 2nd D spine; esca bulbous with filamentous tentacles.

This cryptic species is covered with thin filamentous protruberances and splotches of color, but always bears a slightly darker ocellus beneath the 7th-10th dorsal rays. A black phase with white tips on the pectoral rays also occurs. In life, its esca resembles a tiny stout-bodied shrimp. This species occurs from the intertidal zone to depths of at least 25 m on both lagoon and seaward reefs.

Indo-Pacific and E. Atlantic: Red Sea to the Society Is., n. to s. Japan, s. to Lord Howe Is. and n. New Zealand; Marianas and Marshalls in Micronesia.

Antennarius pictus (Shaw & Nodder, 1794)
Painted frogfish; Spotted frogfish   Pl. 13E
(*A. chironectes*)

SL: to 16 cm (6.3 in); D I+I+I, 12-13 (up to last 5 rays branched); A (7)-8; P 9-11(10); bony part of illicium with numerous dark crossbands and nearly twice as long as 2nd D spine; esca an elongate tuft of flattened appendage.

This species also has a black phase with white pectoral ray tips. It is one of the more common antennariids in the Marianas where it occurs on lagoon reefs.

Indo-Pacific: E. Africa to the Hawaiian and Society Is., n. to s. Japan, s. to the Great Barrier Reef; Marianas and Marshalls in Micronesia.

Antennarius randalli Allen, 1970   Figs. 1c, 2
Randall's frogfish

SL: to 21 mm (0.8 in); D I+I+I, 12-13, last 2-3 branched; A 7; P 9; bony part of illicium ca. 1/2 length of 2nd D spine; esca bulbous with 8-10 club-shaped tentacles.

This tiny frogfish has been collected from the outer reef slopes at depths of 8 to 31 m.

West-central Pacific: Taiwan, Philippines, Moluccas, Fiji, Marshall Is., and Easter Is.

Fig. 2. Esca of *A. randalli* (after Allen, 1970).

Antennarius rosaceus (Smith & Radcliffe, 1912)
Spiny-tufted frogfish   Fig. 1d

SL: to 42 mm (1.7 in); D I+I+I, (12)-13; A (7)-8; P 9-(10); bony part of illicium < 1.8 in length of soft D fin base; esca a small bulbous knot of filaments.

This is the only Micronesian antennariid that has an elongate second dorsal spine not connected to the body by a web of skin and bearing numerous spiny tufts and a filamentous tip. It has been collected from the seaward reef flat to a depth of 130m.

Indo-Pacific: Red Sea, Philippines, Timore, Samoa, and Gilbert, Marshall, and Lord Howe Is.

Antennatus tuberosus (Cuvier, 1817)
Bandfin frogfish
(Antennatus bigibbus)

SL: to 6.5 cm (2.6 in); D I+I+I, 12; A 7-8; P 9-12(11); illicium slightly longer than 2nd D spine tapering to a nonfilamentous simple tentacle that lacks an esca.

This is the only Micronesian antennariid that lacks a groove between the upper jaw and base of the illicium. It also has a distinctive color pattern in which there is a a broad dark band and marginal dark bands on the anal and caudal fins.
Indo-Pacific: E. Africa to the Line and Pitcairn Is., n. to the Marshall and Hawaiian Is., s. to Samoa.

Histrio histrio (Linnaeus, 1758)
Sargassumfish

SL: to 14 cm (5.4 in); D I+I+I, 11-13; A 7-8; P 9-11(10). This is the only antennariid adapted to a pelagic existence by riding amongst rafts of floating *Sargassum* seaweed. It looks almost exactly like the weed itself by virtue of a camouflaging color pattern and numerous fleshy weedlike dermal appendages. It occasionally washes into reef waters with detached weed, and post-larvae occasionally settle out on clumps of *Sargassum* still growing on the reef margin.
Indo-west-Pacific and tropical Atlantic: n. to s. Japan, s. to Australia; Marianas in Micronesia.

Order ATHERINIFORMES

ATHERINIDAE (SILVERSIDES)

Silversides are small schooling fishes characterized by two dorsal fins, pelvic fins with I, 5 rays, a small terminal mouth, a broad silvery mid-lateral band, and the absence of a lateral line. They inhabit surface coastal and coral reef waters and feed on zooplankton. Most Micronesian species occur in marine rather than in estuarine situations. (Lit.: Lewis et al., 1983)

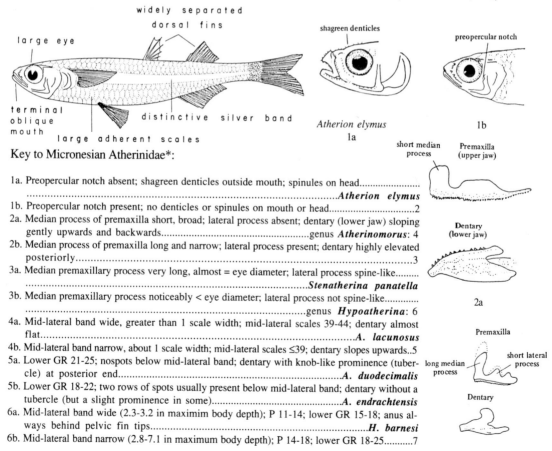

Key to Micronesian Atherinidae*:

1a. Preopercular notch absent; shagreen denticles outside mouth; spinules on head......................
....*Atherion elymus*

1b. Preopercular notch present; no denticles or spinules on mouth or head...............................2

2a. Median process of premaxilla short, broad; lateral process absent; dentary (lower jaw) sloping gently upwards and backwards...genus *Atherinomorus*: 4

2b. Median process of premaxilla long and narrow; lateral process present; dentary highly elevated posteriorly...3

3a. Median premaxillary process very long, almost = eye diameter; lateral process spine-like.........
....*Stenatherina panatella*

3b. Median premaxillary process noticeably < eye diameter; lateral process not spine-like.............
....genus *Hypoatherina*: 6

4a. Mid-lateral band wide, greater than 1 scale width; mid-lateral scales 39-44; dentary almost flat...*A. lacunosus*

4b. Mid-lateral band narrow, about 1 scale width; mid-lateral scales ≤39; dentary slopes upwards..5

5a. Lower GR 21-25; nospots below mid-lateral band; dentary with knob-like prominence (tubercle) at posterior end...*A. duodecimalis*

5b. Lower GR 18-22; two rows of spots usually present below mid-lateral band; dentary without a tubercle (but a slight prominence in some)...*A. endrachtensis*

6a. Mid-lateral band wide (2.3-3.2 in maximim body depth); P 11-14; lower GR 15-18; anus always behind pelvic fin tips...*H. barnesi*

6b. Mid-lateral band narrow (2.8-7.1 in maximum body depth); P 14-18; lower GR 18-25...........7

---

* Based on Lewis et al., 1983.

7a. Premaxillary process long; A 8-11; anus 0.5-2.0 scales in front of pelvic fin tips; mid-lateral band 4.0-7.1 in maximim depth...*H. ovalaua*

7b. Premaxillary process moderate, 2.2-3.7 in eye diameter; A 10-13; mid-lateral band 2.9-5.1 in maximim depth..*H. cylindrica*

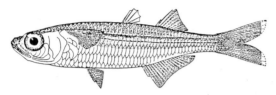

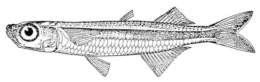

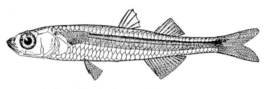

a. *Atherinomorus insularum*, 63 mm, Saipan.

c. *Atherion elymus*, 29 mm, Guam.

b. *Atherinomorus lacunosus*, 90 mm, Guam.

d. *Hypoatherina barnesi*, 52 mm, Rongelap.

Fig. 2. Micronesian silversides (a, c, d, after A. M. Awl *in* Schultz et al., 1953).

Atherion elymus Jordan & Starks, 1901
Bearded silverside

SL: to 36 mm (1.4 in); D III-V-I,8-11; A I,8-11; P 11-13; LR 41-44; GR 2-3+1+10-11.

This species forms loose aggregations in tidepools and along rocky shorelines and reef margins.

Tropical w. Pacific: Philippines to Samoa, n. to s. Japan; Marianas and Marshalls in Micronesia.

Atherinomorus duodecimalis
   (Cuvier & Valenciennes, 1835)
Tropical silverside

SL: to 70 mm (2.8 in); D IV-VI+I, 9-10; A I, 12-13; P 14-17; GR 6+1+21-25; LR <39.

Indo-west-Pacific: Comores and Madagascar to the Solomons, n. to the Philippines and Carolines, s. to New Caledonia.

Atherinomorus endrachtensis
   (Quoy & Gaimard, 1824)
Striped silverside

SL: to 90 mm (3.5 in); D IV-V-I, 7-8; A I, 10-12; LR 35-37; GR 5-6+1+18-22.

Tropical w. Pacific: nw. Australia to the Solomons, n. to the Philippines and Kosrae, s. to Queensland.

Atherinomorus lacunosus (Schneider, 1801)
Hardyhead silverside

(*Pranesus pinguis*; *P. insularum whitei*?)

SL: to 120 mm (4.7 in); D IV-VII-I, 8-11; A I, 12-17; P 14-17; LR 39-44; GR 5-6+1+18-25.

This very common silverside occurs in large schools along sandy shorelines and reef margins in areas of relatively clear water.

Indo-Pacific: Red Sea to the Hawaiian Samoan, and Phoenix

Is.; n. to s. Japan, s. to New Caledonia; throughout Micronesia.

Hypoatherina barnesi Schultz, 1953
Slender silverside

SL: to 54 mm (2.1 in); D V-VII-I, 8-11; A I, 12-17; P 11-14; LR 43-44; GR 3-5+1+15-17.

This species occurs in lagoons and along shorelines of outlying islands.

Indo-Pacific: E. Africa to the n. Cooks, n. to New Guinea and the Marshalls, s. to Fiji.

Hypoatherina ovalaua (Herre, 1935)
Ovalaua silverside

SL: to 70 mm (2.8 in); D V-VII-I,9-10; A I,7-10; P 14-18; LR 40-45; GR 4-6+1+20-26.

This species is relatively common in both high island and atoll lagoons.

West-central Pacific: New Guinea to the Phoenix and Tongan Is., n. to the Carolines and Marshalls, s. to Rowley Shoals and New Caledonia.

Hypoatherina cylindrica
Cylindrical silverside

Recently reported from Pohnpei and the Wallis and Futuna Is.

Stenatherina panatella (Jordan &Richardson, 1908)
Panatella silverside

(*Hypoatherina temmincki*, Schultz, 1953)

SL: to 90 mm (3.5 in); D V-VII-I,8-10; A I,10-12; P 14-18; LR 46-47; GR 5+1+20-22.

This species inhabits high island and atoll lagoons.

West-central Pacific: Sumatra to the n. Cooks, n. to the Philippines, Carolines, and Marshalls, s. to Fiji.

ISONIDAE (KEELED SILVERSIDES)

Iso hawaiiensis Gosline, 1952   Fig. 1
Keeled silverside

SL: to 30 mm (1.2 in); D IV-V-I,16; A I,20-24; P 12-13; LR 38; GR 12.

Isonids have a relatively compressed keeled body. They occur in the surf zone of rocky coasts or seaward reefs.

Pacific Plate: Marshall, Hawaiian, and Rapa Is.

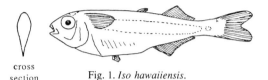

cross
section   Fig. 1. *Iso hawaiiensis.*

Order CYPRINODONTIFORMES

BELONIDAE (NEEDLEFISHES)

Needlefishes have extremely elongate jaws full of needle-like teeth and slender silvery bodies shaded a darker bluish or greenish dorsally. The dorsal and anal fins are located posteriorly, and pelvic fins are abdominal; all fins lack spines.

They are surface dwelling predators of small fishes. They spawn by attaching large adhesive eggs to floating debris. When alarmed or attracted to lights at night, they are capable of skipping across the surface at high speed and have been known to impale fishermen or water skiers with sometimes fatal results. The highly compressed *Ablennes hians* occurs exclusively on the open ocean but most others range into inshore reefs.

Platybelone argalus platyura (Bennett, 1832)
Keeled needlefish   Pl. 13C
(*Belone platyura* Schultz, 1953)

FL: to 37 cm (14.6 in); D 13-15; A 17-19; P 10-11; GR 4-5+6-7.

This is the only Micronesian needlefish that has gill rakers and a distinctly flattened caudal peduncle bearing a prominent keel on each side. It is probably the most common needlefish of reef flats, lagoons and bays where it occurs in groups of a few to several dozen.

Circumtropical: throughout Micronesia; the subspecies *argalus* in the tropical Atlantic.

Strongylura incisa (Valenciennes, 1846)   Fig. 1a,b
Reef needlefish
(*Rhaphiobelone robusta*)

FL: to 100 cm (3.3 ft); D 18-20; A 21-23; P 10-11; GR 0.

Species of *Strongylura* differ from those of *Tylosurus* by having compressed bodies and longer and thinner jaws with more numerous teeth. Their tails are truncate in juveniles

a. *Strongylura incisa*, 354 mm FL, Guam.

b. Head of *Strongylura incisa*, 354 mm FL, Guam.

c. Head of *Tylosurus crocodilis crocodilis*, 745 mm FL, Guam.

d. *Tylosurus crocodilis crocodilis*, 745 mm FL, Guam.

Fig. 1. Micronesian needlefishes.

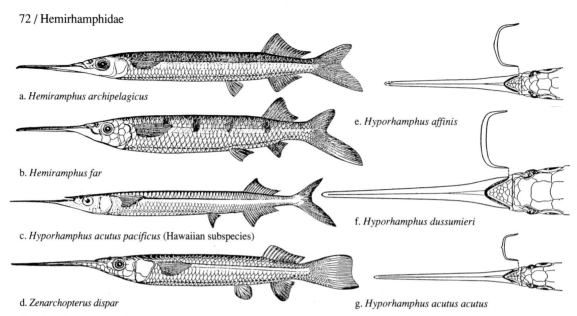

a. *Hemiramphus archipelagicus*

e. *Hyporhamphus affinis*

b. *Hemiramphus far*

f. *Hyporhamphus dussumieri*

c. *Hyporhamphus acutus pacificus* (Hawaiian subspecies)

d. *Zenarchopterus dispar*

g. *Hyporhamphus acutus acutus*

Fig. 1. Micronesian halfbeaks (a, b, d after Fowler, 1959; c, after Jordan and Evermann, 1903; e, f, g, after A. M. Awl *in* Schultz, 1953).

becoming emarginate in adults. This species occurs over both lagoon and seaward reefs.
Indo-Pacific: Eastern Indian Ocean to Mangareva, n. to the Ryukyus, s. to the s. Great Barrier Reef; throughout Micronesia.

Strongylura leiura leiura (Bleeker, 1850)
Littoral needlefish
D 18-21; A 22-26; P 11-12; GR 0.
This species occurs in bays and other inshore waters of high islands and continental coastlines.
Indo-west-Pacific: E. Africa to Fiji; n. to Taiwan, s. to New Caledonia; in Pohnpei in Micronsia; the subspecies *ferox* in Australia.

Tylosurus crocodilis crocodilis (Lesueur, 1821)
Crocodile needlefish; Houndfish   Pl. 13E;
(*Strongylura gigantea*, Schultz, 1953)   Fig 1c,d (p. 71)
FL: to 130 cm (4.3 ft); D 21-24; A 19-22; P 14-15; GR 0; head 2.0-2.6 in SL.
Crocodile needlefishes have relatively stout, cylindrical bodies, shorter heads, and attain a larger size than other needlefishes. This species occurs singly or in small groups over both lagoon and seaward reefs.
Circumtropical: throughout Micronesia; the subspecies *fodiator* in the tropical e. Pacific.

HEMIRHAMPHIDAE (HALFBEAKS)

Halfbeaks are closely related to needlefishes and flyingfishes. They differ from the needlefishes by having a small upper jaw and relatively large scales. The lower jaw of most species is an elongate flattened spike that lacks teeth (at least

externally) and is often tipped in red. Some species are capable of gliding through the air on outstretched pectoral fins like the flyingfishes. They are surface-dwelling omnivores that feed on floating bits of algae and seagrasses, zooplankton, and small fishes. Two strictly offshore species, the flyingfish-like *Euleptorhamphus viridis* and the short-jawed (lacking the beak-like lower jaw) *Oxyporhamphus micropterus* are not included. The surface-dwelling flyingfishes (Exocoetidae) are closely related to halfbeaks. They commonly enter deep lagoons, but seldom venture over shallow coral reefs.

Hemiramphus archipelagicus Collette & Parin, 1978
Island halfbeak   Fig 1a
FL: 25 cm (9.8 in); D 11-15 (usually 13-14); A 10-13 (Usually 11-12); P 11-13.
Hemiramphus is distinguished from *Hyporhamphus* by lacking scales on the snout, having a more deeply forked tail and often a deeper body, and a dorsal fin that originates in front of, rather than over, the origin of the anal fin. This halfbeak occurs in schools in lagoons and relatively sheltered seaward waters.
Indo-Pacific: E. Africa to Samoa, n. to the Philippines, s. to Tonga; Marianas in Micronesia.

Hemiramphus far (Forsskål, 1775)   Fig. 1b
Spotted halfbeak
FL: to 40 cm (15.7 in); D 13-15; A 11-13; P 11-12; LL 50-55; GR 6-8+17-23=24-31.
The spotted halfbeak has a series of 4-9 black blotches on it sides. It inhabits coastal waters of high islands and continental shorelines.
Indo-west-Pacific: Red Sea to Samoa, n. to the Ryukyus, s. to New Caledonia; Belau in Micronesia.

Hemiramphus lutkei (Valenciennes, 1846)
Lutke's halfbeak
Indo-Pacific: E. Africa to Kiribati; n. to Marcus Is.; Kapingamarangi in Micronesia.

Hyporhamphus acutuc acutus (Günther, 1871)
Pacific halfbeak   Fig 1c,g (p. 72)
FL: to 25 cm (9.8 in).
Pacific Plate: Marshalls, Gilberts, and Tonga to the Marquesas, and Easter Is.; the subspecies *pacificus* in the Hawaiian Is.

Hyporhamphus affinis (Günther, 1866)
Insular halfbeak   Fig. 1e (p. 72)
(*H. dussumieri*, Schultz *in* Schultz et al, 1953)
FL: to 26 cm (10.2 in); D 15-17; A 15-17; P 11-13; pred. scales 38-41; GR 8-10+22-27=31-36.
Indo-Pacific: E. Africa to the Tuamotus, n. to the Ryukyus and Hawaiian Is., s. to the Australs, absent from coastal waters of the Indo-Australian region; throughout Micronesia.

Hyporhamphus dussumieri (Valenciennes, 1846)
Dussumier's halfbeak   Fig. 1f (p. 72)
(*H. laticeps*)
FL: to 25 cm (9.8 in); D 15-17; A 14-16; P 11-13; pred. scales 36-43.
This species occurs in schools on the surface of lagoon and seaward reefs.
Indo-Pacific: E. Africa to the Tuamotus, n. to the Ryukyus, s. to the Australs; throughout Micronesia.

Zenarchopterus dispar Valenciennes, 1846
Estuarine halfbeak   Fig. 1d (p. 72)
FL: to 12 cm (4.7 in).
This species inhabits estuaries, mangroves, and rivers.
Indo-west-Pacific: Sri-Lanka to Samoa, n. to the Marianas, s. to New Caledonia; Belau, Carolines, and Marianas in Micronesia.

Order BERYCIFORMES

ANOMALOPIDAE (FLASHLIGHTFISHES)

Flashlightfishes are a primitive group of black fishes that possess a luminous organ under each eye, blunt snouts, large mouths, and a forked tail. A lime-green light is produced biochemically by bacteria that live within the light organ. The light enables them to attract as well as see their zooplankton prey and may also be used for communication and to confuse predators. Two genera, each with one species, occur in the Indo-Pacific: *Anomalops* which has two dorsal fins and a light organ that rotates on or off and *Photoblepheron* with a single dorsal fin and a flap of skin that moves over the light organ to turn it on or off. Throughout most of their range both species occur at depths below 30 m, but in certain areas they live as shallow as 2 m. They remain hidden during the day and venture out at night to feed, tending to occur shallower on dark, moonless nights. (Lit.: McCosker and Rosenblatt, 1987)

Anomalops katoptron Bleeker, 1856   Pl. 14A;
Flashlightfish   Fig. 1a
SL: to 266 mm (10.6 in); D V to VI-I, 14; A II, 9-11; P 18; V I,5; LL ca. 75; GR 8-11+23-24=32-34.
This species occurs in two forms, a small shallow water form (≤91 mm), and a large deep water form. At Guam, the deep water form is occasionally collected by fishing at depths of 200 to 400 m. However, small individuals of an undetermined flashlightfish have been observed by divers at night as shallow as 25 m in the vicinity of the "Blue Hole", a large cave in the face of a dropoff.
Indo-Pacific: Philippines and Moluccas to the Tuamotus, n. to s. Japan; s. to the Great Barrier Reef; Marianas in Micronesia.

Photoblepheron palpebratus(Boddaert, 1781)
Flashlightfish   Fig. 1b
SL: to 90 mm (3.5 in); D II-III, 16-20; A I-II, 13-15; P 15-17; V I,5-6; LL ca. 40; LR ca. 110.
In Micronesia this species has been observed at depths of 7 to 25 m along the seaward reef at Oroluk and Kwajalein atolls.
Indo-Pacific: Philippines, Moluccas, c. Carolines, s. Marianas (?), s. Marshalls, New Guinea, Great Barrier Reef, Society Is., and Rarotonga; the species *steinitzi* from the Red Sea and Comore Is.

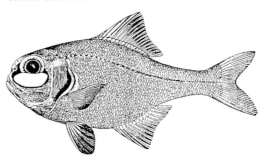

a. *Anomalops katoptron*, 255 mm SL, Guam.   b. *Photoblepheron palpebratus*

Fig. 1. Micronesian flashlightfishes (after Fowler, 1959).

HOLOCENTRIDAE (SOLDIERFISHES and SQUIRRELFISHES)

Holocentrids are relatively deep bodied fishes with large eyes and mouths, small teeth, large coarse scales, and stout dorsal and anal fin spines. All have I, 7 pelvic rays and IV anal spines, and most are predominately red in coloration. The family is divisible into two subfamilies: the Myripristinae (soldierfishes; including *Myripristis*, *Plectrypops*, and *Ostichthys*) which lack a well developed preopercular spine and are relatively blunt snouted, and the Holocentrinae (squirrelfishes; including *Neoniphon* and *Sargocentron*) which possess a stout, sometimes venemous preopercular spine and a more pointed snout. Holocentrids are nocturnally active; during the night soldierfishes occupy the water column above the reef where they feed on large zooplankton, primarily crustacean larvae, and squirrelfishes forage closer to the bottom for crustaceans, worms, or small fishes. During the day, most holocentrids hover in or near caves and crevices or among branching corals. Species of *Myripristis* are able to produce a variety of clicking, grunting, and growling sounds which may be used as warning or recognition signals. In Belau, at least one species of *Myripristis* is reputed to spawn a few days after each new moon. The larval stage probably lasts for several weeks since most species are widely distributed and settlement occurs at the relatively large size of 30 mm or more. At least 13 species of soldierfishes and 16 species of squirrelfishes occur in Micronesia. Not included is the deepwater soldierfish *Ostichthys kaianus*, from depths of 310 to 640 m. (Lit.: Randall and Greenfield, 1981; Shimizu and Yamakawa, 1979).

Subfamily Myripristinae

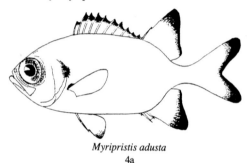

Myripristis adusta
4a

symphysial tooth
patches
frontal view of mouth

Myripristis hexagona
5a

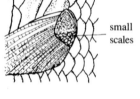

small
scales

pectoral fin folded forward
6b

Key to the Micronesian species of Myripristinae*:

1a. D spines 12; D continuous, though deeply notched; lower limb GR 11-18..............2
1b. D spines 11; D divided to the base between spines 10 and 11; lower limb GR 19-32...
....genus ***Myripristis*** (3)
2a. Premaxillary groove (between nasal bones) broadly V-shaped (deep water).................
....***Ostichthys kaianus***
2b. Premaxillary groove narrow and elongate or rhomboidal.................***Plectrypops lima***
3a. LL 26-32 (except 30-34 in *woodsi*)..4
3b. LL 32-44..9
4a. Spinous D blackish with a submarginal unpigmented zone; margin of median fins
   broadly black, especially on lobes of C and elevated parts of soft D and A; a single
   scale (rarely 2) on inner side of P base.....................................***M. adusta***
4b. Spinous D not blackish; margin of median fins not broadly black (but black blotch or
   streak may be present distally); either no scales or numerous small scales in P axil...5
5a. Two pairs of symphysial tooth patches, one above the other, outside gape at tip of
   lower jaw (but may be absent at under 7.5 cm); LL 25-29....................***M. hexagona***
5b. A single pair of tooth patches, 1 at each side of symphysis on lower jaw just outside
   gape; LL 27-32...6
6a. No scales in axil of P fins; LL 30-34; in life, a white spot in front of upper P axil.....
   ....***M. woodsi***
6b. Small scales present in axil of P fins); LL 27-31; no white spot on upper pectoral
   axil...7

---

* *M. woodsi* keys out in two places; drawings 4-13 redrawn from Greenfield, 1974.

Myripristis kuntee
9a

9b

7a. Scales on upper sides of body with broad blackish rims (purplish to blue to dark brown in life), interorbital space and nape almost completely dark; upper-limb GR 12-16 (modally 14); LL 27-29...*M. violacia*

7b. Scales on upper sides of body without broad blackish rims; upper-limb GR 11-15 (modally 12-13); LL 27-32 (modally 29)...8

8a. Least bony interorbital width 4.3-5.8 in head; lower jaw of adults strongly projecting when mouth fully closed; horizontal diameter of orbit=vertical diameter; outer part of spinous D broadly orangish yellow...*M. berndti*

8b. Least bony interorbital width 3.7-4.4 in head; lower jaw of adults slightly projecting when mouth fully closed; horizontal diameter of orbit < vertical diameter; outer part of spinous D red..*M. murdjan*

9a. Dark brown bar from upper end of gill opening to P axil; LL 37-44; A rays 14-16; D rays 15-17..*M. kuntee*

9b. Dark brown pigment in region of gill opening, if present, confined to opercular membrane; LL 32-40; A rays 10-15; D rays 13-16..10

10a. Dark brown pigment of opercular membrane ending at or slightly below opercular spine; A rays 13-15; D rays 14-16...*M. pralinia*

10b. Dark brown area of opercular membrane, when present, extending well below opercular spine (usually to level of upper P base); A rays 10-13; D rays 13-15..........11

11a. Third A spine distinctly longer than 4th; front of lower jaw (symphysial teeth) fits into deep notch in upper jaw; LL 32-38...12

11b. Third A spine not longer than 4th; front of lower jaw (symphysial teeth) does not fit into deep notch in upper jaw; LL 30-34..13

12a. Least bony interorbital width ≤3.3 in head; opercular membrane red, not dark brown; fins orange-red, the spinous D tips white..................................*M. vittatus*

12b. Least bony interorbital width ≥4.0 in head; opercular membrane dark brown; C and much of D, A, and V yellow; spinous D not tipped in white..............*M. chryseres*

13a. Soft D and A fins with white leading edges; in life a white spot in front of upper P axil...*M. woodsi*

13b. Soft D and A fins uniformly red without white leading edges; no white spot in front of P axil..*M. amaena*

Myripristis pralinia
10a

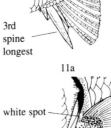

3rd
spine
longest

11a

white spot

Myripristis woodsi

13a

Plectrypops lima (Valenciennes, 1831)   Pl. 14B
Cardinal soldierfish
SL: to 12 cm (4.7 in); D XII, 14-16; A IV, 10-12; P 16-17; V I,7; LL 39-42; GR 7-8+14-15=22-25; depth 2.3-2.6.
Plectrypops is easily distinguished from *Myripristis* by its relatively long straight forehead, small tail with greatly rounded lobes, and over 40 pored lateral line scales. The deep dwelling (310-640 m) *Ostichthys kaianus* has a similar body shape, but has much larger scales (LL 28-30), broken white stripes on its sides, and reaches a size of 29 cm. During the day the cardinal soldierfish inhabits deep recesses of caves and ledges of lagoon and seaward reefs from the reef flat to depths of 25 m or more. At night it roams the reef remaining close to the substrate to feed on small crustaceans, crustacean larvae, and an occasional small fish.
Indo-Pacific: E. Africa to the Hawaiian and Easter Is., n. to s. Japan, s. to Lord Howe Is.; throughout Micronesia.

Myripristis adusta Bleeker,1853   Pl. 14C
Bronze soldierfish
SL: to 25 cm (9.8 in); D X-I, 14-16(15); A IV, 12-14(13); P 15-16, 1(rarely 2) scale on inner axil ; LL 27-29; GR 10-13+23-27=35-40.
This soldierfish is easily distinguished by its unique coloration. Although it occasionally occurs on exposed reef flats and shallow lagoon reefs, its usual habitats are areas of rich coral growth of dropoffs and steep channel slopes from be-

low the effects of surge to over 25 m. It occurs singly or in small groups in the vicinity of caves and crevices and is less abundant than many other *Myripristis*. In the Marshalls, it is known only on the basis of an underwater photograph taken at Kwajalein.
Indo-Pacific: E. Africa to the Line and Tuamotu Is., n. to the Ryukyus, s. to New Caledonia; throughout Micronesia.

Myripristis amaena (Castlenau, 1873)   Pl. 14D
Brick soldierfish
(*M. argyromus*)
SL: to 21 cm (8.3 in); D X-I,13-15; A IV, 12-13; P 14-16, inner axil naked; LL 32-34; GR 13-15+26-28=40-43.
This species differs from all other Micronesian soldierfishes by the uniform red coloration of its fins which lack white leading edges or darker tips. It inhabits reef flats and seaward slopes to depths of at least 52 m where it occurs in small aggregations in caves or under ledges or boulders.
West-central Pacific: Indonesia and the Philippines to the Hawaiian and Ducie Is., n. to the Ryukyu and Marcus Is.; throughout Micronesia.

Myripistis berndti Jordan & Evermann, 1903
Bigscale soldierfish   Pl. 14E
SL: to 24 cm (9.4 in); D X-I, 13-15; A IV, 11-13; P 14-16 (15), inner axil scaled; LL 28-31; GR 12-14+24-27=35-42.
This is the largest and among the more common of Micro-

nesian soldierfishes. It is easily distinguished from *M. murdjan* by its orange rather than red spinous dorsal fin and lighter body coloration. During the day it occurs in loose aggregations in caves and under ledges of subtidal reef flats, channels and margins to outer reef slopes at depths of 50 m or more.

Indo-pan Pacific: E. Africa to Central America, n. to s. Japan and the Hawaiian Is., s. to Pitcairn and Lord Howe Is.; throughout Micronesia.

Myripristis chryseres Jordan & Evermann, 1903
Yellowfin soldierfish Pl. 14F

SL: to 20 cm (7.9 in); D X-I, 13-14; A IV, 11-13; P 14-16 (15), inner axil naked; LL 32-38; GR 12-15+23-27=33-38.

This is the only Micronesian soldierfish with bright yellow fins. It rarely occurs in caves at depths of 12 m or less. Its usual habitat is steep outer reef slopes at depths of over 30 to at least 235 m. On rare occasions it turns up in nighttime catches of small bottomfishes.

Indo-Pacific: E. Africa to the Hawaiian and Samoan Is., n. to s. Japan; Guam in Micronesia.

Myripristis hexagona (Lacepède, 1802) Pl. 15A
Doubletooth soldierfish

SL: to 153 mm (6.0 in); D X-I, 13-15(14-15); A IV, 12-13; P 14-16(14-15), inner axil scaled; LL 25-28(27-28); GR 12-15+24-29=36-43.

This is the only Micronesian *Myripristis* that has two pairs of symphysial tooth patches outside the gape at the tip of the lower jaw (the smaller lower pair absent in juveniles under 75 mm). The individual in the photograph differs from typical examples by lacking white on the anterior margins of the soft portions of the dorsal and anal fins. It is known from Micronesia on the basis of a photograph taken at a depth of 15 m along Belau's Ngemelis Wall. Elsewhere it has been reported from a depth of 40 m.

Indo-west Pacific: E. Africa to Samoa, n. to the Ryukyus, s. to the Great Barrier Reef; Belau in Micronesia.

Myripristis kuntee Cuvier, 1831 Pl. 15B
Pearly soldierfish, Shoulderbar soldierfish
(*M. multiradiatus*)

SL: to 17 cm (6.7 in); D X-I, 15-17; A IV, 14-16; P 14-16 (15), inner axil naked; LL 37-44; GR 12-15+22-26=33-41.

This is among Micronesia's most abundant soldierfishes. It inhabits subtidal reef flats as well as lagoon and seaward reefs below the surge zone to depths of 26 m or more. It is less secretive than most other *Myripristis* and during the day often occurs in large aggregations in the vicinity of rich foliaceous or cavernous coral growth.

Indo-Pacific: E. Africa to the Line and Tuamotu Is., n. to s. Japan and the Hawaiian Is., s. to Lord Howe Is.; throughout Micronesia.

Myripristis murdjan (Forsskål, 1775) Pl. 15C
Red soldierfish
(*M. bowditchae*)

SL: to 22 cm (8.5 in); D X-I, 13-15(14-15); A IV, 11-14 (12-13); P 14-16(15), inner axil scaled; LL 27-32(28-30);

GR 13-14+24-29=36-43.

This species differs from *M. amaenus* by possessing prominent white leading edges of its soft dorsal, anal, and tail fins, and from *M. berndti* by having a deep red spinous dorsal fin. It inhabits reef flats as well as shallow lagoon and seaward reefs to a depth of at least 37 m (in the Red Sea). It is relatively secretive by day, hovering under ledges and in caves. It is not as common as some of the other soldierfishes in Micronesia.

Indo-Pacific: Red Sea to the Marshalls and Samoa, n. to the Ryukyus and Bonins, s. to the s. Great Barrier Reef; throughout Micronesia.

Myripristis pralinia Cuvier, 1824 Pl. 15D

SL: to 17 cm (6.7 in); D X-I, 14-16; A IV, 13-15; P 15, inner axil naked; LL 34-40; GR 13-15+23-26=35-42.

This species closely resembles *M. kuntee*, but unlike that species, its black opercular bar seldom extends beyond the preopercular spine. During the day, *M. pralinius* occurs in small groups in caves or under ledges of reef flats, lagoons, and outer reef slopes to depths 40 m. It is relatively rare in Micronesia.

Indo-Pacific: E. Africa to the Marquesas and Mangareva, n. to the Ryukyus, s. to New Caledonia; Marshalls and Marianas in Micronesia.

Myripristis violacea Bleeker, 1851 Pl. 15E
Violet soldierfish, Orangefin soldierfish
(*M. microphthalmus*)

SL: to 17 cm (6.7 in); D X-I, 14-16; A IV, 12-14; P 14-16 (15), inner axil usually scaled; LL 27-29; GR 12-15+27-31=38-48.

The combination of silvery-violet sheen, orange tips on the fins, and dark orange-red opercular bar are distinctive. This soldierfish inhabits lagoons, channels, and semi-protected seaward reefs in areas of rich coral growth from depths of 4 to 25 m. It is relatively common near large bushes of arborescent *Acropora* or layered *Porites rus* corals.

Indo-Pacific: E. Africa to the Tuamotus, n. to the Ryukyus, s. to New Caledonia and the Australs; throughout Micronesia.

Myripristis vittata Cuvier, 1831 Pl. 15F
White-tipped soldierfish

SL: to 15 cm (5.9 in); D X-I, 13-15; A IV,11-13(12); P 14-16, inner axil naked; LL 35-40; GR 11-13+21-25=34-39.

This is the only species of soldierfish that lacks a dark opercular bar (except for perhaps a deeper red). It forms large aggregations in caves and ledges of steep dropoffs at depths generally below 15 m, but is known from the depth range of 3 to at least 80 m.

Indo-Pacific: E. Africa to the Marquesas and Tuamotus, n. to s. Japan, s. to New Caledonia; throughout Micronesia.

Myripristis woodsi Greenfield, 1974 Pl. 16A
White-spot soldierfish

SL: to 21 cm (8.3 in); D X-I, 13-14; A IV, 10-13; P 15, inner axil naked; LL 30-34; GR 13-16+27-32=41-48.

This is the only Micronesian large-scaled (ave. LL <32) *My-*

ripristis that lacks scales on its inner pectoral axil. It also differs by having a white spot on the upper inner pectoral axil and the combination of dark red (vs. black) opercular membrane, dark red or purple pectoral axil, distinct white ring around the iris, and white anterior margins of its pelvic and soft rayed fins. It typically inhabits reef flats and the shallowest portions of lagoon and seaward reefs.

Pacific Plate: Carolines to the Line Is., n. to the Bonins and Marcus Is., s. to Samoa and the Tuamotus; throughout Micronesia.

Subfamily Holocentrinae

Key to the Micronesian species of Holocentrinae*:

1a. Last D spine about equidistant from penultimate spine and 1st soft-ray; jaws about equal or lower jaw slightly protruding; body depth 2.3-3.5 in SL..............
....genus *Sargocentron*(5)

1b. Last D spine much closer to 1st soft ray than to penultimate spine; lower jaw projecting; body depth 2.9-3.7 in SL................................genus *Neoniphon*(2)

2a. Scales above LL to base of middle D spines 3 1/2; LL scales 42-47; body silvery pink with wellow longitudinal stripes.....................................*N. aurolineatus*

2b. Scales above LL to base of middle D spines 2 1/2; LL 36-43; no yellow stripes on body..3

3a. P rays usually 13; spinous D clear with some dark red streaks distally, but no black markings (Fig. 1b)..*N. argenteus*

3b. P rays usually 14; spinous D with large black markings...............................4

4a. A rays 7 or 8; a large black spot on 1st 3 D membranes (Fig. 1d)......*N. sammara*

4b. A rays 9; a broad median black band across entire spinous D (Fig. 1c)...............
....*N. opercularis*

5a. Scales above LL to base of middle D spines 3 1/2; lower jaw slightly projecting; spinous D uniformly dark red (Fig. 1m), without markings; large oval dark red spot on preopercle behind eye...*S. spiniferum*

5b. Scales above LL to base of middle D spines 2 1/2; lower jaw not projecting; color or not as in 5a...6

6a. LL 32-39...7

6b. LL 38-55..10

7a. Margin of nasal fossa (nostril) with 1 or more spinules................................8

7b. Margin of nasal fossa usually without spinules..............................*S. praslin*

8a. Spinous D membrane not incised between spines; D rays 14 (rarely 13); body dark brown to purplish red with a silvery white vertical line on each scale; depth 2.3-2.6 in SL...*S. violaceum*

8b. Spinous D membrane distinctly incised between spines; D rays 13; body not as above; depth 2.4-2.8 in SL...9

9a. Upper margin of 1st suborbital with serrations; body red without distinct stripes or dark markings; dark blotch between D spines 1 and 2.........*S. dorsomaculatum*

9b. Upper margin of 1st suborbital smooth; body yellowish orange with white stripes and distinct dark blotches at bases of soft D, soft A and C fins; D without dark blotch..*S. melanospilos*

10a. LL 38-43; preopercular spine usually > 2/3 eye diameter.............................11

10b. LL 41-55; preopercular spine < 2/3 eye diameter (except in *S. tiere*)..............12

11a. Premaxillary groove not reaching past a vertical at front edge of orbit; oblique rows of scales on cheek 5; D rays usually 14; edge of nasal fossa with or without spinules; body red without stripes; prominent silvery white spot on peduncle at D base, or C peduncle and entire rear 1/3 of body silvery white........
....*S. caudimaculatum*

11b. Premaxillary groove reaches well past verical at front edge of orbit; oblique rows of scales on cheek 4; D rays usually 13; no spinules at edge of nasal fossa; alternating stripes of red and silvery white on body; no silvery spot on peduncle...*S. tieroides*

12a. Preopercular spine of adults 2/3 or more of eye diameter; longest D spine 2.6-3.5 in head; body red with faint silvery striupes, those on lower part showing

Sargocentron
1a

all others   *aurolineatus*
Neoniphon
1b

margins with   margins
spinules   smooth
7a   7b

upper margin
serrated

S. dorsomaculatum
9a

smooth
upper margin
S. melanospilos
9b

premaxillary
groove

S. caudimaculatum   *S. tieroides*
11a   11b

---

* Drawings for couplets 7a, 9a, and 13a redrawn from Shimizu and Yamakawa, 1979.

blue irridescence; attains 27 cm SL...*S. tiere*

12b. Preopercular spine of adults 1/2 or less of eye diameter; longest D spines 1.5-2.3 in head; body distinctly striped with red and silvery white; not exceeding 16 cm SL...13

13a. Medioposterior margin of nasal bone with 1 or 2 spinules; LL 48-55; body elongate, the depth 2.9-3.5 in SL...*S. microstoma*

13b. Medioposterior margin of nasal bone without spinules; LL 41-49; body depth 2.7-3.3 in SL...14

14a. Interorbital width greater than snout length; V 1.5-1.75 in head; body usually covered with blackish dots...*S. punctatissimum*

14b. Interorbital width subequal to or shorter than snout length; V 1.25-1.5 in head; body not covered with blackish dots...15

15a. P rays usually 14; spinous D reddish black (membrane tips white), with a more or less distinct longitudinal white band along front half of fin usually present (Fig. 1f); longitudinal body stripes distinct on preserved specimens....*S. diadema*

15b. P rays usually 15; spinous D red with a curved white band along middle formed by a series of white spots (1 per interspinous membrane) beginning at base of 1st membrane, mem- brane tips white (Fig. 1h); longitudinal body stripes faint on preserved specimens and usually a dusky blotch on 1st 1 or 2 interspinous D membranes..*S. ittodai*

spinous
inner
margin

S. microstoma
13a

smooth
inner
margin

13b

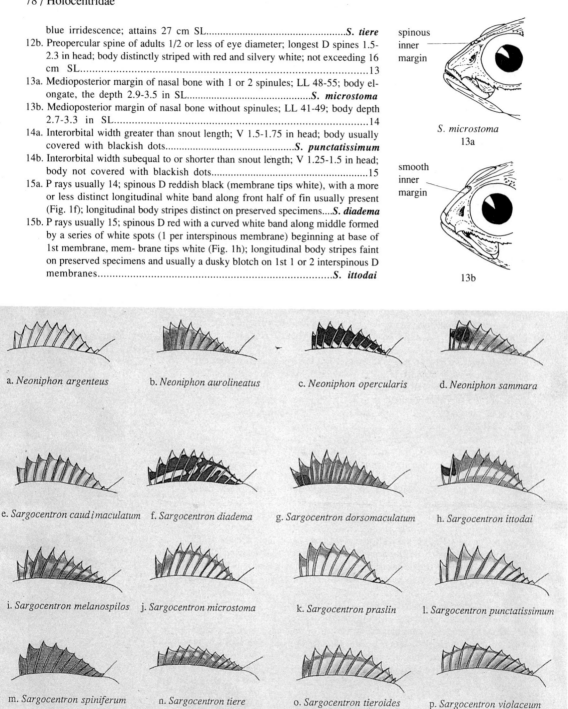

a. *Neoniphon argenteus*

b. *Neoniphon aurolineatus*

c. *Neoniphon opercularis*

d. *Neoniphon sammara*

e. *Sargocentron caudimaculatum*

f. *Sargocentron diadema*

g. *Sargocentron dorsomaculatum*

h. *Sargocentron ittodai*

i. *Sargocentron melanospilos*

j. *Sargocentron microstoma*

k. *Sargocentron praslin*

l. *Sargocentron punctatissimum*

m. *Sargocentron spiniferum*

n. *Sargocentron tiere*

o. *Sargocentron tieroides*

p. *Sargocentron violaceum*

Fig. 1. Typical pigmentation patterns of spinous dorsal fins of Micronesian holocentrinae. Shading indicates various intensities of orange, red, or black. Unshaded areas are white or clear.

Neoniphon argenteus (Valenciennes, 1831)
Clearfin squirrelfish   Pl. 16B; Fig. 1a
(*Holocentrus laevis*)
SL: to 19 cm (7.5 cm); D X-I, 11-13(12); A IV, 7-9; P 12-14(13); LL 38-43(41-42); GR 5-7+9-12=14-18(16-17); depth 3.0-3.7.
Neoniphon differs from *Sargocentron* in the position of the last dorsal fin spine (see key) as well as in coloration. *N. argenteus* is very similar to *N. sammara*, but has a uniformly clear dorsal fin. It inhabits reef flats and lagoon and semi-sheltered seaward reefs to depths of over 20 m. It is generally found in areas of rich coral growth, particularly among the branches of large staghorn *Acropora* corals with the more abundant *N. sammara*.
Indo-Pacific: E. Africa to the Marquesas, n. to the Ryukyus, s. to the Tuamotus and Samoa; throughout Micronesia.

Neoniphon aurolineatus (Liénard, 1839)
Yellowstriped squirrelfish   Pl. 16C; Fig. 1b
SL: to 20 cm (7.8 in); D X-I, 12-14(13); A IV, 8-9(9); P 13-15; LL 42-47; GR 5-7+11-13=16-18; depth 3.0-3.3.
This is the only species of *Neoniphon* with yellow body stripes, 3 1/2 instead of 2 1/2 scale rows above the lateral line, and a last dorsal spine that is shorter than the second to last one. It is also confined to relatively deep outer reef slopes from over 30 to 160 m.
Indo-Pacific: Comore Is. to the Hawaiian Is. n. to s. Japan, s. to the Great Barrier Reef; Guam in Micronesia.

Neoniphon opercularis (Valenciennes, 1831)
Blackfin squirrelfish   Pl. 16D; Fig. 1c
SL: to 27 cm (10.6 in); D X-I, 12-14(13); A IV, 8-9; P 13-(14); LL 36-41; GR 5-8+11-13=18-19; depth 2.9-3.3.
This large *Neoniphon* inhabits subtidal reef flats and lagoon and seaward reefs to depths of 20 m or more. It is moderately common in areas of rich coral growth where it occurs singly or in small groups near shelter during the day.
Indo-Pacific: E. Africa to the Tuamotus, n. to the Ryukyus, s. to New Caledonia; throughout Micronesia.

Neoniphon sammara (Forsskål, 1775)
Bloodspot squirrelfish   Pl. 16E; Fig. 1d
SL: to 24 cm (9.4 in); D X-I, 11-13(12); A IV, 7-(8); P 13-15; LL 38-43(41-42); GR 6-8+10-13=16-19(16-18); depth 3.0-3.6.
This is one of the most common and ubiquitous of Micronesia's squirrelfishs. It occurs in seagrass beds and most hard-bottomed habitats from the reef flat to depths of 46 m or more on lagoon and seaward reefs. It is less secretive than most other species of squirrelfishes. During the day it hovers in small groups in the vicinity of branching corals, rocks, or ledges and feeds primarily on isopods. During the night, it disperses over the reef to feed on small crabs and shrimps.
Indo-Pacific: Red Sea to the Marquesas and Ducie, n. to s. Japan and the Hawaiian Is., s. to Lord Howe Is.; throughout Micronesia.

Sargocentron caudimaculatum (Rüppell, 1838)
Tailspot squirrelfish   Pl. 16F; Fig. 1e
SL: to 20 cm (7.8 in); D X-I, 13-15; A IV, 9; P 13-15(14); LL 38-43(41-42); GR 5-8+11-13=16-21; depth 2.4-2.9.
This distinctive squirrelfish inhabits outer reef slopes and dropoffs at depths of 6 to over 40 m. It is relatively common in areas of rich coral growth where it occurs singly or in small groups in the vicinity of holes and ledges during the day. It occasionally occurs on lagoon reefs as shallow as 5 m.
Indo-Pacific: Red Sea to the Line, Marquesan, and Tuamotu Is., n. to s. Japan and Marcus Is., s. to the s. Great Barrier Reef; throughout Micronesia except for the n. Marshalls.

Sargocentron diadema (Lacepède, 1802)
Crown squirrelfish   Pl. 17A,B; Fig. 1f
SL: to 13 cm (5.1 in); D X-I, 12-14; A IV, 8-10(9); P 13-15(14); LL 46-50; GR 5-7+12-14=17-21(19-20); depth 2.7-3.2.
The reddish-black to black dorsal fin with two white streaks is distinctive. The crown squirrelfish is a common inhabitant of subtidal reef flats and lagoon and seaward reefs to depths of 30 m or more. During the day, it occurs singly or in small groups under ledges or in crevices and feeds lightly on isopods; at night it roams over open sand and low-profile reef areas to feed on polychaetes and small crabs.
Indo-Pacific: Red Sea to the Hawaiian, Marquesan, and Tuamotu Is., n. to the Ryukyus and Bonins, s. to Lord Howe Is.; throughout Micronesia.

Sargocentron dorsomaculatum
(Shimizu & Yamakawa, 1979)   Fig. 1g
Spotfin squirrelfish
SL: to 20 cm (7.9 in); D X-I, 13; A IV, 9; P 13-14(14); LL 32-35; GR 5-7+10-12=15-18; depth 2.4-2.8.
This recently discovered squirrelfish is nearly uniformly red with indistinct lighter stripes and usually bears a distinctive dark spot on the front of its dorsal fin. It differs greatly in coloration from the three other Micronesian *Sargocentron* (*melanospilos*, *praslin*, and *violaceum*) with 37 or fewer lateral line scales. It appears to be quite secretive during the day. It spawns during the summer in the Ryukyus.
Tropical w. Pacific: Known only from the Ryukyus, Pohnpei and Kosrae.

Sargocentron ittodai (Jordan & Fowler, 1903)
Samurai squirrelfish   Pl. 17C; Fig. 1h
SL: to 14.5 cm (5.7 in); D X-I, 12-14(13); A IV, 8-10(9); P 14-16(15); LL 43-47; GR 5-7+ 12-14=17-20(19-20); depth 2.8-3.3.
This species is close to *S. microstoma* but differs in the coloration of the dorsal fin and in having fewer lateral line scales (49-56 in *microstoma*) and a relatively deeper body. In tropical regions, this species inhabits outer reef slopes at depths exceeding 16 m.
Indo-west-Pacific: Sri Lanka to Pohnpei and the Great Barrier Reef, n. to s. Japan.

Sargocentron melanospilos (Bleeker, 1858)
Blackspot squirrelfish   Pl. 17D; Fig. 1i
SL: to 20 cm (7.9 in); 25 cm (9.8 in) in Japan; D X-I, 12-

14; A IV, 9-(10); P 14; LL 33-36; GR 6-8+10-12=18-20; depth 2.6-3.0.

This is the only Micronesian squirrelfish with orange stripes and distinctive black blotches at the bases of the soft dorsal and anal fins, the base of the tail, and on the pectoral axil. It is a relatively uncommon inhabitant of coral rich areas.

Indo-Pacific: Red Sea to Samoa, n. to the Ryukyu and Bonin Is., s. to New Caledonia and the s. Great Barrier Reef; Carolines and Marshalls in Micronesia.

Sargocentron microstoma (Günther, 1859)
Finelined squirrelfish   Pl. 17E,F; Fig. 1j
SL: to 16 cm (6.3 in); D X-I, 12-14; A IV, 9-10; P 14-(15); LL 48-55; GR 6-8+13-15=19-21; depth 3.0-3.5.

This species differs from other white-striped species of *Sargocentron* in the coloration of its spinous dorsal fin. In addition, an orange tinge usually present on its operculum distinguishes it from *S. diadema*. This is one of the most common and ubiquitous of Micronesian squirrelfishes. It occurs in virtually all coral reef zones where there is sufficient shelter to a depth of 183 m. During the day it generally remains hidden among corals, in holes, or under ledges. It is one of the more commonly encountered squirrelfishes in thickets of staghorn *Acropora* or in large heads of *Pocillopora eydouxi*. At night it solitarily roams the reef to feed on small crustaceans, worms, and fishes.

Indo-Pacific: Chagos, Astove, and Maldive Is. to the Hawaiian, Line, and Tuamotu Is., n. to the Ryukyus and Bonins, s. to the Australs; throughout Micronesia.

Sargocentron praslin (Lacepède, 1802)
Dark-striped squirrelfish   Pl. 18A; Fig. 1k
SL: to 28 cm (11.0 in); D X-I, 12-13; A IV, 8-9; P 13-15; LL 33-36; GR 6-8+10-12; depth 2.5-2.8.

This species occurs on reef flats and on shallow lagoon patch reefs and protected seaward reefs, often in "dead" reef areas. It is not particularly common in Micronesia and quite secretive during the day. The closely related *S. rubrum* prefers continental coastal reefs and is not known from Micronesia.

Indo-Pacific: E. Africa to the Phoenix and Samoan Is., n. to s. Japan, s. to Queensland; throughout Micronesia, except the n. Marshalls.

Sargocentron punctatissimum (Cuvier, 1829)
Speckled squirrelfish   Pl. 18B; Fig. 1l
(*Holocentrus lacteoguttatus*)
SL: to 13 cm (5.1 in); D X-I, 12-14(13); A IV, 9; P 14-16; LL 41-47; GR 5-7+10-12=15-19(17-18); depth 2.7-3.1.

This small *Sargocentron* is the only species in the genus that is primarily silvery below with scattered silver flecks on its sides. It is a relatively common inhabitant of surge-swept tunnels and crevices of the reef margin and reef front. It rarely occurs below 30 m, but has been observed at depths of 101-183 m from a submersible in the Hawaiian Is. At night, it disperses over sand flats and open reef bottom to feed on small crustaceans, crustacean larvae, and polychaete worms.

Indo-Pacific: Red Sea to Easter Is., n. to s. Japan and the Hawaiian Is., s. to the Australs; throughout Micronesia.

Sargocentron spiniferum (Forsskål, 1775)
Long-jawed squirrelfish   Pl. 18C; Fig. 1m
SL: to 36 cm (14.1 in); D X-I, 14-16(15); A IV, 9-(10); P 14-16; LL 41-47(43-45); GR 6-7+12-14=17-20; depth 2.4-2.6.

This is the largest species of squirrelfish and the highest-bodied *Sargocentron*. Its long preopercular spine is venemous and in certain areas the flesh may be ciguatoxic. It inhabits a variety of reef zones from reef flats to lagoon and seaward reefs to a depth of at least 122 m and is fairly common in areas not subjected to heavy spearfishing. Juveniles occur on shallow protected reefs. During the day, solitary individuals hover under ledges or in caves. At night, it actively forages for crabs, shrimps, and small fishes.

Indo-Pacific: Red Sea to the Hawaiian and Ducie Is., n. to s. Japan, s. to New South Wales; throughout Micronesia.

Sargocentron tiere (Cuvier, 1829)   Pl. 18D; Fig. 1n
Blue-lined squirrelfish
SL: to 26 cm (10.2 in); D X-I, 13-15; A IV, 9; P 13-15 (14); LL 46-52; GR 7-9+13-16=19-23(21-22); depth 2.7-3.0.

Several irridescent blue streaks adorn the sides of this squirrelfish when seen under the right lighting conditions. It is fairly common along exposed reef margins and outer reef slopes, and in Hawaii, has been observed at a depth of 183 m from a submersible. During the day, it is more secretive than most squirrelfishes and typically seen in the far reaches of holes and crevices of surge channels. At night it roams open reef areas in search of crustaceans, crustacean larvae, polychaete worms, and small fishes.

Indo-Pacific: E. Africa to the Hawaiian, Marquesan, and Ducie Is., n. to s. Japan, s. to the Australs; throughout Micronesia.

Sargocentron tieroides (Bleeker, 1853)
Pink squirrelfish   Figs. 1o, 2
SL: to 16 cm (6.3 in); D X-I, 13-14(14); A IV, 9; P 13-14 (14); LL 40-41; GR 7+13-14= 20-21; depth 2.7-3.0.

In the Marianas, this small squirrelfish inhabits relatively deep waters of outer reef slopes and is rarely observed by divers, but on atolls in the Carolines, it has been collected on reef flat and lagoon patch reefs.

Indo-Pacific: E. Africa to the Line and Society Is., n. to the Ryukyus and Wake Is., s. to Vanuatu; throughout Micronesia.

Fig. 2. *Sargocentron tieroides*, 125 mm, Guam.

Sargocentron violaceum (Bleeker, 1853)   Pl. 18E
Violet squirrelfish
SL: to 19 cm (7.5 in); D X-I, 12-(14); A IV, 9; P 13-14; LL 33-37; GR 6-8+12-13=18-20; depth 2.3-2.6.

The violet squirrelfish has a high body similar to that of *S. spiniferum*, but differs in coloration and does not get as large. It is a relatively uncommon inhabitant of atoll reef flats, lagoon patch reefs, and steep outer reef slopes to a depth of at least 20 m.

Indo-Pacific: Aldabra to Vanuatu, n. to the Ryukyus, s. to the Great Barrier Reef; Belau to the e. Carolines and Marshalls in Micronesia.

Order SYNGNATHIFORMES

AULOSTOMIDAE (TRUMPETFISHES)

Aulostomus chinensis (Linnaeus, 1766)   Pl. 19A,B
Trumpetfish
SL: to 62 cm (25 in); DVIII to XII (each spine a seperate fin), 24-27; A 26-29; V 6.

The trumpetfish occurs in three basic color phases: uniformly brown to green, mottled brown to green, or uniformly yellow (the latter rare in Micronesia). It inhabits rocky and coral habitats of protected and seaward reefs from below the surge zone to a depth of 122 m. It is a solitary ambushing predator of small fishes and crustaceans. Prey are literally sucked into its greatly expansable tubed snout. It is adept at hanging vertically among the branches of corals, seagrass, or other shelter in order to approach unwary prey. It may also hide within schools of herbivorous fishes or behind larger fishes and use them as moving "blinds" in order to approach unsuspecting prey.

Indo-pan-Pacific: E. Africa to Panama, n. to s. Japan and Hawaii, s. to Lord Howe and Easter Is.; throughout Micronesia.

FISTULARIIDAE (CORNETFISHES)

Fistularia commersonii Rüppell, 1838   Pl. 19C
Cornetfish; Smooth flutemouth
(*F. petimba* Schultz, 1953)
SL: to 107 cm (3.5 ft); TL: to 150 cm (4.9 ft); D 14-17; A 14-16; P usually 15; V 6.

Cornetfishes are characterized by a vertically flattened rather than laterally compressed body, a long whiplike tail filament, and a bluish coloration. The single Micronesian species occurs in virtually all reef habitats to a depth of at least 128 m except in areas of heavy surge. It is usually seen in relatively open sandy areas and often occurs in schools of similarly sized individuals. It feeds on small fishes and crustaceans.

Indo-pan-Pacific: Red Sea to Panama, n. to s. Japan and Hawaii, s. to Lord Howe and Easter Is.; throughout Micronesia.

CENTRISCIDAE (SHRIMPFISHES)

Aeoliscus strigatus (Günther, 1860)   Pl. 19D
Shrimpfish
TL: to 15 cm (5.9 in); D III-10; A 12; V 4.

The bizarre little shrimpfishes have extremely thin, contorted bodies covered with bony plates. The soft dorsal, caudal, and anal fins are positioned underneath and in front of the spinous dorsal fin. Shrimpfishes always swim head-down and occur in schools among the spines of *Diadema* sea urchins or staghorn corals. They feed primarily on minute crustaceans in the zooplankton and are popular in the aquarium trade.

Indo-west-Pacific: w. Indian Ocean to New Caledonia, n. to s. Japan, s. to New South Wales; Belau to Pohnpei in Micronesia.

SOLENOSTOMIDAE (GHOST PIPEFISHES)

Solenostomus cyanopterus Bleeker, 1852   Pl. 19E;
Ghost pipefish   Fig. 1
(*S. armatus* Schultz, 1953)
SL: to 16 cm (6.3 in).

Ghost pipefishes resemble outstretched seahorses with thin bodies and large fins. In females, the upper margin of the pelvic fins are united to the body and the lower margins are attached to each other to form a brood pouch for fertilized eggs. This species ranges in coloration from black to tan or light green. It usually occurs in pairs in sheltered waters among seaweeds or seagrasses and feeds on minute crustaceans. It is quite rare in Micronesia.

Indo-west-Pacific: E. Africa to the Marshalls, n. to s. Japan, s. to s. the Great Barrier Reef; Marshalls and Marianas in Micronesia, but expected throughout the Carolines.

Fig. 1. *Solenostomus cyanopterus* (after Weber and DeBeaufort, 1922).

SYNGNATHIDAE (PIPEFISHES AND SEAHORSES)

Pipefishes and seahorses typically have long tubular snouts and elongate bodies encased in rings of bony plates. Parental care is highly unusual: males possess a ventral brood pouch in which the eggs are fertilized and incubated after being deposited by the female. Nearly all species are small and generally inconspicuous bottom dwellers that feed on minute benthic and planktonic animals. Many species are rarely seen and can be identified only with the aid of a microscope. There are two subfamilies: the Hippocampinae (seahorses) in which the head is clearly bent downward from the main axis of the body, and the Syngnathinae (pipefishes) in which the head is more or less along the same axis as the rest of the body. A key is provided for the identification of the 15 genera and 37 species known from Micronesia. Species of *Hippichthys* and *Microphis* inhabit fresh and brackish water and are not discussed. The meristic symbol "R" stands for rings. (Lit.: Dawson, 1984, 1986)

Key to Micronesian Syngnathidae*:

1a. Tail tapered and prehensile, its tip without a fin..2
1b. Tail not tapered or prehensile, its tip with a distinct fin..4
2a. Head clearly angled ventrally from longitudinal axis of body (seahorses); lateral trunk ridge confluent with inferior tail ridge................................genus *Hippocampus*: 3
2b. Head essentially in line with longitudinal axis of body; lateral trunk ridge confluent with lateral tail ridge..*Syngnathoides biaculeatus*
3a. Body rings with long spines; snout longer than remainder of head..............*H. histrix*
3b. Body rings without long spines; snout not as long as remainder of head........*H. kuda*
4a. Superior trunk and tail ridges continuous..5
4b. Superior trunk and tail ridges discontinuous..8
5a. Inferior trunk and tail ridges continuous, lateral trunk ridge not confluent with inferior tail ridge...7
5b. Inferior trunk and tail ridges discontinuous, lateral trunk ridge confluent with inferior tail ridge...genus *Choeroichthys*: 6
6a. Scutella without keels; rings 14-18+17-20; D rays 18-26..................*C. brachysoma*
6b. Scutella with keels; rings 18-21+21-25; D rays 27-34..........................*C. sculptus*
7a. D and A fins present; mouth terminal on projecting snout....*Phoxocampus diacanthus*
7b. D and A fins absent in subadults-adults; mouth inferior, not on projecting snout.......
....*Bulbonaricus brauni*
8a. Inferior trunk and tail ridges continuous..9
8b. Inferior trunk and tail ridges discontinuous, the lateral trunk ridge confluent with inferior tail ridge...21
9a. Snout without dorsolateral spines or spinules, without bony platelets in gill membranes...10
9b. Snout with dorsolateral spines and spinules, adults with bony platelets in gill membranes...*Bhanotia nuda*
10a. Without lateral snout ridge or dermal flaps...13
10b. With lateral snout ridge and/or dermal flaps.....................genus *Cosmocampus*: 11
11a. Snout short, its length 2.1-4.0 in HL; P rays 9-16 (<16 in 99%).....................12
11b. Snout longer, its length 1.6-1.9 in HL; P rays 16-18 (usually 16-17)..*C. maxweberi*
12a. Trunk rings 16-17; D rays 22-23..*C. darrosanus*
12b. Trunk rings 15; D rays 16-20...*C. banneri*
13a. A rays 2-3, pouch plates present, everted pouch-closure.........genus *Hippichthys*: 14
13b. A rays 4, pouch plates absent, semi pouch-closure...........genus *Corythoichthys*: 15
14a. Trunk rings 14-16 (modally 15), total rings 51-57, D fin origin usually on tail (in 99%)...*H. spicifer*
14b. Trunk rings 12-14 (modally 13), total rings 45-48, D fin origin on trunk...............
....*H. cyanospilus*
15a. Snout short, its length averages 2.3-2.5 in HL, its depth averages 4.6-4.9 in snout length..*C. flavofasciatus*
15b. Snout longer, its length averages 1.7-2.1 in HL, its depth averages 5.3-9.1 in snout length..16

5a

5b

6a

6b ← keel

7a

7b

8a

8b

9a

* Adapted from Dawson, 1984 and 1986; figures after Dawson, 1986.

16a. Trunk rings modally 16 (in 96%)...17

16b. Trunk rings modally 17-18 (in 95%)..20

17a. Snout long and slender, its length averages 1.7-1.8 in HL, its depth averages 8.0-9.1 in snout length...18

17b. Snout shorter and deeper, its length averages 2.0-2.1 in HL, its depth averages 5.3-7.0 in snout length..19

18a. Total rings 48-55 (modally 51); D rays average 28; venter of anterior trunk rings plain or with faint bars, spots or ocelli..*C. schultzi*

18b. Total rings 45-48 (modally 46); D rays average 23; venter of anterior trunk rings usually shaded with dark brown...*C. ocellatus*

19a. Head with prominent stripes or reticulations; venter of anterior trunk rings spotted, barred, or streaked with brown; tail with indications of reticulate bars..*C. intestinalis*

19b. Head plain or dusky; venter of anterior trunk rings blackish; tail without reticulate bars..*C. nigripectus*

20a. Head usually with prominent stripes or reticulations; both sexes with brown to black bars, spots or small blotches on venter of anterior 1-4 trunk rings..*C. haematopterus*

20b. Head markings faint or obsolete; males with small blotches on venter of anterior 5-8 trunk rings, venter plain in females...*C. polynotatus*

21a. C rays typically 8 or 9...22

21b. C rays typically 10...28

22a. C rays typically 8...*Minyichthys myersi*

22b. C rays typically 9...23

23a. C often stuby or rudimentary; trunk rings 21-24, the 1st clearly longer than 2nd; male brood area under tail.......................................*Trachyrhamphus bicoarctatus*

23b. C well-developed; trunk rings 15-21, the 1st not much longer than 2nd; male brood area under trunk..genus *Microphis*: 24

24a. Opercular ridge distinct, typically complete; pectoral-fin base with 1-2 distinct ridges; lateral and inferior trunk ridges distinct.......................................25

24b. Opercular ridge vestigial or obsolete; pectoral-fin base without distinct ridges in sub-adults- adults; lateral and inferior trunk ridges indistinct............................... ....*M.* (subgenus *Coelonotus*) *leiaspis*

25a. Snout relatively long and slender, its depth averages 4.3-10.6 in snout length; scutella without keels...*M.* (subgenus *Oostethus*): 26

25b. Snout relatively short and deep, its depth averages 3.5-4.1 in snout legth; usually with some keeled scutella....................................*M.* (subgenus *Lophocampus*): 27

26a. Snout length 1.6-1.7 in HL, snout depth >8.6 (ave. = 9.2) in snout length............. ....*M. brachyurus brachyurus*

26b. Snout length 1.8-2.0 in HL, snout depth <8.5 (ave. = 6.7) in snout length............. ....*M. manadensis*

27a. D rays 32-42...*M. retzii*

27b. D rays 25-29..*M. brevidorsalis*

28a. First trunk ring not much longer than 2nd; P rounded; C fin not large, dermal flaps usually present; male brood area under tail...32

28b. First trunk ring much longer than 2nd; P typically emarginate; C fin large, the membranes broad; dermal flaps absent; male brood area under trunk...................... ....genus *Doryrhamphus*: 29

29a. Snout with 1-5 rows of dorsolateral spinules; body without banded color pattern; membranous pouch folds present in brooding male.....(subgenus *Doryrhamphus*): 30

29b. Snout without rows of dorsolateral spinules; body with banded color pattern; membranous pouch folds absent in brooding males... ....*D.* (subgenus *Dunkerocampus*) *dactyliophorus*

30a. With one well-developed spine on superior ridges of the posterior 4-6 predorsal trunk rings..*D. excisus excisus*

30b. With two well-developed spines on superior ridges of the posterior 4-6 predorsal trunk rings..31

31a. Tail rings 13-26..*D. negrosensis negrosensis*

31b. Tail rings 21-23..*D. janssi*

32a. Median dorsal snout ridge low, entire, essentially concave in lateral profile; lateral snout ridge absent; without dermal flaps on eye.................genus *Micrognathus*: 33

32b. Median dorsal snout ridge not essentially concave in lateral profile, often elevated or spiny; lateral snout ridge or spine usually present; usually with dermal flaps on eye..genus *Halicampus*: 34

33a. Trunk rings 15-16 (15 in 99%); dark blotches above the lateral trunk ridge absent; ridges on distal part of tail developed into prominent plates..................................
....*M. brevirostris pygmaeus*

33b. Trunk rings 15-17 (16-17 in 99.7%); dark blotches frequently present above the lateral trunk ridge; ridges on distal part of tail not well-developed............*M. andersonii*

34a. Median dorsal snout ridge discontinuous, with semi-isolated spines or ridge-like elevations...35

34b. Median dorsal snout ridge essentially continuous, sometime emarginate but without separated spines or ridges...*H. dunckeri*

35a. Trunk rings usually 14 (96%), margins of superior trunk ridges with spines or serrations..36

35b. Trunk rings 15, margins of superior trunk ridges without spines or serrations..........
....*H. mataafae*

36a. Tail rings 33-37, dermal flaps simple or branched..................................*H. brocki*

36b. Tail rings 30-32, dermal flaps simple, flat and somewhat spatulate..........*H. nitidus*

32a

33a

33b

Subfamily Hippocampinae (Seahorses):

Hippocampus histrix Kaup, 1856   Pl. 19F
Thorny seahorse

TL: to 150 mm (5.9 in) (stretched); R 11+33-34; D 17-19; A 4; P 17-18.

The long spines on the rings easily distinguish this species from *H. kuda* which has blunt knobs instead. Some individuals have dark bars on the snout. The thorny seahorse is a rarely encountered inhabitant of shallow sheltered reefs, where it occurs among clumps of algae or in seagrass beds. Occasionally large individuals occur pelagically, probably associated with drifting debris.

Indo-Pacific: Red Sea to the Hawaiian and Society Is., n. to s. Japan; s. to Papua New Guinea; Guam in the Micronesia.

Hippocampus kuda Bleeker, 1852   Pl. 19G
Yellow seahorse

TL: to 300 mm (11.8 in) (stretched); R 11+34-37; D 15-18; A 4; P 15-17.

This seahorse ranges in coloration from a dirty yellow to reddish brown to black, and may be blotched or banded. It occurs from estuaries to seaward reefs at depths of 30 m or more, and has been found pelagically.

Indo-Pacific: Red Sea to New Caledonia and the Hawaiian Is., n. to s. Japan, s. to Lord Howe Is.(?); Belau and Pohnpei in Micronesia.

Subfamily Syngnathinae (Pipefishes):

Bhanotia nuda Dawson, 1978   Fig. 1a
Naked pipefish

SL: to 70 mm (2.8 in); R 13-14+37-40=51-55; D 26-30; P 12-14.

Planktonic juveniles attain a length of 60 mm and bear lateral spines on the snout. Metamorphosed individuals have been reported from tidepools to a depth of at least 14 m.

Belau and Papua New Guinea

Bulbonaricus brauni (Dawson & Allen, 1978)
Pugheaded pipefish

SL: to 55 mm (2.2 in); R 17+44-46; HL ca. 14; SnL ca. 6.4.

The dorsal fin, pectoral fins, and elongate snout are lost upon metamorphosis to the demersal stage. This rare species is apparently commensal with dendrophylliid corals and the coral *Galaxea musicalis*. It has been collected in the depth range of 0.6 to 10 m.

Indo-Australian: Sumatra, n.w. Australia, and Belau

Choeroichthys brachysoma (Bleeker, 1855)
Short-bodied pipefish   Fig. 1b

SL: to 63 mm (2.5 in); males begin brooding at 30 mm (1.8 in); R 14-18+17-20; D 18-26; P 18-23(19-20); HL 4.1-5.9; SnL 1.8-2.4.

This species is known from tidepool, seagrass, and coral reef habitats to a depth of 25 m.

Indo-Pacific: Red Sea to the Society Is., n. to the Philippines, s. to Queensland; Belau and Guam in Micronesia.

Choeroichthys sculptus (Günther, 1870)   Fig. 1c
Sculpted pipefish

SL: to 80 mm (3.2 in); males begin brooding at 46 mm (1.8 in); R 18-21+21-25; D 27-34; P18-23(20-21); HL 4.9-7.1; SnL 2.0-2.5.

Males are characterized by vertical rows of silver spots. This species inhabits intertidal reef flats to a depth of 2 to 3 m.

Indo-Pacific: E. Africa to the Line and Gambier Is., n. to s. Japan, s. to Tonga; throughout Micronesia.

Corythoichthys flavofasciatus (Rüppell, 1838)
Network pipefish   Pl. 20A; Fig. 2a,h

SL: to 116 mm (4.6 in); males mature at 70 mm (3.8 in); R 15-17+32-39; D 26-36; P 13-17; HL 6.8-10.9; SnL 1.9-2.6.

This intricately patterned pipefish is fairly common among algal-matted rock and living corals of lagoon and seaward reefs from the low tide line to a depth of 25 m or more.

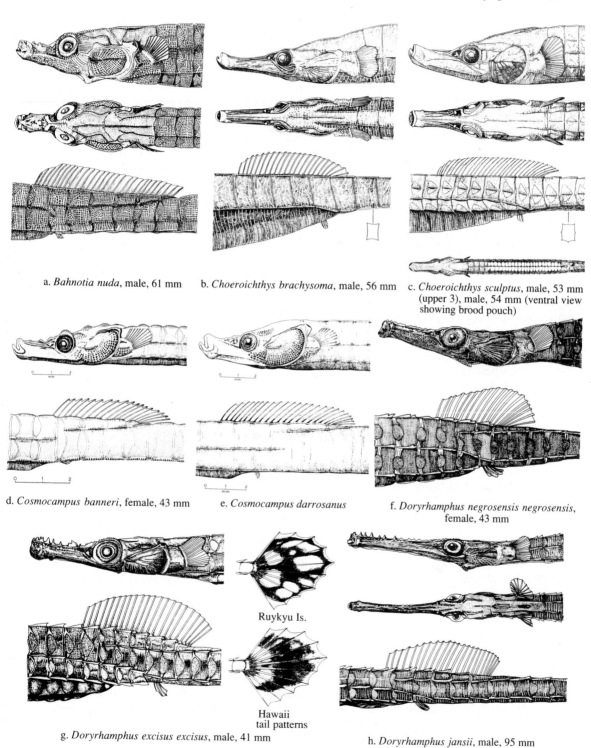

a. *Bahnotia nuda*, male, 61 mm

b. *Choeroichthys brachysoma*, male, 56 mm

c. *Choeroichthys sculptus*, male, 53 mm (upper 3), male, 54 mm (ventral view showing brood pouch)

d. *Cosmocampus banneri*, female, 43 mm

e. *Cosmocampus darrosanus*

f. *Doryrhamphus negrosensis negrosensis*, female, 43 mm

Ruykyu Is.

Hawaii tail patterns

g. *Doryrhamphus excisus excisus*, male, 41 mm

h. *Doryrhamphus jansii*, male, 95 mm

Fig. 1. Micronesian pipefishes (a, after Dawson, 1978; b, c, after Dawson, 1976; d, e, after Dawson and Randall, 1975; f-h, after Dawson, 1981).

Indo-Pacific: Red Sea to Tuamotus, n. to the Ryukyus, s. to the Australs; throughout Micronesia.

Corythoichthys haematopterus (Bleeker, 1851)
Pipefish Fig. 2b

SL: to 198 mm (7.8 in); males mature at 90 mm (3.6 in); R 16-18+32-37; D 23-33; P13-18; HL 6.3-9.4; SnL 1.9-2.4. Most specimens have been collected from depths of 0 - 3 m, but it may occur to a depth of at least 20 m.
Indo-west-Pacific: E. Africa to Vanuatu, n. to s. Japan; Belau and Yap in Micronesia.

Corythoichthys intestinalis (Ramsay, 1881)
Scribbled pipefish Pl. 20B; Fig. 2c,i

SL: to 160 mm (6.3); males mature at 68 mm (2.7 in); R 15-17+31-37; D 26-32; P 14-18; HL 6.6-9.8; SnL 1.8-2.4. The intricate color pattern of this species is highly variable. This is probably the most common pipefish in the Marianas and Marshalls. It is abundant in certain shallow sandy or mixed sand, rubble, or coral areas of reef flats and lagoons, and occasionally occurs on seaward reefs to a depth of at least 20 m.
West-central Pacific: Borneo to Samoa, n. to the Marshalls and Marianas, s. to Rowley Shoals and New Caledonia; throughout Micronesia.

Corythoichthys nigripectus Herald, 1953 Fig. 2d,j
Black-breasted pipefish

SL: to 110 mm (4.3 in); males mature at 87 mm (3.4 in); R 16+56-40; D 25-31; P 13-17; HL 6.8-9.8; SnL 1.9-2.3. This uncommon species occurs on lagoon and seaward reefs and has been collected in the depth range of approximately 4 to 28 m.
Indo-Pacific: Red Sea to the Society Is., n. to the Marianas; throughout Micronesia.

Corythoichthys ocellatus Herald, 1953 Fig. 2e,k
Ocellated pipefish

SL: to 103 mm (4.1 in); males mature at 58 mm (2.3 in); R 15-16+29-32; D 22-25; P 14-17; HL 5.7-7.1; SnL 1.7-2.0. This species has a color pattern very similar to that of *C. schultzi*, but can usually be separated on the basis of meristics. It has been collected to a depth of 12 m.
Indo-Australian: Philippines to Solomon Is., s. to Queensland; Belau in Micronesia.

Corythoichthys polynotatus Dawson, 1977
Many-spotted pipefish Fig. 2f

SL: to 136 mm (5.4 in); R 16-17+32-36; D 23-29; P 13-16; HL 7.1-9.0; SnL 2.0-2.2.
Belau and Philippines

Corythoichthys schultzi Herald, 1953 Fig. 2g,l
Guilded pipefish, Schultz' pipefish

SL: to 149 mm (5.9 in); males mature at 90-95 mm (3.6-3.7 in); R 15-17+32-39; D 25-31; P 14-18; HL 6.0-8.1; SnL 1.5-2.0. This species has been photographed among the branches of the orange sea fan, *Melithea* sp. It inhabits coralline areas

of lagoon and seaward reefs to a depth of at least 30 m.
Indo-Pacific: Red Sea, Ryukyus, Rowley Shoals, Belau, Marshalls, and Tonga.

Cosmocampus banneri (Herald & Randall, 1972)
Roughridge pipefish Fig. 1d

SL: to 58 mm (2.3 in); males begin brooding at 23 mm (.9 in); R 15+27-30; D 16-20; P 11-14(12-13); HL 7.1-8.3; SnL 2.2-2.7. This species inhabits coral reefs to a depth of 30 m.
Indo-Pacific: Red Sea to Fiji; n. to the Ryukyus, s. to New Caledonia; Marshalls in Micronesia.

Cosmocampus darrosanus (Dawson & Randall, 1975) Fig. 1e
D'Arros pipefish

SL: to 74 mm (2.9 in); males mature at 43 mm (1.7 in); R 16-17(16)+29-31; D 22-23; P 11-12(11); HL 7.9-10.1; SnL 2.6-3.1. This species has been collected on reef flats at depths of less than 3 m.
Indo-west Pacific: East Africa to Queensland; Guam in Micronesia.

Cosmocampus maxweberi (Whitley, 1933)
Maxweber's pipefish

SL: to 79 mm (3.2 in); males mature at 62 mm (2.4 in); R 14-15(15)+29-32; D 23-27; P16-18(16); HL 5.3-6.8; SnL 1.6-1.9. Most collections of this species are from coral bottoms at less than 4 m, but it has been collected as deep as 36 m. The only Micronesian record is from the lagoon of Bikini Atoll at a depth of 6 to 8 m.
Indo-Pacific: Red Sea to Samoa, s. to Queensland; Marshalls in Micronesia.

Doryrhamphus excisus excisus Kaup, 1856
Bluestripe pipefish Pl. 20C; Fig. 1g

(*D. melanopleura*)
SL: to 66 mm (2.6 in); males begin brooding at 33 mm (1.3 in); R 17-19(17-18)+13-17; D 23-26; P 19-23; HL 3.9-4.9; SnL 2.0-2.4. Species of *Doryrhamphus* are secretive inhabitants of the recesses of caves and crevices. They usually occur in pairs and tend to hover just above the substrate rather than crawl over it. This common species as well as others in the subgenus have the unusual habit of picking parasites from the skin of other fishes, particularly moray eels. Their large, colorful fanlike tails and habit of swimming with a distinctive bobbing motion may help advertise their trade. *D. excisus* occurs on lagoon and seaward reefs in the depth range of 0 to at least 45 m.
Indo-pan-Pacific: E. Africa to Mexico, n. to the Ryukyu and Hawaiian Is., s. to the Tuamotus and s. Great Barrier Reef; throughout Micronesia; the subspecies *abbreviatus* in the Red Sea and *paulus* in the Revilagigedos Is.

Doryrhamphus janssi (Herald & Randall, 1972)
Janss' pipefish Fig. 1h

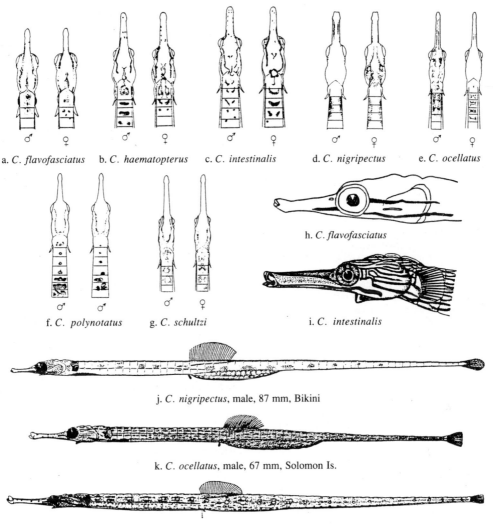

a. *C. flavofasciatus*   b. *C. haematopterus*   c. *C. intestinalis*   d. *C. nigripectus*   e. *C. ocellatus*

h. *C. flavofasciatus*

f. *C. polynotatus*   g. *C. schultzi*

i. *C. intestinalis*

j. *C. nigripectus*, male, 87 mm, Bikini

k. *C. ocellatus*, male, 67 mm, Solomon Is.

l. *C. schultzi*, male, 122 mm, Bikini

Fig. 2. Micronesian species of *Corythoichthys*. Drawings a-g show ventral surface of head and anterior trunk rings. (a-g after Dawson, 1977; h-l after Herald *in* Schultz et al., 1953; h, by P. Bravo; i, by A. M Awl).

SL: to 127 mm(5 in); males begin brooding at 80 mm (3.2 in); R 16+21-23; D 22-25; P 19-21; HL 4.2-5.2; SnL 1.5-1.8.

This uncommon species has been reported from tide pools to a depth of 35 m.

Indo-Australian: Gulf of Thailand to the Solomons, n. to the Philippines, s. to Queensland; Belau and Truk in Micronesia.

Doryrhamphus negrosensis negrosensis
Herre, 1934   Fig. 1f
Negros pipefish
SL: to 47 mm (1.9 in); males begin brooding at 22 mm (.9 in); R 14-16+13-15; D 16-19; P 17-20; HL 3.5-4.2; SnL

1.9-2.2.

This miniscule species occurs on mud and reef flats.

West Pacific: Borneo to Vanuatu, n. to the Yaeyamas, s. to Rowley Shoals; Belau and Yap in Micronesia; the subspecies *malus* in Queensland.

Doryrhamphus (Dunkerocampus) dactyliophorus
(Bleeker, 1853)
Banded pipefish   Pl. 20F
SL: to 176 mm (6.9 in); males begin brooding at 90 mm (3.5 in); R 15-17(16)+18-22; D 22-26; P 18-22(19-21); HL 3.7-4.6; SnL 1.4-1.8.

Members of the subgenus *Dunkerocampus* have alternating white and red to black bars. This spectacular pipefish has been collected from tidepools and lagoons as well as outer reef slopes to a depth of 56 m. It is uncommon in Micronesia.

Indo-Pacific: Red Sea to the Australs; n. to the Izus, s. to New Caledonia; throughout Micronesia.

Halicampus brocki (Herald, 1953) Fig. 3a,b
Brock's pipefish

SL: to 110 mm (4.3 in); males begin brooding at 90 mm (3.5 in); R14+33-37; D 21-23; A 4; P 11-14(12-14); HL 8.5-12.4; SnL 2.4-3.0.

This species has been reported from both lagoon and seaward reefs in the depth range of 2 to 23 m.

West-Pacific: Philippines and n.w. Australia to Queensland, n. to the Yaeyamas; Marshalls and Marianas in Micronesia.

Halicampus dunckeri (Chabanaud, 1929) Fig. 3c,d
Duncker's pipefish

SL: to 115 mm (4.5 in); males begin brooding at 75 mm (3 in); R 14+31-36(<36); D 16-20; A 2-3; P 10-13; HL 9.6-14.7; SnL 3.0-4.4.

As presently accepted, this is a highly variable species consisting of four basic morphological types. Two occur in Micronesia, one in Belau and the other in Pohnpei. *H. dunckeri* has been reported from sand, rubble, or reef habitats to a depth of at least 14 m.

Indo-west-Pacific: Red Sea to the Solomons, n. to s. Japan, s. to the s. Great Barrier Reef; Belau and Pohnpei in Micronesia.

Halicampus mataafae (Jordan & Seale, 1906)
Samoan pipefish Fig. 3e

SL: to 128 mm (5 in); males mature at 92mm (3.6 in); R 15+33-36(34-36); D 21-26(21-24); A (3); P 12-14; HL 10.2-13.0; SnL 2.5-4.0.

This species has been collected from reef pool, rock, and coral habitats to a depth of over 15 m.

Indo-Pacific: Red Sea to Samoa, n. to Taiwan, s. to Queensland; Belau and the Marshalls in Micronesia.

Halicampus nitidus (Günther, 1873) Fig. 3f
Glittering pipefish

SL: to 73 mm (2.9 in); R 13-15(14)+30-32; D 18-22(20-21); A (3); P 11-14(12-13); HL 8.2-10.7; SnL 2.9-3.7.

This species has been reported from reef flats to a depth of over 17 m.

West-Pacific: Vietnam to Fiji, n. to the Ryukyus, s. to Rowley Shoals and New Caledonia; Belau in Micronesia.

Micrognathus andersonii (Bleeker, 1858) Fig. 3g
Anderson's short-nosed pipefish

SL: to 78 mm (3.1 in); males begin brooding at 34 mm (1.3 in); R 15-17(16-17)+27-32(28-32); D 17-24; A (3); P 11-13; HL 8.1-10.4; SnL 2.7-2.9.

This species has been reported from tidepools, reef flats, and shallow sand flats among algae or seagrasses to a depth of 5 m or more.

Indo-Pacific: Red Sea to Samoa, n. to s. Japan, s. to Tonga; Belau, to the e. Carolines and Marianas in Micronesia.

Micrognathus brevirostris pygmaeus
Fritzsche, 1981 Fig. 3h
Pigmy short-nosed pipefish

SL: to 55 mm (2.2 in); males begin brooding at 23 mm (.9 in); R 15-16(15)+28-31; D 18-21; A (3); P 10-13(11-12); HL 7.2-10.2; SnL 2.6-3.3.

This species occurs on lagoon and seaward reefs from tidepools to a depth of at least 8 m.

West-central Pacific: Moluccas to the Society Is., n. to the Marshalls, s. to New Caledonia; Belau, Marianas, and Marshalls in Micronesia; the subspecies *M. b. brevirostris* from the Red Sea and Persian Gulf.

Minyichthys myersi (Herald & Randall, 1972)
Myers' pipefish Fig. 3i

SL: to 58 mm (2.3 in); males begin brooding at 40 mm (1.6 in); R 17-19(18)+36-42; D 25-33; P 12-13(13); HL 7.0-8.5; SnL 2.3-3.2.

This species has been collected from coral and rubble habitats in the depth range of 6 to 35 m.

Indo-west Pacific: Cargados Carajos, Philippines, Moluccas, Papua New Guinea, and Guam.

Phoxocampus diacanthus (Schultz, 1943)

SL: to 87 mm (3.4 in); males begin brooding at 55 mm 2.2 in); R 15-16(16)+25-28; D 20-24; P 13-15(14); HL 6.4-7.9; SnL 2.2-2.6.

This species inhabits rock and coral habitats of lagoons and seaward reefs from the surf zone to a depth of 40 m.

Indo-Pacific; Sri Lanka to Samoa, n. to Hong Kong, s. to New Caledonia; Belau, Marianas, and Marshalls in Micronesia.

Syngnathoides biaculeatus (Bloch, 1785) Pl. 20D
Alligator pipefish

SL: to 283 mm (11.1 in); males begin brooding at 180 mm 7.1 in); R 15-18+ca. 40-54; D 38-48; P 20-24(22); HL ca. 4.9-6.3; SnL ca. 1.7-1.8.

This large, ugly pipefish inhabits protected coastal shallows over or among algae, seagrasses, or floating weeds. Juveniles are occasionally found among debris floating offshore.

Indo-Pacific: Red Sea to Samoa, n. to s. Japan, s. to New South Wales; throughout Micronesia except the n. Marshalls.

Trachyramphus bicoarctata (Bleeker, 1857)
Double-ended pipefish Pl. 20G; Fig. 3j

SL: to 385 mm 15.2 in); males begin brooding at 260 mm (10.2 in); R 21-24+55-63=76-86; D 24-32; P 15-19; HL 9.9-13.0; SnL 1.5-2.0.

This bizarre creature resembles a thin bent waterlogged stick. It is the longest, but not the heaviest syngnathid in the tropical Indo-Pacific. It occurs on sand, rubble, or mixed reef substrates, usually among algae or seagrasses in the depth range of 1 to 42 m.

Indo-west-Pacific: Red Sea to New Caledonia, n. to s. Japan; Marianas in Micronesia.

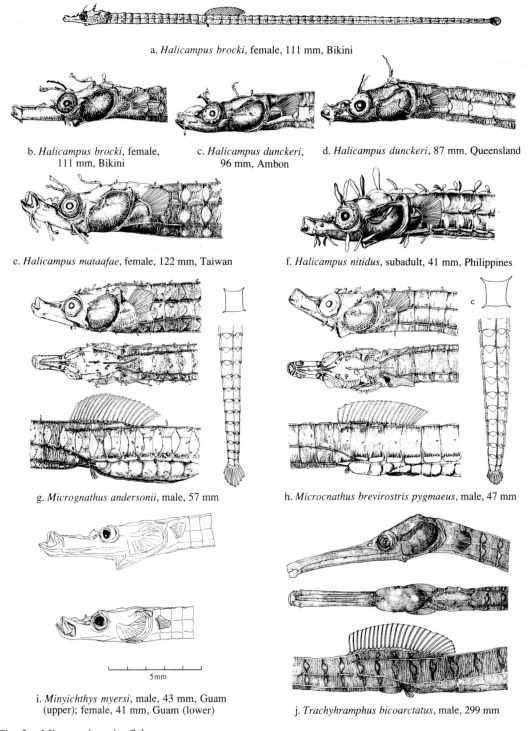

a. *Halicampus brocki*, female, 111 mm, Bikini

b. *Halicampus brocki*, female,
111 mm, Bikini

c. *Halicampus dunckeri*,
96 mm, Ambon

d. *Halicampus dunckeri*, 87 mm, Queensland

e. *Halicampus mataafae*, female, 122 mm, Taiwan

f. *Halicampus nitidus*, subadult, 41 mm, Philippines

g. *Micrognathus andersonii*, male, 57 mm

h. *Microcnathus brevirostris pygmaeus*, male, 47 mm

5mm

i. *Minyichthys myersi*, male, 43 mm, Guam
(upper); female, 41 mm, Guam (lower)

j. *Trachyhramphus bicoarctatus*, male, 299 mm

Fig. 3. Micronesian pipefishes (a, after Herald *in* Schultz et al, 1953, drawn by A. M. Awl; b-f after Dawson, 1985; g, h after Dawson, 1982; i after Herald and Randall, 1972; j after Dawson, 1984).

Order PEGASIFORMES

PEGASIDAE (DRAGONFISHES)

Eurypegasus draconis (Linnaeus, 1758)
Short dragonfish   Pl. 20E; Fig. 1
SL: to 6 cm (2.4 in); D 5; A 5; P 10-12; body rings, 3; tail rings, 8.

These bizarre little fishes are characterized by a somewhat flattened body covered with hard bony plates, a proboscis-like snout, a tiny toothless mouth, and large somewhat colorful wing-like pectoral fins. They are rarely seen dwellers of sandy or muddy bottoms that feed on minute invertebrates. One of the five known species occurs in Micronesia. **Indo-Pacific:** Red Sea to the Marquesan and Society Is., n. to s. Japan, s. to Lord Howe Is.; throughout Micronesia.

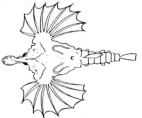

Fig. 1. *Eurypegasus draconis*, underside (after Gloerfelt-Tarp and Kailola, 1984).

Order SCORPAENIFORMES

DACTYLOPTERIDAE (HELMET GURNARDS)

Dactyloptena orientalis (Cuvier, 1829)   Pl. 20H
Common helmet gurnard
SL: to 35 cm (13.8 in); D I+I+V+I, 8; A 6-7; P 32-35, V I, 4; LL 47.

These unusual fishes are characterized by a heavily armored box-like body and enormous winglike pectoral fins. Although sometimes called flying gurnards, they do not fly at all, but "walk" along sandy bottoms on highly modified leg-like pelvic fins. They are well-camouflaged and usually slow moving, but capable of rapid bursts of speed when alarmed. They feed on small sand-dwelling crustaceans, molluscs, worms, and occasionally on fishes. The common helmet gurnard inhabits sandy expanses of lagoon and seaward reefs at depths of 1 to at least 40 m. It is solitary and not often seen on Micronesian reefs. Another of the three Indo-Pacific species, *D. petersoni*, has been reported from the Marianas at depths below 90 m. **Indo-Pacific:** E. Africa to the Tuamotu, Marquesan, and Hawaiian Is., n. to s. Japan, s. to n. New Zealand; reported from Belau, Pohnpei, and the Marianas in Micronesia.

PLATYCEPHALIDAE (FLATHEADS)

Flatheads are characterized by an elongate body with two dorsal fins, a large dorso-ventrally flattened head ornamented with numerous spines or bony ridges, and a large mouth with villiform teeth. The eyes of many of the shallow water species have a characteristic iris lappett, a branched tassle-like organ which hangs over the eye and expands or contracts as necessary to shade the eye from excessive sunlight or to camouflage it from prospective prey. All species are cryptically colored and tend to rest on, or partially buried in, sand or rubble. They are ambushing predators of small fishes and crustaceans, and in turn, are important food fishes in certain parts of the world. At least five species occur in Micronesia, none of which seem particularly common. Most species lack distinctive markings and are difficult to identify without consideration of certain morphological characters as indicated in the following key. (Lit.: Knapp, 1973, *in* Smith and Heemstra, 1986)

Key to Micronesian Platycephalidae:

1a. Suborbital ridge finely serrate along its entire length..............*Sorsogona welanderi*
1b. Suborbital ridge not finely serrate...2
2a. A distinct pit behind each eye (not well developed in juveniles).........................
....*Cymbacephalus beauforti*
2b. No distinct pit behind each eye.....genus *Platycephalus* (subgenus *Thysanophrys*): 3
3a. Edges of both lips with papillae; least width of bony interorbital space 2.1 to 2.9 in greatest diameter of eye; dorsal soft rays usually 11..........................*P. otaitensis*
3b. Edges of lips without papillae...4
4a. Bony interorbital space narrow, its least width 5.5 to 5.9 in greatest diameter of eye; dorsal soft rays 11-12..*P. chiltonae*
4b. Bony interorbital space wide, its least width 1.1 to 2.0 in greatest diameter of eye; dorsal soft rays usually 12..*P. arenicola*

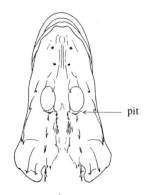

pit

2a

Head morphology of
Cymbacephalus beauforti
(after Knapp, 1973)

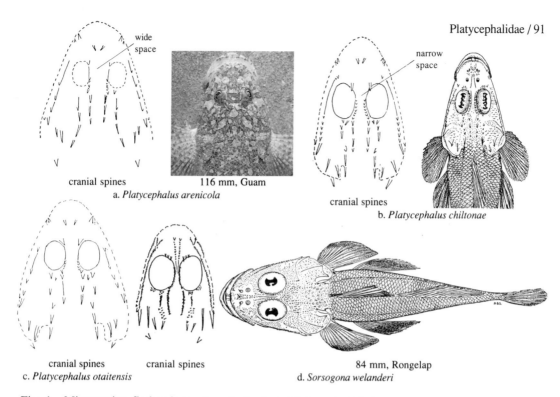

Fig. 1. Micronesian flatheads (drawings after Schultz *in* Schultz et al., 1966; right sides of b, d, by D. B. Schultz).

Cymbacephalus beauforti (Knapp, 1973)   Pl. 21A
Crocodile fish

SL: to >45 cm (>18 in); D I, VIII (rarely IX)+11; A 11; P 19-21; LP 50-55; interorb. width 1.5 (juv.) to 3.2 (lg. adult) in eye.

This intricately patterned flathead is the only Micronesian species that develops a distinctive pit behind each eye and attains a size of over 30 cm. It occurs on sand or rubbble substrates in the vicinity of mangroves, seagrasses, or scattered corals of sheltered to semi-exposed reefs to a depth of at least 8 m.

Indo-Australian: Singapore and Philippines to New Caledonia; Belau and Yap in Micronesia.

Platycephalus arenicola (Schultz, 1966)   Fig. 1a
Broadhead flathead

SL: to 26 cm (10.2 in); D IX+11-(12); A (12)-13; P 19-22; LL 51-54; GR 1+4-6; interorb. width 1.1-2.0 in eye.

This species inhabits sand patches of lagoon and semi-sheltered seaward reefs to depths of at least 15 m.

Indo-Pacific: E. Africa to the Marshalls, n. to Taiwan and the Ryukyus; Marianas, Marshalls, and e. Carolines in Micronesia.

Platycephalus chiltonae (Schultz, 1966)
Longsnout flathead   Pl. 21C; Fig. 1b

SL: to 20 cm (7.7 in); D VIII-IX+11; A 12; P 19-21; LP 50-57; GR 1+5-6; interorb. width 5.5-5.9 in eye.

Chilton's flathead inhabits sandy areas of lagoon and shel-

tered reefs at depth of 1 to at least 80 m. Although seldom seen, it is the flathead most often encountered on shallow sandy reef flats and channels of Guam. It has the habit of burying itself with only its eyes and nostrils protruding, and is capable of amazing bursts of speed when disturbed.

Indo-Pacific: Red Sʆa to the Marquesan and Tuamotu Is., n. to Taiwan and the Yaeyamas, s. to the s. Great Barrier Reef; Marianas and Marshalls in Micronesia.

Platycephalus otaitensis (Bleeker, 1853)   Fig. 1c
Fringelip flathead

(*Thysanophrys papillolabium* Schultz)

SL: to 21 cm (8.3 in); D IX+(11)-12; A 12; P 20-22; LP 51-53; GR 1+5-6; interorb. width 2.1-2.9 in eye.

The dark markings on the fins of this species tend to show up as series of distinct widely-spaced dark reddish to black checks. This species occurs in shallow sandy areas of lagoon and seaward reefs to a depth of at least 15 m.

Indo-Pacific: E. Africa to the Tuamotus, n. to Taiwan, s. to Queensland; Marshalls and Carolines in Micronesia.

Sorsogona welanderi (Schultz, 1966)   Fig. 1d
Welander's flathead

SL: to 11 cm (4.3 in);D I, VIII+11; A 11; P 22; LP 54; interorb. width 5.5-6.0 in eye; iris lappet bilobed.

This species has been collected in sandy areas of lagoon and seaward reefs at depths of 6 to 12 m.

West-central Pacific: w. Indonesia to Samoa; Marshalls in Micronesia.

CARACANTHIDAE (CORAL CROUCHERS)

The velvetfishes are small compressed ovoid fishes characterized by venomous dorsal spines and small tubercles covering the body. They are found exclusively among the branches of certain *Stylophora*, *Pocillopora*, and *Acropora* corals, and will tightly wedge themselves in the corals when disturbed.

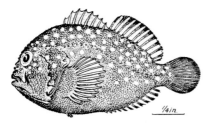

Fig. 1. *C. maculatus* (after Jordan and Evermann, 1903).

Caracanthus maculatus (Gray, 1831)
Spotted coral croucher
SL: to 44 mm (1.7 in); D VII-VIII, 12-13; A II, 11-12; P 13-15; V I, 2.
This species is a tan to light gray covered with numerous small reddish-brown spots and has a notched dorsal fin. It is common among the branches of large pocilloporid corals such as *P. eydouxi* as well as *Stylophora mordax* and certain ramose species of *Acropora*.
West-central Pacific: E. Indies to the Line, Marquesan, and Austral Is., n. to s. Japan; throughout Micronesia; closely related to *C. madagascariensis* of the Indian Ocean.

Caracanthus unipinna (Gray, 1831)
Pigmy coral croucher
SL: to 29 mm (1.1 in); D VII-VIII, 12-13; A II, 11-12; P 12-13; V I, 2.

This uniformly dark species has smaller, but longer tubercles than *C. maculatus* and lacks a notch in the dorsal fin. It inhabits *Stylophora mordax* and ramose species of *Acropora*.
Indo-Pacific: E. Africa to the Tuamotus, n. to s. Japan, s. to the s. Great Barrier Reef; throughout Micronesia.

TETRAROGIDAE (WASPFISHES)

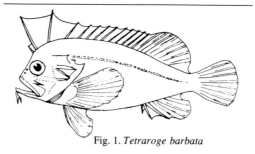

Fig. 1. *Tetraroge barbata*

Tetraroge barbata (Cuvier, 1829)
Mangrove waspfish
SL: to 8.4 cm (3.3 in); D XIII, 8; A III, 5; P 12-13(12); V I, 5; LP 14-16; GR 7-8 (on lower limb only); prickles instead of scales.
Waspfishes are closely related to scorpionfishes, but have dorsal fins that originate over or in front of the eyes, typically lack scales, and tend to be more compressed. Their spines are venomous and they feed on small fishes and crustaceans. This species inhabits muddy inshore waters of mangrove swamps and penetrates freshwater rivers. The closely related family Aploactinidae, which differs by having a fleshy papillae in front of the isthmus, is also known from Micronesia on the basis of an undescribed species of *Cocotropus* recently collected at Kwajalein.
West Pacific: Sumatra to New Caledonia, n. to the Ryukyus; Belau in Micronesia.

SCORPAENIDAE (SCORPIONFISHES)

Scorpionfishes are typically stout-bodied bottom-dwelling carnivores characterized by venomous dorsal, anal, and pelvic fin spines, a large head with numerous ridges and spines including a suborbital stay (a distinctive bony plate extending from beneath the eye to the preopercle; Fig. 1), and a large mouth full of small villiform teeth. Most species are well-camouflaged by possessing numerous dermal flaps and tassles as well as a highly variable coloration that perfectly matches the background on which they rest. A few (*Rhinopias* spp.; *Taenianotus triacanthus*) are highly compressed. The spectacular lionfishes of the subfamily Pteroinae (*Pterois* and *Dendrochirus* spp.) are characterized by greatly enlarged pectoral fins, elongate dorsal fin spines, are often brightly colored, and may swim well above the bottom. Many small cryptic species of the subfamily Scorpaeninae are quite common in shallow rubbly areas but are seldom noticed and difficult to identify. At least 30 species of scorpionfishes are known from Micronesia. Two species of *Pontinus* inhabit depths below 100 m and are not included here. (Lit.: Eschmeyer *in* Smith and Heemstra, 1986; Eschmeyer and Randall, 1975, Eschmeyer and Rao, 1973; Eschmeyer et al., 1973, 1979)

Subfamily Scorpaeninae

Key to shallow-water Micronesian Scorpaeninae:

1a. Palatine teeth present..2
1b. Palatine teeth absent..9
2a. Body not highly compressed; ≤ 65 vertical scale rows................................4
2b. Body highly compressed; ≥ 70 vertical scale rows or scales as small papillae.....3
3a. Scales normal, ≥ 70 vertical scale rows.............................***Rhinopias frondosa***
3b. Scales as small spiny papillae...................................***Taenianotus triacanthus***
4a. Rear lachrymal spine hooked forward; scales cycloid, at most feebly crenulate......
....genus ***Parascorpaena***: 5
4b. Rear lachrymal spine retrorse; scales mostly ctenoid.........genus ***Sebastapistes***: 6
5a. Supraocular tentacle absent or small; vertical scale rows < 40; distinct dark blotch
    near end of spinous D fin of males...............................***P. mcadamsi***
5b. Supraocular tentacle longer than orbit diameter; vertical scale rows ≥ 40; no dis-
    tinct dark blotch on D fin..***P. mossambica***
6a. Coronal spines present; coronal ridge strong...............................***S. mauritiana***
6b. Coronal spines absent; coronal ridge weak...7
7a. Lachrymal with 2 spines; lower opercular spine preceded by a ridge.................8
7b. Lachrymal with ≥ 3 spines; lower opercular spine preceded by a scaly area instead
    of a ridge..***S. cyanostigma***
8a. Scales on sides ctenoid; normally 15 P rays....................................***S. strongia***
8b. Scales on sides cycloid to emarginate; normally 16 P rays............***S. galactacma***
9a. 12 D spines...genus ***Scorpaenopsis***: 15
9b. 13 D spines...genus ***Scorpaenodes***: 10
10a. Nasal spine absent; mid P rays abruptly longer than those above; head length
    much longer than length of spinous D fin.................***S. (Hypomacrus) minor***
10b. Nasal spine present; P normal; head length about equal to length of spinous D
    fin..11
11a. Vertical scale rows ≤ 35; head almost completely scaled.............................14
11b. Vertical scale rows ≥ 38; head normally only partly scaled..........................12
12a. Vertical scale rows 38-40; dark spot at rear of spinous D fin............***S. varipinis***
12b. Vertical scale rows ≥ 42; no dark spot at rear of spinous D fin....................13
13a. D soft rays usually ≤ 8; no interorbital spine; ≤ 4 spines on suborbital ridge;
    vertical scale rows ≤ 44; a dark blotch on operculum; scattered skin flaps on
    body, but appearance not furry...............................***S. guamensis***
13b. D soft rays 9; interorbital spine present at posteror edge of interorbital ridge; ≥ 5
    spines on suborbital; vertical scale rows ≥ 48; numerous small skin flaps on
    body giving a furry appearance...............................***S. parvipinnis***
14a. P rays usually 17, rarely 18-19; suborbital ridge with 4 spines plus extra spine
    below main ridge..***S. hirsutus***
14b. P rays 18-20, usually 19; suborbital ridge usually with 3 (rarely 4) spines........
....***S. kelloggi***
15a. P rays 16, all unbranched; vertical scale rows ca. 35.....................***S. fowleri***
15b. Normally ≥ 17 P rays, uppermost branched; vertical scale rows > 40............16
16a. Back distinctly humped in front of dorsal fin; interorbital broad (> 1.1 x orbit di-
    ameter); inner face of P fin brilliantly colored in yellow, orange, and black.....17
16b. Back slightly humped at most; interorbital narrow (≤ 1.1 x orbit diameter); in-
    ner face of P fin not brilliantly colored as above..18
17a. Submarginal black band on inner face of P fin restricted to upper portion..........
....***S. diabolus***
17b. Submarginal black band on inner face of P fin complete...............***S. macrochir***
18a. P rays usually 20; vertical scale rows ca. 60; orbit smaller than snout length.....
....***S. oxycephala***
18b. P rays 17-18; vertical scale rows ca. 45-50; orbit wider than snout length.........
....***Scorpaenopsis*** n. sp. (Eschmeyer & Rao, in press)

---

* Excludes *S. papuensis* which will be reported from Belau and Guam by Eschmeyer
  and Rao (MS).

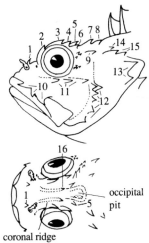

1 nasal
2 preocular
3 supraocular
4 postocular
5 postfrontal
6 tympanic
7 parietal
8 nuchal
9 pterotic

10 lachrymal
11 suborbital
   (on stay)
12 preopercular
13 opercular
14 postemporal
15 humeral
16 coronal

occipital pit

coronal ridge

Fig. 1. Cranial spines of
Scorpaenidae.

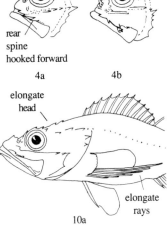

rear
spine
hooked forward

4a   4b

elongate
head

elongate
rays

10a

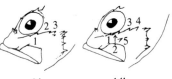

14a   14b

Parascorpaena mcadamsi (Fowler, 1938)
McAdam's scorpionfish

SL: to 5.8 cm (2.3 in); D XII, 8-(9); A III, 5; P 15-17(16); LP 23-24; LR ca. 36; supraocular tentacles absent or short. This small species differs from *P. mossambica* by lacking or having a poorly developed tentacle above each eye and a dark spot at the rear of the spinous dorsal fin in males.
Indo-Pacific: E. Africa to Ducie, n. to the Ryukyus, s. to Rapa; Belau and Marshalls in Micronesia.

Parascorpaena mossambica (Peters, 1855)
Mozambique scorpionfish Pl. 21E

(*Sebastapistes mcadamsi* Schultz)
SL: to 7.3 cm (2.9 in); D XII, 9; A III, 5; P 14-16; LR 40-41; supraocular tentacles well developed.
On Guam, this small scorpionfish is common in areas of mixed sand and rubble of reef flats, shallow lagoons, and channels to a depth of at least 18 m. During the day it usually stays hidden, but ventures out in the open at night.
Indo-Pacific: E. Africa to the Society Is., n. to the Izus, s. to Australia; throughout Micronesia.

Sebastapistes cyanostigma (Bleeker, 1856) Fig. 2b
Yellowspotted scorpionfish

(*Sebastapistes albobrunnea* Günther)
SL: to 6.4 cm (2.5 in); D XII, 9-10; A III, 5-6; P 16; LP 24-25; LR 42-45; lachrymal spines us. 5.
The numerous tiny white spots on a mottled yellow-green and reddish-brown background are distinctive. This species lives exclusively among the branches of robust *Pocillopora* corals in surgy areas of seaward reefs from depths of 2 to at least 15 m.
Indo-Pacific: Red Sea to the Line Is, n. to the Ryukyus, s. to Samoa; throughout Micronesia.

Sebastapistes galactacma Jenkins, 1903 Fig. 2c
Galactacma scorpionfish

SL: to 4.9 cm (1.9 in); D XII, (9)-10; A III, 5; P 15-17(16); LR ca. 45; lachrymal spines, 2.
This is the only Micronesian *Sebastapistes* with cycloid to emarginate scales on its sides. It has been collected from coral and rubble areas of seaward reefs at depths of 6 to 29 m.
Pacific Plate: Guam, Pohnpei, Hawaii, and Rapa.

Sebastapistes mauritiana (Cuvier, 1829)
Mauritius scorpionfish

(*S. corallicola* Schultz, 1966)
SL: to 5.4 cm (2.1 in); D XII, 9; A III, 5; P 15-16; LP 21-23; LR 42-45; strong coronal ridges with spine; lachrymal spines usually 3; distinct occipital pit, deepening with age.
This small scorpionfish usually has a dark blotch at the rear of its spinous dorsal fin as well as a distinct occipital pit. It has been collected from outer intertidal reef flats and shallow lagoon reefs exposed to wave action.
Indo-Pacific: E. Africa to the Marquesas and Rapa; Guam and Marshalls in Micronesia; close to *S. ballieui* of the Hawaiian Is. (Fig. 2a).

Sebastapistes strongia (Cuvier, 1829)
Barchin scorpionfish Pl. 21E; Fig. 1d

(*S. bynoensis* Schultz, 1966 (in part))
SL: to > 4 cm (1.6 in); D XII, 8-9(9); A III, 5; P 14-17(15); LP 20-22; LR 40-44; lachrymal spines, 2.
This is among the most common of small scorpaenids of mixed sand and rubble areas of reef flats, shallow lagoons, and channels to a depth of at least 18 m. During the day it usually stays hidden, but ventures out in the open at night.
Indo-Pacific: Red Sea to the Society Is., n. to Taiwan, s. to Queensland; Carolines and Marianas in Micronesia.

Scorpaenodes hirsutus (Smith, 1957)
Hairy scorpionfish

SL: to 5.6 cm (2.2 in); D XIII, (8)-9; A III, 5-6; P 17-19 (17); LP ca. 23; LR 30-32; us. 4 spinous points on suborbital ridge.
This species has been collected on both lagoon and seaward reefs to a depth of at least 40 m.
Indo-Pacific: Red Sea to the Marquesas and Pitcairn, n. to the Ryukyu and Hawaiian Is.; throughout Micronesia.

Scorpaenodes kelloggi (Jenkins, 1903) Fig. 1e
Kellogg's scorpionfish

SL: to 3.9 cm (1.5 in); D XIII, 7-8(8); A III, 5; P 18-20 (19); LP 20; LR 30-31; 3-4 spinous points on suborbital ridge.
This species has been reported from coralline areas from near shore to the outer reef slope at a depth of at least 24 m.
Indo-Pacific: E. Africa to the Hawaiian, Line, and Society Is.; n. to Taiwan; throughout Micronesia.

Scorpaenodes minor (Smith, 1958) Fig. 1f
Minor scorpionfish

(*Hypomacrus brocki* Schultz, 1966)
SL: to 4.0 cm (1.6 in); D XII-XIV, 7-9(8); A III, 5; P 14-16(15); LP 21-22; LR 29-32.
This is the only Micronesian scorpionfish with elongate lower pectoral fin rays. It is an uncommon species known from a few specimens collected from lagoon and seaward reefs at depths of less than 15 m.
Indo-Pacific: E. Africa to the Samoan and Austral Is., n. to the Philippines; Pohnpei, Marianas, and Marshalls in Micronesia.

Scorpaenodes parvipinnis (Garrett, 1864) Fig. 1g
Coral scorpionfish

SL: to 12 cm (4.7 in); D XIII, 9; A III, 5; P 17-19(18); LR 45-55; ≥ 5 spinous points on suborbital ridge.
This species has been collected from areas of rich coral growth from near shore to the outer reef slope at a depth of 49 m. It is relatively uncommon and remains hidden during the day.
Indo-Pacific: Red Sea to the Marquesas and Tuamotus. n. to the Ryukyu and Hawaiian Is., s. to Lord Howe Is.; throughout Micronesia.

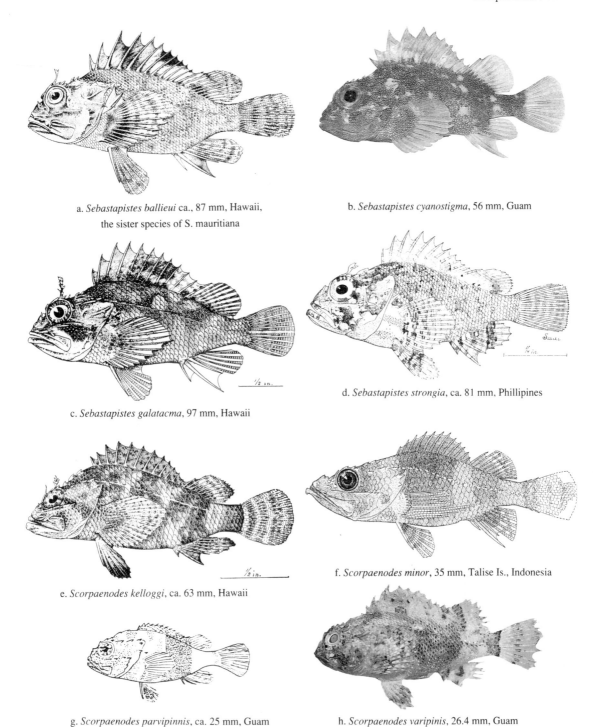

a. *Sebastapistes ballieui* ca., 87 mm, Hawaii, the sister species of S. mauritiana

b. *Sebastapistes cyanostigma*, 56 mm, Guam

c. *Sebastapistes galatacma*, 97 mm, Hawaii

d. *Sebastapistes strongia*, ca. 81 mm, Phillipines

e. *Scorpaenodes kelloggi*, ca. 63 mm, Hawaii

f. *Scorpaenodes minor*, 35 mm, Talise Is., Indonesia

g. *Scorpaenodes parvipinnis*, ca. 25 mm, Guam

h. *Scorpaenodes varipinis*, 26.4 mm, Guam

Fig. 2. Micronesian species of *Sebastapistes* and *Scorpaenodes* (a, c, e, after Jenkins, 1903; d, after Jordan and Seale, 1906; f, after D. B. Schultz in Schultz et al., 1966).

Scorpaenodes varipinis Smith, 1957 — Fig. 1h
Blotchfin scorpionfish

SL: to 7.5 cm (3 in); D XIII, 8; A III, 5; P 17-18; LP 23-25; LR ca. 38-40.

This species has been collected from shallow coralline areas to a depth of 200 m (the latter taken from the gut of a deep-water snapper).

Indo-west Pacific: E. Africa to Guam.

Scorpaenodes guamensis (Quoy & Gaimard, 1824)
Guam scorpionfish — Pl. 21F

SL: to 12 cm (4.7 in); D XIII-XIV, 7-9(8); A III, 4-5(5); P 18-19(19); LP 22-24; LR 41-47; two forms: form *guamensis* with longest D spine=12-14% of SL and= max. diameter of eye; dark opercular blotch distinct; form *scabra* with longest D spine=14-18% of SL and > max. diameter of eye; dark opercular blotch obscure.

Some ichthyologists regard the two forms as separate species; both occur in Micronesia. In the Marianas and much of Micronesia, the *guamensis* form is the most common scorpaenid of rubble or rocky areas of reef flats, shallow lagoons, and channels. It normally rests hidden in cracks and under ledges, often upside down. It feeds primarily at night on small shrimps, small crabs, and polychaetes.

Indo-Pacific: Red Sea to the Pitcairn group, n. to the Izus, s. to New South Wales; throughout Micronesia.

Scorpaenopsis diabolus (Cuvier, 1829) — Pl. 22A
Devil scorpionfish — Fig. 3a
(*S. gibbosa* Schultz, 1966)

SL: to 18.5 cm (7.3 in), 24 cm (9.5 in) in s. Japan; D XII, 8-10(9); A III, (5)-6; P 17-19(18); LP 22-25; LR 43-48; submarginal black band on inner pectoral fin surface incomplete.

This exceedingly ugly creature has a colorful surprise for those that disturb it: it flashes the undersides of its pectoral fins that are brilliantly colored in yellow, orange, and black. Presumably this is an effective warning that would-be predators learn after their first experience with a mouthful of venomous spines! Both this species and *S. macrochir* belong to the "humpbacked" group of *Scorpaenopsis*, and both have colorful inner surfaces to their pectoral fins. *Scorpaenopsis diabolus* is a relatively uncommon inhabitant of rubbly or weedy coralline-rock bottoms of reef flats and lagoon and seaward reefs to a depth of 70 m.

Indo-Pacific: Red Sea to the Line, Marquesan and Pitcairn Is., n. to s. Japan, s. Korea, and the Hawaiian Is., s. to Queensland; throughout Micronesia.

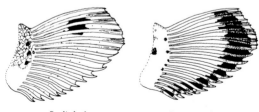

S. diabolus   S. macrochir
Fig. 3. Inner face of right pectoral fin.

Scorpaenopsis macrochir Ogilby, 1910
Flasher scorpionfish — Pl. 22B; Fig. 3b

SL: to 10.4 cm (4.1 in); submarginal black band on inner pectoral fin surface complete.

In addition to the differences already noted, this species has a relatively larger eye, shorter snout, and less obviously humped back than does *S. diabolus*. At Guam, it is a relatively uncommon inhabitant of mixed sand and rubble areas of reef flats and shallow lagoons.

West-central Pacific: nw. Australia, Moluccas, and Philippines to the Marquesan and Society Is., n. to the Ryukyus, s. to Rowley Shoals, Queensland, and Tonga; Marianas and Carolines in Micronesia.

Scorpaenopsis fowleri (Pietschmann, 1934) — Fig. 4
Pigmy scorpionfish

SL: to 2.8 cm (1.1 in); D XII, 9; A III, 5; P 16; LR ca. 35; shallow pit below front of eye.

This tiny scorpionfish matures at a size of 2.4 cm or less. It has been collected around mixed sand and rubble, coral, or rocks to a depth of at least 27 m.

Indo-Pacific: W. Indian Ocean to Oeno, n. to the Philippine and Hawaiian Is.; throughout Micronesia.

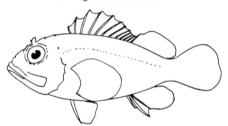

Fig. 4. *Scorpaenopsis fowleri.*

Scorpaenopsis oxycephala (Bleeker, 1849)
Tassled scorpionfish — Pl. 22C,D
(*S. cirrhosa* Myers and Shepard)

SL: to 19 cm (7.5 in); D XII, 9; A III, 5; P (19)-20; LR 60-65.

The coloration of this species is quite variable, ranging from an orange-red to a dark brown or green. Juveniles generally possess a broad white band across the nape and an irregular white band extending from each eye to the upper lip; adults may retain some of the white under the eye. This species prefers rock and coral substrates of clear-water outer reef slopes and channels from depths of 1 to at least 35 m. At least two other closely related species, *S. papuensis* (Cuver) and an undescribed species, will be reported from Micronesia by Eschmeyer and Rao.

Indo-west Pacific: Red Sea to Guam, n. to Taiwan; Belau and Guam in Micronesia; probably more widespread.

Scorpaenopsis sp. — Fig. 5
Spinycrown scorpionfish

SL: to ca. 13 cm (5.1 in); D XII, 9; A III, 5; P 17-18; LR ca. 45-50; orbit ≥ snout length.

This is the only species of *Scorpaenopsis* that has extra spines above the tympanic spines.

Indo-Pacific: Red Sea to the Marquesan and Pitcairn Is., n. to the Ryukyus; throughout Micronesia.

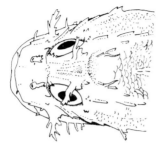

Fig. 5. Head of *Scorpaenopsis* sp., 95 mm (redrawn from Eschmeyer *in* Smith and Heemstra, 1986).

Rhinopias frondosa (Günther, 1891)   Pl. 21E
Weedy scorpionfish

SL: to 19 cm (7.5 in); D XII, 9; A III, 5; P 16; LR ca. 70-75.

The intricate color pattern of this fish is truly remarkable. Its body is highly compressed and covered with weed-like tassles. Underwater it must look exactly like a clump of algae. It is extremely rare; fewer than a dozen specimens exist in museum collections. The only Micronesian specimen came from a depth of 60 m at Condor Reef, Caroline Islands. Elsewhere it has been collected from rocky or coraline habitats at depths of 13 to 90 m.

Indo-west Pacific: E. Africa to the Caroline Is., n. to s. Japan; Condor Reef, Caroline Is., in Micronesia.

Taenianotus triacanthus Lacepède, 1802   Pl. 22E
Leaf fish

SL: to 7.1 cm (2.8 in); D XII, 8-11(10); A III, 5-(6); P 14-15(14); has prickly papillae instead of scales.

This unusual little fish resembles a leaf in structure as well as behavior. Its body is quite compressed and it has the habit of mimicking a leaf or blade of algae by swaying from side to side. Although they are usually a cryptic yellowish-green or brown, some individuals may be black, red, or a silvery white and stand out in stark contrast against their background, yet still resemble an innanimate object. The leaf fish is relatively uncommon in Micronesia where it occurs on reef flats, outer reef slopes, current-swept channels, or rarely on lagoon reefs. Elsewhere it has been reported from as deep as 134 m. It does well in captivity only if offered a steady diet of small live fishes or crustaceans and kept in high quality water. It has the peculiar habit of sloughing off its outer layer of skin from time to time.

Indo-pan-Pacific: E. Africa to the Galapagos Is., n. to the Ryukyu and Hawaiian Is., s. to the Tuamotus and n. New South Wales; Marianas and Marshalls in Micronesia.

Subfamily Synanceiinae (Stonefishes)

Synanceia verrucosa Bloch & Schneider, 1801
Stonefish   Pl. 22F

SL: to 35 cm (13.8 in); D XII-XIV (XIII), 5-7(6); A III, 5-6

(5); P 17-19(18); LL 8-10, but pores buried.

This large hideous creature is probably the world's most venemous fish. Beneath its warty skin are 12 to 14 stout grooved spines, each with a large venom sack at its base. Its pelvic and anal fin spines are similarly developed. The stonefish has been responsible for numerous debilitating and occasionally fatal injuries. The wounds are extremely painful and may result in death of the surrounding tissue or loss of wounded fingers or toes. Although the spines can easily penetrate a tennis shoe, the stonefish usually rests under or against rocks, reducing the chances of it being stepped on. The stonefish is fairly common on sandy or rubbly areas of reef flats and shallow lagoons, but its excellent camouflage and habit of partially burying itself in the sand make it virtually invisible. It is normally solitary and feeds on fishes and crustaceans that are engulfed in its enormous upturned mouth.

Indo-Pacific: Red Sea to Mangareva, n. to the Ryukyus, s. to New Caledonia and the Australs; throughout Micronesia.

Subfamily Choridactylinae (Devilfishes)

Inimicus didactylus (Pallas, 1769)   Pl. 23A; Fig. 6
Spiny devilfish

SL: to 148 cm (5.8 in); D XV to XVII, 7-9; A II, 10-12; P 12, lower 2 entirely free; GR 1-3+7-9=9-11.

In this subfamily, the lower 2 to 3 pectoral rays are entirely free and used as "walking" legs. *Inimicus* is further characterized by long extremely venemous dorsal spines, the first three of which are connected by a membrane, the remainder deeply incised; bulbous eyes on top of the head; an upward projecting snout; and the absence of scales, except for 13 to 15 buried lateral line scales and scattered buried scales seen as warts or tufts. They inhabit open sandy or silty substrates at depths of 5 to 40 m or more and often lie buried up to their eyes waiting to ambush small fishes.

West Pacific: Thailand to Vanuatu, n. to se. China; Belau in Micronesia.

Fig. 6. Inner face of right pectoral fin of *I. didactylus*.

Subfamily Pteroinae (Lionfishes)

Members of this subfamily have greatly enlarged pectoral fins, elongate dorsal fin spines, are often brightly colored, and may swim well above the bottom. Species of *Dendrochirus* differ from those of *Pterois* by possessing shorter pectoral fin rays that do not extend past the base of the tail, that are connected for most of their lengths, and are branched. They also tend to be smaller and less colorful.

Dendrochirus biocellatus (Fowler, 1938)
Ocellated lionfish   Pl. 23B; Fig. 7

SL: to 8 cm (3.2 in),12 cm (4.7 in) in s. Japan; D XIII, 9;
A III, 5; P 20-21; LP 24-25; LR 47-48; mid-dorsal spines
shorter than body depth.

This is the only species of *Dendrochirus* with a pair of distinct occelli on the soft-rayed dorsal fin. It inhabits exposed
areas of rich coral growth and clear water from depths of 1 to
at least 40 m. It is secretive by day, but active at night. It
seems to be relatively uncommon in Micronesia.

Indo-Pacific: Sri Lanka to the Society Is., n. to s. Japan;
s. to Scott Reef; throughout Micronesia.

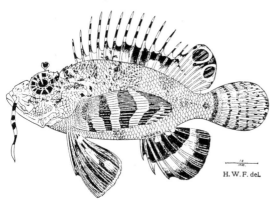

Fig. 7. *Dendrochirus biocellatus*, ca. 64 mm (after Fowler,
1938).

Dendrochirus brachypterus (Cuvier, 1829) Pl. 23C
Shortfin lionfish

SL: to 15 cm (5.9 in); D XIII, 9-10; A III, 5-6; P (17)-18;
LR 40-45; mid-dorsal spines shorter than body depth.

The shortfin lionfish is relatively common around isolated
weed-covered rocks on sandy areas of reef flats and shallow
lagoons. During the day, it tends to remain innactive, often
hiding in an upside-down position with the pectoral fins
folded. At night it actively roams the reef in search of small
crustaceans.

West Pacific: Red Sea to Samoa and Tonga, n. to s. Japan,
s. to Lord Howe Is.; Marianas in Micronesia.

Dendrochirus zebra (Cuvier, 1829)   Pl. 23D
Zebra lionfish

SL: to 25 cm (9.8 in); D XIII, 10-11; A III, 6-7; P 16-(17);
LP 45-55; LR 46-49; mid-dorsal spines longer than body
depth.

This is the only Micronesian *Dendrochirus* in which the
longest dorsal spines are longer than the body depth, the
body has distinct white bars like those in species of *Pterois*,
and the coloration of the pectoral fin consists of concentric
bands. It is common in the Philippines where it is exported
for the aquarium trade, but rare in Micronesia. Courtship
and spawning occur at night. Males are quite aggressive and
patrol a home range within which they attempt to drive out
other males and court any females. The females are smaller
and develop an almost white face when in courtship. Spawn-

ing occurs at the apex of a short and rapid paired ascent resulting in a gelatinous mass of 2,000 to 15,000 eggs left to
drift with the current. Hatching occurs some 36 hours later
and the larvae probably settle out in a few weeks at a size of
10-12 mm. This species has been spawned in captivity.

Indo-Pacific: E. Africa to Samoa, n. to s. Japan, s. to Lord
Howe Is.; Belau and the Marshalls in Micronesia.

Pterois antennata (Bloch, 1787)   Pl. 23E
Spotfin lionfish

SL: to 19 cm (7.5 in); D XIII, 11-12; A III, 6; P 16-18(17);
LP 26; LR 50-54; scales mostly ctenoid.

This common lionfish inhabits lagoon and seaward reefs
from the reef flat to a depth of at least 50 m. During the day
it is relatively inactive, occuring singly or in small groups,
usually under ledges and in holes. In the late afternoon and
at night it forages for shrimps and crabs.

Indo-Pacific: E. Africa to Marquesas and Mangareva, n. to s.
Japan, s. to the Australs and s. Queensland; throughout Micronesia.

Pterois radiata Cuvier, 1829   Pl. 23F
Clearfin lionfish

SL: to 20 cm (7.9 in); D XII-XIII, 10-12(11); A III, 5-(6); P
(16)-17; LP 27; LR 50-55; scales mostly ctenoid.

This is the only species of *Pterois* that lacks markings between its fin rays and has a pair of horizontal white stripes
at the base of its tail. It is the least common of the three
species of *Pterois* in Micronesia. It occurs on lagoon and
seaward reefs from the reef flat to a depth of over 15 m,
sometimes in the same hole with *P. antennata*. It feeds almost exclusively on small crabs and shrimps. Limited observations of reproductive behavior suggests that it is similar to that of *Dendrochirus zebra*.

Indo-Pacific: Red Sea to the Society Is., n. to the Ryukyus,
s. to New Caledonia; throughout Micronesia.

Pterois volitans (Linnaeus, 1758)   Pl. 24
Lionfish, Turkeyfish

SL: to 30 cm (11.8 in); D XIII, 10-11(11); A III, 6-7(7); P
14-16(14, but us. 15-16 in s. Pacific); LP 27-30; LR 90-
120; scales cycloid.

The lionfish is among the reef's most spectacular inhabitants. It occurs on both lagoon and seaward reefs from turbid inshore areas to depths of over 50 m. During the day it
often hangs under ledges, but may also actively forage as it
does at night. It feeds on small fishes, shrimps, and crabs.
Lionfish are popular aquarium pets and are relatively easy to
maintain, particularly if they learn to take non-live foods.
They are capable of inflicting extremely painful, in some
cases fatal, wounds and will stand their ground if harassed.

West-central Pacific: w. Australia and Malaysia to the Marquesas and Oeno (Pitcairn group), n. to s. Japan and s. Korea, s. to Lord Howe, the Kermadec, and Austral Is.;
throughout Micronesia; replaced by the very similar *P.
miles* from the Red Sea to Sumatra.

ORDER PERCIFORMES

SERRANIDAE (FAIRY BASSLETS and GROUPERS)

Members of this family generally possess a single dorsal fin with well-developed spines, a continuous lateral line, two or three small flattened opercular spines, and relatively small ctenoid scales. The lower jaw generally projects beyond the upper jaw and the rear part of the upper jaw (maxillary) is fully exposed. Micronesian species fall in one of two subfamilies, the Anthiinae (fairy basslets) and the Epinephelinae (groupers), or in a genus of uncertain placement, *Liopropoma*, each of which will be treated separately.

Subfamily Anthiinae (Fairy basslets)

Most members ot this subfamily are relatively small (<10 cm SL) colorful inhabitants of steep outer reef slopes. Species of *Pseudanthias** are laterally compressed, sexually dichromatic, diurnally active planktivores that commonly aggregate a few meters above prominent coral heads or ledges. Although occasionally found in channels or deep, clearwater lagoons, they reach their greatest abundance along current-swept dropoffs of the outer reef slope. In the Carolines and Belau, some species are abundant in as little as 3 m along leeward reefs where the reef margin plunges precipitously to depths of several hundred meters, but in the Marianas they are seldom found in less than 20 m. Aggregations typically consist of one or more brilliantly hued territorial males and numerous slightly less colorful females. Males are sex-reversed females, with sex-reversal socially controlled and terminal. At the approach of danger and at night fairy basslets shelter within the reef. Species of *Luzonichthys* are relatively elongate with separate spinous and soft-rayed dorsal fins, and *Serranocirrhitus* and *Holanthias* are deep-bodied (the latter occur at depths of 100 to 300 m). Species of *Plectranthias* possess a deeply notched dorsal fin, a large mouth, and in most, a robust body and thickened lower pectoral rays. Most are deep-dwelling, sedentary or cryptic predators of small benthic fishes and crustaceans. At least 29 species in 7 genera occur in Micronesia. Not included are two species of *Holanthias*, two *Plectranthias*, and four undescribed *Pseudanthias* that occur at depths exceeding 90 m. (Lit.: Katayama and Amaoka, 1986; Randall, 1979)

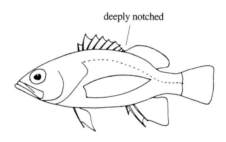

deeply notched

1a *Plectranthias*

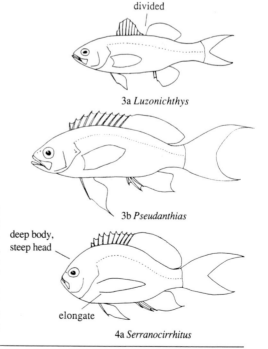

divided

3a *Luzonichthys*

3b *Pseudanthias*

deep body,
steep head

elongate

4a *Serranocirrhitus*

Key to Micronesian genera of Anthiinae:

1a. LL ≤ 31; D deeply notched......................***Plectranthias***
1b. LL ≥ 33-74; D divided or continuous, not notched.......2
2a. Body elongate, depth 2.3-3.8 in SL............................3
2b. Body deep, depth 1.9-2.35 in SL...............................4
3a. D divided to base between spinous and soft rayed parts....
....***Luzonichthys***
3b. D continuous......................................***Pseudanthias****
4a. P elongate, < 2.6 in SL, all rays unbranched................
....***Serranocirrhitus***
4b. P not elongate, > 2.8 in SL, most rays branched (occurs
below 90 m)...***Holanthias***

* Includes the Indo-Pacific species of *Anthias*, *Franzia*, and *Mirolabrichthys* of contemporary authors. Recent studies have shown *Anthias* to be confined to the Atlantic and Mediterranean. The Indo-Pacific species belong in *Pseudanthias* (Fig. 5). Some authors elevate the subgenera *Franzia* and *Mirolabrichthys* to genera.

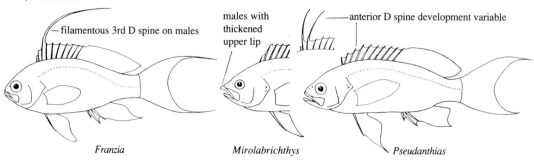

Fig. 1. Subgenera of *Pseudanthias*.

Luzonichthys waitei (Fowler, 1931)   Pl. 25A
Magenta slender basslet

SL: to 45 mm (1.8 in); D X+15-16; A III,7-8; P 18-20(19); LL 52-57; GR 7-10+20-22; depth 3.3-3.8.

Species of *Luzonichthys* are more elongate than other anthine fishes and possess separate spinous and soft-rayed portions of the dorsal fin. They occur in large zooplankton feeding aggregations along steep outer reef slopes at depths of 10 to 55 m. In Micronesia, *L. waitei* has been observed at a depth of 16m off the south tip of Peleliu, Belau and at 46 to 55 m at Kwajalein.

Indo-Pacific: Aldabra and Astove to the Loyalty Is., n. to the Philippines; Belau and the s. Marshalls in Micronesia (the Indian Ocean population regarded by some as *L. addisi*).

Luzonichthys whitleyi Smith 1961
Whitlêy's slender basslet

SL: to 45 mm (1.8 in); D X+15-16; A III, 8(II, 9?); P 20-22(21); LL 65-74; GR 7-8+20-22.

This species is easily separated from *L. waitei* on the basis of number of lateral line scales (≥65 vs ≤57) and usual number of pectoral fin rays (21 vs 19) as well as certain details of coloration. It is provisionally included here on the basis of a few individuals photographed in a mixed aggregation with *L. waitei* at a depth of 16 m off the south tip of Peleliu, Belau.

Indo-Pacific: Aldabra, Christmas Is., Belau, Nauru, and the Line Is. (the w. Indian Ocean population regarded by some as *L. microlepis*).

Pseudanthias huchtii (Bleeker, 1856)   Pl. 25B,C
Red-cheeked fairy basslet

(*Anthias mortoni*)

SL: to 76 mm (3 in); D X, 17; A III, 7; P 17-18; LL 36-40; GR 9-10+24-26; depth 2.3-2.6.

Pseudanthias huchtii and *P. squammipinnis* are members of the subgenus *Franzia* which is characterized by heavily scaled dorsal and anal fins and lunate tails. The third dorsal spine becomes greatly developed in males. Females of *P. huchtii* lack the red head band of males. In Belau, where this species is rare, it was observed singly or in small groups around coral outcrops of clear outer reef slopes at depths of 4 to 20 m. On inshore reefs of the Philippines and Indonesia, *P. huchtii* is one of the most abundant fairy basslets.

Indo-Australian: Moluccas and Philippines to Vanuatu, s. to the Great Barrier Reef; Belau in Micronesia.

Pseudanthias squammipinnis (Peters, 1855)
Scalefin or Lyretail fairy basslet   Pl. 25D,E

SL: to 108 mm (4.3 in); D X, 15-17; A III, 6-8; P 16-18 (17); LL 38-43(41-43); GR 8-11+23-26; depth 2.4-3.0.

In Belau, this species occurs in small aggregations a few meters off coral outcrops of steep dropoffs below 12 m. Elsewhere in its range it may form enormous aggregations above coral outcrops or patch reefs of clear lagoons, channels, or outer reef slopes at depths of 4 to 20 m. It is a well-known aquarium fish. On the Great Barrier Reef and off southern Japan, spawning takes place during the summer, but in the Red Sea it occurs in winter. Successful males spawn nightly with successive females.

Indo-west Pacific: Red Sea to the Solomons, n. to s. Japan, s. to New South Wales; Belau in Micronesia.

Pseudanthias cooperi (Regan, 1902)   Pl. 25E,F
Red-bar fairy basslet

(*Leptanthias kashiwae* Tanaka; *Anthias taeniatus* Myers and Shepard, 1980)

SL: to 64 mm (2.5 in),105 mm (4.1 in) in s. Japan; D X, 15-17(16); AIII, 7-8; P 18-20(19); LL 48-52; GR 8-11+22-27; depth 2.8-3.2.

This fairy basslet occurs in small, loose aggregations along current-swept dropoffs from depths of 16 to 60 m. Males develop an incomplete crimson bar in the middle of their sides. This species is relatively rare in Micronesia.

Indo-Pacific: E. Africa to the Line Is., n. to s. Japan, s. to the Great Barrrier Reef; Belau, Marshalls, and Marianas in Micronesia.

Pseudanthias pleurotaenia (Bleeker, 1857)
Square-spot fairy basslet   Pl. 26A,B,C

SL: to 100 mm (3.9 in); D X, (16)-18 (3rd spine somewhat elongate in males); A III, 6-(7); P 17-19; LL 44-49; GR 11-13+27-30; depth ca. 2.5.

This spectacular fairy basslet occurs in aggregations a few meters above the edges of current-swept dropoffs at depths of 15 to 180 m. In the Marianas, it is rare in less than 30 m. Nowhere common, aggregations typically consist of 6 to 30 individuals with females outnumbering males. Juveniles are solitary and remain close to shelter. Underwater the large magenta blotch of males appears to glow, creating a breathtaking sight. This species is highly prized, but seldom encountered in the aquarium trade due to the difficulty of safely bringing it to the surface.

West-central Pacific: Indonesia to Samoa, n. to the Ryukyus, s. to Rowley Shoals and New Caledonia; throughout Micronesia.

Pseudanthias ventralis ventralis (Randall, 1979)
Long-finned fairy basslett   Pl. 26D

SL: to 58 mm (2.3 in); D X, 17; A III, 9; P 15; LL 39-46; GR 7-8+21-24; depth 2.9-3.1.

This small fairy basslet typically inhabits caves or coral rubble along steep dropoffs or channel walls at depths of 40 to perhaps 120 m. On rare occasions it has been collected as shallow as 26 m but it is somewhat secretive and rarely encountered by divers. Based on observations from a submersible, this (or a closely related species) is the dominate fish along the steep submarine slopes of Enewetak Atoll at depths of 90 to 120 m.

West-central Pacific: Marianas and Marshalls to Pitcairn, s. to the Great Barrier Reef and New Caledonia; the subspecies *hawaiiensis* from the Hawaiian and Johnston Is.

Pseudanthias randalli (Lubbock & Allen, 1978)
Randall's fairy basslet   Pl. 27A,B

SL: to 70 mm (2.8 in); D X, 15-17(16); A III, 7-8(7); P 16-18(17); LL 38-46; GR 8-10+1+21-23; depth 2.6-3.0.

This small fairy basslet occurs in small aggregations in or near caves of current-swept dropoffs at depths of 15 to 68 m. It generally remains close to the substrate and is relatively uncommon. Juveniles and females are a uniform yellowish- to reddish-orange with yellow outer caudal rays. Males develop a slightly protruding upper lip.

West-central Pacific: Philippines and Moluccas to the Marshalls; Belau and Kwajalein in Micronesia.

Pseudanthias sp.
Cave fairy basslet   Pl. 26E

(*Anthias randalli* Myers and Shepard, 1980)
SL: to 60 mm (2.4 in).

This species closely resembles *P. randalli* both in morphology and behavior, but differs in coloration. Further study is needed to determine whether or not it is a distinct species. It is currently known only from the vicinity of the "Blue Hole", Guam at depths of 25 to 45 m.

Guam

Pseudanthias bartlettorum
(Randall & Lubbock, 1981)   Pl. 27C,D
Bartlett's fairy basslet

SL: to 62 mm (2.4 in); D X, 17-18 (17); A III, 7; P 20-21 (21); LL 54-58; GR 10-11+23-26; depth 2.9-3.1.

This and the following species are members of the subgenus *Mirolabrichthys* which is characterized by a forked tail and a thickened, protruding upper lip in males. Off leeward Kosrae, Bartlett's fairy basslet is abundant along steep outer reef slopes and dropoffs at depths of 4 to over 30 m. It forms large aggregations that typically consist of a few males and up to several dozen females and juveniles that often mingle with *P. dispar*. In Belau, it was observed only at the south tip of Peleliu in small numbers.

Pacific Plate: Belau, Kosrae, Kwajalein, Nauru, and Fanning Is.

Pseudanthias dispar Herre, 1955   Pl. 28A,B
Peach fairy basslett

SL: to 67 mm (2.6 in); D X, 16-18(17); A III, 7-8; P 18-20 (19-20); LL 55-63; GR 9-12+22-26; depth 2.7-3.3.

This spectacular fairy basslet occurs in large aggregations above coral outcrops along the upper portions of steep outer reef slopes, dropoffs, and channel walls at depths of 3 to over 15 m. Males seem to spend a great deal of their time in courtship and often occur in small groups at the perimeter of larger aggregations. This is probably the most abundant shallow water fairy basslet off leeward reefs throughout the Caroline Islands.

West-central Pacific: Christmas Is., Indian Ocean to the Line Is., n. to the Yaeyamas, s. to the n. Great Barrier reef, Fiji and Samoa; Belau, e. Carolines, and s. Marshalls in Micronesia.

Pseudanthias bicolor (Randall, 1979)   Pl. 27E
Bicolor fairy basslet

SL: to 82 mm (3.2 in), 111 mm (4.4 in) in Hawaii; D X, 16-18(17); A III, 7-8; P 19-21(19-20); LL 57-64; GR 11-12+26-29; depth 2.7-3.0.

The bicolor fairy basslet is a relatively uncommon inhabitant of lagoon patch reefs and outer reef slopes from depths of 5 to 68 m. It occurs in small groups above coral outcrops or near crevices or ledges.

Indo-Pacific: Mauritius to the Hawaiian and Line Is., s. to the Loyalty Is.; Marshalls and e. Carolines in Micronesia.

Pseudanthias lori (Lubbock & Randall, 1976)
Lori's anthias   Pl. 27F

SL: to 66 mm (2.6 in); D X, 16-17(16), A III, 7-8; P 16-18(17-18); LL 47-52; GR 8-9+21-24; depth 3.4-4.0.

Lori's fairy basslet typically occurs in small aggregations in the vicinity of caves or ledges of steep outer reef slopes at depths of 20 to 70 m. In Belau, an aggregation was observed at a depth of 18 m at The Corner, a spectacular dive site near the Ngemelis Islands.

Weest-central Pacific: Philippines and Moluccas to the Tuamotus, s. to Rowley Shoals, the n. Great Barrier Reef, and Loyalty Is.; Belau in Micronesia.

Pseudanthias pascalus (Jordan & Tanaka, 1927)
Purple queen   Pl. 28C,D

SL: to 117 mm (4.6 in); D X, 15-17(16); A III 7-8; P 16-19; LL 48-52; GR 9-11+23-27; depth 2.9-3.4.

The purple queen inhabits outer reef slopes and dropoffs at depths of 5 to 60 m, particularly in the vicinity of large caves or coral outcrops exposed to currents. It occurs in large aggregations that may venture several meters above the bottom. Its diet consists primarily of copepods and other planktonic crustaceans or crustacean larvae, and fish eggs.

West-central Pacific: Bali and the Ryukyus to the Tuamotus, n. to s. Japan, s. to New Caledonia; throughout Micronesia.

Pseudanthias smithvanizi
(Randall & Lubbock, 1981)   Pl. 28E
Smithvaniz' fairy basslet
SL: to 59 mm (2.3 in); D X, 15-17(16); A III, 7-8; P 16-18(16-17); LL 44-48; GR 8-9+20-24; depth 3.1-3.3.
This small fairy basslet inhabits steep outer reef slopes and dropoffs at depths of 6 to 70 m. It typically occurs in small aggregations of less than 20 which tend to remain within a meter of the reef. It is quite common along the walls of the Ngemelis area of Belau.
West-central Pacific: Cocos-Keeling Is. to the s. Marshalls, n. to the Philippines, s. to the Great Barrier Reef; Belau and the s. Marshalls in Micronesia.

Pseudanthias tuka Herre & Montalban, 1927
Yellowstriped fairy basslet   Pl. 29A,B
SL: to 80 mm (3.1 in); D X, 15-17(16); A III, 7-8; P 15-17; LL 45-49; GR 8-10+22-26; depth 2.8-3.3.
This species is closely related to the purple queen, but differs in details of coloration: primary phase P. tuka possess a broad yellow stripe along the back and caudal fin lobes and males have a yellowish proboscis and lower jaw and a purple spot at the base of the soft dorsal fin, features that are lacking in P. pascalus. In Belau, P. tuka is relatively common along the dropoffs of the southwest portion of the barrier reef at depths of 10 to 15 m where it frequently aggregates with the more abundant P. pascalus.
Indo-Australian: Philippines and Bali to the Solomon Is., s. to Rowley Shoals and the Great Barrier Reef; Belau in Micronesia.

Serranocirrhitus latus Watanabe, 1949   Pl. 29C
Hawkfish anthias
SL: to 82 mm (3.2 in); D X, 18-20; A III, 7; P 13-14; LL 33-38; GR 9-10+23-26; depth 1.9-2.2.
Serranocirrhitus latus is easily distinguished from all other anthiines by the combination of its deep body and elongate pectoral fins which reach at least as far back as the 5th anal ray. It typically occurs in small groups in the vicinity of caves and ledges of steep outer reef slopes at depths of 15 to 70 m. It seems to be relatively rare at Belau.
Indo-Australian: Moluccas to Fiji, n. to the Izus, s. to New Caledonia and the Great Barrier Reef; Belau in Micronesia.

Fig. 2. *Plectranthias fourmanoiri* 38 mm, Guam.

Plectranthias fourmanoiri Randall, 1980   Fig. 2
Fourmanoir's basslet
SL: to 38 mm (1.5 in); D X, 16-18(16); A III, 7; P 12-13

(13); LLp 25; GR 4-7+10-12; depth 2.7-3.0.
Species of *Plectranthias* are characterized by deeply notched dorsal fins, large mouths, and usually robust bodies and thickened lower pectoral fin rays. They are probably carnivores of small fishes and crustaceans and most are deep-dwelling. The four known shallow water Micronesian species are included here; two additional species, P. kamii and an undescribed species, occur in deep water. P. fourmanoiri is a secretive species known only from poison stations made in lagoon or seaward reefs at depths of 5 to 44 m.
West-central Pacific: Christmas Is., e. Indian Ocean to Pitcairn; Marianas and Marshalls in Micronesia.

Plectranthias longimanus (Weber, 1913)
Long-finned basslet
SL: to 28 mm (1.1 in); D X, 13-15(13-14); A III, 6-7; P 12-13(13); LP 12-15; GR 1+4-7; depth 2.6-3.1.
This species closely resembles P. nanus, but has lower numbers of pectoral fin rays and pored lateral line scales. It is known primarily from poison stations made at depths of 6 to 73 m. Its behavior is reported to be similar to that of a small hawkfish.
Indo-west Pacific: primarily continental areas from E. Africa to Fiji, n. to S. Japan, s. to Queensland; Ulithi in Micronesia.

Plectranthias nanus Randall, 1980   Fig. 3
Pigmy basslet
SL: to 40 mm (1.6 in); D X, 13-15(14-15); A III, 6-8(7); P 14-16(14-15); LLp 16-22; GR 4-7+11-14; depth 2.9-3.6.
This secretive little species is known from coral or rubble habitats of deep channels and exposed reefs at depths of 3 to 57 m.
West-central Pacific: primarily insular areas from Cocos-Keeling and Christmas Is., to the Hawaiian, Line, and Pitcairn Is.; throughout Micronesia.

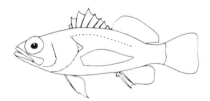

Fig. 3. *Plectranthias nanus*.

Plectranthias winniensis (Tyler, 1966)
SL: to 40 mm (1.6 in); D X, 16-17; AIII, 7; P 16-18(17); LL incomplete, LP 14-20; GR 4-6+11-15; depth 3.0-3.4.
This small cryptic species differs from the preceding species in color pattern as well as certain counts. In life it is a mottled orange anteriorly, blotched with red posteriorly which forms diagonal bars on the lower sides posteriorly. All specimens have been collected with ichthyocides along outer reef slopes at depths of 23 to 58 m.
Indo-Pacific: Red Sea, Seychelles, Mauritius, and Hawaiian, Tuamotu, Austral, Pitcairn, and Marshall Is.

Subfamily Epinephelinae (Groupers)

This subfamily includes large-mouthed, robust-bodied bottom dwellers ranging in length from several centimeters to 3 meters. They inhabit a wide range of habitats from the shoreline to depths of 200 m or more. They are carnivores of crustaceans and fishes, and will readily take a baited hook. Species of *Cephalopholis* and *Epinephelus*, and probably the remaining genera are sequential hermaphrodites, maturing first as females, then changing to males. Small species may reach maturity in as little as a year, and large ones may take several years. Groupers weighing over 50 kg (110 lb) must certainly be decades old. Spawning in groupers is typically seasonal and synchronized by moon phase. In certain areas, some species migrate from miles around to congregate at favored spawning sites. Eggs are small (<1mm) and pelagic. The planktonic larval stage lasts up to several weeks in the widespread species. Some of the large species, particularly the piscivores, are frequently ciguatoxic in certain areas. Their voracious appetites, curiosity, and life histories combine to render large species highly vulnerable to depletion in heavily fished areas. Once the larger individuals of a reef are harvested to the point where only small or immature females remain, the reproductive potential of the population may be lost and new stocks must depend on recruitment or migration from less exploited areas. Large species are thus rare or absent from heavily fished islands such as Guam, but are conspicuous elements of lightly fished areas. At least 43 species in 9 genera occur in Micronesia. The following Micronesian species are confined to deep water and are not considered further: *Cephalopholis analis, C. igarashiensis, Epinephelus morrhua, E. retouti, E. septemfasciatus,* and *Saloptia powelli.* Pectoral counts exclude the rudimentary upper ray which is often only visible by dissection, longitudinal scale rows are counted immediately above the lateral line, and gill raker counts include all countable elements, except intercalary rakers. (Lit.: Morgans, 1982; Randall, 1987; Randall and Hoese, 1986).

Key to Micronesian genera of Epinephelinae:

1a. D VII-VIII, 10-11; lower edge of preopercle with 3 or 4 large, antrorse spines..2
1b. D IX-XI; lower edge of preopercle without large antrorse spines (except *E. septemfasciatus* with 1 to 4 moderate spines)..3
2a. Large canine teeth on edge of lower jaw.....***Plectropomus***
2b. No large canine teeth on edge of lower jaw (below 100 m)...***Saloptia***
3a. Rear nostril a long vertical slit; head profile strongly concave; D X...***Cromileptes***
3b. Rear nostril round or oblong, head profile straight or convex (slightly concave in *C. sonnerati*); D IX-XI......4
4a. C lunate, lobes produced in adults; GR all rudimentary...
....***Variola***
4b. C truncate, emarginate, or rounded; GR not all rudimentary...5
5a. Palatine teeth absent; body elongate, the depth 3.3-3.7 in SL...***Anyperodon***
5b. Palatine teeth present; body depth 2.1-3.7 (rarely > 3.3) in SL...6
6a. Body depth 2.1-2.5 in SL; P assymetric, the 5th or 6th rays longest; C truncate; D IX.................***Aethaloperca***
6b. Body depth 2.3-3.6 in SL (except 2.0-2.3 in *C. igarashiensis*); P rounded, the middle rays longest; C emarginate to rounded, truncate in a few species; D IX or XI...7
7a. D IX...8
7b. D XI...***Epinephelus***
8a. C truncate to slightly emarginate; head small, its length 2.8-3.2 in SL...***Gracila***
8b. C rounded (truncate in *polleni* and *igarashiensis*); head larger, 2.3-2.8 in SL.............................***Cephalopholis***

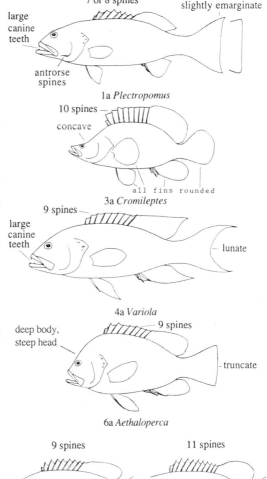

7 or 8 spines

truncate to slightly emarginate

large canine teeth

antrorse spines

1a *Plectropomus*

10 spines

concave

all fins rounded

3a *Cromileptes*

9 spines

large canine teeth

lunate

4a *Variola*

9 spines

deep body, steep head

truncate

6a *Aethaloperca*

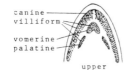

canine
villiform

vomerine
palatine

upper   5b

lower

canine
or
villiform

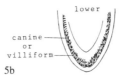

9 spines

7a *Gracila; Cephalopholis*

11 spines

7b *Epinephelus*

Aethaloperca rogaa (Forsskål, 1775)   Pl. 29D
Redmouth grouper

SL: to 50 cm (19.7 in); Wt.: to 2.1 kg (4.6 lb); D IX, 17-(18); A III, 8-(9); P 17-(18); LP 48-55; LR 95-97; GR 9-12+15-16.

The relatively deep body and truncate tail as well as color pattern readily distinguish this species from all other Micronesian groupers. The inside of this grouper's mouth ranges from light pink to crimson. Juveniles have a white border on the caudal fin and some adults may have a broad white band extending from the belly to half way up each side. *A. rogaa* prefers coral rich areas characterized by caves and crevices and clear water in the depth range of 1 to 54 m. It feeds on fishes and crustaceans. In East Africa it matures at 34 cm and spawns the year round. It is relatively common on certain current-swept reefs of southwestern Belau, but rare elsewhere in Micronesia.

Indo-Pacific: Red Sea to Kiribati and Vanuatu, n. to s. Japan, s. to the Great Barrier Reef; Belau, Kapingamarangi, and the n. Marianas (1 specimen) in Micronesia.

Anyperodon leucogrammicus (Valenciennes, 1828)
White-lined grouper   Pl. 29E,F

SL: to 41 cm (16.1 in); D XI, 14-16; A III, 8-9; P 15-17; LP 63-71; LR 120-122; GR 8-10+16-17.

The absence of palatine teeth and unique color pattern distinguish *Anyperodon* from *Epinephelus*. Juveniles and subadults are characterized by three to five thin white longitudinal stripes on their sides. In certain areas small juveniles are aggressive mimics of females of the similarly colored wrasses *Halichoeres melanurus*, *H. purpurascens*, and *H. richmondi*. Prospective prey may mistake the grouper for the harmless microcarnivorous wrasses. This grouper is fairly secretive, preferring areas of rich coral cover and clear water on both lagoon and seaward reefs at depths of 5 to 50 m. It feeds on fishes and probably on crustaceans. It is relatively common on lagoon patch reefs of Enewetak Atoll, but uncommon in most other areas of Micronesia.

Indo-Pacific: Red Sea to the Line Is., n. to the Ryukyus, s. to New Caledonia and Samoa; Belau to e. Carolines and Marshalls in Micronesia.

Cephalopholis argus (Schneider, 1801)   Pl. 30A,B
Peacock grouper; Blue-spotted grouper

SL: to 42 cm (16.4 in); D IX, 15-17(16); A III, 9; P 16-18 (17); LP 46-51; LR 95-110; GR 9-11+17-19.

The combination of 9 dorsal spines and rounded tails (except truncate in *C. polleni* and nearly truncate in the deepwater *C. igarashiensis*) distinguish Micronesian species of *Cephalopholis* from all other Micronesian groupers. The peacock grouper occurs on both lagoon and seaward reefs at depths of 1 to at least 40 m, particularly in areas of rich coral growth and clear water. The brilliantly hued juveniles seem to prefer shallow, protected coral thickets. Adults may occur in pairs or in small groups. They feed at night as well as during the day, primarily on small fishes and to a lesser extent on crustaceans. Off east Africa, females ripen at about 22 cm. Although common throughout most of its range, the peacock grouper is becoming scarce on most of the heavily fished reefs of Guam.

Indo-Pacific: Red Sea to Ducie and the Marquesas, n. to s. Japan, s. to Lord Howe and Rapa Is.; throughout Micronesia; introduced to the Hawaiian Is.

Cephalopholis boenak (Bloch, 1790)   Pl. 30C
Brownbarred grouper
(*C. pachycentron* Masuda et al., 1984)

SL: to 17 cm (6.7 in); D IX, 15-17; A III, 8; P 16-18; LP 47-51; LR 86-100; GR 7-8+14-17.

This small grouper inhabits rocky and coral rich areas of sheltered, often turbid regions of lagoon reefs at depths of 1 to 20m. It somewhat more secretive than other *Cephalopholis* and feeds primarily on crustaceans.

Indo-west Pacific: E. Africa to Vanuatu, n. to s. Japan, s. to Queensland; Belau in Micronesia.

Cephalopholis leopardus (Lacepède, 1802)
Leopard grouper   Pl. 30D

SL: to 20 cm (7.9 in); D IX, 14-15; A III, (9)-10; P 16-18; LP 46-53; LR 79-90; GR 7-8+14-16.

Some color phases of the leopard grouper closely resemble that of *C. urodeta*, but always bear the distinctive dark saddle on the caudal peduncle. This small grouper inhabits lagoon pinnacles, channels, and outer reef slopes in areas of rich coral growth at depths of 3 to over 20 m. It is generally solitary and more secretive than *C. urodeta* and does not seem to be particularly common anywhere in Micronesia.

Indo-Pacific: E. Africa to the Line and Tuamotu Is., n. to the Yaeyamas, s. to Samoa; throughout Micronesia.

Cephalopholis miniata (Forsskål, 1775)   Pl. 30E
Coral grouper

SL: to 31 cm (12.2 in); D IX, 14-(15); A III, 9; P 17-(18); LP 47-54; LR 99-115; GR 7-8+14-16.

This gorgeous grouper is the only Micronesian *Cephalopholis* with relatively large, round, evenly spaced blue spots on a red background. The coral grouper typically inhabits channels and outer reef slopes in areas of rich coral growth and clear water at depths of 3 to 150 m or more. It occurs solitarily or in small groups. It is quite common on the leeward barrier reefs of Belau and the Carolines, but rare in the Marianas.

Indo-Pacific: Red Sea to the Line Is., n. to s. Japan, s. to Lord Howe Is.; throughout Micronesia.

Cephalopholis polleni (Bleeker, 1868)   Pl. 31A
Harlequin grouper
(*Gracila polleni*)

SL: to 30 cm (11.7 in); D IX, 15; A III, 9; P 17-19; LP 65-75; LR 111; GR 7-8+14-16.

This gorgeous little grouper inhabits caves and crevices of deep dropoffs at depths of 27 to 120 m. It seems to have a predilection for swimming upside-down against the roofs of caves or archways. Although uncommon, it may occur in small groups.

Indo-west Pacific: Comores to the Line Is., n. to the Ryukyus, s. to Christmas Is. and New Britain; Guam and Belau in Micronesia.

Cephalopholis sexmaculata (Rüppell, 1830)
Cave grouper; Six-banded grouper   Pl. 31B

SL: to 38 cm (15 in); D IX, 14-16; A III, 9; P 16-18(17); LP 49-56; LR 99-109; GR 7-8+14-17.

Although sometimes confused with *C. miniata*, *C. sexmaculata* has smaller blue spots (which often form streaks on the head) on a more somber orange body with up to six dusky bars. This species is relatively common but secretive, inhabiting caves and crevices of steep outer reef slopes from as little as 6 to 137 m. It may occur solitarily or in small groups. The cleaner shrimp *Periclimenes elegans* may occasionally be seen on its head.

Indo-Pacific: Red Sea to the Marquesas and Tuamotus, n. to s. Japan, s. to Lord Howe Is.; throughout Micronesia.

Cephalopholis sonnerati (Valenciennes, 1828)
Tomato grouper   Pl. 31C; Fig. 4b

SL: to 47 cm (18.5 in); 3.4 kg (5.5 lb); D IX, 14-16(15); A III, 9; P 18-20(19); LP 66-67; LR 115-140; GR 7-10+14-16.
This colorful grouper inhabits deep lagoon reefs and steep outer reef slopes at depths of 12 to 150 m. It is uncommon in less than 30 m, but shows up regularly in catches of bottom fish. It feeds on small fishes and crustaceans including shrimps, crabs, and stomatopods. Off East Africa females mature at 28 cm, males at 34 cm (suggesting sex-reversal), and spawning coincides with the April-May and October rainy seasons.

Indo-Pacific: E. Africa to Samoa, n. to s. Japan, s. to Queensland and Tonga; throughout Micronesia.

Cephalopholis spiloparaea (Valenciennes, 1828)
Orange-red pigmy grouper   Pl. 31D

(*C. aurantius*, Masuda et al., 1984)
SL: to 19 cm (7.4 in); D IX, (15)-16; A III, (9)-10; P 17-19(17-18); LP 48-53; LR 87-100; GR 7-8+14-16.
The color of this little grouper may range from a dull orange to a deep maroon or crimson. It is the deep water counterpart of *C. urodeta*, inhabiting steep outer reef slopes at depths of 16 to at least 108 m. It is rare in less than 30m, but quite common deeper.

Indo-Pacific: E. Africa to the Pitcairn group, n. to the Ryukyus, s. to New Caledonia and Rapa; throughout Micronesia.

Cephalopholis urodeta (Bloch & Schneider, 1801)
Flagtail grouper   Pl. 31E,F

(*C. urodelus*)
SL: to 19 cm (7.4 in); D IX, 15; A III, 9; P 17-18; LP 54-64; LR 94-107; GR 7-10+14-15.
This small grouper occurs on lagoon and seaward reefs at depths of 1 to at least 36 m. It is particularly common on shallow clearwater seaward reefs at depths of 3 to 15 m. It is generally solitary and feeds on small fishes and crustaceans.

Indo-Pacific: E. Africa to Mangareva, the Marquesas, and Line Is., n. to s. Japan, s. to New Caledonia and Rapa; throughout Micronesia.

Cromileptes altivelis (Valenciennes, 1828)
Pantherfish; Polkadot grouper   Fig. 4a; Pl. 32A

SL: to 70 cm (28 in); D X, 17-19; A III, 10; P 17-18; LP 53-55; LR 110-120; GR 8-10+15-17.
The disproportionately small head and deep body give this grouper an unmistakable profile. Its black polkadots become proportionately smaller and more numerous with age. The pantherfish has been reported from lagoon and outer reef slope habitats in the depth range of 2 to at least 40 m. It feeds on fishes and crustaceans. It is relatively common on continental reefs of the Indo-Australian region where it is a popular export for the aquarium trade, but is relatively rare in Micronesia.

Indo-west Pacific: E. Africa to Vanuatu, n. to s. Japan, s. to New Caledonia; Belau and Guam in Micronesia; a recent record from the Hawaiian Is. is probably the result of an aquarium release.

Epinephelus fasciatus (Forsskål, 1775)   Pl. 32B
Black-tipped grouper

(*E. emoryi*)
SL: to 29 cm (11.4 in); D XI, 15-17(16); A III, 8; P 18-20 (18-19); LP 50-58 & LR 92-125 (Belau to west), LP 61-75 & LR 114-135 (Oceania); GR 6-9+15-18.

This is one of the most common groupers of outer reef slopes at depths below 15 m. In protected bays and lagoons, it may occur as shallow as 4 m and has been fished from as deep as 160 m. It is generally solitary and feeds primarily on crustaceans and fishes, and to a lesser extent on octopods and ophiuroids, by day as well as at night. A similar species, *E. retouti*, has been collected at Belau, and could be expected throughout Micronesia at depths below 80m. It differs from *E. fasciatus* by having a straight rather than convex dorsal head profile, and a truncate rather than rounded or slightly truncate tail. Off East Africa females of *E. fasciatus* mature at 16 cm, males at 17.5 cm, and spawning takes place seasonally prior to the major rainy season.

Indo-Pacific: Red Sea to the Line, Marquesan, and Ducie Is., n. to s. Japan, s. to Lord Howe and the Austral Is.; throughout Micronesia.

Epinephelus caeruleopunctatus (Bloch, 1790)
Snowy grouper   Fig. 4c; Pl. 32C

SL: to 64 cm (25.2 in); D XI, 15-17(16); AIII, 8; P 17-19 (18); LP 51-61; LR 86-106; GR 8-10+15-17.
This uncommon grouper inhabits coral rich areas of deep lagoons, channels and outer reef slopes at depths of 4 to 65 m.
Indo-Pacific: E. Africa to Kiribati, n. to s. Japan, s. to New Caledonia; Belau to e. Carolines and s. Marshalls in Micronesia.

Epinephelus ongus (Bloch, 1790)   Fig. 4d
Wavy-lined grouper

(*E. summana* Schultz, 1953, Masuda et al., 1984)
SL: to 40 cm (15.7 in); D XI, (15)-16; A III, 8; P 15-17 (16); LP 48-53; LR 90-109; GR 8-10+15-17.
In most recent books, this species has been confused with *E. summana*, a Red Sea endemic. Juveniles are black with white polkadots; these become more numerous, smaller in relative size, and coalesce to form a pattern of wavy lines on the sides with increasing age. At all sizes, a black region

underlies and borders the maxillary (rear of upper lip). *E. ongus* occurs primarily on inner coastal and lagoon reefs, even in brackish water, where it frequents ledges and caves at depths of 5 to 25 m.

Indo-Pacific: E. Africa to the Marshalls, n. to the Ryukyus; s. to New Caledonia; Pohnpei and the Marshalls in Micronesia.

Epinephelus socialis (Günther, 1873)   Pl. 32D
Tidepool grouper

SL: to 42 cm (16.5 in); D XI, 14-(15); A III, 8; P 18-(19); LP 65-70; LR 97-111; GR 8-9+16-19.

The tidepool grouper inhabits reef flats and surge pools to a depth of about 3 m. It seems to be more common on atolls than at high islands. It feeds on crabs, particularly grapsids, and on octopuses and fishes.

Pacific plate: Insular areas from the n. Marianas to the Line and Ducie Is., s. to Kiribati, Samoa, and Rapa; n. Marianas and Marshalls in Micronesia.

Epinephelus macrospilos (Bleeker, 1855)   Pl. 33A

SL: to 35 cm (13.8 in): D XI, 16; A III, 8; P 18-(19); LP 50-52; LR 98-102; tot. GR 21-24.

The groupers identified as *E. macrospilos* in the first edition of this book are actually *E. corallicola* (Pl. 32F) and *E. howlandi* (Pl. 32E). The fish in Pl. 33A is provisionally identified as *E. macrospilos*. *E. corallicola* may be separated by its higher LP count (54-63), and *E. howlandi* usually has a lower P count (18), higher GR count (modally 25), and more compressed body than *E. macrospilos*. The status of these species will be clarified in a forthcoming issue of Indo-Pacific Fishes (J. E. Randall, pers. com.). *E. howlandi* occurs throughout Micronesia, *E. corallicola* is at Belau.

Indo-Pacific: Nicobars to the Marshalls, n. to the Ryukyus; Belau and Marshalls in Micronesia.

Epinephelus tauvina (Forsskål, 1775)
Greasy grouper   Pl. 33A,B
(*E. elongatus*)

SL: to 64 cm (25.2 in); D XI, 14-16(14-15); A III, 8; P 18-19; LP 65-74; LR 93-113; GR 8-10+18-20.

In many recent works, this species has been thoroughly confused with the larger spotted species *E. salmoides* as well as with *E. lanceolatus*. The greasy grouper is a much smaller species that more closely resembles some of the "honeycomb" groupers before its fully grown. It occurs primarily in coral rich areas of lagoon and seaward reefs at depths of 1 to at least 46 m. It feeds primarily on fishes, to a lesser extent on crustaceans, and may occasionally be ciguatoxic. It is solitary and fairly common in lightly fished areas.

Indo-Pacific: Red Sea to the Marquesas and Ducie, n. to s. Japan, s. to New Caledonia and Rapa; throughout Micronesia.

Epinephelus miliaris (Valenciennes, 1830)   Fig. 4h

SL: to 45 cm (in); D XI, 16-18; A III, 17-18; LP 48-51; LR 94-108; GR 8-9+15-16; depth 2.9-3.2.

This species is unique among Micronesian groupers by having a honeycomb pattern of large spots on the soft-rayed portions of the fins and a very fine pattern of small close-set spots on the spinous portions of the fins and on the body. It is reported from the depth range of 1 to 90 m, but is apparently rare in Micronesia.

Indo-Pacific: E. Africa to the Gilbert and Samoan Is., n. to the Ryukyus; Belau and Yap in Micronesia.

Epinephelus maculatus (Bloch, 1790)   Pl. 33C
Highfin grouper
(*E. medurensis*)

SL: to 45 cm (17.7 in); D XI, 15-17(16); A III, 8; P 17-(18); LP 48-51; LR 103-120; GR 8-10+15-17.

This grouper possesses a somewhat elevated spinous dorsal fin and is particularly colorful as a juvenile with large white blotches on a tan background punctuated by numerous black spots. Large individuals resemble the hexagon grouper, but the spots are more evenly arranged. Juveniles may occur in shallow coral rubble, while adults occur mainly around isolated coral heads of lagoon or seaward reefs to depths of 82 m. *E. maculatus* feeds primarily on sand dwelling fishes and crustaceans and occasionally on octopuses. It is relatively uncommon and may be ciguatoxic in certain areas.

West-central Pacific: S. China Sea to Samoa, n. to s. Japan, s. to Lord Howe Is.; throughout Micronesia.

Epinephelus chlorostigma (Valenciennes, 1828)
Brown-spotted grouper

SL: to 60 cm (23.6 in); D XI, 16-18(17); A III, 8; P 17-19 (17-18); LP 49-53; LR 96-119; GR 8-10+15-18.

This species resembles the adult of *E. maculatus*, but has much smaller and more closely packed spots and a more emarginate caudal fin. It is reported to occur over a wide range of habitats, including seagrass beds and outer reef slopes in the depth range of 4 to 280 m.

Indo-west Pacific: E. Africa to Rotuma, n. to s. Japan, s. to New Caledonia; Belau to Kosrae in Micronesia.

The "honeycomb" complex:

This complex consists of five or more small (<30 cm SL) closely related species that bear a pattern of closely packed hexagonal brown spots. In all of them the individual spots become proportionately smaller and more closely packed with age. In addition, various behaviorally induced patterns of light and dark blotches, bars, or diagonal bands may be superimposed over the constant background of brown hexagons. None of them seem to be easily separable meristically, but each possesses distinctive elements of coloration that seem to be consistently present. The four Micronesian species may be distinguished as follows:

E. hexagonatus: small but conspicuous triangular white spots on the corners of the brown hexagons of the vertical fins and all of the body except the belly; four to six dark blotches along the dorsal fin base.

E. melanostigma: a single large black blotch along middle of dorsal fin base.

E. spilotoceps: two to four black blotches along dorsal fin base, the first largest, the last one or two absent in

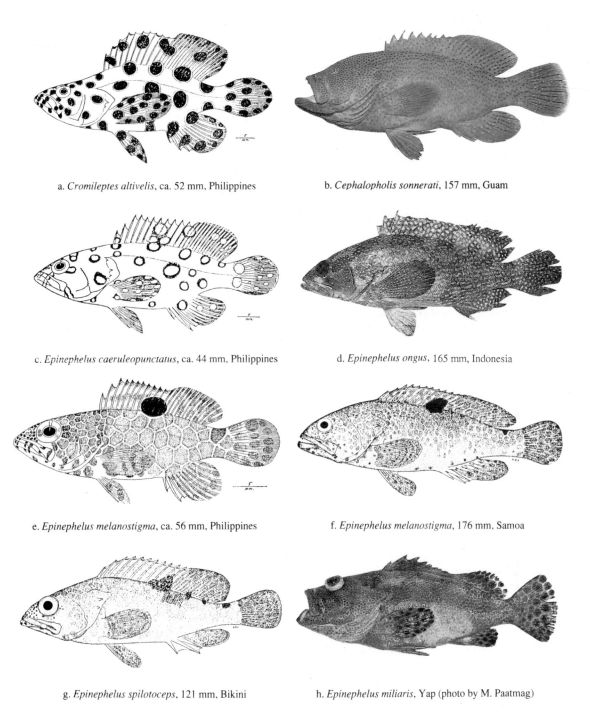

a. *Cromileptes altivelis*, ca. 52 mm, Philippines

b. *Cephalopholis sonnerati*, 157 mm, Guam

c. *Epinephelus caeruleopunctatus*, ca. 44 mm, Philippines

d. *Epinephelus ongus*, 165 mm, Indonesia

e. *Epinephelus melanostigma*, ca. 56 mm, Philippines

f. *Epinephelus melanostigma*, 176 mm, Samoa

g. *Epinephelus spilotoceps*, 121 mm, Bikini

h. *Epinephelus miliaris*, Yap (photo by M. Paatmag)

Fig. 4. Micronesian groupers (a, c, e, after Fowler and Bean, 1930; d, after Gloerfelt-Tarp and Kailola, 1984; f, g, after D. B. Schultz in Schultz et al., 1953).

juveniles; small conspicuous dark spots on snout and sometimes between or below the eyes.

E. merra: none of the above characteristics; often a series of about five darker diagonal bands, each two to five hexagons wide, superimposed on sides and radiating from eye; hexagons on sides may coalesce into short rows.

Two larger species may closely resemble the "honeycomb" groupers at some stage in their lives. They may be distinguished as follows:

E. maculatus: brown spots evenly distributed and packed into hexagonal shapes only on adults which are generally larger (>25 cm); front portion of spinous dorsal fin about 50% taller at all sizes.

E. tauvina: hexagonal spots only on soft dorsal, anal, and caudal fins and on posterior portion of body of individuals <30 cm; body relatively elongate.

Epinephelus hexagonatus (Schneider, 1801)
Hexagon grouper   Pl. 33D

SL: to 29 cm (11.4 in); D XI, 15-(16); A III, 8; P (18)-19; LP 61-68; LR 93-109; GR 7-9+16-19.
This small well-camouflaged grouper is common on outer reef flats and clear lagoon areas as well as seaward reefs to depths of 6 m or more. It is solitary and feeds primarily on fishes and crustaceans by day or night.
Indo-Pacific: E. Africa to the Line, Marquesan, and Gambier Is., n. to the Ryukyus, s. to New Caledonia and Rapa; throughout Micronesia.

Epinephelus melanostigma Schultz, 1953
Blackspot honeycomb grouper   Fig. 4e,f

SL: to 30 cm (11.8 in); D XI, 14-16(15); A III, 8; P 17-19 (18); LP 56-68; LR 83-98; GR 7-10+17-19.
This honeycomb grouper is an uncommon resident of shallow lagoon and seaward reefs. Information on it is sparse due in part to confusion with *E. hexagonatus*.
Indo-Pacific: E. Africa to the Gambier and Line Is., n. to s. Japan, s. to Lord Howe Is.; Belau to e. Carolines and Marshalls in Micronesia.

Epinephelus merra Bloch, 1790   Pl. 33E
Honeycomb grouper

SL: to 22.5 cm (8.9 in); D XI, 15-17(16); A III, 8; P 16-18; LP 48-52; LR 100-114; GR 6-8+14-16.
The honeycomb grouper is a common resident of shallow lagoon and semi-protected seaward reefs that occasionally occurs as deep as 50 m. Juveniles often occur in thickets of staghorn *Acropora* corals. *E. merra* feeds primarily on fishes and crustaceans, tending to feed more heavily on fishes as it grows.
Indo-Pacific: E. Africa to the Line and Gambier Is., n. to s. Japan, s. to Rapa and Lord Howe Is.; throughout Micronesia.

Epinephelus spilotoceps Schultz, 1953   Fig. 4g
Foursaddle grouper   Pl. 33F

SL: to 25 cm (9.8 in); D XI, 14-(15); A III, 8; P (18)-19; LP 60-69; LR 86-100; GR 7-8+15-18.
This relatively uncommon grouper inhabits lagoon patch reefs, the upper slopes of channels, and reef margins. Information is sparse due to confusion with *E. hexagonatus*.
Indo-Pacific: E. Africa to the Line Is., s. to Scott Reef; Carolines and Marshalls in Micronesia.

Epinephelus malabaricus (Schneider, 1801)
Malabar grouper   Fig. 5c

(*E. cylindricus* Fourmanior and Laboute, 1976; *E. salmoides* Katayama, 1984; ?*E. abdominalis* Peters, 1855)
SL: to 170 cm (5.6 ft), possibly 200 cm (6.6 ft); Wt.: to 90 kg (198 lb), possibly >136 kg (300 lb); D XI, 14-16(15); A III, 8; P 18-20(19); LP 54-64; LR 102-117; GR 8-11+15-18.
Considerable confusion has surrounded the identity of this species. Small individuals closely resemble *E. tauvina* and *E. suillus*; reports of giant individuals of those species may refer to either this species or *E. lanceolatus*. In Belau, individuals of about 40 kg or more occur along the edges of sandy channels of the outer reef slope. They are quite wary and difficult to approach. In New Caledonia, this species gathers in groups of 100 or more in channels at depths of 12 to 30 m to spawn during December and January.
Indo-west Pacific: Red Sea to Fiji, s. to New Caledonia, n. to the Ryukyus; Belau in Micronesia.

Epinephelus fuscoguttatus (Forsskål, 1775)
Blotchy grouper   Pl. 34A; Fig. 5a

SL: to 89 cm (35 in); Wt.: to > 15.4 kg (34 lb); D XI, (14)-15; A III, 8; P 18-20(19); LP 52-58; LR 102-115; GR 10-12+18-21.
This species closely resembles the marbled grouper, *E. microdon*, but differs by having more pectoral rays (18-19 vs 16-17) and lower limb gill rakers (19-21 vs 16-17). It also tends to be a lighter, more yellowish brown in coloration and reaches a larger size. *E. fuscoguttatus* inhabits lagoon pinnacles, channels, and outer reef slopes at depths of 1 to 60 m, generally in areas of rich coral growth and clear water. It feeds on fishes, crabs, and cephalopods. In some areas it may be ciguatoxic. It is relatively uncommon and extremely wary.
Indo-Pacific: Red Sea to the Line Is., n. to the Ryukyus, s. to New Caledonia and Samoa; throughout Micronesia.

Epinephelus polyphekadion (Bleeker, 1849)
Marbled grouper   Pl. 34B; Fig. 5b

(*E. horridus*; *E. microdon*; *E. fuscoguttatus* Schultz, in part)
SL: to 61 cm (24 in); D XI, 14-15; A III, 8; P 16-(17); LP 47-52; LR 95-111; GR 9-10+15-17.
The marbled grouper inhabits lagoon and seaward reefs at depths of 2 to over 46 m, generally in areas of rich coral growth. It is solitary and feeds primarily on fishes and crustaceans, occasionally on cephalopods and gastropods. Although it is one of the most common groupers of unfished reefs in the Marshall Islands, it is uncommon at heavily fished islands such as Guam. It is extremely curious and in areas of little spearfishing can be closely approached or even petted. In the Marshall Islands it is one of the most fre-

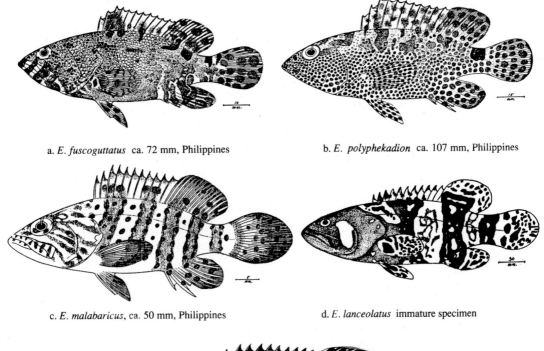

a. *E. fuscoguttatus* ca. 72 mm, Philippines

b. *E. polyphekadion* ca. 107 mm, Philippines

c. *E. malabaricus*, ca. 50 mm, Philippines

d. *E. lanceolatus* immature specimen

e. *E. lanceolatus* immature specimen

Fig. 5. Some Micronesian species of *Epinephelus* (a, b, c, d, after Fowler and Bean, 1930; c, drawing from the *Albatross* Philippine collection, after Schultz et al., 1966).

quently ciguatoxic groupers.

Indo-Pacific: Red Sea to the Line and Gambier Is., n. to s. Japan, s. to Rapa and Lord Howe Is.; throughout Micronesia.

Epinephelus cyanopodus (Richardson, 1846)
Yellowfin grouper (juv.);
Speckled grouper (adult)   Pl. 34C
(*E. hoedti* Masuda et al., 1984; *E. kohleri* Schultz, 1953)
SL: to >75 cm (29.5 in); D XI, 16-17; A III, 8; P 18-20; LP 63-75; LR 130-147; GR 8-11+15-17.
Juveniles are mostly yellow becoming gray with dark spots anteriorly. The spotted gray area increases in extent with in-

creasing size until only the fins remain yellow on individuals of 15-20 cm. *E. cyanopodus* occurs around isolated coral heads of lagoons and seaward reefs at depths of 8 to 150 m or more. It characteristically swims out in the open, often several meters above the bottom, and is somewhat difficult to approach. It is an uncommon solitary species that feeds primarily on sand dwelling fishes and crustaceans such as snake eels and box crabs. Large individuals may be ciguatoxic.

West-central Pacific: s.e. China and Lesser Sunda Is. (Indonesia) to Kiribati, n. to the Ryukyus and Bonins, s. to Lord Howe Is.; Marshalls and e. Carolines in Micronesia; replaced by *E. flavocaeruleus* in the Indian Ocean.

Epinephelus lanceolatus (Bloch, 1790)
Giant grouper
Pl. 34E; Fig. 5d,e

(*Promicrops lanceolatus*)

SL: to ca. 260 cm (8.5 ft; 300 cm TL (9.8 ft); Wt.: to >400 kg (882 lb); D XI, 14-16(15); A III, 8; P 18-19; LP 53-67; LR 89-110; GR 9-10+14-16

This is the only *Epinephelus* in which the dorsal fin spines of large individuals progressively increase in size from front to back. *E. lanceolatus* is the largest of all coral reef dwelling bony fishes. As a small juvenile it has an unmistakable pattern of bold yellow blotches on a dark background; as it grows, the yellow becomes dull and speckled with brown and the brown becomes speckled with yellow, until the entire fish becomes mottled in dull shades of light and dark brown at a size of 100 cm or more. *E. lanceolatus* is a solitary inhabitant of lagoon and seaward reefs at depths of a few to at least 50 m. Large individuals often have a "home" cave or wreck that they frequent. *E. lanceolatus* feeds on crustaceans, particularly spiny lobsters, fishes, small sea turtles, and even small sharks, all of which are swallowed whole. There are unconfirmed reports of pearl divers being swallowed as well. Since a large area of reef is required to maintain such a large predator, its numbers are always low, even in unexploited areas. In many places, it has all but disappeared, due primarily to the thoughtless efforts of a few overzealous spearfishermen. Large individuals may be ciguatoxic, and their flesh is of inferior quality, so there is little justification for their slaughter. Since they take decades to grow, and juveniles are rare to begin with, there is little chance of giant individuals reappearing in unprotected areas.

Indo-Pacific: Red Sea to the Hawaiian, Line, and Pitcairn Is., n. to s. Japan, s. to New Caledonia; throughout Micronesia.

Gracila albomarginata (Fowler & Bean, 1930)
White-margined grouper
Pl. 34D

SL: to 36 cm (14.2 in); D IX, 14-(15); A III, 9; P 18-(19); LP 67-73; LR 101-117; GR 8-9+15-17.

Gracila differs from all shallow water Micronesian *Cephalopholis* (except *C. polleni*) by having a truncate rather than rounded tail. This grouper's color pattern is unmistakable, but fades rapidly upon death or can be "turned off" when the fish is alarmed. *G. albomarginata* inhabits steep outer reef slopes and channels adjacent to deep water at depths of 6 to 120 m. It has the habit of hovering or swimming a few meters off the bottom. Although usually solitary, groups of three or four have been observed. It is rather uncommon at Belau and the Carolines, and quite rare in the Marianas.

Indo-Pacific: E. Africa to the Marquesas and Tuamotus, n. to the Ryukyus, s. to New Caledonia; throughout Micronesia.

Plectropomus areolatus (Rüppell, 1830)
Pl. 35A
Squaretail grouper; Squaretail coral trout

(*P. truncatus*)

SL: to 60 cm (23.6 in); D VIII, 11; A III, 8; P 15-16; LP 83-97; LR 107-128; GR 0-2+2-7.

Species of *Plectropomus* differ from all other groupers by the combination of 8 dorsal spines, antrorse spines on the lower margin of the preopercle, and conspicuous canine teeth on the sides of the lower jaw. They feed almost exclusively on fishes, some of which may be surprisingly large. Large individuals of all Micronesian species may be ciguatoxic in certain areas. This relatively small *Plectropomus* is distinguished by its truncate tail with a narrow white posterior margin, and relatively large, crowded, dark-edged circular blue spots covering its body and fins. It inhabits both lagoon and seaward reefs at depths of 2 to over 20 m. For a few days before new moon in May, large numbers gather in the seaward end of Ulong Channel, Belau to spawn. At this time, males may display light bodies with about five irregular dark saddles and dark dorsal and anal fins.

Indo-Pacific: Red Sea to the Phoenix Is. and Samoa, n. to the Ryukyus, s. to Rowley Shoals and the Great Barrier Reef; throughout Micronesia.

Plectropomus laevis (Lacepède, 1801)
Pl. 35B,C,D
Saddleback grouper; Giant coral trout

(*P. melanoleucus*)

SL: >100 cm (39.4 in); Wt.: to 22 kg (48.5 lb); D VIII, 11; A III, 8; P 16-18(17); LP 92-115; LR 123-153; GR 1-3+4-10.

The saddleback grouper occurs in two basic color phases: the saddleback phase and a blue spotted reddish-brown phase with fainter dark saddles. In some recent books the reddish-brown phase is incorrectly identified as *P. leopardus*. The saddleback phase seems to be characteristic of juveniles and young adults. Generally at a length of about 40 to 60 cm, the white and yellow portions of the body and fins begin to assume a reddish cast, but there is a great deal of variability at all but the largest sizes. The number and intensity of blue spots may be behaviorly controlled. *P. laevis* inhabits lagoon and seaward reefs in areas of rich coral growth at depths of 4 to at least 90 m. Juveniles seem to be more frequently encountered in relatively turbid areas of deep lagoons; adults prefer clearer lagoon and outer reef areas. Large adults sometimes occur in pairs. This grouper is a voracious piscivore: in one study, stomachs of individuals of 64 to 79 cm contained relatively large fishes such as parrotfishes, large wrasses, surgeonfishes, and other groupers ranging in length from 15 to 31 cm! Not surprisingly *P. laevis* is one of the most notorious of ciguatera offenders throughout much of Oceania. It may be moderately common in lightly fished areas, but is rare around heavily fished islands such as Guam.

Indo-Pacific: E. Africa to Mangareva, n. to the Ryukyus, s. to the s. Great Barrier Reef, New Caledonia, and Rapa; throughout Micronesia.

Plectropomus leopardus (Lacepède, 1802)
Leopard coral trout
Pl. 35E

SL: to 68 cm (26.8 in); D VIII, 11; A III, 8; P 14-17(16); LP 89-99; LR 112-127; GR 1-3+6-10.

This the only *Plectropomus* with a nearly complete blue ring around each eye. Its blue spots are also smaller and more numerous than those of the other species. At Belau, *P. leopardus* inhabits coral rich areas of lagoon reefs. Elsewhere it has been reported in the depth range of 3 to 100 m. At night, it sleeps under ledges while assuming a dappled pattern of pink blotches. It appears to be less prone to develop ciguatera than the larger species of *Plectropomus*.

West Pacific: Indochina to Fiji, n. to s. Japan. s. to the Abrolhos Is., s. Queensland, and New Caledonia; Belau and Mortlocks (s. of Truk) in Micronesia.

Plectropomus oligacanthus Bleeker, 1854
Blue-lined coral trout   Pl. 35F

SL: to 65 cm (25.6 in); D VIII, 11; A III, 8; P 14-16(15); LP 86-96; LR 115-126; GR 1-3+7-9.

This uncommon *Plectropomus* is characterized by blue wavy lines on the head and blue vertical lines on the sides.

West-central Pacific: e. Java to the Solomons, n. to the Philippines, s. to Scott Reef and the n. Great Barrier Reef; Belau, Truk, and s. Marshalls in Micronesia.

Variola albimarginata Baissac, 1956   Pl. 36A
Whitemargin lyretail grouper

SL: to 45 cm (17.8 in); D IX, 14; A III, 8; P 18-19; LP 68-75; LR 110-130; GR 7-9+13-16.

The two species of *Variola* are the only Micronesian groupers with lunate tails. *V. albimarginata* is relatively rare and can be distinguished from *V. louti* by the thin white submarginal band on its tail. It inhabits outer reef slopes and coastal reefs at depths of 12 to 90 m.

Indo-west Pacific: E. Africa to Samoa, n. to s. Japan, s. to Indonesia and Vanuatu; Guam in Micronesia.

Variola louti (Forsskål, 1775)   Pl. 36B,C
Lyretail grouper; lyretail coral trout

SL: to 56 cm (22 in); D IX, 13-15(14); A III, 8; P 16-19; LP 64-78; LR 113-135; GR 7-10+15-19.

This gorgeous grouper inhabits deep lagoon pinnacles, channels, and seaward reefs at depths of 4 to at least 150 m. Adults seem to prefer areas of rich coral growth below 15m; but juveniles may occur in as little as 4m. Its diet consists primarily of fishes, including relatively large spiny or venemous species such as squirrelfishes and scorpionfishes, and to a lesser extent on crabs or spiny lobsters. Large individuals may be ciguatoxic in certain areas.

Indo-Pacific: Red Sea to the Marquesas and Pitcairn group, n. to s. Japan, s. to New Caledonia and Rapa; throughout Micronesia.

Genus *Liopropoma* (Swissguard basslets)

Members of this genus are small, secretive carnivores of motile invertebrates. They have D VIII spines but in most, the first is embedded and the seventh is isolated and also embedded. Western Atlantic species appear to be secondary gonochorists, that is, their sex is predetermined although their gonad morphology reveals a hermaphroditic ancestry. An additional species not described below, *L. lunulatum*, occurs in deeper reef waters. GR counts include rudiments.

Liopropoma mitratum Lubbock & Randall, 1978
SL: to 72 mm (2.8 in); D VI+I+I, 11-(12); A III, 8; P 13-15(14); LL 45-48; GR 5-7+12-14; depth 3.2-4.2.

This species and *L. pallidum* are uniformly reddish brown to

reddish gray, becoming redder posteriorly. *L. mitratum* differs from *L. pallidum* by having 14 rather than 15-16 P rays and 19-30 rather than 8-13 preopercular serrae. All Micronesian species inhabit caves and crevices and are seldom seen by divers. *L. mitratum* has been collected at depths of 3 to 46 m, usually below 15 m.

Indo-Pacific: Red Sea to the Tuamotus, n. to the Philippines, s. to the Great Barrier Reef; Belau to Pohnpei in Micronesia.

Liopropoma multilineatum Randall & Taylor, 1988
SL: to 65 mm (2.6 in); D VI+I+I, 11-(12); A III, 8; P 13-(14); LL 46-47; GR 5-6+13-14; depth 3.0-3.5.

This species closely resembles *L. tonstrinum*, but differs by having numerous red pinstripes on its sides, a less pronounced white lateral stripe, and a serrate posterior preopercular margin. It has been collected at depths of 25 to 46 m.

West Pacific: Philippines to Fiji, s. to Rowley Shoals and the Coral Sea; Belau in Micronesia.

Liopropoma pallidum (Fowler, 1938)
Pallid basslet

SL: to 64 mm (2.5 in); D VI+I+I, 11-(12); A III, 8; P 15-16; LL (46)-47; GR 5-6+12-13; depth 3.1-3.5.

This species has been collected from shallow lagoon and seaward reefs at depths of 6 to 40 m.

Pacific Plate: e. Caroline, Mariana, Marshall, Line, Society, Tuamotu, Austral, and Pitcairn Is.

Liopropoma susumi (Jordan & Seale, 1906)
Pinstriped basslet   Fig. 6

(*Ypsigramma brocki*; *Ypsigramma lineata*)

SL: to 76 mm (3.0 in); D VI+I+I, 11-(12); A III, 8; P (15)-16; LL 44-47; GR 4-6+13-15; depth 3.3-3.7.

This striped species has been collected from lagoon coral heads and seaward reefs at depths of 2 to 34 m.

Indo-Pacific: Red Sea to the Line Is. and Samoa, n. to the Ryukyus, s. to Reunion and New Caledonia; Belau to the e. Carolines and Marshalls in Micronesia.

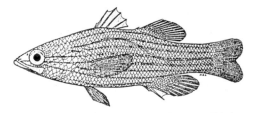

Fig. 6. *L. susumi*, 65 mm (after D. B. Schultz *in* Schultz et al., 1953).

Liopropoma tonstrinum Randall & Taylor, 1988
Redstriped basslet   Pl. 36D

SL: to 65 mm (2.6 in); DVI+I+I, 12; AIII, 8; P 14; LL 46-47; GR 5-6+13-15; depth 3.5-3.7.

This colorful basslet has been collected from crevices and caves at depths of 11 to 50 m.

West-central Pacific: Christmas Is., Indian Ocean, Fiji, Samoa, and throughout Micronesia.

GRAMMISTIDAE (SOAPFISHES)

The soapfishes are small grouper-like fishes that produce a toxic mucus which renders them unpalatable to predatory fishes. When frightened, some species can produce enough mucus to kill all the inhabitants of an aquarium except other soapfishes of the same species. Some authors place *Pseudogramma* in a separate family, Pseudogrammatidae. Six species are known from Micronesia.

Belonoperca chabanaudi Fowler & Bean,1930
Chabanaud's soapfish Pl. 36E
SL: to 120 mm (4.7 in); D VIII-IX, 10; A II, 8; P 13-15; LR 69-76; GR 6-8+13-15.
The bright yellow saddle on the caudal peduncle and black ocellus on the dorsal fin are striking on this otherwise drab fish. It occurs in small caves and under ledges of outer reef slopes at depths of 4 to 45 m. It is secretive and solitary and has the habit of hovering in the center of its cave. It ventures more out in the open at night.
Indo-Pacific: E. Africa to Samoa, n. to the Ryukyus, s. to New Caledonia; throughout Micronesia.

Grammistes sexlineatus (Thünberg, 1792)
Skunkfish; yellowstriped soapfish Pl. 36G
SL: to 270 mm (10.6 in).D VII, 12-14; A II, 8-9; P 14-18; LR 60-72; GR 1-3+7-9.
The skunkfish inhabits reef flats and shallow lagoon and seaward reefs to a depth of at least 12 m. Near New Caledonia an exceptional individual was once fished from 130 m of water over a depth exceeding 4,000 m! The skunkfish is relatively common but secretive during the day when it is usually seen in a hole or crevice. It is more apt to venture out into the open at night. In makes a fearless and hardy, but voracious aquarium fish that will devour any fish or crustacean it can catch, even ones nearly as large as itself!
Indo-Pacific: Red Sea to the Marquesas and Mangareva, n. to s. Japan, s. to New Caledonia; throughout Micronesia.

Pogonoperca punctata (Valenciennes, 1830)
Spotted soapfish Pl. 36F
SL: to 300 mm (11.8 in); D VII, 12-13; A III, 8; P 14-15; LP 59-70; LR 90-100; GR 1-2+7-8.
This is the largest of the soapfishes. Juveniles are a deep chocolate brown with several large white spots. *P. punctata* is known from Micronesia on the basis of an individual photographed at Kwajalein and a specimen taken at a depth of 120 m off Guam. It is a secretive fish known from outer reef slopes at depths of 25 to 150 m.
Indo-Pacific: Comores to the Line, Marquesan, and Society Is., n. to s. Japan, s. to New Caledonia; Guam and Kwajalein in Micronesia.

Grammistops ocellatus Schultz, 1953
Ocellate soapfish Fig. 1
SL: to 107 mm (4.2 in); D VI-VII, 11-13; A II, 8-9; P 14-15; LP 58-67; LR 82-100; GR 1-2+6-9.

This species is quite secretive and seldom encountered without the use of an ichthyocide. It has been collected from coral heads of lagoon and seaward reefs at depths of 3 to over 15m.
Indo-Pacific: E. Africa to the Society Is., n. to the Ryukyus; throughout Micronesia.

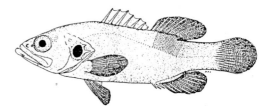

Fig. 1. *Grammistops ocellatus*, 86 mm SL, Bikini (after D. B. Schultz *in* Schultz et al., 1953).

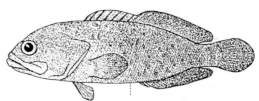

Fig. 2. *Pseudogramma bilinearis*, Phoenix Is. (after A. M. Awl *in* Schultz, 1943).

Pseudogramma bilinearis (Schultz, 1943)
Twolined soapfish Fig. 2
SL: to 96 mm (3.8 in); D VII, 23-24; A III, 19-21; P 15-17; LR 59-71; GR 5-6+11-12=16-18.
This species occurs among corals of wave-washed seaward reefs.
West-central Pacific: Rowley Shoals and Caroline Is. to the Hawaiian, Marquesan, and Tuamotu Is.; throughout Micronesia.

Pseudogramma polyacantha (Bleeker, 1856)
SL: to 86 mm (3.4 in); D VII-VIII, 19-22; A III, 15-18; P 16-17; LR 50-54; GR 6+11-12.
This species occurs among the corals of shallow reef flats and lagoons. It is reported to be abundant in the Marshalls, but is secretive and unlikely to be seen by divers. An additional currently undescribed species of *Pseudogramma* has recently been discovered in the Marshalls.
Indo-Pacific: E. Africa to the Line, Marquesan, and Ducie Is., n. to s. Japan and the Hawaiian Is., s. to Lord Howe Is.; throughout Micronesia.

PLESIOPIDAE (PRETTYFINS; LONGFINS)

Plesiopids are characterized by a disjunct lateral line, preopercle with a double border, and long pelvic fins. The three Micronesian species are secretive by day but venture out at night to feed. Several Australian warm-temperate species are large and spectacularly conspicuous.

Calloplesiops altivelis (Steindachner, 1903)
Comet Pl. 37A

(*C. argus*)

SL: to 108 mm (4.3 in); D XI, 8-10; A III, 10; P 17-20; LP 19-21+9-11; GR 2-4+9.

This beautiful little fish inhabits outer reef slopes at depths of 3 to 45 m. It remains hidden within holes by day, but begins to venture out near sunset. When frightened it may adopt a posture that results in its rear half resembling the head of a young moray eel, *Gymnothorax meleagris*. The comet is a popular aquarium fish but is relatively uncommon in Micronesia.

Indo-Pacific: Red Sea to the Line Is., n. to s. Japan, s. to the s. Great Barrier Reef and Tonga; throughout Micronesia.

Plesiops caeruleolineatus Rüppell, 1835
Red-tipped longfin Fig. 1

(*P. melas*)

SL: to 58 cm (2.3 in); D XI, 7; A III, 8-9; P 21; LP 19+10-13; GR 5+8.

The bright red tips and blue submarginal band on the spinous dorsal fin distinguish this black to brown plesiopid from all other Micronesian species. It is a common, but seldom seen inhabitant of exposed outer reef flats and outer reef slopes to a depth of 23m. It ventures out in the open at night to feed on small crustaceans, fishes, and gastropods.

Indo-Pacific: Red Sea to Samoa, n. to s. Japan, s. to the s. Great Barrier Reef; throughout Micronesia.

Fig. 1. *Plesiops caeruleolineatus*, Guam.

Plesiops corallicola Bleeker, 1853 Pl. 37B
Bluegill longfin

(*P. nigricans* Schultz, 1953)

SL: to 129 mm (5.1 in).

D VII, 7; A III, 8; P 20; LP 17-18+13-14; GR 4-5+7-9=11-14.

This species' coloration can range from a pale grey with black blotches and blue dots to an almost uniformly black except for the ever-present blue ocellus on the edge of its operculum. The bluegill longfin is relatively common on reef flats where it lurks under rocks or in crevices for the small fishes and crustaceans upon which it feeds.

Indo-Pacific: Madagascar to the Line Is., n. to s. Japan, s. to the s. Great Barrier Reef and Tonga; throughout Micronesia.

PSEUDOCHROMIDAE (DOTTYBACKS)

This family consists of small elongate fishes with a long continuous dorsal fin with 1 to 3 spines and 21 to 37 rays, and pelvic fins with a spine and 3 to 5 rays. *Pseudochromis* has a disjunct lateral line; *Pseudoplesiops* lacks one. Species of *Pseudoplesiops* are quite secretive and generally encountered only with the aid of ichthyocides. Many species of *Pseudochromis* are also secretive but the brilliantly colored ones may be quite conspicuous as they hover near shelter. Pseudochromids are carnivores of small crustaceans, polychaete worms, and zooplankton. Females of *Pseudochromis* produce a spherical mass of eggs that is guarded by the male. Pseudochromids are easily maintained in aquaria and the colorful ones make a stunning display once they overcome their shyness. (Lit.: Gill, pers. com.)

Pseudochromis cyanotaenia Bleeker, 1857
Surge dottyback Fig. 1a

(*P. tapienosoma* Schultz, 1953)

SL: to 45 mm (1.8 in); D III, (22)-23; A III, 12-(13); P 17-19(18-19); LP 22-34+5-11; LR 29-40; GR 3-5+10-11=13-16.

This little dottyback is sexually dichromatic: the male is a dirty yellowish anteriorly with a stripe of the same color extending posteriorly along the back into an almost black ground color bearing deep blue irridescent bars, and the female is a dark brown becoming dirty yellowish anteriorly. It is relatively common in the vicinity of holes and crevices of exposed outer reef flats and reef margins to a depth of 4 m, but is seldom noticed due to its secretive habits. It often occurs in pairs and feeds on small crabs, isopods, and copepods.

Indo-Pacific: Maldives and Laccadives to Fiji, n. to the Ryukyus, s. to the Great Barrier Reef; throughout Micronesia.

Pseudochromis fuscus Müller & Troschel, 1849
Dusky dottyback Pl. 37C

(*Pseudochromis aurea*)

SL: to 65 mm (2.6 in); D III, 25-28(26-27); A III, 13-15 (14); P 17-20; LP 23-36+4-13; LR 34-43; GR 5-9+11-15=17-21.

This secretive species lives among corals of lagoon and seaward reefs to a depth of 30 m. It is relatively common in the vicinity of small patches of branching corals on shallow sandy subtidal reef flats and lagoons.

Indo-west Pacific: India to the Solomons, n. to Taiwan, s. to the s. Great Barrier Reef; Belau to the e. Carolines in Micronesia.

Pseudochromis marshallensis (Schultz, 1953)
Marshall Is. Dottyback Pl. 37D

SL: to 65 mm (2.6 in); DIII, 24-26; A III, 11-14(12-13); P 17-19; LP 24-32+6-15; LR 35-39; GR 4-7+11-15=15-22.

P. marshallensis has been collected from both lagoon and seaward reefs to a depth of at least 10 m.

West-central Pacific: Philippines and Taiwan to Vanuatu, s. to nw. Australia and New Caledonia; e. Carolines and Marshalls in Micronesia.

Pseudochromis polynemus Fowler, 1931
Long-finned dottyback Pl. 37E

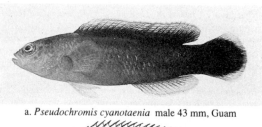

a. *Pseudochromis cyanotaenia* male 43 mm, Guam

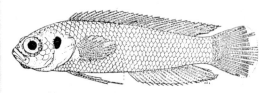

c. *Pseudoplesiops revellei* holotype, 31 mm, Bikini

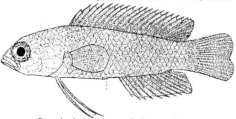

c. *Pseudoplesiops rosae* holotype, Samoa

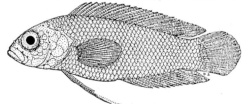

d. *Pseudoplesiops typus* 40 mm, Bikini

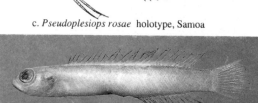

e. *Pseudoplesiops* sp. A, 40 mm, Guam

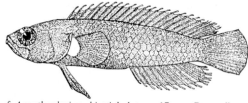

f. *Acanthoplesiops hiatti* holotype, 17 mm, Rongerik

Fig. 1. Micronesian species of *Pseudochromis* and *Pseudoplesiops* (a, c, e, after D. B. Schultz and d, f, after A. M. Awl, *in* Schultz et al., 1953; b, after Fowler, 1931).

SL: to 105 mm (4.1 in); D III, 27; A III, 14; P 18; LP 31-32+15-17; LR 38-39; GR 5+11 (based on holotype only).
This large deep-bodied dottyback occurs among dense coral growth of seaward reefs to depths of 15 m or more.
Indo-Australian: Philippines to the Moluccas and Belau.

Pseudochromis porphyreus
Lubbock & Goldman, 1974   Pl. 37F
Magenta dottyback
SL: to 45 mm (1.8 in); D III, 21-22; A III, 11-12; P 16-18; LP 20-27+0-7; LR 35-40; GR 6-8+13-15=19-23.
This stunning creature stands out like a jewel as it hovers a few centimeters above coral or rubble. It inhabits steep outer reef slopes and outer channel walls at depths of 6 to 65 m. It is quite common off leeward Belau, but relatively uncommon in the eastern Carolines.
West Pacific: Philippines to Samoa, n. to the Ryukyus, s. to the Moluccas and Admiralty Is.; Belau and Carolines in Micronesia.

Pseudochromis tapienosoma Bleeker, 1853
Black-banded dottyback
(*P. melanotaenia*)
SL: to 44 mm (1.7 in) D III, 22; A III, 13; P 17-18; LP 21-25+7-10; GR 4+12.
This small species has a dark brown body and bright yellow fins with a broad black margin on the dorsal fin which continues as a submarginal band around the tail. It inhabits tidepools and lagoons.

West Pacific: Ryukyus s. to Timor; Belau to Pohnpei in Micronesia.

Pseudoplesiops revellei Schultz, 1953   Fig. 1b
Revelle's basslet
SL: to 32 mm (1.3 in); D I, 27-28; A I-III, 17-18; V I, 4; P 17-18; LR 34-38; GR 2-3+9-10=11-13.
This small species has been collected from from lagoon and seaward reefs.
Pacific plate: Marianas, Marshalls, and e. Carolines to the Pitcairn Group.

Pseudoplesiops rosae Schultz, 1953   Fig. 1c
Rose Island basslet
SL: to 26 mm (1.0 in); D I, 22--23; A I, 13-14; V I, 3; P 16-18(16-17); LR 26-29; GR 2-4+7-9=9-12.
This species has been collected from reef margins exposed to wave action and currents to a depth of 10 m.
Indo-Pacific: Maldives to Samoa, n. to the Yaeyamas, s. to nw. Australia and the s. Great Barrier Reef; throughout Micronesia.

Pseudoplesiops typus Bleeker, 1858   Fig. 1d
Hidden basslet
(*P. sargenti*)
SL: to 46 cm (1.8 in); D II, (24)-26; A II-III, 14-16(II, 15); P 16-18; V I, 4; LR 33-39; GR 2-4+9-12=12-16.
This species has been collected from coral heads at depths of 6 to 9 m.

West-central Pacific: Borneo to the Marshall and Solomon Is., n. to the Philippines, s. to nw Australia and Queensland; Marshalls in Micronesia.

Pseudoplesiops sp. A   Fig. 1e
Yellowtail basslet

SL: 40 mm (1.6 in); D 27; A 15; V I, 3; P 18; LL continuous.

This undescribed species is a gorgeous pink anteriorly and yellow posteriorly with clear fin membranes. It has been observed only inside Guam's "Blue Hole" at depths of 24 to 29 m, and collected once. It typically hovers a few centimeters in front of a small hole into which it immediately darts when disturbed.

Guam; possibly widespread in the west-central Pacific.

ACANTHOCLINIDAE (SPINY BASSLETS)

Acanthoclinids differ from the closely related pseudochromids by having more dorsal and anal fin spines and 1 or 2 instead of 3 to 5 pelvic rays. Most of the 10 known species occur in New Zealand, but the 3 species of *Acanthoplesips* occur in the tropical Indo-Pacific, with one in Micronesia. (Lit.: Hardy, 1984).

Acanthoplesiops hiatti Schultz, 1953   Fig. 1f
Hiatt's basslet

SL: to 21 mm (.8 in); D XIX-XXI, 3-5; A VIII-X, 3-5; P 17-18; LP 7-13; ca. GR 2+7; depth at 1st A spine 4.3-4.8. This tiny species has been collected from shallow wave-washed seaward reefs.

West-central Pacific: Philippines, Moluccas, s. Japan, Izus, and Marshalls.

CIRRHITIDAE (HAWKFISHES)

Hawkfishes are small grouper-like fishes characterized by numerous short filaments at the tip of each their 10 dorsal spines, thickened and elongate lower pectoral rays, a single continuous dorsal fin, and continuous lateral line. They derive their common name from their habit of perching on the outermost branches of coral heads or other prominences. All are carnivores of small benthic crustaceans and fishes. The few species studied are protogynous hermaphrodites. Males are territorial and maintain a harem of females. Courtship and spawning occur at dusk or early night throughout the year in the deep tropics, but only during the warmer months in warm temperate areas. Spawning occurs at the apex of a short, rapid paired ascent. The pelagic larval stage probably lasts a few to several weeks. At least 10 species occur in Micronesia. (Lit.: Randall, 1963)

Amblycirrhitus bimacula (Jenkins, 1903)   Pl. 37G
Two-spotted hawkfish

SL: to 67 mm (2.6 in); D X, 12; A III, 6; P 14; LL 40-42;

GR 3-5+11-12.

Unlike most hawkfishes this species is secretive, remaining in or near interstices of rock, coral, or rubble. It is a moderately common, though seldom noticed inhabitant of seaward reefs in areas exposed to moderate surge or currents at depths of 2 to at least 15 m.

Indo-Pacific: E. Africa to Mangareva and the Hawaiian Is., n. to Taiwan; throughout Micronesia.

Cirrhitichthys falco Randall, 1963   Pl. 38A
Falco hawkfish

SL: to ca. 50 mm (2.0 in); D X, 12; A III, 6; P 14; LL 42-45; GR 3-4+10-11.

This colorful hawkfish is a common inhabitant of areas of moderate to rich coral growth of seaward reefs at depths of 4 to at least 46 m. It typically rests at the bases of coral heads rather than in or on them. Current studies indicate that it is haremic and spawns nightly.

West Pacific: Philippines, Scott Reef (?), and Sundas to Samoa, n. to the Ryukyus and Bonins, s. to the s. Great Barrier Reef and New Caledonia; Belau to the e. Carolines and Marianas in Micronesia.

Cirrhitichthys oxycephalus (Bleeker, 1855)
Pixy hawkfish   Pl. 38B,C

SL: to 70 mm (2.8 in); D X, 12-13(12); A III, 6; P 14; LL 41-45; GR 3-5+10-12.

The coloration of this species varies from one of solid dark spots on a light background to one of less conspicuous light-centered spots. *C. oxycephalus* inhabits areas of rich coral growth and clear water of lagoons, channels, or seaward reefs from below the surge zone to depths of at least 40 m. It may rest on, in, or beneath hard or soft corals or other reef growth. Males are territorial and haremic. It is common at Belau and the Carolines, but rare in the Marianas.

Indo-pan-Pacific: Red Sea to Panama, n. to the Marianas, s. to New Caledonia and the Marquesas; Belau to the e. Carolines and Marianas in Micronesia.

Cirrhitus pinnulatus (Bloch &Schneider,1801)
Stocky hawkfish   Pl. 38D

SL: to 230 mm (9.1 in); D X, 11; A III, 6; P 14; LL 39-44; GR 5-7+12-14.

This is the largest Micronesian hawkfish and is often fished for food. It is a common inhabitant of reef fronts and rocky shorelines exposed to moderate to strong surge to depths of about 3 m. It is an ambushing predator that feeds primarily on crabs, but will also take other crustaceans, small fishes, sea urchins or brittle stars.

Indo-Pacific: Red Sea to the Marquesas and Mangareva, n. to s. Japan and the Hawaiian Is., s. to the Kermadec and Rapa Is.; throughout Micronesia.

Neocirrhites armatus Castlenau, 1873   Pl. 38E
Flame hawkfish

SL: to 75 mm (3.0 in); D X, 13; A III, 6-7; P 14; LL 42-45; GR 5+11-12.

This spectacular hawkfish is fairly common along surge-swept reef fronts and submarine terraces to a depth of about

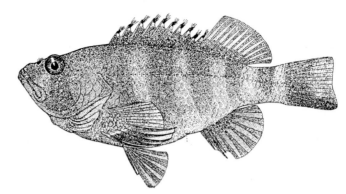

Fig. 1. *Isocirrhitus sexfasciatus*
holotype, 78 mm SL
(after A. M. Awl *in*
Schultz et al., 1953).

11 m. It inhabits heads of the corals *Stylophora mordax*, *Pocillopora elegans*, *P. eydouxi*, or *P. verrucosa* but is fairly secretive and will retreat to the innermost recesses of the coral when approached. It is a highly prized aquarium fish, but requires well-oxygenated water and tends to fade in captivity.
Pacific Plate: Ryukyus to the Line Is. and Mangareva, s. to the Great Barrier reef and Australs; Carolines, Marianas, and Wake Is. in Micronesia.

Oxycirrhites typus Bleeker, 1857   Pl. 38F
Longnose hawkfish
SL: to 84 mm (3.3 in); D X, 13; A III, 7; P 14; LL 51-53; GR 5+12-13.
This distinctive little hawkfish inhabits steep outer reef slopes exposed to strong currents. It lives in large gorgonians and black corals, and in Micronesia at least, it is confined to depths below 30 m. Elsewhere it has been found as shallow as 10 m to at least 100 m. It feeds on small benthic or planktonic crustaceans.
Indo-pan-Pacific: Red Sea to Panama, n. to s. Japan and the Hawaiian Is., s. to New Caledonia; throughout Micronesia.

Isocirrhitus sexfasciatus (Schultz, 1960)
Six-banded hawkfish   Fig. 1
SL: to 78 mm (3.1 in).; D X, 11; A III, 6; P 14; LL 44-45; GR 4-5+12.
This rare hawkfish inhabits the surge zone of the reef margin and reef front.
Pacific plate: Marshalls and Tuamotus.

Paracirrhites arcatus (Cuvier, 1829)   Pl. 39A
Arc-eye hawkfish
SL: to 111 mm (4.4 in); D X, 11, A III, 6; P 14; LL 45-50; GR 4-5+12-13.
This little hawkfish occurs in a variety of color morphs, but always has the distinctive ring extending around and behind the eye. The most common morph in Micronesia is the one shown with the white streak, but others may lack this or have a more olive ground color. The arc-eyed hawkfish occurs on lagoon and seaward reefs at depths of 1 to at least 33 m wherever there are suitable corals. It is perhaps the most common hawkfish inhabiting heads of small branching corals, particularly *Pocillopora* spp., ramose *Acropora* spp., or *Stylophora mordax*. It characteristically perches conspicuously on the outermost branches.

Indo-Pacific: E. Africa to the Hawaiian, Line, and Mangareva Is., n. to s. Japan, s. to New Caledonia and Rapa; throughout Micronesia.

Paracirrhites forsteri (Schneider, 1801)
Freckled hawkfish; Blackside hawkfish
(*P. typee*)   Pl. 39B,C,D
SL: to 172 mm (6.8 in); D X, 11, A III, 6; P 14; LL 45-49; GR 5-6+11-13.
The coloration of the freckled hawkfish changes with growth as well as varies among adults. In Oceania, juveniles are a golden green dorsally and white ventrally; in continental areas juveniles may be red dorsally. Adults may range from a light pink to brown or olive as shown, or a to a deep maroon becoming yellow distally. The maroon and yellow phase was originally described as a distinct species, *P. typee* Randall, but further study is needed to determine its true status. The spotting on the face is always present and may range from red to black. The freckled hawkfish occurs on lagoon or seaward reefs at depths of 1 to at least 33 m wherever suitable corals are present. Like *P. arcatus*, it is most common on outer reef slopes and tends to perch conspicuously on the outermost branches of corals, particularly *Pocillopora eydouxi*, ramose or tabular *Acropora* spp., and *Millepora dichotoma*. It feeds on small fishes and crustaceans, and is territorial and haremic.
Indo-Pacific: Red Sea to the Hawaiian, Line, Marquesan, and Ducie Is., n. to s. Japan, s. to Norfolk and the Austral Is.; throughout Micronesia.

Paracirrhites hemistictus (Günther, 1874)
Whitespot hawkfish   Pl. 39E,F
(*P. polystictus*)
SL: to 195 mm (7.7 in); D X, 11, A III, 6; P 14; LL 48-51; GR 6-7+12-14.
This large hawkfish occurs in two basic color morphs: a light phase with a broad white longitudinal band and a maroon to black phase (*polystictus*) with a conspicuous white blotch on each side. The white spot hawkfish is a relatively uncommon inhabitant of exposed reef fronts and outer reef slopes to a depth of about 18 m. It perches on rocks as well as corals. Males maintain harems of up to four females.
West-central Pacific: Cocos-Keeling and Christmas Is., to the Line, Marquesan, and Ducie Is., n. to the Bonins, s. to New Caledonia and the Australs; throughout Micronesia.

APOGONIDAE (CARDINALFISHES)

Cardinalfishes are characterized by two dorsal fins, the first with VI to VIII spines, II anal spines, large eyes, a large mouth, and double-edged preopercles. They derive their name from the red coloration of some of the species, although most are rather drab and many are striped. Most species tend to remain hidden under ledges or in holes during the day; a few form dense aggregations immediately above mounds of branching corals. They typically disperse over the reef at night to feed on zooplankton and small benthic crustaceans. In most if not all species, the male broods the eggs in his mouth until they hatch. At least 58 species in 12 genera occur in Micronesia; the classification of some is still under study. Counts follow the method of Hayashi (1984) in which only the developed gillrakers are counted. (Lit.: Frazer and Lachner, 1985; Fraser and Randall, 1976; Randall, et al., 1985; Randall and Lachner, 1986; Shao and Chen, 1987)

Subfamily Apogoninae

Apogonichthys ocellatus (Weber, 1913)   Pl. 40A
Ocellated cardinalfish
SL: to 32 mm (1.3 in); D VIII-I, 9; A II, 8; P 16; LP 24; GR 1+6.
Members of the genera *Apogonichthys*, *Foa*, and *Fowleria* are typically secretive, cryptic inhabitants of seagrasses, algal beds, or rubble of sheltered reefs. This species inhabits shallow sheltered lagoons and harbors where it hides among rocks, rubble, or clumps of brown algae.
Indo-Pacific: E. Africa to the Marquesas and Tuamotus, n. to s. Japan, s. to the s. Great Barrier Reef and Rapa; throughout Micronesia.

Apogonichthys perdix (Bleeker, 1854)   Fig. 3a
Perdix cardinalfish
SL: to 36 mm (1.4 in); D VIII-I, 9; A II, 8; P 13-14; LP 23-25; GR 1-2+5-7= 7-10.
This species occurs among rubble of reef flats and "dead" reefs to a depth of 65 m.
Indo-Pacific: Red Sea to the Hawaiian Is. and Rapa, n. to s. Japan; throughout Micronesia.

Foa brachygramma (Jenkins, 1903)   Fig. 3b
Bay cardinalfish
SL: to ca. 40 mm (1.6 in), 63 mm (2.5 in) in the Hawaiian Is.; D VIII+I, 9; A II, 8-9; P 10-12; LP 9-12; GR 1+1+5-7.
Foa differs from *Apogonichthys* and *Fowleria* by having palatine teeth and also from *Apogonichthys* by having an incomplete lateral line. The species typically live among seagrasses, heavy algal growth, or rubble of shallow sheltered areas. This species has recently been collected on the inner subtidal reef flat at Tumon Bay, Guam. Elsewhere it is an abundant reef flat species that occasionally occurs as deep as 79 m. A possibly undecribed species was recently collected from a *Halimeda* bed in Kwajalein lagoon at a depth of 19 to 27 m.
Indo-Pacific: E. Africa to the Hawaiian Is., n. to s. Japan; Marianas in Micronesia.

Fowleria punctulata (Rüppell, 1838)
Spotcheek cardinalfish *(F. isostigma)*   Fig. 1a
SL: to 85 mm (3.4 in); D VII-I, 9; A II, 8; P 14; LP 11-12; GR 0+4.

Fowleria is characterized by a reduced lateral line and prominent black ocellus on the operculum. At least three closely related species, distinguishable primarily by color, occur in Micronesia. The ground color of this species is light brown with or without 3 to 4 rows of black spots on the sides.
Indo-Pacific: Red Sea to the Tuamotus, n. to s. Japan, s. to Rapa; throughout Micronesia.

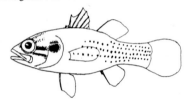

a. *F. punctulata*

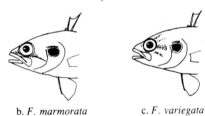

b. *F. marmorata*   c. *F. variegata*

Fig. 1. Micronesian species of *Fowleria*.

Fowleria marmorata (Alleyne & MacLeay, 1876)
Marbled cardinalfish   Fig. 1b
SL: to 40 mm (1.6 in); D VII-I, 9; A II, 8; P 14; LP 12; GR 1+5.
This species has a marbled, reddish, color pattern. It occurs on rocky bottoms.
Indo-Pacific: Red Sea to the Line, Marquesan and Society Is., n. to the Ryukyus, s. to the s. Great Barrier Reef; throughout Micronesia.

Fowleria variegata (Valenciennes, 1832)
Variegated cardinalfish   Figs. 1c, 3c
SL: to 65 mm (2.6 in); D VII-I, 9; A II, 8; P 13; LP 10-11; GR 1+5.
This species is reported from coral reefs and seagrass beds of inner bays and shallow lagoons.
Indo-west Pacific: Red Sea to Samoa, n. to the Ryukyus, s. to the s. Great Barrier Reef; Guam in Micronesia.

Rhabdamia cypselurus Weber, 1909
Luminous cardinalfish

SL: to 51 mm (2.0 in); D VI-I, 9; A II, 9; P 14-15; LR 25; GR 2-3+11-12=13-15.

Members of *Rhabdamia* are transparent in life and occur in large shoals among rocks or above corals of lagoon patch reefs. They have a pair of luminous organs beneath the end of the operculum.

Indo-Pacific: E. Africa to the Marshalls, n. to the Ryukyus. s. to New Guinea; Belau east to the Marshalls and Kapingamarangi in Micronesia.

Rhabdamia gracilis (Bleeker, 1856)   Fig. 3d
Graceful cardinalfish

SL: to 51 mm (2.0 in); D VI-I, 9; A II, 12; P 13; LR 26; GR 7+28.

This species lacks the dark markings on the head and tail of *R. cypselurus*.

Indo-Pacific: E. Africa to the Marshalls, n. to s. Japan, s. to Indonesia; Marshalls and Kapingamaringi in Micronesia.

Subgenus *Pristicon*:

Apogon trimaculatus (Cuvier, 1828)   Fig. 3e
Threespot cardinalfish

SL: to 128 mm (5.0 in); D VI-I, 9; A II, 8; P 14-15; LP2 5-26; LR 23-24; GR 2+10.

In life, this large species is a dark reddish in coloration. It inhabits lagoons and outer reef slopes. It seems to be relatively rare in the Marianas.

West-central Pacific: Malaysia to Samoa, n. to the Ryukyus, s. to Rowley Shoals; throughout Micronesia.

Apogon melas Bleeker, 1848   Fig. 3f
Black cardinalfish

SL: to 92 mm (3.6 in); D VII-I, A II, 8; P 14-15; LP 26-27; GR 5+15.

This distinctive species occurs in coastal bays.

West-central Pacific: Malaysia to the Moluccas, n. to the Ryukyus, s. to Rowley Shoals; Belau in Micronesia.

Subgenus *Zapogon*:

Apogon evermanni Jordan & Snyder, 1904
Evermann's cardinalfish   Fig. 3g

SL: to 110 mm (4.3 in); D VI-I, 9; A II, 8; LP 25; GR 5+16.

This species inhabits the deep recesses of caves in the outer reef slope, rarely in as little as 8 m, usually much deeper to at least 50 m.

Indo-Pacific & tropical w. Atlantic: Christmas, Marshall, Hawaiian, and Marquesan Is.

Subgenus *Jaydia*

Apogon ellioti Day, 1875   Fig. 3h
Elliot's cardinalfish

SL: to ca. 113 mm (4.5 in); D VII+I, 9; A II, 8; P 16-17; LP 25; GR 11-17.

This species normally inhabits sandy to muddy bottoms at depths of 50 to 80 m, but has been recorded from as little as 18 m. It has luminous organs on the thorax and abdomen

which contain luciferin obtained from *Cypridina* plankton.

Indo-Pacific: E. Africa to the s. Marshalls, n. to s. Japan, s. to nw. Australia; s. Marshalls in Micronesia.

Subgenus *Apogon*:

Apogon coccineus Rüppell, 1838
Cryptic cardinalfish   Pl. 40B; Fig. 3i

(*A. erythrinus*)

SL: to 45 mm (1.8 in); D VI-I, 9; A II, 8; P 13-14; LP 24-26; GR 2+7-8.

This cardinalfish inhabits sheltered reef flats, lagoons, and seaward reefs to a depth of at least 17 m. During the day, it remains hidden under rocks or deep in holes. At night it ventures over the reef to feed on small benthic crustaceans, but always remains close to the substrate.

Indo-Pacific: Red Sea to Marquesas and Easter Is., n. to s. Japan and the Hawaiian Is., s. to Lord Howe Is.; throughout Micronesia.

Apogon doryssa (Jordan & Seale, 1906)   Fig. 2
Longspine cardinalfish

SL: to ca. 40 mm (1.6 in); D VI-I, 9; A II, 8; P 11-12; LP 24; GR 1+8.

This species differs from *A. coccineus* by having fewer pectoral rays and much longer dorsal and anal spines, with the 2nd dorsal spine reaching the mid-base of the second dorsal fin when laid flat. Its ecology is similar to that of *A. coccineus*.

West-central Pacific: Christmas Is. to the Tuamotus, n. to the Ryukyus, s. to Rapa; Marianas and Marshalls in Micronesia.

Fig. 2 *Apogon doryssa.*

Subgenus *Pristiapogon*:

Apogon taeniopterus Bennett, 1835   Fig. 3j
Bandfin cardinalfish

(*A. menesemops*; *A. menesemus*)

SL: to 150 mm (5.9 in); D VII-I, 9; A II, 8; P (13)-14; LP 25; GR 2-4+12-14 =15-17.

The bandfin cardinalfish inhabits rocky and coralline areas of seaward reefs. It is uncommon throughout Micronesia, but common in certain other areas of the Pacific. It hovers in small groups among branching corals or rocks during the day and roams the reef at night to feed on free swimming crustaceans.

Indo-Pacific: Mauritius to the Line, Marquesan, and Tuamotu Is., n. to the Hawaiian Is., s. to New Caledonia and the Cook Is.; throughout Micronesia.

Apogon exostigma (Jordan & Starks, 1906)
Eyeshadow cardinalfish   Pl. 40C

(*A. frenatus* Lachner, 1953)

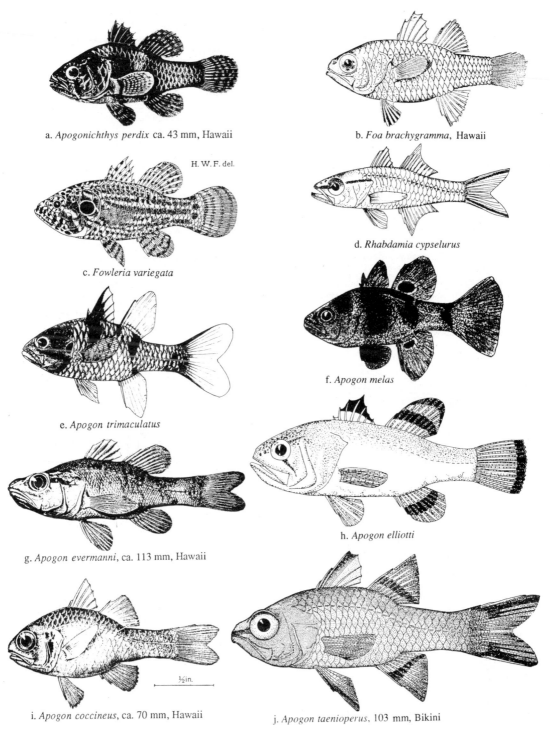

a. *Apogonichthys perdix* ca. 43 mm, Hawaii

b. *Foa brachygramma*, Hawaii

H. W. F. del.

c. *Fowleria variegata*

d. *Rhabdamia cypselurus*

e. *Apogon trimaculatus*

f. *Apogon melas*

g. *Apogon evermanni*, ca. 113 mm, Hawaii

h. *Apogon elliotti*

½in.

i. *Apogon coccineus*, ca. 70 mm, Hawaii

j. *Apogon taenioperus*, 103 mm, Bikini

Fig. 3. Micronesian cardinalfishes (a, b, g, i, after Jordan and Evermann, 1903; c, after Fowler, 1959; j after A. M. Awl in Schultz et al., 1953).

SL: to 94 mm (3.7 in); D VII-I, 9; A II, 8; P 12-14(13); LP 23-25; GR 2+8-11=10-13.

In this species, the spot on the caudal peduncle is centered slightly above the level of the lateral stripe. It is relatively common under ledges or among isolated coral heads in relatively silty inner reef areas.

Indo-Pacific: Red Sea to the Line and Mangareva Is., n. to the Ryukyus, s. to the s. Great Barrier Reef and Australs; throughout Micronesia.

Apogon fraenatus Valenciennes, 1832 Pl. 40D
Bridled cardinalfish

SL: to 85 mm (3.4 in); D VII-I, 9; A II, 8; P 13-16(14); LP 23-25; GR 2-3+7-11=9-13.

In this species, the spot on the caudal peduncle is centered at the level of the lateral stripe. *A. fraenatus* inhabits reef flats and lagoon and seaward reefs to a depth of at least 25 m. It is one of the most common cardinalfishes of relatively clear water areas of mixed sand, rubble, or coral. During the day it occurs under ledges in small groups or as solitary individuals.

Indo-Pacific: Red Sea to the Line and Tuamotu Is., n. to the Ryukyus, s. to New South Wales; throughout Micronesia.

Apogon kallopterus Bleeker, 1878 Pl. 40E
Iridescent cardinalfish

(*A. snyderi*)

SL: to 122 mm (4.8 in); D VII-I, 9; A II, 8; P (13)-14; LP 23-25; GR 2+8-12=10-14.

This relatively large cardinalfish inhabits clear water lagoon patch reefs and seaward reefs from the lower surge zone to a depth of 45 m. It is generally solitary by day as well as night. It usually hovers near the entrance to crevices during the day and roams the reef over sandy patches to feed on small benthic and free swimming crustaceans by night.

Indo-Pacific: Red Sea to the Line, Marquesan, and Pitcairn Is., n. to s. Japan and the Hawaiian Is., s. to New Caledonia and Rapa; throughout Micronesia.

Subgenus *Nectamia*:

Apogon dispar Fraser & Randall, 1976 Pl. 40F
Redspot cardinalfish

SL: to 48 mm (1.9 in); D VII-I, (8)-9; A II, (8)-9; P 13-14; LP 25; GR 4-5+17-20=21-25.

The redspot cardinalfish has a lustrous sheen as well as a distinctive red spot on its caudal peduncle. It hovers in small groups in caves of dropoffs at depths of 18 to 58 m. It may belong in a separate subgenus with *A. melanoproctus*.

Indo-Australian: Cocos-Keeling, Solomons, and Belau.

Apogon hartzfeldii Bleeker, 1852
Hartzfeld's cardinalfish

SL: to 82 mm (3.2 in); D VI-I, 9; A II, 8; LP 21-22+4-5 on C ped.; GR 15-17.

This species is grey with thin white stripes, all but the uppermost fading posteriorly. It occurs in small groups among debris or corals of sheltered reef flats and shallow lagoons.

Indo-Australian: Philippines, Borneo, Moluccas, and w. New Guinea, s. to nw Australia; Belau in Micronesia.

Apogon lateralis Valenciennes, 1832 Pl. 40H
Inshore cardinalfish

SL: to ca. 80 mm (3.1 in); D VI-I, 9; A II, 8; P 14; LR 23; GR 3+4+15-16.

This species is abundant in shallow sheltered inshore reefs or river mouths where it lives among clumps of algae or algal covered rubble.

Indo-W. Pacific: E. Africa to Samoa, n. to Taiwan; Marianas and Carolines in Micronesia.

Apogon sangiensis Bleeker, 1857 Pl. 40G
Sangi cardinalfish

SL: to 66 mm (2.6 in); D VI-I, 9; A II, 8; P 13-14; LP 24; GR 5+16 (not Illustated).

This species occurs in small schools among rocks or coral of shallow sheltered lagoons.

Indo-W. Pacific: E. Africa to Vanuatu, n. to the Ryukyus; Belau, Yap, and Truk in Micronesia.

Apogon bandanensis Bleeker, 1854 Fig. 4a
Bigeye cardinalfish

SL: to 77 mm (3.0 in); D VII-I, 9; A II, 8; P 13; LP 26; GR 6-7+19=25-26.

This species has a larger eye than either *A. fuscus* or *A. guamensis* as well as a differently shaped eye mark and darker vertical fins. It inhabits outer reef slopes generally at depths below 30 m.

West Pacific: Moluccas and Philippines to Samoa, n. to the Ryukyus, s. to the s. Great Barrier Reef; Marianas and Carolines in Micronesia.

a. *A. bandanensis* b. *A. fuscus* c. *A. guamensis*

Fig. 4. Facial patterns of the *Apogon bandanensis* complex.

Apogon fuscus (Quoy & Gaimard, 1825)
Gray cardinalfish Pl. 41A; Fig. 4b

(*A. savayensis*)

SL: to 77 mm (3.0 in); D VII-I, 9; A II, 8; P 13; LP 26; GR 7+20=27.

This species inhabits outer reef slopes where it tends to remain hidden in crevices among the corals during the day. At night it emerges to feed in the water column on free-swimming invertebrates such as ostracods, amphipods, shrimps, and certain polychaetes.

Indo-Pacific: Red Sea to the Line and Tuamotu Is., n. to the Ryukyus, s. to the s. Great Barrier Reef and Rapa; throughout Micronesia.

Apogon guamensis Valenciennes, 1832
Guam cardinalfish Pl. 41B; Fig. 4c

(*A. nubilus*)

SL: to 79 mm (3.1 in); D VII-I, 9; A II, 8; P 13; LP 26; GR 5-6+18=23-24.

Although this species is one of the most common cardinalfishes of reef flats and shallow lagoons, its rarely seen during the day when it shelters deep within *Acropora* thickets and other corals as well as in holes or crevices. At night it emerges to feed on free-swimming invertebrates in the water above the reef.

Indo-Pacific: Red Sea to Samoa, n. to the Ryukyus, s. to the s. Great Barrier Reef; throughout Micronesia.

Apogon angustatus (Smith & Radcliffe, 1911)
Broad-striped cardinalfish   Pl. 41C

SL: to 78 mm (23.1 in); D VII-I, 9; A II, 8; P 14; LL 28; GR 11-15.

There are at least 4 very similar looking striped species of *Apogon* in Micronesia. Field identification is based on shape, thickness, and orientation of the stripes, particularly in the caudal region. *A. angustatus* is relatively common on seaward reefs in areas of clear water from the outer reef flat to a depth of 65 m. During the day it remains under ledges or in holes; at night it ventures out to feed on polychaetes and other small benthic invertebrates.

Indo-Pacific: Red Sea to the Line and Mangareva Is., n. to Taiwan, s. to New Caledonia; throughout Micronesia.

Apogon taeniophorus Regan, 1905   Pl. 41D
(*A. saipanensis*; *A. robustus* Lachner, 1953)

SL: to 93 mm (3.7 in); D VII-I, 9; A II, 8; P 14; LR 23-24; GR 2+10 (17-19 total incl. rudiments).

In large specimens of this species, a secondary dark line extends backwards as far as the first dorsal fin. *A. taeniophorus* inhabits ledges or holes of outer reef flats in areas exposed to surge. In the Marianas, it is the least common of the striped species of *Apogon*.

Indo-Pacific: Red Sea to the Line and Pitcairn Is., n. to s. Japan, s. to New South Wales and Rapa; throughout Micronesia.

Apogon nigrofasciatus Lachner, 1953   Pl. 41E
Black-striped cardinalfish
(*A. aroubiensis* Lachner, 1953)

SL: to 70 mm (2.8 in); D VII-I, 9; A II, 8; P 13-(14); LP 24-(25); GR 7+21.

This species occurs on reef flats and shallow outer lagoon reefs but is not as abundant as *A. novemfasciatus*. It also seems to be less gregarious and is usually seen under ledges or in crevices, singly or in pairs. It emerges at night to feed on small benthic invertebrates.

Indo-Pacific: Red Sea and Christmas Is. to the Tuamotus; n. to s. Japan, s. to New Caledonia and Rapa; throughout Micronesia.

Apogon novemfasciatus Cuvier, 1828   Pl. 41F
Seven-striped cardinalfish

SL: to 73 mm (2.9 in); D VII-I, 9; A II, 9; P 14; LP 27; GR 3+13.

This is one of the most common cardinalfishes of reef flats and shallow lagoons to a depth of about 4 m. During the day, it occurs in small groups under rocks and ledges or in holes, particularly near sandy or rubbly areas. At night it

disperses to feed on small crustaceans and fishes.

West-central Pacific: Christmas Is. (Indian Ocean) to the Line Is., n. to the Izus, s. to the Great Barrier Reef and Samoa; throughout Micronesia.

Apogon compressus (McCulluch, 1915)   Pl. 41G
Ochre-striped cardinalfish

SL: to ca. 85 mm (3.4 in); D VII-I, 9; A II, 9; P 13-14; LP 25; GR 7+21.

This species occurs in small groups among or near mounds of branching corals such as *Porites cylindrica* or *P. nigrescens*.

West Pacific: Malaysia to the Solomons, to the Ryukyus, s. to the Great Barrier Reef; Belau in Micronesia.

Apogon sealei Fowler, 1918   Pl. 41H
Seale's cardinalfish

SL: to ≥ 60 mm (3.4 in); D VII-I, 9; A II, 8; P 14; LP 23; GR 6+14.

This uncommon species lives among branching corals of sheltered lagoon reefs.

West Pacific: Malaysia to the Solomons, n. to s. Japan, s. to nw. Australia; Belau in Micronesia.

Apogon cyanosoma Bleeker, 1853   Pl. 42A
Yellow cardinalfish
(*A. novae-guinea* Lachner, 1953)

SL: to 50 mm (2.0 in); D VII-I, 9; A II, 8; P 14; LP 26; GR 3+14.

Micronesian populations are uniformly yellow rather than conspicuously striped in yellow and white as are populations from elsewhere. The yellow cardinalfish inhabits sheltered clearwater areas of lagoon and seaward reefs from depths of 1 to at least 49 m. During the day, it gathers in small to large aggregations under ledges, in holes, or even among the spines of sea urchins. It feeds on planktonic crustaceans and small invertebrates by day and night.

Indo-Pacific: Red Sea to the Marshalls, n. to s. Japan, s. to the s. Great Barrier Reef; throughout Micronesia.

Subgenus *Zoramia*:

Key to Micronesian species:

1a. Dark line dorsally from first dorsal fin onto caudal peduncle and on ventral margin of caudal peduncle............
....*leptacanthus*
1b. Dark dorsal and ventral lines absent.........................2
2a. Gular area dark; short vertical dark lines above insertion of some anal rays...*perlitus*
2b. Gular area pale; no vertical lines above anal rays.........3
3a. Prominent diffuse dark spot on opercular flap; diffuse melanophores surrounding small spot on caudal peduncle...*gilberti*
3b. No spot on opercular flap; spot on caudal peduncle not surrounded by melanophores...........................*fragilis*

Apogon fragilis Smith, 1961
Fragile cardinalfish

SL: to 43 mm (1.7 in); D VI-I, 9; A II, 9; P 14; LP 24; GR

4-7+19-24=23-28.

This and the following three species occur in large, often mixed-species aggregations above branching corals in sheltered lagoons and bays.

Indo-Pacific: E. Africa to Samoa, n. to the Yaeyamas, s. to the Great Barrier Reef; Belau east to the s. Marshalls in Micronesia.

Apogon gilberti (Jordan & Seale, 1905) Pl. 42B
Gilbert's cardinalfish

SL: to 42 mm (1.7 in); D VI-I, 9; A II, 9; P 13-(14); LP 24; GR 5-7+21-23= 26-30.

Indo-Australian: Philippines, Moluccas, Belau, and Yap.

Apogon leptacanthus Bleeker, 1856 Pl. 42C
Bluestreak cardinalfish

SL: to 45 mm (1.8 in); D VI-I, 9; A II, 9; P 13-14; LP 24; GR 5-7+21-24=27-31.

This exquisite little cardinalfish occurs in dense aggregations above mounds of the branching corals *Porites cylindrica* and *P. andrewsi* in sheltered, often turbid bays and lagoons. It frequently occurs in mixed species aggregations with *Archamia fucata*, *A. zosterophora.*, or other species of the subgenus *Zoramia*.

Indo-Pacific: Red Sea to Samoa, and Tonga, n. to the Ryukyus, s. to New Caledonia; throughout Micronesia.

Apogon perlitus Fraser & Lachner, 1985 Fig. 2a
Pearly cardinalfish

SL: to 42 mm (1.7 in); D VI-I, 9; A II, 9; P (14)-15; LP 24; GR 5-6+19-21= 25-27.

The dark gular area distinguishes this species from others in the subgenus.

Indo-Australian: Philippines, Moluccas, and Belau.

Archamia biguttata Lachner, 1951 Pl. 42D
Twinspot cardinalfish

SL: to 87 mm (3.4 in); D VI-I, 9; A II, 16-17; P 13; LP 25-26; GR 3-4+16-17=19-21.

The large dark spot on the upper corner of the operculum is distinctive. This species inhabits inshore reefs of bays or lagoons to a depth of 18 m. It typically hovers in small groups in the recesses of caves. It is relatively common along Guam's southwest coast.

West Pacific: Sumatra to Samoa, n. to the Ryukyus; Belau and Marianas in Micronesia.

Archamia fucata (Cantor, 1850) Pl. 42E
Orange-lined cardinalfish

SL: to 59 mm (2.3 in); D VI-I, 7-8; A II, 15-18; P 13-14; LP 25-26; GR 4-5+15-16=19-21.

This species inhabits sheltered bays and lagoon patch reefs at depths of 2 to 60 m. It typically occurs in dense aggregations in the entrances of caves, but may also occur close above densely branching corals such as *Porites cylindrica*. It is relatively uncommon in the Marianas and Marshalls, but common throughout the high Caroline Islands.

Indo-Pacific: Red Sea to Samoa, n. to the Ryukyus, s. to Scott Reef and New Caledonia; throughout Micronesia.

Archamia zosterophora (Bleeker, 1858) Pl. 42F
Blackbelted cardinalfish

SL: to 61 mm (2.4 in); D VI-I, 9; A II, 16-17; P 14; LP 26-27; GR 6+16.

Species of *Archamia* have a higher number of soft anal rays, higher number of gill rakers, and more compressed bodies than species of *Apogon* (except the subgenus *Zoramia* for the latter two characters). The blackbelted cardinalfish inhabits sheltered lagoons and inshore bays where it typically occurs in dense aggregations immediately above or among the branches of large stands of *Porites cylindrica* and other branching corals. They rise further above the corals at dusk, then disperse to feed in the water column at night.

West Pacific: Moluccas and Philippines to the Solomons, s. to New Caledonia, n. to the Ryukyus; Belau and Yap in Micronesia.

Sphaeramia nematoptera (Bleeker, 1856) Pl. 43A
Pajama cardinalfish

SL: to 61 mm (2.1 in); D VII-I, 9; A II, 9; P 13-14; LP 26-27; GR 7+27.

This spectacular cardinalfish aggregates among the branches of the corals *Porites nigrescens* and *P. cylindrica* in sheltered bays and lagoons at depths of 1 to 6 m. At night it disperses to feed close to the substrate. It is a popular aquarium export from the Philippines.

West-Pacific: Java to New Guinea, n. to the Ryukyus; Belau to Pohnpei in Micronesia.

Sphaeramia orbicularis (Cuvier, 1828) Pl. 43B
Orbiculate cardinalfish

SL: to 89 mm (3.5 in); D VII-I, 9; A II, 9; P 12-13; LP 23-24; GR 6+19.

This strictly coastal species hovers in small aggregations among mangroves, rocks, debris, or piers of shallow sheltered shorelines. It feeds in the early evening and just before dawn, primarily on planktonic crustaceans and to a lesser extent on insects, polychates, small fishes, and fish eggs. Courtship and spawning occur on a semi-lunar cycle, shortly before full and new moons. Males incubate up to 12,000 eggs for a period of about 8 days. After the pelagic larval phase, juveniles settle and grow at a rate of 3 to 6 mm per month. Males mature at 7cm, females at 6 cm.

Indo-Pacific: E. Africa to Kiribati, n. to the Ryukyus, s. to New Caledonia; Belau to e. Carolines and Marianas in Micronesia.

Cheilodipterus isostigma Schultz, 1940 Fig. 6b

SL: to 93 mm (3.7 in); D VI-I, 9; A II, 8; P 13; LR 25; GR 5+13-14.

Species of *Cheilodipterus* possess numerous large needle-like canine teeth in both jaws and elongate bodies. They attain a larger size than most other shallow-water apogonids and feed primarily on small fishes. *C. isostigma* is nearly indistinguishable from *C. quinquelineata* , differing only by possessing canine teeth at the end of the lower jaw (fig. 6). It has been collected from lagoon reefs to depths of 12 m or more where it is generally less common than *C. quinquelineata*.

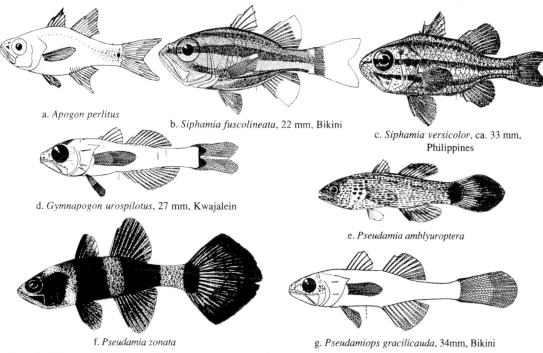

a. *Apogon perlitus*

b. *Siphamia fuscolineata*, 22 mm, Bikini

c. *Siphamia versicolor*, ca. 33 mm, Philippines

d. *Gymnapogon urospilotus*, 27 mm, Kwajalein

e. *Pseudamia amblyuroptera*

f. *Pseudamia zonata*

g. *Pseudamiops gracilicauda*, 34mm, Bikini

Fig. 5. Micronesian apogonids (b, d, g, after A. M. Awl *in* Schultz et al., 1953; c, after Smith and Radcliffe, 1911).

West-central Pacific: Philippines, Moluccas, New Guinea, Belau, Carolines, and Marshalls.

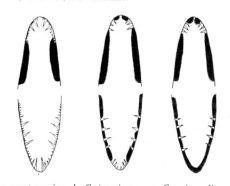

a. most species b. *C. isostigma* c. *C. quinquelineata*

Fig. 6. Dentition of species of *Cheilodipterus* (after Lachner *in* Schultz et al, 1953).

Cheilodipterus artus Smith, 1961
Lined cardinalfish
Pl. 43D,F

SL: to 187 mm (7.4 in); D VI-I, 9; A II, 8; P 12-(13); LP 27-28; dev. GR 7-10(reduced in adults); depth 2.5-3.5.

Juveniles have a small black spot surrounded by a large gold blotch on the caudal peduncle. *C. artus* inhabits sheltered bays and lagoon patch reefs at depths of 5 to over 20 m. It typically occurs in small loose aggregations that hover in mid-water in caves or just above the branches of certain corals.

Indo-Pacific: Red Sea to the Tuamotus, n. to the Ryukyus, s. to the Great Barrier Reef; Belau and Marianas in Micronesia.

Cheilodipterus macrodon (Lacepède, 1802)
Large-toothed cardinalfish
Pl. 43C

SL: to 174 mm (6.9 in); D VI-I, 9; A II, 8; P 13; LP 24-25; LR 23-26; GR 5-6+15-16=20-22 (12 dev.).

Juveniles have a large black blotch on the caudal peduncle which becomes diffuse with age. Adults closely resemble the adults of *C. artus*, but have alternating stripes of slightly unequal width that tend to be more gray than bronze in color. *C. macrodon* inhabits caves and ledges of clear lagoon and seawards reefs at depths of .5 to at least 40 m. It is generally solitary and hovers in mid water.

Indo-Pacific: Maldives to the Marshalls, n. to the Ryukyus, s. to the Great Barrier Reef; throughout Micronesia.

Cheilodipterus quinquelineata (Cuvier,1828)
Five-lined cardinalfish
Pl. 43G; Fig. 6c

SL: to 76 mm (3.0 in); D VI-I, 9; A II, 8; P 12-13; LP 25-26; LR 24-25; GR 4-5+14.

This cardinalfish is common on reef flats and lagoon and seaward reefs to a depth of at least 40 m. It occurs in small to large aggregations among corals, rocks, the spines of the sea urchin *Diadema setosum*, or under ledges. It feeds during the day and night on small crustaceans and gastropods as well as small fishes.

Indo-Pacific: Red Sea to Ducie, n. to s. Japan, s. to Lord Howe Is. and Rapa; throughout Micronesia.

Cheilodipterus singapurensis Bleeker, 1860
Truncate cardinalfish (*C. truncatus*)
SL: to ≥153 mm (7.4 in); D VI-I, 9; A II, 8-9; P 12-13; LR 23-25; GR 4-6+14-16.
This species differs from *C. quinquelineatus* by possessing a dark spot around the anus and a truncated dorso-posterior corner of the maxillary.
West-central Pacific: Sumatra and Philippines to New Guinea and the Marshalls, n. to the Ryukyus.

Siphamia fuscolineata Lachner, 1953   Fig. 5b
Crown-of-thorns cardinalfish
SL: to 40 mm (1.6 in); D VII-I, 9; A II, 8;P 13-15; LR ca. 23; GR 3+7-9.
Species of *Siphamia* possess unique bioluminescent bands. Most are small (≤30 mm) and relatively deep bodied. This rare species occurs among the spines of the crown-of-thorns starfish, *Acanthaster planci*, in groups of up to 31 from lagoon depths of 7 m or more.
West-central Pacific: Sumatra, s. Taiwan, and the Marshalls.

Siphamia versicolor (Smith & Radcliffe, 1911)
Sea urchin cardinalfish   Fig. 5c
SL: to 56 mm (2.2 in); D VII-I, 8-9; A II, 8-9; P 14; Lp 20-23; GR 1+7-9.
This rare species lives in small groups exclusively among the spines of the long-spined sea urchin *Diadema setosum* in shallow sheltered waters.
Indo-west Pacific: Maldives to the Marianas, n. to the Ryukyus, s. to nw. Australia; Marianas and e. Carolines in Micronesia.

Siphamia fistulosa (Weber, 1909)
SL: to 16 mm (0.6 in).
This species is known from Micronesia on the basis of a single collection of post-larval specimens from the branches of the coral *Pocillopora damicornis* at a depth of 18 m in Apra Harbor, Guam.
Indo-Australian: Indonesia and Guam.

Subfamily Pseudaminae

Gymnapogon philippinus (Herre, 1939)
Philippine cardinalfish
SL: to 37 mm (1.5 in); D VI-I, 9; A II, 8; P 14; GR 1+8.
Gymnapogon, *Pseudamiops*, and *Pseudamia* constitute an aberrant group of small delicate cardinalfishes characterized by elongate bodies and large round fins. Species of *Gymnapogon* lack both scales and a lateral line. This species occasionally occurs in schools of *Rhabdamia gracilis*.
Indo-Australian: Philippines, Taiwan, Ryukyus, Kapingamarangi.

Gymnapogon urospilotus Lachner, 1953   Fig. 5d
SL: to 27 mm (1.1 in); D VI-I, 9; A II, (9)-10; P 14-15; GR 1+9.
This species has a distinctive dark B-shaped spot on the caudal fin base. It occurs among schools of juveniles of other apogonids.

West-central Pacific: Taiwan and Ryukyus to the Society Is.; throughout Micronesia.

Pseudamia amblyuroptera (Bleeker, 1856)
SL: to 80 mm (3.1 in); D VI-I, 8;   Fig. 5e
A II, (9)-10; P 16; LR 39-41; GR 2+9-10.
Species of *Pseudamia* have small cycloid scales over most of the body and a reduced lateral line consisting of about 20 pores. This small species occurs in shallow mangrove creeks and nearby shallow lagoon reefs and seagrass beds.
Indo-Australian: Malaysia and Philippines to the Solomons, Belau, and Yap.

Pseudamia hayashii
    Randall, Lachner, & Fraser, 1985
Hayashi's cardinalfish
SL: to 62 mm (2.4 in); D VI-I, 8; A II, 7-(8); P 15-17(16); LR 23-24; GR 1+7 (not illustrated).
This species resembles *P. amblyurptera* and *P. gelatinosa* but has larger scales (LR≤24). It has been collected from lagoon and seaward reefs at depths of 2 to 64 m. During the day it remains hidden in small caves or beneath ledges.
Indo-west Pacific: G. of Aden to Samoa, n. to s. Japan, s. to Rowley Shoals and Queensland; Belau to Kosrae in Micronesia.

Pseudamia gelatinosa Smith, 1955
Gelatinous cardinalfish
SL: to 79 mm (3.1 in); D VI-I, 8; A II, 8; P 15-17(16); LR 39-43; GR 1+(7)-8 (not illustrated).
This species has fewer gill rakers and anal fin rays than *P. amblyuroptera*. It has been collected from protected bay and lagoon reefs in areas of clear water at depths of .5 to 40 m, usually with the aid of ichthyocides.
Indo-Pacific: Red Sea to the Line and Society Is., n. to s. Japan, s. to New South Wales and Rapa; Belau to the e. Carolines in Micronesia.

Pseudamia zonata Randall, Lachner,& Fraser,1985
Paddlefin cardinalfish   Fig. 5f
SL: to 87 mm (3.4 in); DVI-I, 9-10; A II, 9; P 15-16; LR 23-25; GR 6+16-18.
This boldly marked cardinalfish has been collected from caves in the depth range of 10 to 31 m. It has recently been observed at Belau.
Indo-Australian: Ryukyus, Philippines, Ninigo Is. (n. Papua New Guinea), Solomon Is., Vanuatu, and Belau.

Pseudamiops gracilicauda (Lachner, 1953)
Graceful-tailed cardinalfish   Fig. 5g
SL: to ca. 34 mm (1.3 in); D VI-I, 8; A II, 7-(8); P 15-17; LR 23-24; GR 1+7.
Pseudamiops is similar to *Pseudamia* but lacks a lateral line and has large exfoliate cycloid scales. This species occurs in caves and among corals of lagoon and seaward reefs at depths of 5 to 30 m. It rises in the water to feed at night.
Indo-Pacific: Chagos Is. to the Hawaiian Is., n. to Taiwan and the Ryukyus, s. to Rapa; Marianas and Marshalls in Micronesia.

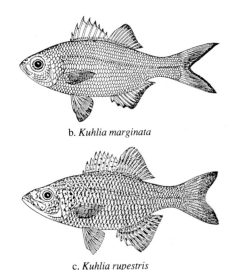

b. *Kuhlia marginata*

c. *Kuhlia rupestris*

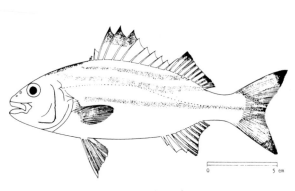

a. *Terapon jarbua*, 16 cm

Fig. 1. Micronesian grunters and flagtails (a, after FAO, 1972; b, c, after Fowler, 1959).

THERAPONIDAE (GRUNTERS)

Terapon jarbua (Forsskål, 1775)   Fig. 1a
Crescent-banded grunter
SL: to 30 cm (11.8 in); D XII, 10; A III, 8; P 13; LL 90-93; GR 6-7+13.
Grunters have oblong compressed bodies, strongly ctenoid scales, a notched dorsal fin, sharply serrated preopercular margins, 1 to 2 strong opercular spines, and a pattern of dark bands on a silvery body. This species schools over shallow sandy bottoms, particularly in the vicinity of river mouths, and feeds on sand-dwelling invertebrates. Juveniles are common in sandy intertidal areas.
Indo-west Pacific: Red Sea to Samoa, n. to s. Japan, s. to Lord Howe Is.; Belau in Micronesia.

KUHLIIDAE (FLAGTAILS)

Flagtails are silvery compressed fishes with a deeply notched dorsal fin, forked tail, and large eyes. Two species occur on Micronesian coral reefs; another (*K. rupestris*; Fig. 1b) occurs in turbid coastal bays and rivers.

Kuhlia marginata (Cuvier, 1829)   Fig. 1c
Dark-margined flagtail
SL: to 20 cm (7.9 in); D X, 10-12; A III, 11-12; P 13-15; LP 48-53; GR 7-9+15-20.
The dusky margin of the soft dorsal, anal, and caudal fins, and absence of bars on the caudal fin are distinctive. Juveniles occur in tidepools; adults occur in deeper water as well as in fresh water. This species is rare in the Marianas where it is known from one individual observed with an aggregation of *K. mugil* inside Saipan's "Blue Grotto".

Indo-Pacific: Sri Lanka to the Line, Johnston, and Ducie Is., n. to s. Japan, s. to Rapa; Belau, Marshalls, and Marianas in Micronesia.

Kuhlia mugil (Forster, 1801)   Pl. 44A
Barred flagtail
(*K. taeniura*)
SL: to 23 cm (9.1 in); D X, 9-11; A III, 9-11; P 14; LP 48-56; GR 8-10+21-26.
Flagtails occur in tightly packed schools along the reef margin or rocky shorelines, from just beneath the breaking surf to a depth of a few meters. They are frequently seen in the entrances of caves along the waterline. Juveniles commonly occur in tidepools or at the heads of surge channels. Flagtails disperse at night to feed on free-swimming crustaceans.
Indo-pan-Pacific: Red Sea to Panama, n. to s. Japan, s. to Lord Howe and Rapa; throughout Micronesia.

PRIACANTHIDAE (BIGEYES)

Bigeyes have moderately deep compressed bodies covered with small ctenoid scales, oblique mouths with a projecting lower jaw, small conical teeth in a narrow band in each jaw, very large eyes, and a continuous dorsal fin. During the day, they generally remain under ledges or close to coral cover; at night they enter the water column and migrate above and away from the reef to feed on larger zooplankton such as the larvae of crabs, fishes, and cephalopods. When close to the reef during the day, they generally assume a predominantly red coloration but at night become silvery or mottled or barred in silver. This change in coloration can occur in a matter of seconds. Two species occur on shallow Micronesian coral reefs; a third, *Pristigenys multifasciata*, has recently been taken off Rota at a depth of over 200 m.

Heteropriacanthus cruentatus (Lacepède, 1801)
Glasseye Pl. 44B
(*Priacanthus cruentatus*)
SL: to 23 cm (9.1 in); D X, 12-13; A III, 14; LP 56-62;
GR 4-5+17-18.
The glasseye inhabits lagoon or seaward reefs from below
the surge zone to a depth of at least 20 m. During the day
it usually occurs singly or in small groups but at dusk it
may gather in large numbers as it prepares to migrate into
the water column to feed.
Circumtropical: n. to the Ryukyu, Bonin, and Hawaiian Is.,
s. to Lord Howe and Easter Is.; throughout Micronesia.

Priacanthus hamrur (Forsskål, 1775) Pl. 44C,D
Goggle-eye
SL: to 26 cm (10.2 in); D X, 14-15; A III, 14-15; LP 75-
80; GR 5+19.
The goggle-eye is a relatively uncommon inhabitant of outer
reef slopes and deep lagoon pinnacles at depths of 8 to 80 m
or more.
Indo-Pacific: Red Sea to the Marquesas and Mangareva, n. to
s. Japan, s. to New Caledonia; throughout Micronesia.

MALACANTHIDAE (SAND TILEFISHES)

Sand tilefishes have elongate bodies with a long continuous
dorsal fin, small mostly ctenoid scales, jaws with villiform
and canine teeth, and a single opercular spine. They usually
occur in pairs on sandy and rubbly areas of outer reef slopes
and retreat to a burrow when pursued. Four species occur on
Micronesian coral reefs. (Lit.: Conde and Terver, 1983;
Randall, 1981)

Hoplolatilus cuniculus Randall & Dooley, 1974
Pale sand tilefish
SL: to 129 mm (5.1 in); D III-V, 29-34; A I, 19-20; P 16-
18; LL 116-140; GR 21-24.
Hoplolatilus is characterized by a compressed body and
forked caudal fin. Some species construct a large mound of
rubble within which they live. *H. cuniculus* is variable in
coloration, ranging from pale olive brown to yellowish or
light greenish or a mixture with some geographic variation.
It is a rarely seen inhabitant of muddy to rubbly areas of
outer reef slopes that is known from depths of 28 to 115 m.
Indo-Pacific: S. Africa (postlarvae only) and Mauritius to the
Society Is., n. to the Ryukyus; Marshalls in Micronesia.

Hoplolatilus fronticinctus (Günther, 1887)
Stocky sand tilefish
SL: to 169 mm (6.7 in); D X, 13; A II, 12; P16-17; LL 85-
92; GR 26-29.
This rare species has the deepest body in the genus and a
thicker tail than *H. cuniculus* and *H. starcki*. It is lavender-
gray above and deep blue below a line extending from the
snout to the origin of the anal fin. It lives in groups that
hover above huge mounds of rubble that it apparently builds
(up to 5.5 m long x 3 m wide and over 1 m high). It has

been collected in the depth range of 40 to at least 70 m.
Indo-west Pacific: Mauritius, India, Philippines, Solomons,
and Belau.

Hoplolatilus starcki Randall & Dooley, 1974
Purple-headed sand tilefish Pl. 44E
SL: to 116 mm (4.6 in); D VIII, 21-23; A II, 15-16; P 18-
19; LL 100-118; GR 22-27.
This striking fish is an uncommon inhabitant of patches of
talus or rubble of steep outer reef slopes at depths of 21 to
105 m. It usually occurs in pairs that quickly dive headfirst
into their burrow when approached. The uniformly pur-
plish-blue juveniles occasionally school with the similarly
colored juvenile *Pseudanthias pascalus* (p. 101).
Tropical W. Pacific: Moluccas and Philippines to Timoe, n.
to the Marianas, s. to Rowley Shoals and New Caledonia;
throughout Micronesia.

Malacanthus brevirostris (Guichenot. 1848)
Quakerfish Pl. 44F
(*M. hoedti*)
SL: to 265 mm (10.4 in); D I-IV, 52-60; A I, 46-55; P 15-
17; LL 146-181; GR 9-20.
Species of *Malacanthus* are more round in cross-section and
less colorful than those of *Hoplolatilus*. The quakerfish is
easily distinguished by its relatively blunt snout and two
equally thin black bars on the tail. It is a relatively uncom-
mon inhabitant of barren, open areas of outer reef slopes at
depths of 14 to 45 m.
Indo-pan-Pacific: Red Sea to Panama, n. to s. Japan and the
Hawaiian Is., s. to Lord Howe and the Australs; throughout
Micronesia.

Malacanthus latovittatus (Lacepède, 1798)
Striped blanquillo Pl. 44G; Fig. 1
SL: to 380 mm (15.0 in); D III-IV, 43-47; A I, 37-40; P
16-(17); LL 116-132; GR 6-14.
This large sand tilefish has a long, pointed snout and a broad
black band extending from the operculum to the tip of the
tail. In juveniles the band covers most of the body leaving
two thin white lateral stripes. The striped blanquillo occurs
on relatively barren rubble or pavement bottoms of outer
reef slopes at depths below 6 m. It is quite wary and tends
to swim away from its pursuer rather than enter its burrow.
Indo-Pacific: Red Sea to the Line Is., n. to s. Japan, s. to
New Caledonia and the Cook Is.; throughout Micronesia.

Fig. 1. *Malacanthus latovittatus* 294 mm, Guam.

ECHENEIDIDAE (REMORAS)

The spinous dorsal fin of remoras is modified into a unique sucking disc in which the spines are split and flattened to form a series of paired transverse laminae. This disc is used to attach to sharks, rays, large bony fishes, sea turtles, or aquatic mammals. Some species are host specific while others utilize a variety of hosts or are free-swimming. Two species associated with coral reef dwellers are included below.

Echeneis naucrates Linnaeus, 1758   Pl. 44H
Sharksucker

SL: to 90 cm (35.4 in); 20-28 pr. laminae; D 32-42; A 32-38; P 22-23.
This large striped remora is often encountered free living in coastal waters as well as attached to a variety of hosts including sharks, rays, large bony fishes, or sea turtles.
Circumglobal

Remora remora (Linnaeus, 1758)
Remora
SL: to 40 cm (15.7 in); 17-19 pr. laminae; D 22-27; A 23-30; P 26-30; GR 5-6+26-28 incl. rudim.; depth ca. 6.2-6.5.
This remora is is uniformly dark and deeper-bodied than *E. naucrates*. It is usually associated with sharks.
Circumglobal

CARANGIDAE (JACKS; TREVALLYS)

Jacks are strong-swimming open water carnivores of fishes and crustaceans. Most are characterized by a silvery laterally compressed to fusiform body, two dorsal fins, small (sometimes embedded) cycloid scales, complete lateral line, slender caudal peduncle reinforced by a series of bony scutes, and strongly forked caudal fin. Many species have a streamlined adipose eyelid. The presence of scutes in most species and two stout spines in front of the anal fin as well as the absence of two or more sets of dorsal and ventral finlets distinguish the jacks from the superficially similar tunas (p. 253). Many species are economically important food fishes, but large individuals of a few may be ciguatoxic in certain areas. Although most of the approximately 30 species known from Micronesia range into or occur primarily in coral reef waters, a few are strictly oceanic. All counts of scutes are for the straight portion of the lateral line only. (Lit.: Berry et al., 1983; Gloerfelt-Tarp and Kailola, 1984; Smith-Vaniz *in* Smith and Heemstra, 1986.)

Key to Micronesian genera of Carangidae*:

1a. Posterior straight part of LL with scutes; in adults, P long and falcate, in most genera longer than head (except about equal in *Selar* and shorter in some *Decapterus* spp.)...2
1b. No scutes on LL; P usually shorter than head (ca. .9-2.0 in HL)...................9
2a. Second D and A with ≥ 1 distinctly separate finlets......................*Decapterus*
2b. Second D and A without finlets...3
3a. Shoulder girdle margin with a furrow ventrally, a large papilla immediately above it and a smaller papilla near upper edge.....................................*Selar*
3b. Shoulder girdle margin smooth...4
4a. In adults, spinous D entirely buried or spines short and disconnected, height of longest spine < pupil diameter; body superficially naked, scales (where present) minute or embedded; opercle scaleless...*Alectes*
4b. In adults, height of erect D usualy > eye diameter and at least anterior spines united by inter-radial membrane; small scales present over most of body; opercle at least partially scaled...5
5a. Tongue, floor, and roof of mouth white, the rest of mouth dark (below 100 m). ....*Uraspis*
5a. Tongue and mouth not as above...6
6a. Upper and lower jaws without teeth, except a few feeble teeth in lower jaw in young...*Gnathanodon*
6b. Jaw teeth always present, varying from 1 or 2 rows to a band of minute teeth (difficult to detect in some species of *Carangoides*)....................................7
7a. Fleshy adipose eyelid completely covering eye except for vertical slit centered on pupil; terminal ray of D and A finlet-like, a little more separated from other rays, but not detached. and about twice the length of penultimate ray......*Atule*

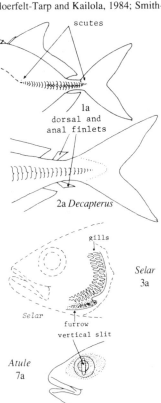

scutes

1a
dorsal and
anal finlets

2a *Decapterus*

gills

Selar
3a

Selar

furrow
vertical slit

Atule
7a

---

* Modified after Smith-Vaniz *in* Smith and Heemstra, 1986.

7b. Fleshy adipose eyelid, if present, not as developed as above; terminal ray of D and A not finlet-like...8

8a. Upper jaw with an outer series of moderate to strong canines and an inner band of fine teeth; lower jaw with a single row of teeth.............................*Caranx*

8b. Both jaws with a band of teeth, at least anteriorly.......................*Carangoides*

9a. A base about 45-70% of D base length; C peduncle grooves present, dorsally and ventrally...10

9b. Base of A as long as, or only slightly shorter than, base of soft D; no C peduncle grooves...12

10a. Single 2-rayed finlet behind end of D and A; maxilla ends distinctly before eye (to below front margin of eye in young)..*Elagatis*

10b. No finlets behind D and A; maxilla ends below eye.................................11

11a. First D spines 4 or 5; A rays 15-17; cutaneous keel laterally on C peduncle well developed (epipelagic)...*Naucrates*

11b. First D spines 7 or 8 (anterior spines may become entirely buried in large fish); A rays 18-22; cutaneous keel laterally on C peduncle absent to moderately developed...*Seriola*

12a. Posterior D and A rays consisting of semi-detached finlets, distal 1/4 to 1/2 of rays not connected by membrane; upper lip joined to snout at midline by a bridge of skin, but crossed by a shallow groove in very young...*Scomberoides*

12b. Posterior D and A rays not consisting of semi-detached finlets; upper lip separated from snout at midline by a continuous deep groove............*Trachinotus*

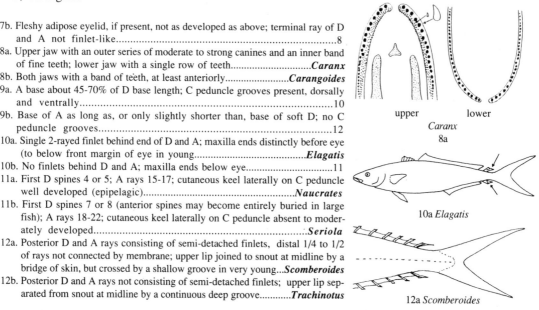

upper   lower
Caranx
8a

10a *Elagatis*

12a *Scomberoides*

Atule mate (Cuvier, 1833)
Yellowtail scad

FL: to 34 cm (13.4 in); D VIII-I, 22-25; A II-I, 18-21; Sc 36-39; GR 10-13+26-31.

This species has heavy adipose tissue over most of the eye and finlet-like last dorsal and anal fin rays. It schools among mangroves and in coastal bays to a depth of perhaps 50 m.

Indo-Pacific: E. Africa to the Hawaiian Is. and Samoa, n. to s. Japan, s. to New Caledonia; Belau and Marshalls in Micronesia.

Decapterus macarellus (Cuvier, 1833)
Mackerel scad

(*D. pinnulatus*)

FL: to 32 cm (12.6 in); D VIII-I, 31-36+1; A II-I, 27-30+1; Sc 24-40, on posterior half of straight portion of LL; GR 10-13+34-38; lower edge of maxillary straight, its distal end slightly-rounded.

Species of *Decapterus* are elongate, nearly round in cross section, and have a one-rayed detached finlet behind the dorsal and anal fins. Three or more species occur in Micronesia, where they inhabit mid-waters of deep lagoons, coastal bays, or offshore waters to depths of 200 m, generally away from coral reefs.

Circumtropical

Decapterus macrosoma Bleeker, 1851   Fig. 1a
Slender scad

FL: to 35 cm (13.8 in); D VIII-I, 33-38+1; A II-I, 27-30+1; Sc 24-40, on posterior 3/4 of straight portion of LL; GR 10-12+34-38; lower edge of maxillary slightly curved, its distal end broadly-rounded.

Indo-pan-Pacific: E. Africa to c. America, n. to s. Japan.

Decapterus maruadsi (Temminck & Schlegel, 1844)
Deep-bodied round scad   Pl. 45A

FL: to 25 cm (9.8 in); D VIII-I, 30-36+1; A II-I, 25-30+1; Sc 30-37, on entire straight portion of LL; GR 12-13+35-39; body deeper, resembles *Selar*.

This species was encountered in large numbers around Guam's first set of fish aggregating devices (FADs), buoys anchored offshore to attract pelagic gamefishes.

West Pacific: S. China Sea to the Marianas.

Selar boops (Valenciennes, 1833)
Yellowband scad

FL: to >18 cm (7.1 in); D VIII-I, 23-25; A II-I, 19-21; Sc 37-46; GR 8-10+25-29.

This species has lower modal dorsal and anal soft ray and gill raker counts, a higher modal straight-line scute count, and a deeper body (depth in FL: ca. 3.3 vs 3.6) than *S. crumenophthalmus*. A broad yellow streak extending from eye to the end of the soft dorsal fin is also often present.

Indo-Australian: Andamans to Vanuatu, n. to the Philippines, s. to nw. Australia; Belau and Pohnpei in Micronesia.

Selar crumenophthalmus (Bloch, 1793)   Fig. 1b
Bigeye scad; Atulai

FL: to 30 cm (11.8 in); D VIII-I, 24-27; A II-I, 21-23; Sc 29-42; GR 9-12+27-31.

The bigeye scad resembles round scads, but has a deeper more compressed body and much larger eye. It is an important foodfish of many tropical coastal regions. In the Marianas, immense schools of subadults appear seasonally from August to November in shallow sandy lagoons, bays, and channels. These may migrate offshore during the night. Adults generally remain offshore to depths of 170 m or more. Bigeye scad feed on small shrimp, benthic invertebrates, and foraminifera when inshore, and zooplankton and fish larvae when offshore.

Circumtropical: n. to s. Japan and the Hawaiian Is., s. to New Caledonia and Rapa; throughout Micronesia.

a. *Decapterus macrosoma*, 233 mm FL, Guam

b. *Selar crumenophthalmus*, 191 mm FL, Guam

c. *Alectis indicus*

d. *Carangoides dinema*

e. *Caranx ignobilis*, 215 mm FL, Guam

f. *Caranx ignobilis*, 835 mm FL, Guam

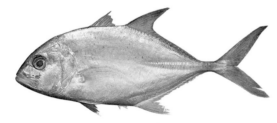

g. *Caranx papuensis*, 194 mm FL, Guam

h. *Caranx sexfasciatus*, 129 mm FL, Guam

i. *Trachinotus blochii*, 68 mm FL, Guam

j. *Trachinotus bailloni*, ca. 400 mm FL, Enewetak

Fig. 1. Micronesian Jacks and Trevallys c, d, after Gloerfelt-Tarp and Kailola, 1984).

Alectis ciliaris (Bloch, 1788)   Pl. 45B; Figs. 2a
Threadfin pompano

FL: to 65 cm (25.6 in), 80 cm (31.5 in) and 18.8 kg (41.5 lb) in Atlantic; D VI (embedded in adults)+I, 18-20; A II-I, 15-17; P 18-20; Sc 12-30; GR 4-6+12-17.

Species of *Alectis* have a pair of small lateral keels on the caudal peduncle and small embedded scales, giving their skin a smooth appearance. In larger individuals the dorsal and anal fin spines disappear under the skin as well. Juveniles of both species are among the most spectacular of jacks. Those under about 16 cm possess long, delicate trailing filamentous dorsal and anal fin rays. These streamers may help the fish resemble a jellyfish and thus gain a certain degree of protection from predation. Juveniles inhabit open seas near the surface; adults usually occur near the bottom at depths of 60 m or more. They are rarely encountered on coral reefs.
Circumtropical: throughout Micronesia.

Alectis indicus (Rüppell, 1830)   Figs. 1c; 2b
Indian threadfish

FL: to 150 cm (59.1 in) and ≥21.4 kg (47.2 lb); D VI (embedded in adult)+I, 18-20; A II-I, 18-20; GR 8-11+21-26; scales minute and embedded.

This species has a distinctly more angular head profile than *A. ciliaris* (Fig. 2b). A school of subadults has been observed at Belau.
Indo-west Pacific: Red Sea and E. Africa to , n. to s. Japan, s. to Australia; Belau in Micronesia.

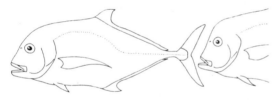

a. *A. ciliaris*   b. *A. indicus*
Fig. 2. Adults of Indo-Pacific species of *Alectis*.

Gnathanodon speciosus (Forsskål, 1775)
Golden trevally   Pl. 45C

FL: to 110 cm (3.6 ft); D VII-I, 18-20; A II-I, 15-17; Sc 15-18; GR 8-9+19-22+27-30.

Juveniles lack teeth in the upper jaw and are bright gold with well-defined black bars. Adults lack teeth entirely and are silvery with a golden sheen and somewhat diffuse dusky bars over the upper half of the body. Tiny juveniles live symbiotically among the tentacles of jellyfish. Those of 5 cm or more often accompany sharks or large groupers. They probably feed on scraps of food and are protected from their host by their small size and maneuverability, and from other predators by the presence of their host. Adults inhabit deep lagoon and seaward reefs where they feed by rooting in the sand for crustaceans and other invertebrates. In Belau, golden trevally aggregate in shallow water to spawn around full moon from November to May.
Indo-pan-Pacific: Red Sea to Panama, n. to the Ryukyu and Hawaiian Is., s. to New Caledonia and the Australs; throughout Micronesia.

Carangoides dinema Bleeker, 1851   Fig. 1d
Shadow kingfish

FL: to 60 cm (23.6 in); D VIII+I, 17-19; A II+I, 15-17; GR 7-9+16-19; str. LL 0-6+Sc 23-30; breast naked to V origin.

Species of *Carangoides* have a band of villiform teeth at least anteriorly in both jaws and lack canines. This trevally is characterized by a series of black rectangular spots at the base of the soft dorsal fin and a dark anal fin. In some individuals the lower half of the pectoral fin and preopercular margin are also dark. At Belau it occurs in large schools at a depth of 15 m or less along steep dropoffs.
Indo-west Pacific: E. Africa to Samoa, n. to s. Japan, s. to Tonga; Belau in Micronesia.

Carangoides ferdau (Forsskål, 1775)
Bar jack   Pl. 45D; Fig. 3b

FL: to >40 cm (15.8 in); D VIII-I, 26-34; A II-I, 21-26; Sc 21-37 small; GR 7-10+17-20; breast naked.

The bar jack occurs in schools in open waters of lagoons and outer reef slopes. It is uncommon in Micronesia.
Indo-Pacific: Red Sea to the Hawaiian and Tuamotu Is., n. to s. Japan, s. to New Caledonia; throughout Micronesia.

a. *C. fulvoguttatus*   b. *C. ferdau* and *C. orthogrammus*
Fig. 3. Naked area of breast of some species of *Carangoides*.

Carangoides fulvoguttatus (Forsskål, 1775)
Yellow-dotted trevally   Fig. 3a

FL: to 82 cm (32.3 in); Wt.: to 18 kg (40 lbs); D VIII-I, 25-30; A II-I, 21-26; Sc 15-21; GR 6-8+17-21; breast naked.

This species is named after the small yellow spots contained within approximately six faint broad dusky bars on its sides. At the Great Barrier Reef, it occurs in large schools along outer reef slopes.
Indo-west Pacific: Red Sea to New Caledonia, n. to the Ryukyus; Belau in Micronesia.

Carangoides orthogrammus Jordan & Gilbert, 1881
Yellow-spotted trevally   Pl. 45E; Fig. 3b
(*C. ferdau jordani*)

FL: to ≥71 cm (28.0 in); Wt.: to 6.1 kg (13.5 lb); D VIII-I, 28-31; A II-I, 24-26; Sc 19-31 small; GR 8-10+20-23; breast naked.

Although this species sometimes has faint chevron bars similar to those of *C. ferdau*, it nearly always has a few small yellow blotches on its sides. Large individuals develop a terminal snout and elongate points on the soft dorsal and anal fins. *C. orthogrammus* occurs in small schools that frequent sandy channels of lagoon and seaward reefs from depths of 3 to 168 m. It is occcasionally observed "rooting" in the sand for small sand-dwelling crustaceans and fishes. Individuals over 40 cm seem to prefer deeper waters. *C. orthogrammus* is a common and important foodfish throughout Micronesia.

Indo-pan-Pacific: w. Indian Ocean to Mexico, n. to s. Japan and Hawaii, s. to Lord Howe Is. and the Australs; throughout Micronesia.

Carangoides plagiotaenia (Bleeker, 1857) Pl. 45F
Barcheek trevally

FL: to >40 cm (15.8 in); D VIII-I, 22-24; A II-I, 18-20; P 20-21; Sc. 11-18 small; GR 8-14+19-27=37-39; breast completely scaled.

This is the only Micronesian carangid with a distinct black bar on the edge of the preopercle, and a nearly, if not completely, scaled breast. It is not uncommon from Belau to the eastern Carolines, but is known from the Marianas on the basis of a specimen fished from a depth of over 200 m. When in shallow water, it typically occurs singly or in small groups along the edges of steep outer reef slopes. At least two other *Carangoides*, the deep-bodied *C. caeruleopinnatus* and *C. talamparoides*, occur in Micronesia but seem to be confined to relatively deep water.

Indo-Pacific: Red Sea to Samoa, n. to the Ryukyus, s. to New Caledonia; throughout Micronesia.

Caranx ignobilis (Forsskål, 1775)
Giant trevally Pl. 46A; Figs. 1e,1f,4a

FL: 165 cm (5 ft 5 in); Wt.: to 68 kg (150 lb); unconfirmed reports of up to 190 cm (6.2 ft) and 95 kg (210 lb); D VIII-I, 17-22(19-20); A II-I, 15-17(16); Sc 26-38; GR 5-7+15-17; breast mostly naked.

Species of *Caranx* are characterized by prominent scutes, a single row of small canines in each jaw and several inner rows of villiform teeth on the upper jaw as well as villiform vomerine and palatine teeth. This is the largest species of *Caranx*. The combination of steep head profile, uniform silver to silvery-black coloration, and mostly naked breast are distinctive. Juveniles occur in small schools over sandy inshore bottoms; adults are usually solitary and range widely over the reef, occuring primarily on seaward reefs to depths of 80 m. They feed primarily on fishes and crustaceans such as crabs and spiny lobsters. Large individuals may be ciguatoxic. *C. ignobilis* gathers to spawn on shallow seaward reefs and offshore banks.

Indo-Pacific: Red Sea to the Hawaiian, Marquesan, and Pitcairn Is., n. to s. Japan, s. to n. New Zealand and Rapa; throughout Micronesia.

 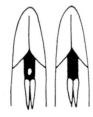

  a. *C. ignobilis*   b. *C. papuensis*
Fig. 4. Naked area of breast of two species of *Caranx*.

Caranx lugubris Poey, 1861 Pl. 46B
Black jack

FL: 91 cm (3.0 ft); Wt.: to 15.5 kg (34.2 lb); D VIII-I, 20-22(21-22); A II-I, 16-19(18); Sc 26-32; GR 6-8+17-22; breast scaled.

This is the only Micronesian *Caranx* that is dull gray to black without a silvery sheen. It occurs singly or in small groups along steep outer reef slopes and offshore banks at depths of 12 to 354 m. It is an important food fish in the Marianas, where it is the most common *Caranx* fished from offshore banks. In certain other areas it may be ciguatoxic.

Circumtropical: n. to s. Japan, s. to New Caledonia; absent from the Red Sea and French Polynesia; throughout Micronesia.

Caranx melampygus (Cuvier, 1833) Pl. 46C
Bluefin trevally
(*C. stellatus*)

FL: to 80 cm (31.5 in); Wt.: to >6.8 kg (15 lb); D VIII-I, 21-24 (22-23); A II-I, 17-21(18-19); Sc 27-42; GR 5-9+17-21; breast scaled.

This is perhaps the most common jack of clear lagoon and seaward reefs. It also occurs in turbid inshore reefs and has been reported from as deep as 190 m. In the Marianas, juveniles, known as Ee, appear in large numbers on shallow sandy inshore reef flats from May to December. Adults often enter channels and inshore reefs during the late afternoon and early morning (and possibly throughout the night) to feed on small free-swimming fishes and crustaceans. They usually occur singly or in small groups, but in Belau, at the south tip of Peleliu (and probably at other current-swept areas), as many as 1,000 or more aggregate during the April new moon to spawn. Large individuals may be ciguatoxic in certain areas.

Indo-pan-Pacific: Red Sea to Panama, n. to the Ryukyu, Izu, and Hawaiian Is., s. to New Caledonia and Ducie; throughout Micronesia.

Caranx papuensis Alleyne & MacLeay, 1877
Brassy trevally Figs. 1g, 4b
(*C. celetus*)

FL: to 80 cm (31.5 in); Wt.: to >6 kg (13.2 lb); D VIII-I, 21-23(22); A II-I, 16-19 (18); Sc 31-39; GR 7-9+18-21; breast mostly or entirely naked.

This species closely resembles the bluefin trevally, but lacks blue on the fins, has a large naked area on the breast, is slightly more elongate, and often has a bronze to greenish cast with scattered black specks. It ranges widely over lagoon and seaward reefs, but is not as common as the bluefin trevally.

Indo-Pacific: E. Africa to the Marquesas, n. to the Ryukyus, s. to New Caledonia and Samoa; Carolines and Marianas in Micronesia.

Caranx sexfasciatus Quoy & Gaimard, 1824
Bigeye trevally Pl. 46D,E; Fig. 1h
(*C. elacate*)

FL: to 85 cm (33.5 in); D VIII-I, 19-22(20-21); A II-I, 14-17 (16-17); Sc 27-36 and black; GR 6-8+15-19; breast scaled.

Juveniles are characterized by six wide dusky bars; adults become somewhat elongate, have dark scutes, and a large patch of adipose tissue behind the eye. Juveniles may be quite abundant around offshore fish aggregating buoys or drifting debris. Adults occur singly or in large schools in deep lagoon, channel, and seaward reef waters to a depth of 96 m. They feed on small fishes and crustaceans, primarily during the night.

Indo-pan-Pacific: Red Sea to Central America, n. to s. Japan and the Hawaiian Is., s. to New Caledonia; throughout Micronesia.

Scomberoides lysan (Forsskål, 1775)   Pl. 47A
Leatherback; Lae
(*S. sanctipetri*)

FL: to ca. 70 cm (27.6 in); D VI to VII-I, 19-21; A II-I, 17-19; scutes absent; GR 3-8+15-20.

The leatherback lacks scutes, has several semi-detached finlets at the end of the dorsal and anal fins, and is covered with tiny needle-like scales imbedded in a tough skin. The dorsal and anal spines are venomous and capable of producing a painful sting. Juveniles occur in shallow inshore and even brackish waters. They have the nasty habit of feeding on scales that they tear off of other fishes such as baitfish or mullet. Adults occur in relatively clear lagoon and seaward reef waters. They are usually seen near the surface but may descend to depths of as much as 100 m. They feed on small fishes and crustaceans. In Kiribati, the leatherback is reported to migrate to the outer reef slope to spawn several days after the full moon.

Indo-Pacific: Red Sea to the Hawaiian, Line, Marquesan, and Tuamotu Is., n. to s. Japan, s. to New South Wales; throughout Micronesia.

Elagatis bipinnulatus (Quoy & Gaimard,1824)
Rainbow runner   Pl. 47B

FL: to 115 cm (3.8 ft); Wt.: to 15.3 kg (33.7 lb); D VI-I, 25-28+2; A I-I, 18-20+2; scutes absent; GR 9-10+25-26.

This small but popular gamefish occurs in large schools from the surface to depths of at least 150 m in clear offshore waters. It occasionally enters deep clear lagoons or seaward reefs as shallow as 3 m. It feeds on pelagic crustaceans and small fishes.

Circumtropical: usually in waters ≥21°C (70°F); entire Indo-Pacific; throughout Micronesia.

Seriola dumerili (Risso, 1810)   Pl. 47C; Fig. 5a
Greater amberjack

FL: to 188 cm (5.3 ft); Wt.: to 80.6 kg (178 lb); D VII-I, 29-35; A II-I, 18-22; GR 5-7 +14-16=20-24 (juvs.), decreasing to 11-19 (adults).

Species of *Seriola* lack scutes. The greater amberjack is a roving predator of deep seaward reefs that occasionally enters coastal bays. It feeds primarily on free-swimming fishes such as bigeye scad. In Micronesia it occurs primarily at depths exceeding 100 m, but in the somewhat cooler Hawaiian Is., it ranges into water as shallow as 8 m and at Johnston Is., has been observed from a submersible as deep as

335 m. In the Marianas, it is an uncommonly caught food-fish that seems to be free of ciguatera, but in areas where it occurs in shallower water, it may often be ciguatoxic.

Circumglobal: n. to s. Japan and the Hawaiian Is., s. to New Caledonia; Marianas and Carolines in Micronesia.

Seriola rivoliana Valenciennes, 1833
Almaco jack   Pl. 47D; Fig. 5b
(*S. songoro*)

FL: to 110 cm (3 ft 6 in); Wt.: to 24 kg (53 lb); D VII-I, 26-33, 1st spine minute or imbedded in adults; A II-I, 18-22; GR 6-9+17-20 =24-29 (juvs.) becoming 22-26 (adults).

The almaco jack differs from the larger greater amberjack by its straighter snout profile, differently shaped maxillary (Fig. 4), lower modal soft dorsal ray count, higher gill raker count, and a more silvery coloration. Juveniles under 18 cm have dark bars on their sides. The almaco jack is a roving predator of small fishes that frequents outer reef slopes and offshore banks to depths of 160 m or more. It rarely occurs at depths of less than 30 m in the Micronesian area.

Circumglobal: n. to the Ryukyus, s. to New Caledonia; absent from the Red Sea and French Polynesia; Marianas and Wake Is. in Micronesia.

a. *S. dumerili*   b. *S. rivoliana*

Fig. 5. Head profiles of Micronesian species of *Seriola* (after Gloerfelt-Tarp and Kailola, 1984).

Trachinotus bailloni (Lacepède, 1802)
Small spotted pompano   Pl. 47E; Fig. 1i

FL: to 33 cm (13.0 in); D V to VI-I, 20-24; A II-I, 20-24; 7-13+15-19.

Species of *Trachinotus* have ovoid bodies and lack scutes. *T. bailloni* is a predator of small fishes that inhabits near surface waters of lagoon and seaward reefs. It is relatively rare in the Marianas.

Indo-Pacific: Red Sea to the Line and Mangareva Is., n. to s. Japan, s. to Lord Howe and Rapa Is.; throughout Micronesia.

Trachinotus blochii (Lacepède, 1802)   Fig. 1j
Silver pompano

FL: to 110 cm (3.6 ft); D VI-I, 18-20; A II-I, 16-18; GR 5-8+8-10.

Juveniles frequent sandy shorelines and shallow sandy or muddy bays in the vicinity of river mouths. Adults move out to clear seaward reefs where they may occur in large schools. Although not particularly common, *T. blochii* is more frequently encountered than *T. bailloni* in the Marianas.

Indo-Pacific: E. Africa to the Marshalls and Samoa, n. to s. Japan, s. to New Caledonia; throughout Micronesia.

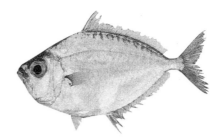

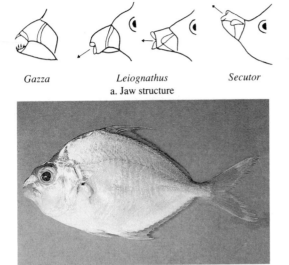

Gazza   Leiognathus   Secutor
            a. Jaw structure

b. *Gazza achlamys*, 133 mm SL

c. *Leiognathus equulus*, 156 mm SL, Guam

d. *Leiognathus stercorarius*, 102 mm SL

Fig. 1. Micronesian ponyfishes (a, after FAO, 1972; b, d, after Gloerfelt-tarp and Kailola, 1982).

LEIOGNATHIDAE
(PONYFISHES; SLIPMOUTHS)

Leiognathids are small highly compressed silvery fishes that have tiny cycloid scales, a highly protrusible mouth, bioluminescent organs in the throat, a single dorsal fin with VIII, 16 rays, and an anal fin with III, 14 rays. The three genera may be differentiated by jaw structure (Fig. 1a). In *Gazza* the mouth contains large canines whereas in *Leiognathus* and *Secutor*, the teeth are close-set and brushlike or small and conical, and the mouth protrudes down and up, respectively. Leiognathids typically occur in schools over muddy or sandy inshore waters, generally away from coral reefs. Some species enter freshwater rivers and some are demersal by day and pelagic by night. The identification of five of the eight species reported from Micronesia requires confirmation. Only Australian material has recently been revised. (Lit.: Dunlap and McFall-Ngai, 1984; Jones, 1985.)

Gazza achlamys Jordan & Starks, 1917   Fig. 1a,b
Large-toothed ponyfish
SL : to ca. 15 cm (5.9 in); D VIII, 16; A III, 14; depth 1.9-2.2 in SL.
Species of *Gazza* feed primarily on small fishes.
Indo-Australian: Sri Lanka to New Guinea, n. to the Philippines; Pohnpei and Guam in Micronesia.

Leiognathus equulus (Forsskål, 1775)   Fig. 1c
Common slipmouth
SL: to 22 cm (8.7 in); D VIII, 16; A III, 14; GR 4-6+13-16=18-21; depth 1.5-2.1 in SL.
This slipmouth has been reported from brackish river

mouths and muddy inshore areas to a depth of 70 m.
Indo-west Pacific: Red Sea to Samoa, n. to the Ryukyus, s. to New Caledonia; Belau to the e. Carolines and Marianas in Micronesia.

Leiognathus stercorarius Evermann & Seale, 1907
Oblong slipmouth   Fig. 1d
SL: to 9.9 cm (3.9 in); D VIII, 16; A III, 14; LL 55-57; depth 2.8-3.7 in SL.
This small, elongate species occurs in inner reef flats and silty coastal waters to a depth of 20 m or more.
Indo-Australian: Indonesia, Philippines, New Guinea, and Guam.

GERREIDAE (MOJARRAS)

Gerreids possess a small protractile mouth like that of the leiognathids, but have large conspicuous cycloid scales and D IX to X spines. They inhabit shallow sandy areas of coral reefs as well as silty inshore areas. They feed by rooting in the sand for small benthic invertebrates. At least five species occur in Micronesia.

Gerres argyreus (Schneider, 1801)   Pl. 47F
Common mojarra
SL: to 19 cm (7.5 in); D IX, 10; A III, 7; P 15-16; LP 41-43; GR 5-6+ ; depth 2.6-2.8 in SL.
This is the most common mojarra of reef flats and shallow lagoons in the Marianas. It occurs singly or in groups and is difficult to approach. In the Gilberts, it forms spawning aggregations for a few days around the new moon.
Indo-Pacific: Red Sea to the Marshalls, s. to Queensland; throughout Micronesia.

a. *Gerres abbreviatus*, Yap (photo by P. N. Paatmag)

b. *Gerres filamentosus*, Yap (photo by P. N. Paatmag)

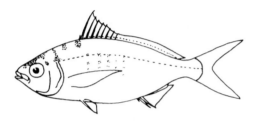

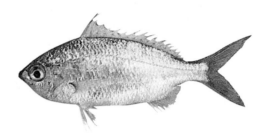

c. *Gerres oblongus* ca. 18 cm SL

d. *Gerres oyena*, 110 mm SL

Fig. 1. Micronesian Mojarras (d, after Gloerfelt-Tarp and Kailola, 1984).

Gerres abbreviatus Bleeker, 1850   Fig. 1a
Deep-bodied mojarra
SL: to 23 cm (9.1 in); D IX, 10; A III, 17; P 17; LP 37-39;
GR 5+7-8; depth 2.1-2.8 in SL.
This species has been reported to a depth of 40 m. In Belau,
it migrates from the mangroves and sand flats to the outer
reef edge to spawn for a few days around full moon.
West Pacific: Indonesia to the Ryukyus; Belau in Micronesia.

Gerres filamentosus Cuvier, 1829   Fig. 1b
Filamentous mojarra
SL: to 25 cm (9.8 in); D IX, 10; A III, 7; P 17; LP 42-47;
GR 5-6+8-9; depth 1.9-2.2.
Indo-west Pacific: Red Sea to Papua New Guinea, n. to s.
Japan; Yap in Micronesia.

Gerres oblongus Cuvier, 1830   Fig. 1c
Oblong mojarra
SL: to 30 cm (11.8 in); D IX, 10; A III, 7; P 17; LP 44-45
(+4-5 on C); GR 5+7; depth 3.0-3.2 in SL.
In Belau this species migrates to specific sandy spots near
the outer reef edge to spawn in late afternoons around full
moon.
Indo-west Pacific: Red Sea to Samoa, n. to the Rykyus, s.
to New Caledonia; Belau and Marianas in Micronesia.

Gerres oyena (Forsskål, 1775)   Fig. 1d
Oyena mojarra
SL: to 20 cm (7.9 in); D IX, 10; A III, 7; P 17; LP 35-39
(+3-4 on C); GR 6+8; depth 2.5-3.0.

Indo-west Pacific: Red Sea to Samoa, n. to s. Japan, s. to
the s. Great Barrier Reef; Carolines in Micronesia.

SILLAGINIDAE (WHITINGS)

Sillago sihama (Forsskål, 1775)   Fig. 1
SL: to 23 cm (9.1 in); D XI to XII-I, 20-21; A II, 21-22; P
14-16; LL 67-69; GR 1-3+8-10.
Whitings are drably colored elongate fishes characterized by
a conical head with small cycloid scales, a small mouth,
small ctenoid scales on the body, a deeply notched dorsal
fin, and a rounded, emarginate, or forked tail. They typically inhabit shallow sandy to muddy inshore waters and river
mouths, generally away from coral reefs. At least one species occurs in Belau, although a recent revision of the family failed to list any Palauan material. The Belauan species
is likely the common and wide-ranging species, *S. sihama*.
(Lit.: McKay, 1986)
Indo-west Pacific: Red Sea to New Caledonia, n. to e. China
and the Ryukyus.

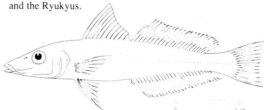

Fig. 1. *Sillago sihama* (after FAO, 1972).

LUTJANIDAE (SNAPPERS)

Snappers are robust perchlike fishes characterized by a continuous dorsal fin, large coarsely ctenoid scales, large canine teeth in both jaws, a maxillary that is mostly covered by the cheek, no spines on the opercle, and an emarginate or forked tail. Most species feed heavily on crustaceans but some feed primarily on fishes and others are planktivores. Some of the larger piscivores may be ciguatoxic. Snappers are among the most important commercial fishes in tropical and subtropical regions. All four subfamilies occur in Micronesia. The Etelinae are primarily deep-dwelling planktivores of pelagic tunicates and crustaceans. *Etelis* (two species), *Pristipomoides* (six species), *Randallichthys filamentosus*, and *Aphareus rutilans* are commercially important bottomfishes found at depths of 90 to 360 m; *Aphareus furca* and *Aprion virescens* occur in shallow to moderately deep water. The Apsilinae is represented in Micronesia by two deepwater planktivores of the genus *Paracaesio*, and the Paradicichthyinae by the shallow water *Symphorichtys spilurus*. The Lutjaninae is represented by two species of *Macolor* and at least 13 species of *Lutjanus* which inhabit shallow to moderately deep reef waters. Gill raker counts in parentheses are for developed rakers only. (Lit.: Allen & Talbot 1985; Johnson, 1980; Kishimoto et al., 1987; Masuda et al., 1984).

Subfamily Etelinae

Aphareus furca (Lacepède, 1802)   Pl. 48A
Blue smalltooth jobfish
SL: to 31.4 cm (12.4 in); D X, 10-11; A III, 8; P 15-16; LP 72-75; GR 6-10+16-18.

This snapper frequently occurs in the open waters close above clear lagoon and seaward reefs at depths of 1 to at least 122 m. It is usually solitary but sometimes occurs in small groups and feeds primarily on small fishes and crustaceans. Small individuals occasionally have bright yellow patches on their snout or head.
Indo-pan-Pacific: E. Africa to Panama, n. to the Ryukyu, Bonin, and Hawaiian Is., s. to Lord Howe and the Austral Is.; throughout Micronesia.

Aprion virescens Valenciennes, 1830   Pl. 48C
Jobfish; Uku
SL: to 80 cm (31.5 in); Wt.: to 22.7 kg (50 lb), rarely > 10 kg (22 lb); D X, 11; A III, 8; P 17-18; LP 48-50; GR 5-9+14-15.

Jobfish occur singly or in small groups in open water above outer reef slopes, channels, and adjacent lagoon waters at depths of 3 to 180 m. They are voracious piscivores that occasionally feed on benthic and planktonic crustaceans and cephalopods and may take a trolled lure as well as a bottom line. Large individuals may be ciguatoxic. In Belau they aggregate to spawn along the outer reef slope from January to May on the full moon and for a few days thereafter.
Indo-Pacific: Red Sea to the Hawaiian, Marquesan, and Tuamotu Is., n. to the Ryukyus, s. to New Caledonia; throughout Micronesia.

Subfamily Paradicichthyinae

Symphorichthys spilurus Günther, 1872
Blue-lined sea bream   Pl. 48B; Fig. 1
SL: to 50 cm (19.7 in); D X, 14-18; A III, 8-11; P 16; LP 53-59; GR 4-6+14-15.

This spectacular snapper has long filamentous rays on the dorsal and anal fins which gradually diminish with age. Juveniles of 10 cm or less are light tan with a broad white

edged black stripe extending from the snout to the upper caudal peduncle. *Symphorichthys* has strong pharyngeal teeth that are used for crushing the mollusks on which it feeds. In Belau, it is reported to undergo a seasonal migration. Throughout most of the year it occurs on inshore lagoon and channel reefs. From March to July, individuals move out from their resident reefs to form large aggregations at specific sites along the reef's edge several days before each new moon. They remain there until they spawn around full moon, then return to their usual territories. These aggregations occur in shallow water in the early morning then move to deeper water each day before noon.
West Pacific: Philippines and Moluccas to New Caledonia, n. to the Ryukyus, s. to Rowley Shoals; Belau in Micronesia.

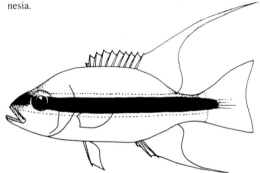

Fig. 1. *Symphorichthys spilurus*, juv. ca 10 cm.

Subfamily Lutjaninae

Macolor macularis Fowler, 1931   Pl. 48D,E
Black-and-white snapper
SL: to >47 cm (18.5 in); D X, 13-14; A III, 10; P 17; LP 50-53; GR 109-122.

Both species of *Macolor* closely resemble one another and undergo the same transition from the black and white juvenile to the nearly black adult. Juveniles under about 10 cm are relatively easy to distinguish from one another: *M. macularis* has elongate pelvic fins, a deeply notched dorsal fin, and clear pectoral fins while *M. niger* has a short pelvic fin, slightly notched dorsal fin and black pectoral fins. Larger juveniles and subadults are more difficult to separate: both species have black pectoral fins and similarly sized pelvic fins, but *M. macularis* generally has more white blotches above the mid-lateral white band (rarely 6, usually >7 vs 4-5 in *M. niger*), and individuals over 25 cm have a slightly different facial pattern consisting of a yellowish background with a reticulate pattern of blue squiggly lines that break up into short dashes and round spots along the lower and rear portions of the operculum (vs light blue squiggly lines on a black background in *M. niger*). Adults are very difficult to separate in the field, differing mainly in details of the facial pattern. Specimens in hand may be separated on the basis of the gill raker count and the size of the exposed portion of the maxillary (larger in *M. niger*). The large eyes and numerous long gill rakers indicate that species of *Macolor* probably feed primarily on larger zooplankton at night. Juveniles of both species closely resemble juvenile *Plectrohinchus picus* which may be toxic, and are solitary. Adults of *M. macularis* usually occur singly or in small groups along steep slopes of lagoons, channels, and seaward reefs at depths of 3 to over 50 m. At Belau, they have been observed among large aggregations of *M. niger*.

West Pacific: Philippines and Bali to the Solomons, n. to Taiwan and the Yaeyamas s. to nw. Australia and New Caledonia; Belau and s. Marianas in Micronesia.

Macolor niger (Forsskål, 1775)   Pl. 48F,G
Black snapper

SL: to >55 cm (21.8 in); D IX-X, 13-15(X 13-14); A III, 10-(11); P 16-18(17); LP 49-58; GR 89-108.

Adult *M. niger* usually occur in aggregations along steep slopes of lagoons, channels, and seaward reefs at depths of 3 to 90 m. They probably disperse to feed at night. Along the vertical wall of the "Corner" off leeward Belau, *M. niger* often forms an enormous aggregation of perhaps 300 or more individuals that stretches from the surface to a depth of over 30 m.

Indo-Pacific: Red Sea to Samoa, n. to the Ryukyus, s. to New Caledonia; throughout Micronesia.

Lutjanus argentimaculatus (Forsskål, 1775)
River snapper   Pl. 49A; Fig. 2a

SL: to > 70 cm (28 in); Wt.: to 16 kg (35.3 lb); D X, 13-14; A III, 7-(8); P 16-17; LP 44-48; GR 6-8+9-12=16-20(0-1+7-8).

The river snapper is easily distinguished from the twinspot snapper by its longer snout and truncate tail as well as a more bronze to greenish coloration. Juveniles may have several blue streaks on the face. This species prefers turbid inshore reefs and continental coastlines to a depth of 120 m. Juveniles are common in brackish or freshwaters of the lower reaches of rivers. In Belau, adults move to deep lagoon or outer reefs to spawn around full moon, with spawning acitivity peaking during the late spring and summer. Its diet consists of benthic invertebrates and fishes.

Indo-Pacific: Red Sea to Samoa and the Line Is., n. to the Ryukyus, s. to New South Wales; Belau to e. Carolines and Marianas in Micronesia.

Lutjanus biguttatus (Valenciennes, 1830)
Two-spot snapper   Pl. 49D

SL: to 173 cm (6.8 in); D XI, 12 A III, 8; P 15-(16); LP 48-50; GR 7-8+16-19=23-25(2+14-15).

This small colorful snapper inhabits outer reef slopes at depths of 3 to 36 m. It appears uncommon at Belau. and Kapingamarangi, but in some areas may occur in schools of 100 or more.

Indo-west-Pacific: Maldives to the Solomons, n. to the Philippines, s. to the n. Great Barrier Reef; Belau and Kapingamarangi in Micronesia.

Lutjanus bohar (Forsskål, 1775)   Pl. 49B,C
Twinspot snapper; Red snapper

SL: to > 76 cm (30 in); Wt.: to 13 kg (28.7 lb); D X, 13-14; A III, 8; P 16-17; LP 48-51; GR 6-7+16=22-23(all distinct).

Juveniles under 20 cm are predominantly gray with two conspicuous white spots beneath the dorsal fin. Occasionally they are bicolored, becoming abruptly pale posteriorly. In certain areas, small juveniles mimic the planktivorous damselfish *Chromis ternatensis* (p. 167). By schooling in midwater with the damselfish, they may be able to approach unwary prey more easily. The twinspot snapper inhabits exposed seaward reefs and adjacent lagoon and channel waters, at depths of 4 to 180 m. It tends to be more abundant around atolls and low islands than around high islands. It occurs singly or in large roving groups and is generally quite wary. When stimulated by food, it can be quite aggressive and will even swim among sharks engaged in a feeding frenzy. It feeds primarily on fishes and to a lesser extent on crustaceans, cephalopods and other mollusks. It is the most frequently ciguatoxic fish in the Indo-Pacific and is banned from sale in many areas. It matures at a size of about 45 cm FL. In Belau, it aggregates to spawn along the outer reef slope around full moon, with peak activity from April to July.

Indo-Pacific: Red Sea to the Line, Marquesan, and Tuamotu Is., n. to the Ryukyus, s. to Lord Howe Is.; throughout Micronesia.

Lutjanus decussatus (Cuvier, 1828)   Pl. 49E
Checkered snapper

SL: to 25 cm (9.8 in); D X, 13-14; A III, (8)-9; P 16-17; LP 47-50; GR 6+8-10=14-16(1+6-8).

The checkered snapper inhabits inshore and offshore reefs at depths of 2 to 30 m. It occurs singly or in schools and is rare at Belau.

Indo-west Pacific: Sri Lanka and e. India to w. New Guinea, n. to the Ryukyus, s. to Rowley Shoals; Belau in Micronesia.

Lutjanus ehrenbergi (Peters, 1869)   Pl. 49F
Blackspot snapper

SL: to 25.5 cm (10.0 in); D X, 13-14; A III, 7-(8); P 15-16; LP 42-47; GR 6-7+10-14=16-22(1+7-10).

This striped species inhabits lagoon and seaward reefs around high islands. Juveniles frequent turbid inshore areas over sand, coral, or rubble and occasionally enter mangroves.

a. *Lutjanus argentimaculatus*, 33.5 cm, Truk

b. *Lutjanus malabaricus*, 53 cm

c. *Lutjanus rivulatus*, 50 cm

d. *Lutjanus vitta*, 22.5 mm

Fig. 2. Micronesian snappers. (b,c,d, after Gloerfelt-Tarp and Kailola, 1984)

Indo-west Pacific: Red Sea to New Ireland, n. to Taiwan, s. to the n. Great Barrier Reef; Belau to Kosrae in Micronesia.

Lutjanus fulvus (Scneider, 1801) Pl. 50A
Flametail snapper
SL: to 34.5 cm (13.6 in); D X, 13-14; A III, 8; P 15-17 (16); LP 47-50; GR 6-7+10-13=16-20(1-2+7-9).
The flame tailed snapper inhabits lagoon and semiprotected seaward reefs at depths of 1 to 75 m. It prefers sheltered areas with deep holes or large boulders and sometimes enters mangroves or the lower reaches of rivers. It feeds primarily at night on benthic crustaceans and fishes. Dominant prey include calapid crabs, mullet, goatfishes, and damselfishes. In Tahiti it spawns around full moon.
Indo-Pacific: Red Sea to the Line, Marquesan, and Tuamotu Is., n. to s. Japan, s. to New South Wales; throughout Micronesia.

Lutjanus gibbus (Forsskål, 1775) Pl. 50B,C
Humpback snapper
(*Anthias heraldi*)
SL: to 41.9 cm (16.5 in); D X, 13-14; A III, 8; P 16-17; LP 47-51; GR 9-10+15-20=25-30(all distinct).
The humpbacked profile and enlarged upper lobe of the tail of adults are distinctive. Coloration ranges from a pinkish grey with maroon fins to a brilliant orange-red. Juveniles are a light gray with numerous oblique dark pinstripes becoming abruptly black along a diagonal running from the soft dorsal fin to the lower caudal peduncle. Juveniles inhabit seagrass beds and mixed sand and coral habitats of shal-low sheltered reefs; adults prefer deeper lagoon and seaward reefs to a depth of 150 m, but occasionally occur on outer reef flats. During the day, adults may occur in large tightly packed aggregations along the upper edges of steep slopes. They probably disperse at night to feed primarily on crustaceans and to a lesser extent on echinoids, gastropods, worms, octopuses, and small fishes. Large adults may be ciguatoxic. In Belau spawning aggregations form along outer reef slopes around full moon throughout the year.
Indo-Pacific: Red Sea to the Line and Tuamotu Is., n. to the Ryukyus, s. to New Caledonia; throughout Micronesia.

Lutjanus kasmira (Forsskål, 1775) Pl. 50D
Bluelined snapper
SL: to 26.1 cm (10.3 in); D X, 14-15; A III, 7-8; P 15-17 (16); LP 48-51; GR 7-8+13-14=20-22(1-2+8-9).
The bluelined snapper occurs in a variety of habitats ranging from shallow inshore lagoons to as deep as 265 m on the outer reef slope. Juveniles may occur in seagrass beds as well as on seaward reefs. During the day it often forms large aggregations around prominent coral formations, isolated patch reefs, or wrecks. At night it disperses to feed on benthic crustaceans and fishes. It is among the most common species fished at night at depths of about 30 to 150 m. Off South Africa, it matures at 17 to 20 cm FL and spawns in late winter and spring.
Indo-Pacific: Red Sea to the Line, Marquesan, and Tuamotu Is., n. to s. Japan, s. to Lord Howe Is., throughout Micronesia; introduced to the Hawaiian Is.

Lutjanus malabaricus (Schneider, 1801)   Fig. 2b
Malabar snapper
SL: to > 49.5 (19.5 in); Wt.: to 13.6 kg (30.0 lb); D XI,
12-14; A III, 8-9; P 16-17; LP 46-50; GR 4-7+12-14=18-
20(1-2+9-11).
This "red" snapper occurs on coastal and offshore reefs at
depths of 12 to over 90 m. Juveniles have a complex color
pattern; adults are uniformly red.
Indo-west Pacific: Persian Gulf to Fiji, n. to Taiwan, s. to
New South Wales; Belau in Micronesia.

Lutjanus monostigmus (Cuvier, 1828)   Pl. 50E
Onespot snapper
SL: to 44.5 cm (17.5 in); D X, (13)-14; A III, 8; P 15-17;
LP 47-50; GR 7+11-12=18-19(1+6-7).
The onespot snapper inhabits outer lagoon and seaward reefs
to a depth of 60 m and enters shallow reef flats at night. It
is fairly common along reef margins where there is an abun-
dance of deep cuts and holes. It occurs singly or in small
groups and feeds primarily on fishes, to a lesser extent on
benthic crustaceans, primarily crabs. In some areas, it may
be severely ciguatoxic.
Indo-Pacific: Red Sea to the Line, Marquesan, and Tuamotu
Is., n. to the Ryukyus, s. to new Caledonia; throughout
Micronesia.

Lutjanus rivulatus (Cuvier, 1838)   Figs. 2c,3
Scribbled snapper
SL: to 63.7 cm (25.1 in); Wt.: to 11 kg (24.3 lb); D X, 15-
16; A III, 8; P 17; LP 47-49; GR 6+11-12=17-18(0-1+7-8).
Juveniles possess a distinctive white spot with a dark anterior border; adults are dirty yellow with a pattern of fine blue
reticulations on the face and white-centered scales on the
sides. It occurs on inshore as well as offshore reefs from
the reef flat to a depth of at least 100 m. It appears to be rare
in Micronesia where it has been recorded from Belau and
possibly observed at Guam.
Indo-Pacific: Red Sea to the Society Is., n. to the Ryukyus,
s. to the Great Barrier Reef; Belau (and the Marianas?) in
Micronesia.

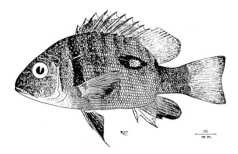

Fig. 3. *Lutjanus rivulatus*, ca. 78 mm (after Fowler, 1931).

Lutjanus semicinctus Quoy & Gaimard, 1824
Half-barred snapper   Pl. 50F
SL: to 27.7 cm (10.9 in); D X, 13; A III, 8; P 16; LP 47-
49; GR 6-7+8-12=14-19(1+6-8).

This unmistakable snapper inhabits reef flats and lagoon and
seaward reefs to a depth of 36 m. It is relatively common in
the eastern Carolines.
West-central Pacific: Philippines and Moluccas to Kiribati
and Fiji, s. to New Caledonia; Truk, Kosrae, Kapingamarangi, and Ebon in Micronesia.

Lutjanus vitta (Quoy & Gaimard, 1824)   Fig. 2d
One-lined snapper
SL: to 27.5 cm (10.8 in); D X, 13-14; A III, (8)-9; P 15-16;
LP 49-51; GR 6-7+9-12=15-19(1-2+8).
This species was reported to be common at Kapingamarangi
lagoon, but is rare or absent from the rest of Micronesia. It
is reported to occur in small groups over flat bottoms with
scattered coral outcrops at depths of 10 to 72 m.
Indo-Pacific: Seychelles(?) and w. India to Vanuatu and New
Caledonia, n. to s. Japan; Belau, Kapingamarangi, and the
Marshalls in Micronesia.

CAESIONIDAE (FUSILIERS)

Fusiliers are closely related to snappers, but possess several
adaptations for a pelagic, planktivorous mode of life. These
include a more elongate fusiform body, small ctenoid scales,
a small terminal mouth with a very protrusible upper jaw,
small conical teeth, and a deeply forked tail. During the day
they occur in large zooplankton feeding schools in mid-water
over the reef, and are particularly abundant along steep outer
reef slopes and around deep lagoon pinnacles. Although
they are generally constant and rapid swimmers, they readily
pause at cleaning stations, and shelter within the reef at
night. At least 10 species in three genera occur in Micronesia. (Lit.: Bell and Colin, 1986; Carpenter, 1987)

Subfamily Caesioninae

Caesio caerulaurea Lacepède, 1801   Pl. 51A
Scissor-tailed fusilier
SL: to 23.5 cm (9.3 in); D X, 14-16(15); A III, (12)-13; P
19-22(≥20); LL 57-65; GR 8-9+22-26; depth 3.0-4.2.
This is perhaps the most common ceasionid in the Marianas
where it occurs in deep lagoons and along outer reef slopes.
Indo-Pacific: E. Africa to Samoa, n. to s. Japan, s. to the
Great Barrier Reef and New Caledonia; throughout Micro-
nesia.

Caesio cuning (Bloch, 1791)   Pl. 51B
(*C. erythrogaster*, Masuda et al., 1984)
SL: to 23.0 cm (9.1 in); D X, 14-16(15); A III, 11; P 17-
20(18-19); LL 45-51; GR 11-13+24-27; depth 2.2-3.1.
This is probably the most common of the deep-bodied spe-
cies of *Caesio* along steep outer reef slopes in Belau.
Indo-west Pacific: Sri Lanka to New Caledonia, n. to the
Ryukyus, s. to nw Australia and the Great Barrier Reef; Be-
lau in Micronesia.

Caesio lunaris Cuvier, 1830   Pl. 51C
Lunar fusilier

SL: to 26.4 cm (10.4 in); D X, 13-15(13-14); A III, 10-(11); P 18-21(19-20); LL 45-53; GR 9+19; depth 2.5-3.5.
This species is fairly common off the steep outer reef drop-offs of Belau.

Indo-west Pacific: Red Sea to Vanuatu, n. to the Ryukyus, s. to Rowley Shoals and the Great Barrier Reef; Belau to Ifaluk in Micronesia.

Caesio teres Seale, 1906   Pl. 51D
Yellowback fusilier

(*C. xanthonotus*, Amesbury and Myers, 1982)

SL: to 26.6 cm (10.5 in); D X, 14-16(15); A III, (12)-13; P 18-23(20-22); LL 51-61; GR 10-11+24-26; depth 2.7-4.2.
Juveniles sometimes occur singly or in small groups that seek shelter near the reef among schools of small plankti-vores. Adults occur in large fast-swimming schools typical of other caesionids. *C. teres* is relatively uncommon in the Marianas but may be abundant elsewhere in Micronesia. At Enewetak, yellowback fusiliers aggregate to spawn near the mouth of the main deep channel for a few days around full moon from March to August. Mass spawning takes place near the surface at the beginning of an outgoing tide.

Indo-Pacific: E. Africa to the Line Is., n. to s. Japan, s. to New Caledonia and Samoa; throughout Micronesia.

Pterocaesio lativittata Carpenter, 1987   Pl. 51E
Yellowstreak fusilier

SL: to 11.4 cm (4.5 in); D X, 14-16(15); A III, (12)-13; P 21-23(21-22); LL 74-88; depth 4.1-5.3.
This species was occasionally observed in large schools off the steep dropoffs of Belau to a depth of over 40 m. It differs from the similar *P. chrysozona* by having a wider lateral yellow stripe that extends above the lateral line anteriorly and a pinker ground color.

Indo-west Pacific: Chagos Arch., Cocos-Keeling Is., Papua New Guinea, and Belau.

Pterocaesio marri Schultz, 1953   Pl. 51F
Twinstripe fusilier

(*P. chrysozona*, Amesbury and Myers, 1982; *P. kohleri*)

SL: to 27.0 cm (10.6 in); D (X)-XI, 14-16(15); A III, 11-13(12); P 22-24(≤23); LL 68-76; GR 8-10+25; depth 3.4-4.6.
This species sometimes schools with *P. tile* above both clear lagoon and seaward reefs.

Indo-Pacific: E. Africa to the Marquesas, n. to s. Japan, s. to Samoa; throughout Micronesia.

Pterocaesio tile (Cuver, 1830)   Pl. 51F
Bluestreak fusilier

SL: to 21.2 cm (8.3 in); D X-XII(XI-XII), 19-22; A III, 13; P 22-24; LL 69-76; GR 9-10+26; depth 3.3-5.4.
The irridescent blue band on the side of this fusilier is un-mistakable. This species occurs in large, often densely packed schools along outer reef slopes and in clear deep atoll lagoons to a depth of 60 m. At Guam, its population has

fluctuated widely in recent years. Although previously considered uncommon, in May 1981, enormous schools of 6 to 7 cm SL juveniles appeared on many of Guam's shallow sandy reef flats for several days after the third lunar quarter and the species has remained relatively common since then. It is fairly common throughout Micronesia.

Indo-Pacific: E. Africa to the Marquesas and Mangareva, n. to s. Japan, s. to New Caledonia and Rapa; throughout Micronesia.

Pterocaesio pisang (Bleeker, 1853)   Pl. 51G
Ruddy fusilier

SL: to 13.8 cm (5.4 in); D (X)-XI, 14-16(15); A III, 11-13 (12); P 18-20(18-19); LL 63-71; GR 10+24; depth 3.6-4.8.
This rather drab reddish fusilier occurs in schools of about 20 to 100 or more above both lagoon and seaward reefs.

Indo-Pacific: E. Africa to Kiribati and Fiji, n. to the Ryukyus, s. to Scott Reef and New Caledonia; Belau and Pohnpei in Micronesia.

Pterocaesio trilineata Carpenter, 1987   Pl. 51H
Three-striped fusilier

SL: to 13.0 cm (5.9 in); D (X)-XI, 14-16(15); A III, 11-(12); P 19-22(≤20); GR 8-11+24-30; LL 62-75; depth 3.3-4.9.
This species occurs in schools of 50 to 100 or more above lagoon and windward seaward reefs of Belau. It was uncommon or absent from the vertical walls of the southwestern barrier reef. It has also been photographed at New Caledonia.

West-central Pacific: Philippines to Kiribati and Fiji, s. to New Caledonia and Norfolk Is.; Belau and Pohnpei in Micronesia.

Subfamily Gymnocaesioninae

Gymnocaesio gymnopterus (Bleeker, 1856)   Fig. 1

SL: to 13.6 cm (5.4 in); D (X-)XI, 14-16(15); A III, 11-13 (12); P 20-22(≥21); LL 64-74; GR 7-9+22-27; depth 3.3-6.0.
Gymnocaesio differs from *Caesio* and *Pterocaesio* by lacking scales on the basal portions of the dorsal and anal fins and by lacking premaxillary teeth. The single species in the genus is known from Micronesia on the basis of a collection of 24 juveniles under 48 mm SL taken in shallow water near the ship pass at Kapingamarangi (Rofen, 1961).

Indo-west Pacific: Red Sea to the Solomons and Vanuatu, n. to the Philippines; Kapingamarangi in Micronesia.

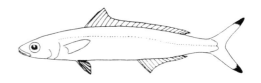

Fig. 1. *Gymnocaesio gymnopterus.*

HAEMULIDAE (SWEETLIPS and GRUNTS)

Haemulids are closely related to lutjanids. They differ by having smaller mouths somewhat lower on the head with small conical teeth and thickened lips, having pharyngeal teeth, and lacking canine and palatine teeth. Some species in this family earn the common name "grunt" by their ability to make grunting sounds by grinding their pharyngeal teeth and amplifying the sound with their gas bladder. Haemulids are primarily nocturnal: during the day they generally hover under or near overhangs or tabular corals, at night they disperse to feed on benthic invertebrates. The are not as wary as most other large fishes. Consequently, they are easy targets for spearfishermen and have become scarce in the heavily fished waters of Guam. Most species of *Plectorhinchus* are colorful and undergo dramatic changes in coloration with growth. Identification of striped juveniles is difficult and their taxonomy remains unresolved. Approximately nine species of *Plectorhinchus*, and one each of *Diagramma* and *Pomadasys* occur in Micronesia. (Lit.: Lee, 1985; Smith, 1962)

Diagramma pictum (Thunberg, 1792)
Slatey sweetlips
Pl. 52A; Fig. 1d,f
SL: to 78 cm (30.7 in); D IX-X, 21-26; A III, 7-8; P 16-17; LS 69-72; LP 116-118; GR 6-9+12-15; depth 2.6-2.7.
The single species of *Diagramma* differs from *Plectorhinchus* by having a much longer and narrower caudal peduncle and fewer dorsal fin spines. Juveniles are colorful and resemble juveniles of certain species of *Plectorhinchus*, but become a dull silvery-gray as they mature. *Diagramma pictum* inhabits lagoon and seaward reefs to a depth of at least 40 m. It prefers sandy to muddy bottoms close to patch reefs where it aggregates during the day.
Indo-west Pacific: Red Sea to New Caledonia, n. to s. Japan, s. to New South Wales; Belau in Micronesia.

Plectorhinchus albovittatus (Rüppell, 1835)
Two-striped sweetlips
Pl. 52C
SL: to ca. 250 cm (9.9 in); D XIII, 17-18; A III, 7; P 17; LP 58; LS ca. 72-85; GR 9+19-21; depth 2.5-2.7.
Two specimens recently collected at Guam are provisionally identified as this species. Until revisionary studies are completed, it is impossible to be certain if they are not juveniles of *P. gaterinoides*. Their color patterns are identical to that of *P. albovittata*, but counts could fit either species (DXIII, 18; A III, 6-7; P 17; GR 6-8+19-20; LS ca. 70; depth 2.8). Unlike *P. gatereinoides*, the color pattern of *P. albovittata* does not change markedly with growth, with only the lowermost white stripe disapearing in adults.
Indo-west-Pacific: Red Sea to Celebes, n. to Taiwan.

Plectorhinchus celebecus (Bleeker, 1873)
Celebes sweetlips
Pl. 52B
SL: to 41 cm (16.3 in); D XII-XIII, 18-21; A III, 7; P 17; LS 56-59; LP ca. 73; GR 12-13+19-20; depth 2.7.
This colorful blue and yellow striped species prefers shel-

tered reefs at depths of 8 to 25 m. It is generally solitary.
West Pacific: Moluccas to Papua New Guinea, n. to the Ryukyus, s. to the Great Barrier Reef; Belau in Micronesia.

Plectorhinchus chaetodonoides (Lacepède, 1800)
Harlequin sweetlips
Pl. 53A,B; Fig. 1g
SL: to 60 cm (23.6 in); D XI-XII, 18-20; A III, 7-8; P 16-17; LP 55-58; GR 10+26-30; depth 2.2-2.5.
Like most *Plectorhinchus*, this species undergoes a dramatic change in coloration with growth. The colorful juveniles swim with a conspicuous exaggerated undulating motion. It has been suggested that this mimics a toxic invertebrate such as a flatworm or that juvenile sweetlips themselves are toxic. In Belau, adults are fairly common in coral rich areas of clear lagoon and seaward reefs at depths of 1 to at least 30 m. They are solitary, and during the day, are usually seen hovering under ledges or tabular corals. They feed primarily at night on crustaceans, mollusks, and fishes.
West Pacific: Sumatra to New Caledonia, n. to the Ryukyus, s. to Rowley Shoals; Belau (and Yap?) in Micronesia.

Plectorhinchus gaterinoides (Cuvier, 1830)
Lined sweetlips
Pl. 52D; Fig. 1e
(*P. lineatus* Gloerfelt-Tarp and Kailola, 1982; *P. diagrammus* Masuda et al., 1984)
SL: to 40 cm (15.7 in); D XII-XIII, 18-22; A III, 7-8; P 16-18; LP 53-65; LS 80-84; GR 6-8+11-20; depth 2.7-2.8.
This species seems to exhibit a wide range of variation in the width and number of stripes. Adults differ from those of *P. orientalis* by lacking stripes on the belly and juveniles are striped rather than blotched. During the day this species occurs under coral ledges of channel and outer reef slopes.
Indo-Pacific: Red Sea (?) to New Caledonia, n. to the Ryukyus; Belau in Micronesia.

Plectorhinchus gibbosus (Lacepède, 1802) Fig. 3d
Gibbus sweetlips
(*P. nigrus*)
SL: to 59 cm (23.3 in); D XIII-XIV, 15-16; A III, 7-8; P 16-17; LP 50-55; LS ca. 59; GR 9-10+18-20; depth 2.35.
This drab sweetlips prefers turbid inshore reefs to a depth of 20 m or more.
Indo-west Pacific: Red Sea to Samoa, n. to the Ryukyus, s. to the Great Barrier Reef; Carolines and Marianas in Micronesia.

Plectorhinchus goldmanni (Bleeker, 1853) Pl. 52E
Goldman's sweetlips
SL: to 60 cm (23.6 in); D XII-XIII, 19-20; A III, 7; P 17; LP 56-58; LS ca. 75; GR 7-9+19-20; depth 2.7-3.0.
This is the only Micronesian sweetlips with diagonal rather than horizontal stripes. During the day it occurs singly or in small groups in coral rich areas of outer reef slopes and channels at depths of 2 to at least 30 m. It forages at night over shallow reef flats for crustaceans. It is somewhat warier than other sweetlips. In Belau, it aggregates to spawn around new moon.
West Pacific: Moluccas and Philippines to New Caledonia, n. to the Ryukyus; Belau in Micronesia.

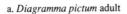
a. *Diagramma pictum* adult

b. *Plectorhinchus obscurus* juv. 152 mm, Guam

c. *Plectorhinchus obscurus* 80.7 cm, Guam

d. *Plectorhinchus gibbosus* 33.4 cm, Truk

e. *Pomadasyus kaakan* 22 cm

f. *Diagramma pictum* juvs. ca. 44 mm

g. *Plectorhinchus chaetodonoides* juv. ca. 125 mm

h. *Plectorhinchus gaterinoides* juv. ca. 50 mm

Fig. 3. Micronesian sweetlips and grunts (a,e, after Gloerfelt-Tarp and Kailola, 1984; f, g, h, after Fowler, 1931).

Plectorhinchus obscurus (Günther, 187 i)
Giant sweetlips   Pl. 52F, Figs. 3b,c
SL: to 83 cm (32.7 in); Wt.: to 15 kg (33 lb); D XII-XIII,
17-20; A III, 7; P 15-17; LS 55-60; LP ca. 85; GR 6-9+19-
23; depth 3.0-3.2.
Small juveniles are dark gray with black fins and one to two
thin oblique white stripes along the back. In life, adults of
this large sweetlips appear slate gray with abruptly black
outer soft dorsal and anal fins. Large solitary adults are rarely observed along outer reef slopes at depths of 2 to 50 m.
In Belau, it aggregates to spawn about once a year around
new moon of April or May.
Indo-Pacific: Red Sea to Fiji, s. to New Caledonia; throughout Micronesia.

Plectorhinchus orientalis (Bloch, 1793)   Pl. 53C,D
Oriental sweetlips
(*P. lineatus* Amesbury and Myers,1982;Masuda et al.,1984)
SL: to 72 cm (28.4 in); D XII-XIV, 17-21; A III, 7-8; P 17-
18; LP 60-65; LS 90-100; GR 8-12+20-23=28-35; depth
2.6-3.1.
This species undergoes a remarkable transformation with
size. Juveniles under about 15 cm have numerous large
cream blotches on a dark brown background; adults are
striped. This species occurs on seaward reefs at depths of 2
to over 25 m.
Indo-west Pacific: E. Africa to Samoa, n. to the Ryukyus,
s. to New Caledonia; Belau to the e. Carolines and Marianas
in Micronesia.

Plectorhinchus picus (Cuvier, 1830)   Pl. 53E,F
Spotted sweetlips
(*P. orientalis* Amesbury and Myers, 1982)
SL: to 70 cm (27.6 in); D XII-XIV, 17-20; A III, 7-8; P 17-
18; LP 70-75; LS 100-120; GR 8-10+23-25; depth 2.9-3.3.
Juveniles under 25 cm are black with a few large white
blotches; adults are a silvery white with numerous small
dark spots. This species inhabits lagoon and seaward reefs
to depths of 3 to at least 50 m. It is generally solitary and
found under or near coral ledges during the day.
Indo-Pacific: Seychelles to the Society Is., n. to Japan, s.
to Lord Howe and Rapa Is; throughout Micronesia.

Pomadasyus kaakan (Cuvier, 1830)   Fig. 3e,h
Common javelinfish
SL: to 32 cm (12.6 in); D XII 13-15; A III, 7-8; P 16-18;
LS 43-49; LP 46-50; GR 5-6+12-13; depth 2.7-2.9.
This silvery species prefers turbid inshore waters with sandy
to muddy bottoms to a depth of 75 m.
Indo-west Pacific: Red Sea to New South Wales, n. to s. Ja-
pan; Belau in Micronesia.

NEMIPTERIDAE
(THREADFIN BREAMS and SPINECHEEKS)

This family consists of small to moderate sized fishes with a

small terminal mouth in which the maxilla never extends
beyond the center of the eye, bands of small conical teeth in
the jaws with or without canines anteriorly, large ctenoid
scales, a continuous unnotched dorsal fin with X spines and
8 to 11 rays, and an emarginate or forked caudal fin. Some
species of *Pentapodus* and *Nemipterus* have a filamentous
upper caudal lobe. Species of *Scolopsis* have a strong back-
ward pointing spine immediately under the eye, hence the
name spinecheek. Protogynous hermaphroditism has been
demonstrated in *Scolopsis bilineatus* and *S. monogramma*,
and is likely in all species. (Lit.: Young and Martin, 1985;
Lee, 1986)

Scolopsis bilineatus (Bloch, 1793)
Twoline spinecheek   Pl. 54A; Fig. 1
SL: to 20 cm (7.9 in); D X, 9; A III, 7; P 17; LL 44-46;
GR 5+5.
Juveniles have three black stripes on a cream background
above the level of the pectoral fin. They occur near the shel-
ter of scattered patches of branching corals in shallow pro-
tected lagoons. Adults occur singly in the vicinity of sand
patches of lagoon and sheltered seaward reefs at depths of 1
to at least 25 m.
West Pacific: Andamans to Fiji, n. to s. Japan, s. to New
Caledonia; Belau to Pohnpei in Micronesia.

Fig. 1. *S. bilineatus* 55 mm (after Fowler, 1931).

Scolopsis ciliatus (Lacepède, 1802)   Pl. 54B
Ciliate spinecheek
SL: to 16 cm (6.2 in); D X, 8-9; A III, 7-8; P 16-17; LL
40-43; GR 5+8-9.
This species occurs singly or in small groups over sandy
lagoon or sheltered seaward bottoms with scattered corals.
Indo-west Pacific: Mauritius (?) and India to New Caledonia,
n. to the Ryukyus; Belau and Yap in Micronesia.

Scolopsis lineatus Quoy & Gaimard, 1824
Black-and-white spinecheek   Pl. 54C,D
(*S. cancellatus*)
SL: to 20 cm (7.9 in); D X, 9; A III, 7; P 14-17; LL 40-
46; GR 5+4.
Juveniles of this species closely resemble those of *S.
bilineatus*. They occur near the shelter of corals on clear
shallow lagoon reefs. Adults often form large shoals on
outer lagoon, reef flat, and semi-protected seaward reefs to
depth of at least 10 m. They feed on benthic invertebrates,
primarily polychaetes, and to a lesser extent on benthic
planktonic crustaceans.
Indo-Pacific: Andamans to the Gilberts, n. to the Ryukyus,
s. to Tuvalu and the s. Great Barrier Reef; throughout
Micronesia.

Scolopsis margaritifer (Cuvier, 1830)   Pl. 54E
Margarite's spinecheek

SL: to 19.5 cm(7.7 in); D X, 9; A III, 7; P 16-17;LL35-39.
This relatively deep-bodied spinecheek is a solitary inhabitant of lagoon patch reefs among the rock islands of Belau.
West Pacific: Sumatra to New Caledonia, n. to se. China and Taiwan, s. to Scott Reef; Belau in Micronesia.

Scolopsis affinis Peters, 1877   Pl. 54F
Spinecheek

SL: to over 20 cm (7.9 in); D X, 9; A III, 7; P 16-18; LL 43-46.
This species occurs singly or in small groups over sandy bottoms with scattered corals in both lagoons and on sheltered seaward slopes.
Indo-Australian: Bali, Molucas, and Belau; undoubtedly more widespread but limits of distribution uncertain due to confusion with *S. monogramma.*

Scolopsis trilineatus Kner, 1868   Pl. 54G
Threeline spinecheek

SL: to 17 cm (6.6 in); D X, 9; A III, 7; P 15-16; LL 41-44.
This generally solitary species occurs over silty bottoms with scattered corals among the inner rock islands of Belau.

West Pacific: Moluccas to Samoa, n. to the Philippines, s. to Scott Reef and New Caledonia; Belau in Micronesia.

Pentapodus caninus (Cuvier, 1830)   Pl. 54H
Canine-toothed mid-water bream

SL: to 22 cm (8.7 in); D X, 9; A III, 7; P 15-16; LL 41-47; GR 5+5.
Species of *Pentapodus* are midwater planktivores. This species inhabits lagoons and sheltered bays around the deeper coral heads.
West-central Pacific: Madagascar to the Gilberts, n. to the Philippines, s. to Papua New Guinea; Belau and the Marshalls in Micronesia.

Pentapodus macrurus (Bleeker, 1852)   Pl. 55A
Redfin mid-water bream

SL: to 30 cm (11.8 in); D X, 9; A III, 7; P 16; LL 45-47; GR 5-6+5-7.
This species occurs in loose aggregations high above patch reefs of lagoons and sheltered bays. It is quite common in Apra Harbor, Guam.
West Pacific: s. South China Sea and Java to Nauru, n. to the Ryukyus; Marianas in Micronesia.

LETHRINIDAE (EMPERORS)

The emperors are closely related to the snappers but differ primarily by possessing a maxillary completely hidden by a naked or near-naked preopercle and conical or molariform teeth on the sides of the jaws. Emperors also have fairly thick lips, canine teeth in the front of the jaws, a continuous dorsal fin with X spines and 9 to 10 rays, and an anal fin with III spines and 8 to 10 rays. Most species feed primarily at night, but some also feed during the day or may rest at night. Those with molariform teeth feed mostly on hard-shelled invertebrates. Others feed on fishes and may be ciguatoxic in certain areas. Protogynous hermaphroditism (sex reversal from female to male) has been demonstrated in several species of *Lethrinus*. At least 3 species of *Gymnocranius*, 13 species of *Lethrinus*, and the monotypic *Gnathodentex*, *Monotaxis*, and the deep water *Wattsia* occur in Micronesia. (Lit.: Sato, 1978; Randall, 1973; Young and Martin, 1982)

Gnathodentex aurolineatus (Lacepède, 1802)
Yellowspot emperor   Pl. 55D

SL: to 21 cm (8.3 in); D X, 10; A III, 10; P 14; LP 60-70.
This relatively common, distinctively marked species inhabits reef flats, lagoons, and seaward reefs to a depth of over 30 m. During the day it generally aggregates between coral heads or in gullies. In certain areas as many as several hundred may hover motionless in a compact mass. At night they disperse to feed on benthic invertebrates such as crabs and gastropods, as well as an occasional small fish.
Indo-Pacific: E. Africa to the Line, Marquesan, and Mangareva Is., n. to s. Japan, s. to n. New South Wales and Rapa Is.; throughout Micronesia.

Monotaxis grandoculus (Forsskål, 1775) Pl. 55B.C
Bigeye emperor

SL: to 45 cm (17.7 in), possibly to 58 cm (22.8 in); Wt.: to ≥ 3.4 kg (7.5 lb); D X, 10; A III, 9; P 13-(14); LP 44-47; TRac 5.

Small juveniles have four permanent black bars and a relatively pointed snout. With growth, the dark bars become dusky, then silvery with white interspaces, and the snout becomes blunt. Adults have the ability to "turn" the white interspaces on or off at will, but large adults are usually an overall silver. The bigeye emperor is relatively common over sandy patches and channels of both lagoon and seaward reefs at to depths of 1 to at least 100 m. Juveniles are solitary, but adults may form loose aggregations during the day that tend to hover along the upper edges of steep slopes or a few meters above the sand at the base of reefs. They disperse at night to feed on hard-shelled sand-dwelling invertebrates such as crustaceans, mollusks, and sea urchins. Occasionally they feed on fishes and may rarely be ciguatoxic in certain areas. In Belau, they aggregate to spawn at the base of reef slopes on the first five days of the lunar month.
Indo-Pacific: Red Sea to the Hawaiian, Marquesan, and Pitcairn Is., n. to the Ryukyus, s. to New Caledonia; throughout Micronesia.

a. *Gymnocranius griseus* 252 mm, Guam

b. *G. euanus*, 475 mm, Rota

c. *Gymnocranius* sp., 402 mm, Guam

d. *Lethrinus lentjan* 256 mm

Fig. 1. Micronesian species of *Gymnocranius* and *Lethrinus* (d, after Glorefelt-Tarp and Kailola, 1984).

Gymnocranius griseus (Schlegel, 1843) Fig. 1a
Gray emperor
SL: to 34 cm (13.4 in); TRac 6; depth 2.1-2.2 (7-30 cm); caudal lobes pointed.

Gymnocranius is characterized by D X, 9-10; A III, 9-10; P 14; LP 46-52; GR 2-4+5-6. *Gymnocranius* differs from *Monotaxis* by lacking denticulated ridges on the lower exposed portion of the maxillary. Both genera are relatively deep bodied and possess stout canines in the front of the jaws and molariform teeth in the sides. *Gymnocranius* is in need of revision. Identification is difficult due to virtually identical meristics and similar coloration among the species. Subtle differences in color, the shape and depth of the body, and shape of the tail seem to be the only useful distinguishing characters. Most species exhibit a dusky bar through the eye, scattered dark scales on the sides, and a certain degree of red on the fins. They occur over sand or rubble substrates of deep lagoon and seaward reefs at depths of about 6 to over 100 m and are uncommon in Micronesia. This species' more ovoid body and pointed caudal lobes are distinctive.

Indo-west Pacific: E. Africa to Vanuatu, n. to s. Japan, s. to nw. Australia and Queensland; Marianas in Micronesia.

Gymnocranius euanus (Günther, 1879) Fig. 1b
Japan sea bream (*G. japonicus*)
SL: to 43 cm (16.9 in); TRac (5)-6; depth 2.3- 2.5; caudal lobes rounded.

This species usually lacks blue markings on the snout and

develops red on the upper and inner portions of the pectoral fins with age.

West-Pacific: s. South China Sea to Tonga; n. to s. Japan; s. to Queensland; Marianas in Micronesia.

Gymnocranius sp. Fig. 1c
Stout emperor (*G. lethrinoides* Masuda et al., 1984)
SL: to 41 cm (16.1 in); TRac 6; depth ca. 2.4 (41 cm); caudal lobes rounded.

This species usually has a broad light blue interorbital band and scattered blue spots on the snout. It is the most frequently encountered *Gymnocranius* in the Marianas.

West-central Pacific: E. Indies to Fiji, n. to s. Japan, s. to New Caledonia; Marianas and Marshalls (?) in Micronesia.

Gymnocranius microdon (Bleeker, 1851)
SL: to 41 cm (16.1 in).
TRac 6; depth ca. 2.7 (33 cm); caudal lobes pointed.

This species has small blue spots densely distributed on its snout and occasionally on its operculum, but differs from *Gymnocranius* sp. by having pointed caudal lobes and a more elongate body.

West-central Pacific: E. Indies, n. to s. Japan; Marshalls in Micronesia.

Genus *Lethrinus*: Many species are capable of rapid changes in coloration and often adopt a pattern of dark reticulations or blotches that render identification in the field difficult.

Even with the specimen in hand, meristics are nearly useless since all species share the following: D X, 9; A III, 8; P 13; LP 45-49; TRa 5-6 (most species have one or the other); GR 4-6+4-6; preopercle naked.

Key to the Micronesian species of *Lethrinus*:*

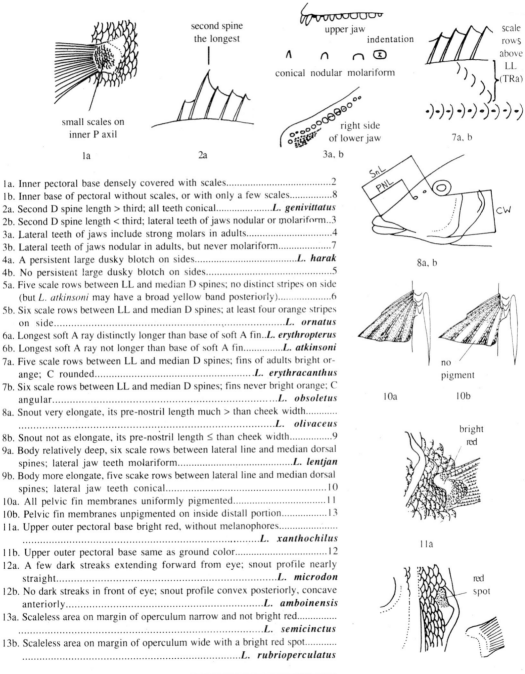

1a. Inner pectoral base densely covered with scales.......................................2
1b. Inner base of pectoral without scales, or with only a few scales..............8
2a. Second D spine length > third; all teeth conical....................*L. genivittatus*
2b. Second D spine length < third; lateral teeth of jaws nodular or molariform..3
3a. Lateral teeth of jaws include strong molars in adults.............................4
3b. Lateral teeth of jaws nodular in adults, but never molariform..................7
4a. A persistent large dusky blotch on sides.........................*L. harak*
4b. No persistent large dusky blotch on sides...5
5a. Five scale rows between LL and median D spines; no distinct stripes on side
   (but *L. atkinsoni* may have a broad yellow band posteriorly)...................6
5b. Six scale rows between LL and median D spines; at least four orange stripes
   on side..*L. ornatus*
6a. Longest soft A ray distinctly longer than base of soft A fin..*L. erythropterus*
6b. Longest soft A ray not longer than base of soft A fin..............*L. atkinsoni*
7a. Five scale rows between LL and median D spines; fins of adults bright orange; C rounded...*L. erythracanthus*
7b. Six scale rows between LL and median D spines; fins never bright orange; C
   angular..*L. obsoletus*
8a. Snout very elongate, its pre-nostril length much > than cheek width...........
   ....*L. olivaceus*
8b. Snout not as elongate, its pre-nostril length ≤ than cheek width..............9
9a. Body relatively deep, six scale rows between lateral line and median dorsal
   spines; lateral jaw teeth molariform.........................*L. lentjan*
9b. Body more elongate, five scake rows between lateral line and median dorsal
   spines; lateral jaw teeth conical..10
10a. All pelvic fin membranes uniformly pigmented.............................11
10b. Pelvic fin membranes unpigmented on inside distall portion.................13
11a. Upper outer pectoral base bright red, without melanophores.....................
   ....*L. xanthochilus*
11b. Upper outer pectoral base same as ground color.............................12
12a. A few dark streaks extending forward from eye; snout profile nearly
   straight...*L. microdon*
12b. No dark streaks in front of eye; snout profile convex posteriorly, concave
   anteriorly..*L. amboinensis*
13a. Scaleless area on margin of operculum narrow and not bright red.............
   ....*L. semicinctus*
13b. Scaleless area on margin of operculum wide with a bright red spot...........
   ....*L. rubrioperculatus*

*Based on Sato, 1978; most figures redrawn from Sato, 1978.

Lethrinus amboinensis Bleeker, 1854
Ambon emperor

(*L. variegatus* Schultz, 1953; ?*L. reticulatus* Schultz, 1953)
SL: to 57 cm (22.4 in); depth 3.0-3.2; teeth conical.
The status of this species is uncertain. It lacks distinctive markings, being an overall dark to light greenish brown becoming paler ventrally, sometimes with widely scattered dark spots and reddish outer fin rays, and has a distinctly convex anterior snout profile. It inhabits rubbly and sandy areas of lagoon and seaward reefs and feeds primarily on fishes and to a lesser extent on mollusks, crustaceans, and sea urchins. It is common at Enewetak and Bikini Atolls.
Tropical W. Pacific: Moluccas to the Marquesas, n. to the Ryukyus; Marianas and Marshalls in Micronesia.

Lethrinus atkinsoni Seale, 1909
Yellowbrow emperor   Fig. 2a

(*L. mahsena* Myers and Shepard, 1980; *L. mahsenoides* Myers, 1988)
SL: to 41 cm (16.1 in); lateral teeth molariform.
The combination of yellow on top of the eye, yellowish sheen from the upper body, and yellowish fins help distinguish this from other lethrinids with 5 scale rows above the lateral line. In the Marianas, it is a relatively uncommon inhabitant of seagrass beds and sandy areas of lagoons and outer reef slopes at depths of 2 to over 18 m.
Indo-west Pacific: Indonesia to the Tuamotus, n. to s. Japan, s. to New Caledonia; Belau and the Marianas in Micronesia.

Lethrinus erythracanthus Cuvier, 1830   Pl. 56B
Orangefin emperor

(*L. kallopterus*)
SL: to 67 cm (26.4 in); Wt.: to ca. 9 kg (19.8 lb); some lateral teeth nodular.
This is probably the largest, though not the longest, species of *Lethrinus*. The deep body, blunt snout with orange spots, and rounded bright orange fins of adults are distinctive. The orangefin emperor occurs in deep lagoons and around sandy areas of channels and outer reef slopes at depths of 23 to 120 m. It feeds on echinoids, mollusks, crinoids, and starfish, and in some areas may be ciguatoxic. It is rare around the heavily fished reefs of Guam.
Indo-Pacific: E. Africa to the Tuamotus, n. to the Ryukyus; throughout Micronesia.

Lethrinus erythropterus Valenciennes, 1830
Masked emperor   Pl. 56A

(*L. hypselopterus*)
SL: to 38 cm (15.0 in); lateral teeth include molars.
At Belau this distinctively patterned *Lethrinus* was observed at depths of 2 to 10 m along the upper edges of steep outer reef slopes along the southwestern barrier reef. It occurred singly or in small groups.
Indo-west Pacific: E. Africa to the Solomons, n. to the Philippines; Belau in Micronesia.

Lethrinus genivittatus Valenciennes, 1830   Fig. 2c
Longspine emperor

(*L. nematacanthus*)

SL: to 20 cm (7.9 in); lateral teeth small and pointed.
This is the only *Lethrinus* in which the second dorsal spine is the longest. It is reported from channels and outer reef slopes at depths of 5 to 25 m.
West Pacific: w. Indonesia to New Caledonia, n. to s. Japan; Kosrae in Micronesia.

Lethrinus harak (Forsskål, 1775)   Pl. 55F
Blackspot emperor

SL: to 49 cm (19.4 in); usually < 30 cm (12 in); lateral teeth molariform.
In the Marianas, this is perhaps the most common emperor of seagrass beds and sandy to rubbly areas of reef flats, shallow lagoons, and channels. It feeds primarily on benthic invertebrates and has been known to exploit the efforts of slower moving fishes such as the cowfish by stealing worms from its victim's mouth as soon as they are pulled free from the sediment. At Belau, it is reported to aggregate in lagoons to spawn during the first five nights of the lunar month throughout much of the year.
Indo-Pacific: Red Sea to Samoa, n. to s. Japan, s. to New Caledonia; throughout Micronesia.

Lethrinus lentjan Lacepède, 1802   Fig. 1d
Redspot emperor

SL: to 42 cm (16.5 in); lateral teeth molariform.
This species inhabits lagoon and seaward reefs at depths of about 20 to 70 m.
Indo-west Pacific: Red Sea to Tonga, n. to the Ryukyus, s. to New Caledonia; Belau in Micronesia.

Lethrinus microdon Valenciennes, 1830   Fig. 2b
Smalltooth emperor

SL: to 53 cm (20.9 in); teeth conical.
This species closely resembles *L. elongatus* but has a shorter head and snout that form a relatively straight profile. At Belau, it spawns during the first five days of the lunar month throughout much of the year with a peak in April.
Indo-west Pacific: Red Sea to the Moluccas, n. to the Ryukyus, s. to nw. Australia; Belau and Kapingamarangi in Micronesia.

Lethrinus obsoletus (Forsskål, 1775)   Pl. 56C
Yellowstripe emperor

(*L. ramak*)
SL: to 34 cm (13.5 in); lateral teeth nodular, but not molariform.
This emperor generally exhibits a broad yellow stripe extending from the pectoral base to the tail. It may also have two thinner stripes above and one below, or can rapidly "turn off" all of its stripes at will. It is common in seagrass beds and sandy or rubbly areas of shallow lagoon and seaward reefs to a depth of over 25 m.
Indo-Pacific: Red Sea to Samoa, n. to the Ryukyus, s. to New Caledonia and Tonga; throughout Micronesia.

Lethrinus olivaceus Valenciennes, 1830   Pl. 55E
Longnose emperor

(*L. miniatus* of most recent authors; *L. elongatus*)

a. *L. atkinsoni*, 261 mm, 8 m, Guam

b. *L. microdon*

c. *L. genivittatus*

d. *L. ornatus* 15 cm

Fig. 2. Micronesian species of *Lethrinus* (b-d, after Glorefelt-Tarp and Kailola, 1984).

SL: to 84 cm (33.1 in); Wt.: to > 7.3 kg (16.1 lb); teeth conical.

This is probably the largest, and certainly the longest-snouted lethrinid. Large courting males may develop a crimson cast on the face and fins. The longnose emperor occurs on both lagoon and seaward reefs at depths of 1 to 20 m. It feeds primarily on fishes as well as on a variety of crustaceans. Large individuals may be ciguatoxic. At Belau, it may occur in large schools and spawns along the edge of the reef for a few days following new moon throughout the year. It is a very wary fish that is rarely seen by divers in heavily fished areas.

Indo-Pacific: Red Sea to Samoa, n. to s. Japan, s. to New Caledonia; throughout Micronesia.

Lethrinus ornatus Valenciennes, 1830   Fig. 2d
Ornate emperor

SL: to 24 cm (9.6 in); lateral teeth molariform.

The combination of broad yellow stripes, red opercular edge, deep body, and short snout are distinctive. In the eastern Carolines, the ornate emperor is a common inhabitant of inshore bays and lagoons.

Indo-west Pacific: India to New Guinea, n. to s. Japan, s. to Queensland; e. Carolines in Micronesia.

Lethrinus rubrioperculatus Sato, 1978   Pl. 56D
Redgill emperor

SL: to 43 cm (16.9 in); teeth conical.

The small red spot on the upper corner of the operculum is distinctive. The redgill emperor inhabits sandy and rubbly areas of outer reef slopes at depths below 12 m. In the

Marianas, it is among the most abundant species taken by bottomfishing at depths of about 25 to 150 m.

Indo-Pacific: E. Africa to the Marquesas, n. to s. Japan, s. to New Caledonia; Marianas in Micronesia.

Lethrinus semicinctus Valenciennes, 1830   Pl. 56E
Reef flat emperor

SL: to 29 cm (11.4 in); teeth conical.

This species inhabits sandy subtidal reef flats and shallow lagoons. It often exhibits a broad dark midlateral stripe.

West Pacific: Moluccas to Vanuatu, n. to the Ryukyu and Bonin Is., s. to Queensland; Marianas in Micronesia.

Lethrinus xanthochilus (Klunzinger, 1870)
Yellowlip emperor   Pl. 56F
(*L. microdon* Schultz, 1953)

SL: to 59 cm (23.2 in); teeth conical.

This large, narrow-bodied emperor differs from *L. elongatus* by having a shorter snout and head with a relatively straight or concave, rather than convex, profile. In addition, it usually has a red spot at the upper base of the pectoral fins and yellowish lips. The yellowlip emperor inhabits shallow lagoon areas of mixed coral rubble and sand as well as seagrass beds. It sometimes occurs in groups of six or more, but is uncommon in heavily fished areas. It is curious but wary and may follow a diver while remaining near the limit of visibility. It feeds on hard-shelled invertebrates such as sea urchins and crabs as well as on small fishes.

Indo-Pacific: Red Sea to the Marquesas, n. to the Ryukyus, s. to New Caledonia; throughout Micronesia.

MULLIDAE (GOATFISHES)

Goatfishes are characterized by an elongate body with relatively large, finely ctenoid scales; a prominent pair of long barbels under the chin; two widely separated dorsal fins with VIII-9 rays (the first spine is often minute); I, 7 anal rays; a small mouth with a slightly protruding upper jaw; and forked caudal fin. The three Micronesian genera are differentiated primarily by dentition: *Mulloides* has several irregular rows of tiny teeth in the jaws and 34 to 36 lateral line scales; *Parupeneus* has a single row of well-spaced conical teeth and 27 to 29 lateral line scales; and *Upeneus* has villiform teeth in both jaws as well as on the prevomer and palatines. The most recognizable feature of the goatfishes is the pair of long barbels located under the chin. These barbels contain chemosensory organs and are used to probe the sand or holes in the reef for the benthic inverte-brates or small fishes on which goatfishes feed. When not in use, the barbels are tucked between the lower portion of the gill covers. Some species of goatfishes are active primarily at night and tend to hover in stationary aggregations or rest on coral ledges by day. Others are most active by day, or active by day or night. Goatfishes are relatively soft bodied and highly esteemed as a food, both by humans as well as by certain predatory fishes. *Parupeneus* and *Upeneus* are in need of revision.

Mulloides flavolineatus (Lacepède, 1801)
Yellowstripe goatfish
Pl. 57A; Fig. 1a

(*Mulloidichthys samoensis*)
SL: to 36 cm (14.1 in), rarely > 23 cm (9.1 in); A I, 7; P 16-18; LL 34-39; GR 7-9+16-21=24-31; depth 3.6-4.7; SnL 1.7-2.6 in HL.

The yellowstripe goatfish is one of the most abundant goat-fishes of shallow sandy flats to a depth of 35 m or more. It differs from the closely related *M. vanicolensis* by having a longer snout, slightly more elongate body, fewer lower limb gill rakers, and certain differences in color. When foraging, *M. flavolineatus* replaces much or all of its lateral yellow stripe with a single oblong black blotch on the middle of each side. It feeds during both the day and night on sand-dwelling invertebrates such as crustaceans, mollusks, worms, and heart urchins as well as foraminiferans, fish eggs, or an occasional small fish. When inactive, it rests in groups on the bottom. In Belau, *M. flavolineatus* spawns over shallow sandy areas near the reef's edge for several days following the new moon. In the Marianas females as small as 123 mm, and males as small as 112 mm, may be ready to spawn. There, spawning occurs from December to September with peaks from March to April. Large schools of sil-very post-larvae, called *tiao*, appear on the reef flats between March and June. The post larvae loose their silvery colora-tion within a few days of settlement. The relatively large size at settlement (6 to 8 cm SL) and wide geographic distri-bution are indicative of a larval period lasting several weeks.
Indo-Pacific: Red Sea to the Hawaiian, Marquesan, and Du-cie Is., n. to the Ryukyus and Bonins, s. to Lord Howe and Rapa Is.; throughout Micronesia.

Mulloides vanicolensis (Valenciennes, 1831)
Yellowfin goatfish
Pl. 57B,C; Fig. 1b

(*Mulloidichthys auriflamma*)
SL: to 31 cm (12.3 in); A I, 7-8; P 16-17; LL 36-42; GR 7-10+21-26=29-36; depth 3.3-3.9; SnL 2.1-2.6 in HL.

This common goatfish varies in coloration from an orange with a pair of thin yellow longitudinal stripes, to white with yellow fins. It inhabits reef flats and lagoon and seaward reefs to a depth of 113 m. During the day it hovers in large inactive aggregations along the reefs edge or near the shelter of large coral mounds. At night it disperses to feed over sand flats on much the same fare as does *M. flavolineatus*.
Indo-Pacific: Red Sea to the Hawaiian, Marquesan, and Tu-amotu Is., n. to s. Japan, s. to Lord Howe Is.; throughout Micronesia.

Mulloides pflugeri (Steindachner, 1900)
Fig. 2
Orange goatfish

SL: to 40 cm (15.7 in); A I, 7-8; P 17-18; LL 36-38; GR 27-30; depth 3.4-3.8; SnL 2.2-2.3 in HL.

This is the only Micronesian goatfish that when freshly caught is a uniform reddish-orange becoming paler ventrally. It occurs at depths exceeding 30 m down to at least 110 m and is rarely encountered by divers. When feeding it displays a pattern of four alternating broad dark and light red bars (Randall, 1986).
Indo-Pacific: Réunion to the Hawaiian, Marquesan, and So-ciety Is., n. to the Ryukyus, s. to Tonga; Marianas and Mar-shalls in Micronesia.

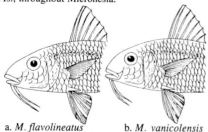

a. *M. flavolineatus*   b. *M. vanicolensis*
Fig. 1. Relative snout length of two species of *Mulloides*.

Fig. 2. *M. pflugeri*, 377 mm FL, Rota Banks, Mariana Is.

Parupeneus barberinoides (Bleeker, 1852)
Half-and-half goatfish   Pl. 57D
SL: to 25 cm (9.8 in); P 14-16(16); LL 28-30; GR 6-7+22-23=27-33; depth 3.2-3.5; SnL 1.0-2.0 in HL.
This spectacular goatfish occurs over mixed sand, rubble, and seaweed covered bottoms. It seems to be relatively rare in Micronesia.
West-central Pacific: Moluccas and Philippines to w. Samoa, n. to the Ryukyus, s. to New Caledonia and Tonga; Belau, Carolines, and Marshalls in Micronesia.

Parupeneus barberinus (Lacepède, 1801)
Dash-and-dot goatfish   Pl. 57E,F; Pl. 59A
SL: to 50 cm (19.7 in); P 16-18(17-18); LL 29-30; GR 6-7+20-23=26-31; depth 3.1-3.5; SnL 1.8-2.1 in HL.
This is one of the most abundant species of *Parupeneus* over large sand patches as well as sand and rubble areas of reef flats, and lagoon and seaward reefs to a depth of about 100 m. During the day it forages singly or in groups for sand dwelling invertebrates, primarily polychaete worms and crustaceans. It is solitary and rests on the bottom at night. Individuals from Belau to the e. Carolines often have a yellow band immediately above the broad black band extending behind the eye. The dark band and spot may become red in large individuals.
Indo-Pacific: E. Africa to the Line, Marquesan, and Tuamotu Is., n. to s. Japan, s. to New Caledonia; throughout Micronesia.

Parupeneus bifasciatus (Lacepède, 1801)
Two-barred goatfish   Pl. 58A,B; Pl. 103H
(*P. crassilabrus* Lachner *in* Schultz et al., 1960)
SL: to 27 cm (10.5 in); P 15-16; LL 27-30; GR 7-10+26-31=34-42; depth 2.7-3.3; SnL 1.7-2.0 in HL.
This species occurs in two color forms that may actually represent different species. The "continental" form has three very distinct dark patches on a light background that do not extend much beyond the level of the upper pectoral axil as well as rows of yellow spots, one in the center of each scale, on the sides. The "Pacific Plate" form usually has two wide bars that extend at least to the belly (these may become indistinct in large individuals) and a ground color that ranges from a light grey to brown or red. *P. bifasciatus* occurs singly or in small groups on both lagoon and seaward reefs at depths of 1 to 80 m. Juveniles range on to reef flats; adults tend to occur around rocky or coralline areas of high vertical relief. They feed primarily on crustaceans during the day and on fishes and crab larvae during the night.
Indo-Pacific: "continental form": E. Africa to Tuvalu and New Caledonia, n. to s. Japan (?); Belau to Kosrae in Micronesia; "Pacific Plate" form: Belau (?) to the Hawaiian, Marquesan, Rapa, and Ducie Is., n. to s. Japan; Marshalls and Marianas in Micronesia.

Parupeneus ciliatus (Lacepède, 1801)   Pl. 58E,F
White-lined goatfish
(*P. porphyreus* Amesbury and Myers, 1982; *P. pleurotaenia* Masuda et al., 1984)
SL: to 32 cm (12.6 in); P 15; LL 28-30; GR 6-7+23-35=30-32.
The white-lined goatfish is one of a complex of four or more similarly colored species. It occurs in seagrass beds as well as coralline areas of lagoon and seaward reefs at depths of 2 to 40 m, but is not particularly common in Micronesia. During the day it is usually seen resting on corals. It probably forages on benthic invertebrates at night.
Indo-Pacific: w. Indian Ocean to the Line, Marquesan, and Tuamotu Is., n. to s. Japan, s. to New Caledonia and Rapa; Marianas in Micronesia; replaced by *P. porphyeus* in the Hawaiian Is.

Parupeneus cyclostomus (Lacepède, 1801)
Yellowsaddle goatfish; Yellow goatfish   Pl. 58C,D
(*P. luteus*; *P. chryserydros*)
SL: to 41 cm (16.1 in); P (16)-17; LL 27-32; GR 5-9+21-25=27-32; depth 3.4-3.9; SnL 1.65-2.0 in HL.
This large goatfish occurs in a variety of primarily clear-water habitats from reef flats and lagoons to a depth of at least 92 m on seaward reefs. It prefers coral, rock, or rubble bottoms and, unlike most goatfishes, feeds primarily on small fishes which are driven from holes with the long, probing barbels. It is inactive at night. It is occasionally accompanied by the bluefin trevally, *Caranx melampygus*, which most likely takes advantage of the goatfishes probing by snatching up fishes driven from hiding before the goatfish can get to them. Small individuals occur singly or in small groups while large ones are usually solitary. Individuals from deeper water may be primarily pink. A brilliant uniformly yellow morph occurs throughout its range except for the Hawaiian Islands.
Indo-Pacific: Red Sea to the Hawaiian, Line, Marquesan, and Tuamotu Is., n. to the Ryukyus, s. to New Caledonia and Rapa; throughout Micronesia.

Parupeneus heptacanthus (Lacepède, 1801)
Redspot goatfish   Fig. 3
(*P. cinnabarinus*)
SL: to 23 cm (9.1 in); P 14-(16); LL 27-28; GR 5-7+20-22=26-29; depth 3.0-3.5; SnL 1.75-2.0 in HL.
This is the only Micronesian goatfish that is light pink with a distinctive small red spot immediately beneath the lateral line under the rear of the first dorsal fin. It occurs singly or in groups over muddy, sandy, rubbly, or seagrass bottoms of lagoon and seaward reefs to a depth of at least 60 m. It is rarely encountered by divers.
Indo-Pacific: Red Sea to Samoa, n. to s. Japan, s. to Lord Howe Is.; throughout Micronesia.

Fig. 3. *P. heptacanthus* 212 mm, Guam.

Parupeneus indicus (Shaw, 1803)   Pl. 58F
Indian goatfish
SL: to 40 cm (15.7 in); P 15-(16); LL 26-31; GR 6+19-21; depth 3.3-3.5; SnL 1.9-2.2 in HL.

The Indian goatfish generally inhabits relatively turbid coastal waters of less than 20 m depth. It occurs singly or in groups and feeds on small benthic invertebrates.

Indo-west Pacific: E. Africa to Samoa and Tonga, n. to the Philippines, s. to New Caledonia; Belau to Kosrae in Micronesia.

Parupeneus multifasciatus (Quoy & Gaimard, 1824)
Multibarred goatfish   Pl. 59A,B,C
(*P. trifasciatus* Lachner *in* Schultz et al., 1960; Amesbury and Myers, 1982)

SL: to 24 cm (9.3 in); P 15-17(16-17); LL 27-30; GR 7-10+28-33=37-42; depth 3.0-3.8; SnL 1.7-1.9 in HL.

This is probably the most common and ubiquitous goatfish throughout its range. It occurs over sand patches as well as rubble, consolidated limestone, or coral bottoms from reef flats and shallow lagoons to a depth of 140 m. During the day it forages singly or in small groups; at night it is inactive. It feeds primarily on small crabs and shrimps, to a lesser extent on fishes, demersal fish eggs, mollusks, and foraminiferans. Males mature at the small size of 18 cm or less. It aggregates to spawn along the sides of deep channels and along steep seaward slopes.

West-central Pacific: Christmas Is., Indian Ocean to the Hawaiian, Line, Marquesan, and Tuamotu Is., n. to s. Japan, s. to Lord Howe and Rapa Is.; throughout Micronesia.

Parupeneus pleurostigma (Bennett, 1830)   Pl. 59D
Sidespot goatfish
SL: to 25 cm (9.8 in).; P 15-17(16); LL 28-32; GR 6-8+22-24=29-32; depth 3.7-3.9; SnL 1.8-2.1 in HL.

This uncommon species closely resembles certain variations of *P. multifasciatus*, but that species always has at least a trace of a dark bar in front of the dark bar preceding the light blotch. The sidespot goatfish occurs in seagrass beds as well as over sand, rubble, or coral and rock bottoms of shallow lagoons and seaward reefs to a depth of at least 46 m. It feeds on a wide variety of benthic animals ranging from small crabs, crab larvae, shrimps, and mantis shrimps, to polychaete worms, heart urchins, peanut worms, gastropods, pelecypods, foraminiferans, brittle stars, and fishes.

Indo-Pacific: E. Africa to the Hawaiian, Line, Marquesan, and Tuamotu Is., n. to the Ryukyus, s. to Lord Howe and Rapa Is.; throughout Micronesia.

Upeneus taeniopterus Cuvier, 1829   Fig. 4a
Band-tailed goatfish
(*U. arge*)

SL: to 25 cm (10.0 in); P 13-(14); LL 36-38(37); GR 5-7+14-17=21-23; depth 3.7-4.3.

Species of *Upeneus* generally inhabit sheltered, often turbid inshore waters over sand or mud bottoms. All Micronesian species have a banded tail. At Tarawa, this species migrates to the outer reef edge to spawn for several days around the new moon. In the Hawaiian Islands, this species is known

as the "nightmare weke": its brain is toxic during certain times of the year and when eaten, causes its victims to hallucinate!

Indo-Pacific: E. Africa to the Hawaiian, Line, and Tuamotu Is., n. to the Yaeyamas; throughout Micronesia.

a. *U. taeniopterus*   b. *U. tragula*   c. *U. vittatus*
Fig. 4. Tail patterns of Micronesian species of *Upeneus*.

Upeneus tragula Richardson, 1846   Pl. 59E; Fig. 4b
Blackstriped goatfish
SL: to 28 cm (11.0 in); P 12-14; LL 29-33; GR 5-6+15-19=21-25; depth 3.7-4.0; SnL 2.3-2.5 in HL.

This unmistakable species occurs singly or in small groups over sandy to muddy bottoms and has been known to enter the lower reaches of rivers. It is relatively common among Belau's Rock Islands.

Indo-Pacific: E. Africa to Vanuatu and New Caledonia, n. to s. Japan; Belau in Micronesia.

Fig. 5. *Upeneus vittatus* (after Fowler, 1959).

Upeneus vittatus (Forsskål, 1775)   Fig. 4c, 5
Yellowbanded goatfish
SL: to 25 cm (9.8 in); P 15-17; LL 32-38; GR 6-9+16-22=25-31; depth 3.6-3.8; SnL 2.6-2.9 in HL.

The less numerous and thicker black bars on the lower caudal lobe (2-4 vs. 5-6), fewer modal lateral line scales, and greater number of gill rakers separate this species from *U. taeniopterus*. This species inhabits sandy lagoons and sheltered coastal waters to a depth of 100 m. It occurs in groups of up to 50 and feeds primarily on small crustaceans.

Indo-Pacific: Red Sea to the Hawaiian, Marquesan, and Society Is., n. to s. Japan, s. to New Caledonia; Belau to the e. Carolines and Marianas in Micronesia.

PEMPHERIDIDAE (SWEEPERS)

Sweepers have moderately ovoid compressed bodies, very large eyes, an oblique mouth with small teeth in bands on the jaws, vomer and palatines, and a single short continuous dorsal fin. There are only two genera, each with one species in Micronesia and a few others elsewhere.

Parapriacanthus ransonneti (Steindachner, 1870)
Pigmy sweeper   Pl. 59F
(*P. beryciformes*)
SL: to 6.3 cm (2.5 in); D V, 7-10; A III, 17-23; P 14-17; LL 63-78+8-10; GR 5-7+14-17.
Species of *Parapriacanthus* have a bioluminous organ on the peritoneum behind the pectoral fin. During the day, this little sweeper hovers in dense swarms under coral overhangs and in caves. At night it disperses in the water above the reef to feed.
West-central Pacific: S. Japan to the Marshalls, s. to Rowley Shoals; Belau, Carolines, and Marshalls in Micronesia.

Pempheris oualensis Cuvier, 1831   Pl. 60A
Bronze sweeper
SL: to 19 cm (7.5 in); D VI, 9; A III, 38-42; P 17-18; LL 62-68; GR 9+21-22=30-32.
The bronze sweeper inhabits shallow clear lagoon and seaward reefs to a depth of at least 36 m. It is quite common along the reef margin. During the day it hovers in schools under ledges of surge channels or in caves. At night it disperses over the reef to feed on benthic and planktonic crustaceans, other small invertebrates, and fishes.
Indo-Pacific: Red Sea to the Line, Marquesan, and Ducie Is., n. to the Ryukyus, s. to Lord Howe and Rapa Is.; throughout Micronesia.

KYPHOSIDAE
(RUDDERFISHES; SEA CHUBS)

Rudderfishes have relatively deep, moderately compressed bodies with a small head, small terminal mouth with stout incisiform teeth, a maxilla that slips partially beneath the preorbital bone, small ctenoid scales extending over most of the soft portions of the median fins, a continuous dorsal fin, and an emarginate to forked tail. They are omnivores characteristic of exposed seaward reefs that feed primarily on benthic algae. Juveniles often occur far out at sea beneath floating debris. Three species of *Kyphosus* occur in Micronesia.

Kyphosus bigibbus Lacepède, 1802   Pl. 60B
Insular rudderfish; Brown chub
SL: to 70 cm (27.6 in); D X-XI, 11-13(12); A III-IV, 10-12 (11); P 18-20; LP 53-59; GR 7-9+18-20=25-27.
The fin ray counts and gill raker counts will separate this species from the lowfin rudderfish, *K. vaigiensis*. Occasionally uniformly yellow, and very rarely, albino individuals

occur. This species is abundant around exposed seaward reefs of isolated high islands such as the northernmost Marianas and Bonins. It feeds on a wide variety of algae including filamentous reds, to coarse browns such as *Sargassum* and *Turbinaria*.
Indo-Pacific: mainly antiequatorial: Red Sea, S. Africa, Taiwan, Izu, Bonin, Mariana, Samoan (?), Hawaiian, Marquesan, New Caledonian, and Rapa Is.

Kyphosus cinerascens (Forsskål, 1775)   Pl. 60C,D
Highfin rudderfish; Snubnose chub
SL: to 37 cm (14.3 in); D XI, 11-(12); A III, 11-(12); P 17-19; LP 48-56; GR 8-10+18-20=26-30.
This is the only Micronesian *Kyphosus* in which the soft dorsal and anal fin rays are considerably longer than the spines. It is probably the most common kyphosid throughout most of Micronesia. The highfin rudderfish occurs in aggregations over hard, algal coated bottoms of exposed, surf-swept outer reef flats, lagoon reefs, and seaward reefs to a depth of at least 24 m.
Indo-Pacific: Red Sea to the Hawaiian, Line, and Tuamotu Is., n. to s. Japan, s. to the s. Great Barrier Reef; throughout Micronesia.

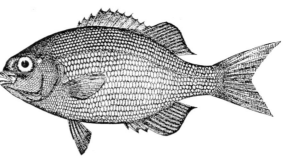

Fig. 1. *K. cinerascens* (after Herre and Montalban, 1927).

Kyphosus vaigiensis (Quoy & Gaimard, 1825)
Lowfin rudderfish; Brassy chub   Pl. 60E; Fig. 1
(*K. lembus* Amesbury and Myers, 1982)
SL: to 49.5 cm (19.5 in); D X-XI, 13-15(14); A III, 12-14 (13); P 18-20; LP 52-58; GR 9-11+22-24=33-35.
The lowfin rudderfish has a similar ecology to that of *K. cinerascens*, but seems to be less common in Micronesia.
Indo-Pacific: Red Sea to the Hawaiian and Tuamotu Is., s. to New Caledonia and Rapa; throughout Micronesia.

MONODACTYLIDAE (MONOS)

Monos are a small family of highly compressed silvery fishes having a small oblique mouth with brush-like teeth in the jaws and villiform teeth on the vomer and palatines, vestigial pelvic fins, a continuous unnotched dorsal fin, and small weakly ctenoid scales that extend over the entire dorsal and anal fins. They occur primarily in estuarine habitats and can live in freshwater.

Monodactylus argenteus (Linnaeus, 1758) Pl. 60F
Mono

SL: to 18 cm (7.1 in); D VII-VIII, 27-31; A III, 27-32; P 16-18; V I, 2-3; LL 50-65; GR 6-8+19-22=25-28.

The mono is an active schooling fish that occurs primarily in estuaries, but may venture over silty coastal reefs.

Indo-west Pacific: Red Sea to Samoa, n. to the Yaeyamas, s. to New Caledonia; Belau to the e. Carolines and Marianas in Micronesia.

SCATOPHAGIDAE (SCATS)

Scats are a small family of compressed fishes possessing a small terminal mouth, continuous dorsal fin, and fine scales covering all but the soft portions of the vertical fins. The larvae undergo a tholichthys stage like that of the chaetodontids. Scats feed on benthic green algae and the associated microfauna; they get the name *Scatophagus*, which literally means "feces eater", from their habit of feeding on human feces in harbors and estuaries.

Scatophagus argus (Linnaeus, 1758) Fig. 1
Scat

SL: to 28 cm (11.1 in); D X-XI, 16-18; A IV, 14-15; P 17; LP 85-120; GR 5+13.

Juveniles live in brackish to fresh water; adults occur in shallow, turbid inshore areas.

Indo-west Pacific: Kuwait to Vanuatu and New Caledonia, n. to s. Japan; Belau to Pohnpei in Micronesia.

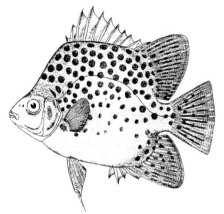

Fig. 1. *Scatophagus argus*, 97 mm (after Herre and Montalban, 1927).

EPHIPPIDAE (BATFISHES; SPADEFISHES)

Batfishes have deep, highly compressed bodies with a small terminal mouth, brushlike teeth (tricuspid in *Platax*), a continuous dorsal fin, and small ctenoid scales extending over the basal portions of the median fins. Juveniles of *Platax*

have very deep bodies and greatly elevated dorsal, anal, and pelvic fins that shorten with age. Three species of *Platax* occur in Micronesia.

Key to Microneisan species of *Platax*:

1a. D 28-34; scales small, 40-45 from LL origin to 1st D spine; all 3 cusps on teeth subequal.....................*teira*
1b. D 35-37; 25-30 scales from LL origin to 1st D spine; middle tooth cusp longest and strongest....................2
2a. Snout convex; chin with 5 mandibular pores on each side...*orbicularis*
2b. Snout concave before eyes; chin with 3-4 mandibular pores each side..*pinnatus*

Platax orbicularis (Forsskål, 1775) Pl. 60A,B
Circular spadefish; Batfish

SL: to 46.5 cm (18.3 in); D V 32-38; A III, 25-28; P 17-19; LL 48-56; GR 9+10; middle cusp on teeth largest.

Juveniles occur singly or in small groups among mangroves and in inner sheltered lagoons. They closely resemble a floating leaf both in appearance and behavior. Subadults move out to deeper channels and lagoons where they aggregate in small tightly-knit schools. Large adults are often solitary and inhabit open water over sandy areas of deep lagoons, channels, and seaward reefs to a depth of at least 30 m. They feed on algae, invertebrates, and small fishes. Adults *Platax* closely resemble one another. The ocular band of adult *P. orbicularis* is made up of a series of dark vermiculations while that of *P. tiera* is solid, and the snout profile of adult *P. pinnatus* is concave rather than convex.

Indo-Pacific: Red Sea to the Tuamotus, n. to s. Japan, s. to New Caledonia; throughout Micronesia.

Platax pinnatus (Linnaeus, 1758) Pl. 61C,D
Pinnate spadefish

SL: to 37 cm (14.6 in); D V, 35-37; A III, 25-28; P 18-20; LL 48-53; GR 9+11.

Juveniles of this batfish are a spectacular dark brown to black with a brilliant crimson margin around the entire fish. It has been suggested that they mimic a large toxic polyclad flatworm when small. They occur among mangroves and on inner sheltered reefs among the Rock Islands of Belau where they seek shelter in caves or under ledges. Adults become a dull silver with short fins. They are generally solitary and occur under overhangs of steep outer reef slopes to a depth of at least 20 m.

Indo-west-Pacific: Red Sea to , n. to the Ryukyus, New Caledonia Belau in Micronesia.

Platax teira (Forsskål, 1775) Pl. 61E,F
Longfin spadefish

SL: to 41 cm (16.3 in); D V-VI, 28-34; A III, 22-28; P 16-18; LL 48-53; GR 9+11-12; ea. cusp on teeth about equal.

Juveniles occur on shallow protected inner reefs. Adults occur on lagoon and seaward reefs to a depth of 20 m or more.

Indo-west-Pacific: Red Sea to Papua New Guinea, n. to the Yaeyamas, s. to the s. Great Barrier Reef; Belau in Micronesia.

CHAETODONTIDAE (BUTTERFLYFISHES)

Butterflyfishes are among the most colorful and conspicuous of coral reef fishes. They have deep, highly compressed bodies covered with moderately small ctenoid scales extending onto the median fins, a small protractile mouth with a band or rows of small brushlike teeth in the jaws, a single continuous dorsal fin with the anteriormost interspinous membranes deeply incised, and a rounded to slightly emarginate tail. Butterflyfishes are typically diurnal. They rest on the bottom among the corals by night while assuming a slightly different, more somber color pattern. During the day most species patrol a home range either individually or in pairs. Diet differs among the species; many feed on a combination of coelenterate polyps or tentacles, small invertebrates, fish eggs, and filamentous algae while others are specialists. Those that feed exclusively on coral polyps are territorial and restricted to the relatively shallow water areas occupied by their food corals. Many of those that feed primarily on zooplankton occur in mid-water aggregations and may range into relatively deep water. Although the exact mode of sexuality in butterflyfishes has not been determined, it appears that they are gonochorists, that is an individual's sex is predetermined and remains the same throughout its life. Most species occur as heterosexual pairs that may stay together for a number of years, if not for life. Spawning generally occurs at dusk at the apex of an ascent during which the male nudges the female in the abdomen. The planktonic eggs most likely hatch within two days and the larval stage probably lasts from several weeks to a few months. All species appear to go through a distinctive late larval stage called the *tholichthys* larva in which the head and front of the body are covered by large bony plates. Settlement occurs at night and juveniles are often found in shallower, more sheltered waters than adults. Coloration typically changes little with growth and nearly all species are easily recognized by color pattern alone. Species recognition for the purpose of reproduction or territorial defense appears to be the primary function of their complex color patterns. Butterflyfishes in general, do not do well in the home aquarium; some of the generalists and planktivores are the easiest to keep and the obligate corallivores are the most difficult. At least 40 species in 5 genera occur in Micronesia*. Not featured is the deep-dwelling *Chaetodon modestus* known from Micronesia on the basis of a single collection made at a depth of 172 m off Guam. (Lit.: Allen, 1979; Burgess, 1978; Maugé and Bauchot, 1984; Nalbant, 1986; Randall et al., 1977; Steene, 1977; Tursch and Tursch, 1982; Yasuda and Zama, 1975)

Chaetodon auriga Forsskål, 1775   Pl. 62A
Threadfin butterflyfish
SL: to153 mm (6.0 in); D XII-(XIII), 22-25(23); A III, 19-21; P 15-17(16); LL 33-43(34-40); LP 29-40(30-37); GR 16-20.
This is one of the most common butterflyfishes of areas of mixed sand, rubble, and coral of shallow reef flats and lagoons. It also occurs on seaward reefs to a depth of at least 30 m. It is a home ranging species that feeds mainly by tearing pieces from polychaetes, sea anemones, coral polyps, and algae.
Indo-Pacific: Red Sea to the Hawaiian, Marquesan, and Ducie Is.; n. to s. Japan, s. to Lord Howe and Rapa Is.; throughout Micronesia.

Chaetodon barronessa Cuvier, 1831   Pl. 62B
Eastern triangular butterflyfish
SL: to 107 mm (4.2 in); D (XI)-XII, 23-26(25); A III, 20-22; P 14-16(15); LL 24-30(26-28); LP 16-23; GR 22-27.
This butterflyfish inhabits lagoon and seaward reefs where there is an abundance of tabular *Acropora* corals. It feeds exclusively on the polyps of these corals, occurs in pairs, and is territorial.
West Pacific: Cocos-Keeling Is. and Indonesia to Fiji, n. to s. Japan, s. to New Caledonia; Belau and Yap in Micronesia.

Chaetodon bennetti Cuvier, 1831   Pl. 62C
Bennett's butterflyfish
SL: to 155 mm (6.1 in); D XIII-(XIV), 15-17(16-17); A III, 14-16(15-16); P 15-17(16); LL 36-40; LP 29-37(31-36); GR 15-20.
Bennett's butterflyfish occurs on both lagoon and seaward reefs in areas of rich coral growth. Juveniles are occasionally found in shallow *Acropora* thickets, adults generally occur as pairs at depths of 5 to 30 m. It feeds primarily on coral polyps.
Indo-Pacific: E. Africa to the Pitcairn group, n. to s. Japan, s. to Lord Howe and Rapa Is.; throughout Micronesia.

Chaetodon burgessi Allen & Starck, 1973   Pl. 62D
Burgess' butterflyfish
SL: to 116 mm (4.6 in); D XIII, 18-19; A III, 15-16; P 16; LP 35-37; GR 17-20.
Like its close relatives, *C. flavocoronatus* and *C. tinkeri*, this species inhabits precipitous dropoffs at depths of 40 to 80 m where there is an abundance of gorgonians and black corals. It was first discovered on the Ngemelis wall of Palau and has since been found in the Philippines where it is exported for the aquarium trade. The individual illustrated was recently collected at Ant Atoll off Pohpei by R. L. Pyle and R. K. Kosaki.
Philippines, Belau, and Pohnpei

---

* Some recent authors (Maugé and Bauchot, 1984; Nalbant, 1986) have split *Chaetodon* into numerous genera, but most authorities do not accept this and other studies in progress indicate that such a split is unjustified. I retain the use of *Chaetodon* in the broad sense.

Chaetodon citrinellus Cuvier, 1831   Pl. 62E
Speckled butterflyfish

SL: to 107 mm (4.2 in); D XIII-(XIV), 20-22(21-22); A III, 16-17; P 14-16(15); LL 36-42(39-41); LP 35-41(37-40); GR 20-22.

This is one of the most common butterflyfishes of relatively shallow exposed reef flats, lagoons, and seaward reefs. It prefers relatively open areas with scattered corals and occasionally occurs to a depth of 36 m. It is usually paired and feeds on small benthic invertebrates, coral polyps, and filamentous algae.

Indo-Pacific: E. Africa to the Hawaiian, Marquesan, and Tuamotu Is., n. to s. Japan, s. to Lord Howe Is.; throughout Micronesia.

Chaetodon ephippium Cuvier, 1831   Pl. 62F
Saddled butterflyfish

SL: to 165 mm (6.5 in); D XII-XIV(XIII), 21-25(23-25); A III, 20-23(21); P 15-17(16); LL 33-40(36-39); LP 31-37; GR 14-17.

The saddled butterflyfish is a common inhabitant of lagoon and seaward reefs to a depth of 30 m. It prefers areas of rich coral growth and clear water and occurs singly, in pairs, or in small groups. It feeds on coral polyps, sponges, small invertebrates, fish eggs, and filamentous algae.

West-central Pacific: Cocos-Keeling Is. to the Hawaiian, Marquesan, and Tuamotu Is., n. to s. Japan, s. to Rowley Shoals and New South Wales and Rapa Is.; throughout Micronesia.

Chaetodon flavocoronatus Myers, 1980   Pl. 63A
Yellow-crowned butterflyfish

SL: to ca. 100 mm (2.9 in); D XIII, 20; A III, 16; P 15; LP 35-38; GR 18 (counts based on the holotype).

This beautiful fish is known only from a few specimens collected at depths of over 30 m along current-swept dropoffs of Orote Peninsula, Guam. It typically occurs singly or in pairs among black corals at depths of 45 to 75 m. Like its closest relative, *C. tinkeri*, it does well in captivity. The first individuals offered for sale were considered so valuable that a Japanese aquarist flew to the dealer in Honolulu to accompany his new fish back to Japan!

Guam.

Chaetodon kleinii Bloch, 1790   Pl. 63B
Klein's butterflyfish

SL: to 109 mm (4.3 in); D (XIII)-XIV, 20-23(21-22); A III, 17-20(18-19); P 14-16(15);LL 33-41(36-40); LP 29-39(32-39); GR 8-23.

Klein's butterflyfish is fairly common in deeper lagoons and channels, and seaward reefs to a depth of 61 m. Although usually found below 10 m, it is occasionally encountered as shallow as 4 m. It is an omnivore that feeds mainly on soft coral polyps (primarily *Sarcophyton tracheiliophorum* and *Litophyton viridis*), algae, and zooplankton, and usually occurs singly or in pairs.

Indo-Pacific: E. Africa to the Hawaiian, Line, and Samoan Is., n. to s. Japan, s. to New South Wales and New Caledonia; throughout Micronesia.

Chaetodon lineolatus Cuvier, 1831   Pl. 63C; Fig. 2a
Lined butterflyfish

SL: to 240 mm (9.4 in); D XII, 24-27(25-27); A III, 19-22; P 16-18(17); LL 26-33; LP 21-30; GR 15-18.

This is the largest species of butterflyfish. It inhabits lagoon and seaward reefs at depths of 2 to 171 m, usually as pairs in areas of heavy coral growth. It is uncommon throughout Micronesia. Although it feeds primarily on coral polyps and small anemones, it also feeds on small invertebrates and algae and is among the easier of the butterflyfishes to maintain in the aquarium.

Indo-Pacific: Red Sea to the Hawaiian, Marquesan, and Ducie Is., n. to s. Japan, s. to Lord Howe Is.; throughout Micronesia.

Chaetodon lunula (Lacepède, 1803)   Pl. 63D
Raccoon butterflyfish

SL: to 159 mm (6.3 in); D X-XIII(XII), 22-25(24); A III, 17-20(18): P 15-17(16-17); LL 35-44 (37-43); LP 31-41.

This common species inhabits lagoon and seaward reefs to a depth of over 30 m. It is quite common in exposed rocky areas of high vertical relief. Juveniles occur among rocks of inner reef flats and in tidepools, and lack the orange-edged black band extending from the operculum to the spinous dorsal fin. It is the only butterflyfish that is nocturnaly active; during the day it may hover inactively in aggregations between boulders as well as forage. It feeds primarily upon opisthobranch gastropods (nudibranchs), tubeworm tentacles, and other benthic invertebrates as well as occasionally on coral polyps and algae. It does relatively well in the aquarium.

Indo-Pacific: E. Africa to the Hawaiian, Marquesan, and Ducie Is., n. to s. Japan, s. to Lord Howe and Rapa Is.; throughout Micronesia.

Chaetodon melannotus Bloch, 1801
Black-backed butterflyfish   Pl. 63E; Fig. 2a

SL: to 135 mm (5.3 in); D (XII)-XIII, 18-21(19-20); A III, 16-18(17); P 13-16(15); LL 33-39; LP 29-36; GR 13-16(14-15).

This species inhabits reef flats, lagoons, and seaward reefs to a depth of over 15 m in areas of rich coral growth. It is fairly common in staghorn coral thickets, but rare on exposed seaward reefs. It is a home-ranging species usually solitary or paired, that feeds primarily on octocorallian and scleractinian coral polyps. It is easier to maintain in the aquarium than most other species that feed heavily on corals.

Indo-Pacific: Red Sea to Samoa, n. to s. Japan, s. to Lord Howe Is.; throughout Micronesia.

Chaetodon mertensii Cuvier, 1831   Pl. 63F
Merten's butterflyfish

SL: to 109 mm (4.3 in); D XII-XIV(XIII), 21-23(22); A III, 16-(17); P (15)-16; LL 35-43; LP 30-41; GR 16-21.

This species is a common inhabitant of deep lagoon reefs and seaward reefs at depths of 10 to 120 m. It occurs singly or in pairs and feeds on small benthic invertebrates and algae. It is very closely related to *C. madagascariensis* from the Indian Ocean, *C. xanthurus* from southeast Asia, and *C. paucifasciatus* from the Red Sea.

A. Young volcanic island with little reef development beyond encrusting coral communities, Pagan.

B. Fringing reef exposed to frequent high surf, Guam. Note the wide reef front with surge channel development.

C. Fringing reef of leeward coast with infrequent surf, Peleliu, Belau. Here the outer reef slope is vertical.

D. Barrier reef enclosing a shallow lagoon with numerous patch reefs and a sand cay, Saipan.

E. Lagoon patch reefs among raised limestone islands, Seventy Islands, Belau (photo by M. Warner).

F. Atoll with a deep lagoon and numerous islands and passes, Ulithi, from an altitude of 39,000 ft.

Plate 1. Types of Reefs

A. Mangrove-lined inner reef flat, Kosrae.
B. Bed of the seagrass *Enhalus acoroides*, inner reef flat, Adelupe, Guam (upper right).
C. Clear inner subtidal reef flat, Uruno, Guam.
D. Shallow lagoon with large stand of staghorn coral (*Acropora formosa*), Saipan (mid right)
E. Reef margin with surge channels, Pago Bay, Guam (above).
F. Top of pinnacle in deep lagoon, Enewetak Atoll. The dominant coral is *Porites rus* (left

Plate 2. Reef zones and habitats

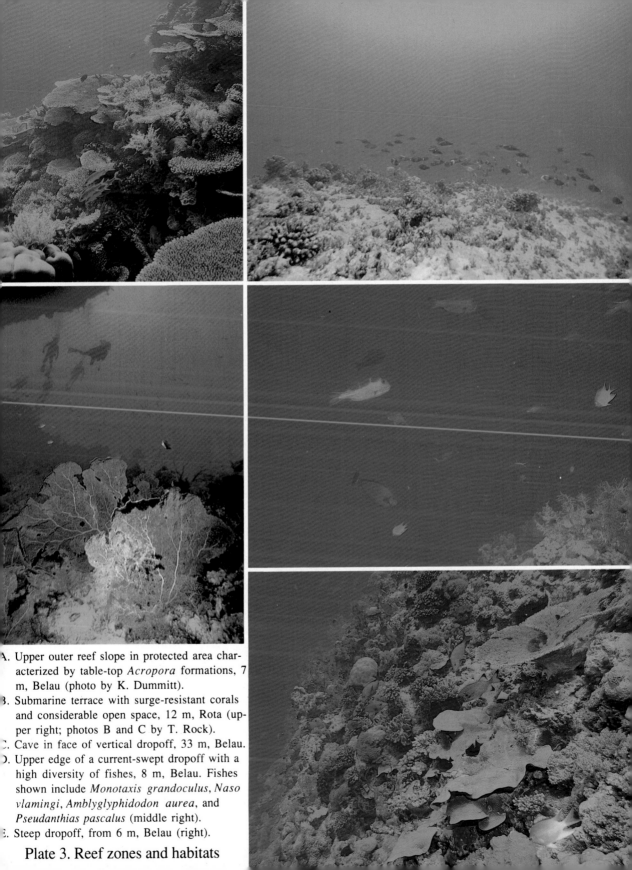

A. Upper outer reef slope in protected area characterized by table-top *Acropora* formations, 7 m, Belau (photo by K. Dummitt).

B. Submarine terrace with surge-resistant corals and considerable open space, 12 m, Rota (upper right; photos B and C by T. Rock).

C. Cave in face of vertical dropoff, 33 m, Belau.

D. Upper edge of a current-swept dropoff with a high diversity of fishes, 8 m, Belau. Fishes shown include *Monotaxis grandoculus*, *Naso vlamingi*, *Amblyglyphidodon aurea*, and *Pseudanthias pascalus* (middle right).

E. Steep dropoff, from 6 m, Belau (right).

Plate 3. Reef zones and habitats

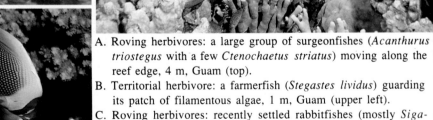

A. Roving herbivores: a large group of surgeonfishes (*Acanthurus triostegus* with a few *Ctenochaetus striatus*) moving along the reef edge, 4 m, Guam (top).

B. Territorial herbivore: a farmerfish (*Stegastes lividus*) guarding its patch of filamentous algae, 1 m, Guam (upper left).

C. Roving herbivores: recently settled rabbitfishes (mostly *Siganus argenteus*) swarm a territorial damselfish's (*Plectroglyphidodon lacrymatus*) patch of algae-covered reef, 4 m, Guam.

D. Omnivores: butterflyfish (*Chaetodon reticulatus*) feeding on coral polyps (*Acropora gravida*). This species' diet also includes small amounts of filamentous algae and invertebrates (left).

Plate 4. Ecology: herbivores and omnivores

A. Diurnal planktivores: fairy basslets (*Pseudanthias dispar* and *Luzonichthys waitei*) above ledge of dropoff, 16 m, Belau.

B. Nocturnal planktivores: soldierfishes (*Myripristis adusta*, *M. berndti*, and *M. vittata*) in cave by day, 16 m, Belau.

C. Sponge and tunicate feeder: an angelfish (*Pygoplites diacanthus*) foraging in a cave, 14 m, Belau (middle right).

D. Cleaner: a cleaner wrasse (*Labroides bicolor*) inspecting a young parrotfish (*Scarus sordidus*), 3 m, Guam (lower right).

Plate 5. Ecology: planktivores and specialists

A. Mid-water carnivores: barracuda (*Sphyraena genie*) schooling by day, 16 m, Belau (top; photo by K. Dummitt).

B. Ambushing predator: a lizardfish (*Saurida gracilis*) swallowing a cardinalfish (*Cheilodipterus lineatus*), 14 m, Guam (middle left).

C. Roving carnivore: whitetip shark (*Triaenodon obesus*), a predator of reef fishes, octopuses, and spiny lobsters,15m, Belau (above)

D. Roving carnivores: goatfishes (*Parupeneus barberinus* and *P. mutifasciatus*) and wrasse (*Halichoeres trimaculatus*), 4 m, Guam.

Plate 6: Ecology: carnivores

A. *Nebrius concolor*, 130 and 160 cm TL, Guam (p. 32; aq. photo).

B. *Stegastoma varium*, ca. 150 cm TL, 15 m, Belau (p. 32; left).

T. Rock

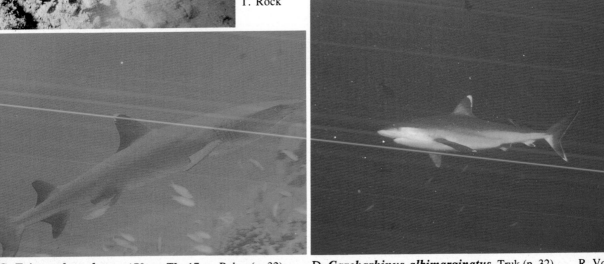

C. *Triaenodon obesus*, 170 cm TL, 17 m, Belau (p. 32).   D. *Carcharhinus albimarginatus*, Truk (p. 32).   R. Voorn

E. *Carcharhinus amblyrhynchos*, 180 cm TL, 18 m, Belau. F. *Carcharhinus melanopterus*, 150 cm TL (p.36; Waikiki Aq.).
(p. 34)

Plate 7. Sharks

A. **_Manta alfredi_**, 350 cm disc width, 2 m, Tumon Bay, Guam (p. 39).

M. Warner

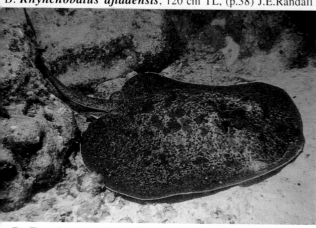

B. **_Rhynchobatus djiddensis_**, 120 cm TL, (p.38) J.E.Randall

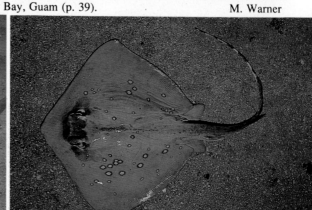

C. **_Dasyatis kuhlii_**, 34.5 cm disc width, Guam (p.38).

D. **_Taeniura melanospilos_**, 100 cm disc width, Truk (p. 38). E. **_Aetobatis narinari_**, 80 cm disc width, Oahu, Hawaii (p. 3
M. Neubauer

Plate 8. Rays

A. **Echidna nebulosa**, 60 cm, 7 m, Rota (p. 41).

B. **Echidna polyzona**, 70 cm, 1.5 m, Guam (p. 42).

C. **Enchelynassa canina**,100cm, Hawaii (p.42). M.Vanderlinden D. **Gymnomuraena zebra**, 75cm, Hawaii (p.42; aq. photo).

E. **Gymnothorax fimbriatus**, 75cm, Guam (p.44; aq. photo). F. **Gymnothorax flavimarginatus**, 120cm, 12m, Belau (p.44).

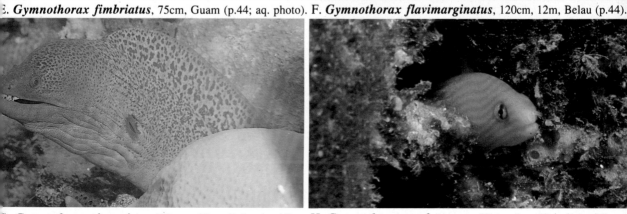

G. **Gymnothorax javanicus**, 170 cm, 18 m, Belau (p. 44). H. **Gymnothorax melatremus**, 20 cm, 9 m, Hawaii (p. 44).

Plate 9. Moray Eels

A. **Gymnothorax meleagris**, 70 cm, 15 m, Guam (p. 44).

B. **Gymnothorax rueppelliae**, 8 m, Oahu, Hawaii (p. 46).

C. **Gymnothorax undulatus**, 75 cm, Guam (p.46; aq. photo).

D. **Rhinomuraena quaesita**, 75 cm, 1.3 m, Indonesia (p. 46

E. **Siderea picta**, 50 cm, Guam (p. 48; aq. photo).

F. **Siderea prosopeion**, 40 cm, Guam (p. 48; aq. photo).

G. **Pseudechidna brummeri**, 50 cm, 1 m, Guam (p. 48).

H. **Uropterygius tigrinus**, 110 cm (p. 50; Waikiki Aq.).

Plate 10. Moray Eels

A. **Conger cinereus**, 50 cm, Hawaii (p. 52; aq. photo).

B. **Heteroconger hassi**, 25 m, Maldives (p. 52).   G. R. Allen

C. **Myrichthys colubrinus**, nw. Australia (p. 56). G.R.Allen

D. **Myrichthys maculosus**, 30 cm, Guam (p. 56; aq. photo).

E. **Albula glossodonta**, 25 cm (p. 58; Waikiki Aq.).

F. **Plotosus lineatus**, 14 cm (p. 59; Noumea Aq.).

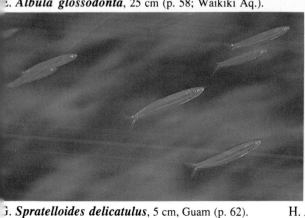

G. **Spratelloides delicatulus**, 5 cm, Guam (p. 62).

H. **Herklotsichthys quadrimaculatus**, 10 cm, 1 m, Pohnpei (p.62).

Plate 11. Conger Eels, Snake Eels, Bonefish, Catfish, and Herrings

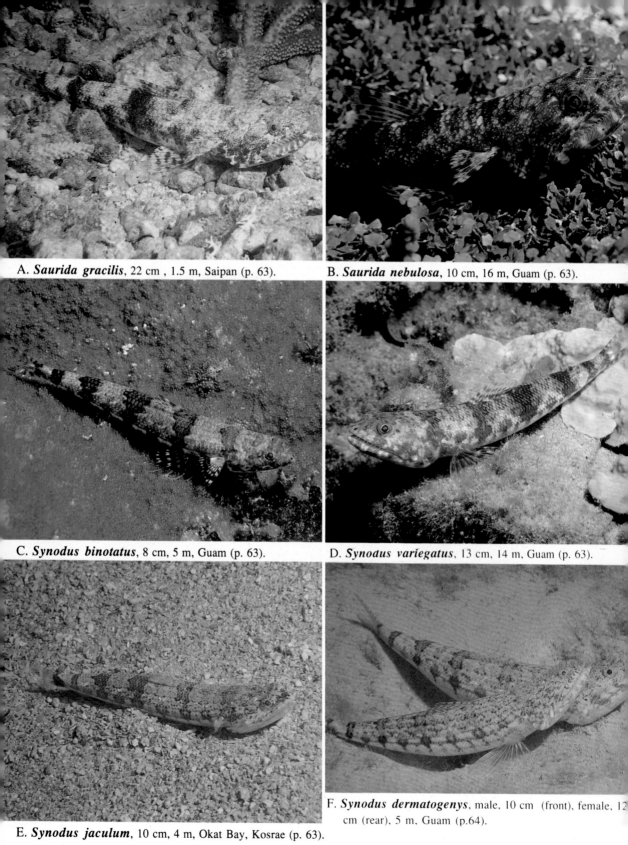

A. **Saurida gracilis**, 22 cm , 1.5 m, Saipan (p. 63).

B. **Saurida nebulosa**, 10 cm, 16 m, Guam (p. 63).

C. **Synodus binotatus**, 8 cm, 5 m, Guam (p. 63).

D. **Synodus variegatus**, 13 cm, 14 m, Guam (p. 63).

E. **Synodus jaculum**, 10 cm, 4 m, Okat Bay, Kosrae (p. 63).

F. **Synodus dermatogenys**, male, 10 cm (front), female, 12 cm (rear), 5 m, Guam (p.64).

Plate 12. Lizardfishes

A. *Antennarius dorehensis*, 4 cm. B. *Antennarius maculatus*, 4 cm. J. LaDouce C. *Histrio histrio*, 1 cm (A-C p. 68).

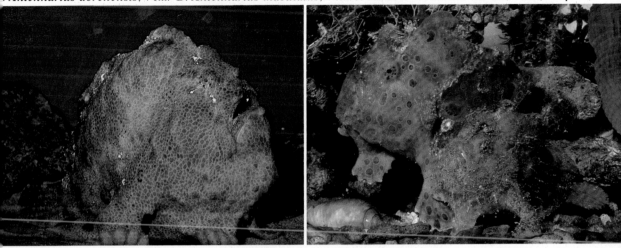

D. *Antennarius commersonii*, 30 cm, (p.68; Steinhart Aq.). E. *Antennarius nummifer*, 5.5 cm (front) and
A. pictus, 6.6 cm (rear), Guam (p. 68; aq. photo).

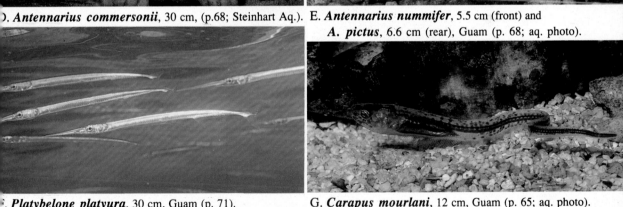

F. *Platybelone platyura*, 30 cm, Guam (p. 71). G. *Carapus mourlani*, 12 cm, Guam (p. 65; aq. photo).

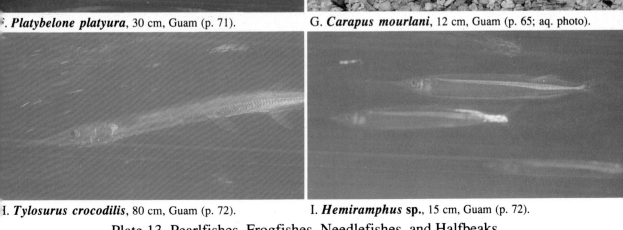

H. *Tylosurus crocodilis*, 80 cm, Guam (p. 72). I. *Hemiramphus* sp., 15 cm, Guam (p. 72).

Plate 13. Pearlfishes, Frogfishes, Needlefishes, and Halfbeaks

A. *Anomalops katoptron*, 8 cm, (p. 73; Steinhart Aq.).

B. *Plectrypops lima*, 10 cm, 8 m, Oahu, Hawaii (p. 75).

C. *Myripristis adusta*, 18 cm, 15 m, Belau (p. 75).

D. *Myripristis amaena*, 18 cm, 18 m, Saipan (p. 75).

E. *Myripristis berndti*, 20 cm, 15 m, Guam (p. 75).

F. *Myripristis chryseres*, 18.5 cm, Guam (p. 76).

Plate 14. Flashlightfishes and Soldierfishes

A. *Myripristis* *hexagona*, 15 cm, 15 m, Belau (p. 76). B. *Myripristis* *kuntee*, 13 cm, 14 m, Guam (p. 76).

C. *Myripristis* *murdjan*, 18 cm, 15 m, Belau (p. 76). D. *Myripristis* *pralinia*, 14 cm, 16 m, Guam (p. 76).

E. *Myripristis* *violacea*, 15 cm, 6 m, Guam (p. 76). F. *Myripristis* *vittata*, 12 cm, 28 m, Guam (p. 76).

Plate 15. Soldierfishes

A. *Myripristis woodsi*, Fanning Atoll (p. 76). J.E.Randall

B. *Neoniphon argenteus*, 13 cm, 1 m, Guam (p. 79).

C. *Neoniphon aurolineatus*, 14 cm, 20 m, Hawaii (p. 79).

D. *Neoniphon opercularis*, 16 cm, 1.5 m, Saipan (p. 79).

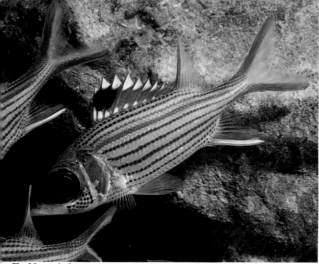

E. *Neoniphon sammara*, 10 cm, 1 m, Guam (p. 79).

F. *Sargocentron caudimaculatum*, 16 cm, 4 m, Belau (p. 79

Plate 16. Soldierfishes and Squirrelfishes

. *Sargocentron diadema*, 12 cm, 27 m, Guam (p.79).　　B. *Sargocentron diadema* courting, 12 cm, 27 m, Guam.

. *Sargocentron ittodai*, 13 cm, Mauritius (p.80). J.E.Randall　D. *Sargocentron melanospilos*, 13 cm, (p.80) J.E.Randall

. *Sargocentron microstoma*, 13 cm, 12 m, Guam (p. 80).　　F. *Sargocentron microstoma* at night, 13 cm, 1 m, Guam.

Plate 17. Squirrelfishes

A. *Sargocentron praslin*, 12 cm, Guam (p. 80; aq. photo). B. *Sargocentron punctatissimum*, 10 cm, 14 m, Hawaii (p.80

C. *Sargocentron spiniferum*,
30 cm, 18 m, Belau (p. 80).

D. *Sargocentron tiere*, 18 cm, 9 m, Guam (p. 80).   E. *Sargocentron violaceum*, 16 cm, 18 m, Belau (p. 81).

Plate 18. Sqirrelfishes

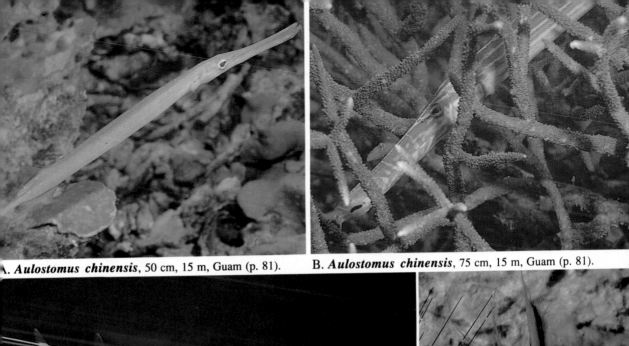

A. *Aulostomus chinensis*, 50 cm, 15 m, Guam (p. 81).   B. *Aulostomus chinensis*, 75 cm, 15 m, Guam (p. 81).

C. *Fistularia commersonii*, 50 cm, 1.5 m, Guam (p. 81).   D. *Aeoliscus strigatus*, 10 cm, Belau (p.81).

E. *Solenostomus cyanopterus*, 6 cm,   F.*Hippocampus histrix*, 6 cm, Guam (p.84).   G.*Hippocampus kuda* (aq. photo; p.84).
Guam (p.81).   Plate 19. Trumpetfishes, Flutemouths, Shrimpfishes, Ghost Pipefishes, and Seahorses

A. *Corythoichthys flavofasciatus*, 9 cm, 1 m, Guam (p.86). B. *Corythoichthys intestinalis*, 12 cm, 1 m, Guam (p. 86).

C. *Doryrhamphus excisus*, 5 cm, 2 m, D. *Syngnathoides biaculeatus*, 18 cm, E. *Eurypegasus draconis*, 4 cm,
   Guam (p. 86).   Guam (p. 88; aq. photo).   Guam (p. 90).

F. *Doryrhamphus dactyliophorus* R.Thresher

G. *Trachyrhamphus bicoarctatus*, 25 cm, 4 m, Guam (p. 88).   H. *Dactyloptena orientalis*, 12 cm, 4 m, Guam (p. 90).

Plate 20. Pipefishes, Dragonfishes, and Helmet Gurnards

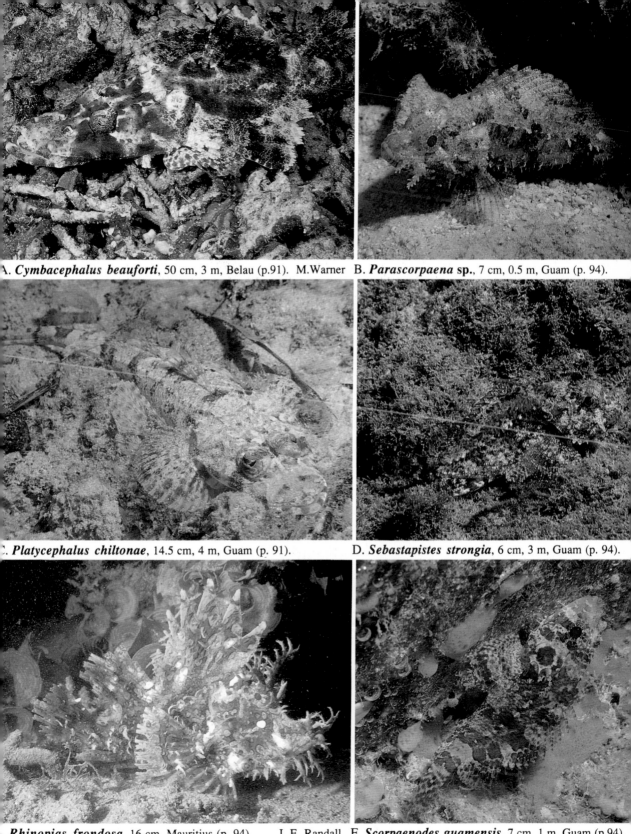

A. *Cymbacephalus beauforti*, 50 cm, 3 m, Belau (p.91).　M.Warner　B. *Parascorpaena* sp., 7 cm, 0.5 m, Guam (p. 94).

C. *Platycephalus chiltonae*, 14.5 cm, 4 m, Guam (p. 91).　　D. *Sebastapistes strongia*, 6 cm, 3 m, Guam (p. 94).

E. *Rhinopias frondosa*, 16 cm, Mauritius (p. 94).　　J. E. Randall　F. *Scorpaenodes guamensis*, 7 cm, 1 m, Guam (p.94).

Plate 21. Flatheads and Scorpionfishes

A. *Scorpaenopsis diabolus*, 16 cm, 3 m, Guam (p. 96).   B. *Scorpaenopsis macrochir*, 10 cm, 4 m, Guam (p. 96).

C. *Scorpaenopsis oxycephala*, 10 cm, 10 m, Guam.   D. *Scorpaenopsis oxycephala*, 18 cm, 12 m, Indonesia (p. 97).

E. *Taenianotus triacanthus*, 7 cm, 3 m, Guam (p. 97).   F. *Synanceia verrucosa*, 20 cm, 3 m, Guam (p. 97).

Plate 22. Scorpionfishes

A. *Inimicus didactylus*, Belau (p. 97).   M. Warner

B. *Dendrochirus biocellatus*, 5 cm, Guam (p. 98; aq. photo).

C. *Dendrochirus brachypterus*, 7 cm, 4 m, Guam (p. 98).

D. *Dendrochirus zebra*, 2 m, Christmas Is. (p. 98). G.R.Aller

E. *Pterois antennata*, 10 cm, 3 m, Indonesia (p. 98).

F. *Pterois radiata*, 10 cm, 1 m, Guam (p. 98).

Plate 23. Devilfishes and Lionfishes

A. *Pterois volitans* dark phase juvenile, 12 cm, 1 m, Indonesia.　B. *Pterois volitans* red phase adult, 20 cm, 4 m, Guam.

C. *Pterois volitans*, 18 cm, 10 m, Guam (p. 98).

Plate 24. Lionfish

A. *Luzonichthys waitei* 6 cm, 2 m, Indonesia (p. 100).   B. *Pseudanthias huchti* female, 5 cm, 7 m, Belau (p. 100).

C. *Pseudanthias huchti* male, 8 cm, 10 m, Indonesia.   D. *Pseudanthias squammipinnis* male, 8 cm, 18 m, Belau.

E. *Pseudanthias squammipinnis* female, 6 cm (top; p. 100);
Pseudanthias cooperi female, 5 cm,15 m, Belau (p. 100).   F. *Pseudanthias cooperi* male, 8 cm, 15 m, Belau.

Plate 25. Fairy basslets

A. *Pseudanthias pleurotaenia* female, 7 cm, 15 m, Guam. B. *Pseudanthias pleurotaenia* male, 9 cm, 25 m, Guam.

C. *Pseudanthias pleurotaenia*
male, 9 cm, 25 m, Guam
(p. 100).

D. *Pseudanthias ventralis* female, 5 cm, 48 m, Guam
(p. 101).   J. E. Randall

E. *Pseudanthias* sp. male, 6 cm, 27 m, Guam (p. 101).

Plate 26. Fairy basslets

A. *Pseudanthias randalli* female, 5 cm,15 m, Belau. B. *Pseudanthias randalli* male, 5 cm, 15 m, Belau (p. 100).

C. *Pseudanthias bartlettorum* females, 6 cm, 5 m, Kosrae. D. *Pseudanthias bartlettorum* male, 7 cm, 15 m, Belau (p. 100).

E. *Pseudanthias bicolor*, 7 cm, 5 m, Kosrae (p. 101). F. *Pseudanthias lori* male, 7 cm, 18 m, Belau (p. 101).

Plate 27. Fairy basslets

A. **Pseudanthias dispar** male, 8 cm (center) courting females, 6 m, Belau (p. 101).

B. **Pseudanthias dispar** male, 8 cm, 1.5 m Indonesia.

C. **Pseudanthias pascalus**, 6 cm, 27 m, Guam (p. 101).

D. **Pseudanthias pascalus** male 9 cm, 16 m, Guam.

E. **Pseudanthias smithvanizi** male 8 cm,15 m, Belau (p.101)

Plate 28. Fairy basslets

A. *Pseudanthias tuka* female, 6 cm, 12 m, Belau (p. 101).   B. *Pseudanthias tuka* male, 8 cm, 14 m, Indonesia.

C. *Serranocirrhitus latus*, 8.5 cm, Belau (p. 102). J.E.Randall   D. *Aethaloperca rogaa*, 30 cm, 12 m, Indonesia (p. 104).

F. *Anyperodon leucogrammicus*, 30 cm,15 m, Belau.

E. *Anyperodon leucogrammicus*, 22 cm, 15 m, Belau (p. 104).

Plate 29. Fairy basslets and Groupers

A. *Cephalopholis **argus***, 28 cm, 18 m, Saipan (p. 104).　　B. *Cephalopholis **argus***, 30 cm, 8 m, Belau.

C. *Cephalopholis **boenak***, 20 cm, 8 m, Belau (p. 104).　　D. *Cephalopholis **leopardus***, 12 cm, 9 m, Guam (p. 104).

E. *Cephalopholis
miniata*, 20 cm, 7
m, Belau (p. 104).

Plate 30. Groupers

Cephalopholis polleni, 18 cm, 35 m, Guam (p. 104).　　B. *Cephalopholis sexmaculata*, 25 cm, 24 m, Belau (p. 105).

Cephalopholis sonnerati, 30 cm (p. 105; Shedd Aq.).　　D. *Cephalopholis spiloparaea*, 12 cm, 30 m, Guam (p. 105).

Cephalopholis urodeta, 16 cm, 9 m, Guam (p. 105).　　F. *Cephalopholis urodeta*, 16 cm, 18 m, Saipan.

Plate 31. Groupers

A. *Cromileptes altivelis*, 50 cm, (p. 105; Steinhart Aq.). B. *Epinephelus fasciatus*, 20 cm, 16 m, Guam (p. 105).

C. *Epinephelus caeruleopunctatus*, 40 cm, 12 m, Belau (p.106). D. *Epinephelus socialis*, 35.4 cm, 12 m, Pagan (p. 10

E. *Epinephelus howlandi*, 15 cm, 8 m, New
  Caledonia (p. 106).

F. *Epinephelus corallicola* , 50 cm, 23 m, Belau (p. 106).

Plate 32. Groupers

A. *Epinephelus macrospilos*, 16 cm, 4 m, Belau (p. 106). B. *Epinephelus tauvina*, 50 cm, 18 m, Saipan.

C. *Epinephelus maculatus*, 43cm, Kwajalein (p.108). J.E.Randall D. *Epinephelus hexagonatus*, 16 cm, 7 m, Guam (p.106)

E. *Epinephelus merra*, 15 cm, 8 m, Belau (p. 108). F. *Epinephelus spilotoceps*, 18 cm, 3 m, Enewetak (p. 108).

Plate 33. Groupers

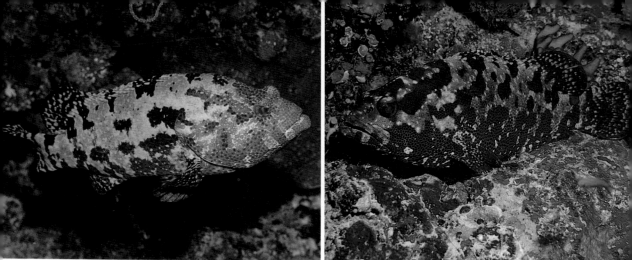

A. *Epinephelus fuscoguttatus*, 60 cm, Truk (p.108). M.Neubauer B. *Epinephelus polyphekadion*, 50 cm, Belau (p. 109)

C. *Epinephelus cyanopodus*, 35 cm, 12 m, Enewetak (p.108). D. *Gracila albomarginata*, 25 cm, 15 m, Belau (p. 110).

E. *Epinephelus lanceolatus*, 100 cm, (p. 110; Steinhart Aq.).

Plate 34. Groupers

A. *Plectropomus areolatus*, 40 cm, 15 m, Belau (p. 110).   B. *Plectropomus laevis*, 20 cm, 10 m, Enewetak (p. 110).

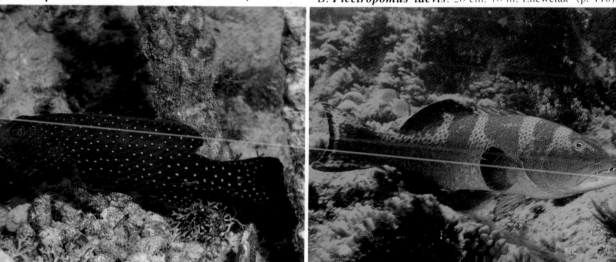

C. *Plectropomus laevis*, 25 cm, 10 m, Guam (p. 110).   D. *Plectropomus laevis*, 60 cm, Enewetak.   J. E. Randall

E. *Plectropomus leopardus*, 36 cm, Great Barrier Reef   F. *Plectropomus oligacanthus*, 35 cm, Philippines (p. 111).
(p. 110).   J: E. Randall   J. E. Randall

Plate 35. Groupers

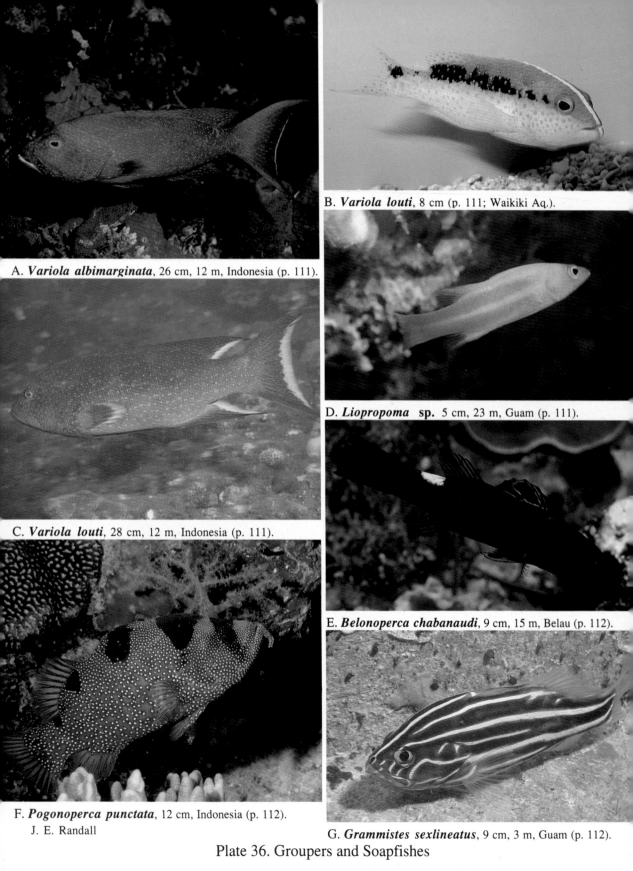

A. *Variola albimarginata*, 26 cm, 12 m, Indonesia (p. 111).

C. *Variola louti*, 28 cm, 12 m, Indonesia (p. 111).

F. *Pogonoperca punctata*, 12 cm, Indonesia (p. 112).
J. E. Randall

B. *Variola louti*, 8 cm (p. 111; Waikiki Aq.).

D. *Liopropoma* sp. 5 cm, 23 m, Guam (p. 111).

E. *Belonoperca chabanaudi*, 9 cm, 15 m, Belau (p. 112).

G. *Grammistes sexlineatus*, 9 cm, 3 m, Guam (p. 112).

Plate 36. Groupers and Soapfishes

. *Calloplesiops altivelis*, 8 cm, (p. 113; aq. photo).

. *Plesiops corallicola*, 12 cm, Guam (p. 113; aq. photo).

. *Pseudochromis fuscus*, light ph., 7cm, 3m, Belau (p113).

. *Pseudochromis marshallensis*, 6 cm, 2 m, Pohnpei (p. 113).

E. *Pseudochromis polynemus*, 7 cm, 13 m, Indonesia (p.113)

F. *Pseudochromis porphyreus*, 6 cm, 18 m, Belau (p. 114).

G. *Amblycirrhitus bimacula*, 7 cm, 10 m, Guam (p. 115).

Plate 37. Prettyfins, Dottybacks, and Hawkfishes

A. *Cirrhitichthys falco*, 7 cm, 15 m, Guam (p. 115). B. *Cirrhitichthys oxycephalus*, 5 cm, 10 m, Belau (p. 115)

C. *Cirrhitichthys oxycephalus*, 7 cm, 3 m, Truk. D. *Cirrhitus pinnulatus*, 13 cm, 6 m, Oahu, Hawaii (p. 115

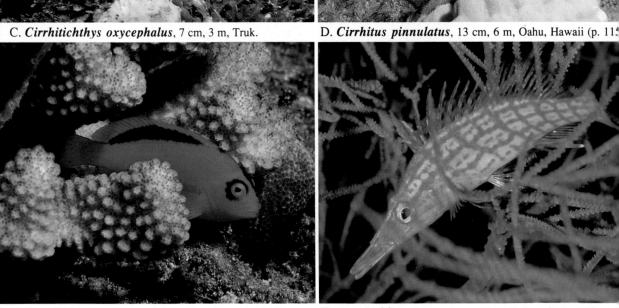

E. *Neocirrhites armatus*, 5.5 cm, 6 m, Guam (p. 115). F. *Oxycirrhites typus*, 6 cm, 12 m, Indonesia (p. 116).

Plate 38. Hawkfishes

M. Neubaue

A. **Paracirrhites arcatus**, 8 cm, 12 m, Guam (p. 116). B. **Paracirrhites forsteri**, 4 cm, 4 m, Guam (p. 116).

C. **Paracirrhites forsteri**, 12 cm, 12 m, Saipan. D. **Paracirrhites forsteri**, *typee* ph., 10 cm, 16 m, Belau.

E. **Paracirrhites hemistictus**, 15 cm, 3 m, Guam (p. 116). F. **Paracirrhites hemistictus**, *polystictus* ph., 13 cm, 3 m, Guam.

Plate 39. Hawkfishes

A. **Apogonichthys ocellatus**, 3.2 cm, Guam (p. 117).

B. **Apogon coccineus**, 3.5 cm, 6 m, Hawaii (p. 118).

C. **Apogon exostigma**, 6 cm, 3 m, Truk (p. 119).

D. **Apogon fraenatus**, 6 cm, 0.5 m, Truk (p. 120).

E. **Apogon kallopterus**, 10 cm, 12 m, Guam (p. 120).

F. **Apogon dispar**, 5 cm, 15 m, Belau (p. 120).

G. **Apogon sangiensis**, 6 cm, 1.5 m, Truk (p. 120).

H. **Apogon lateralis**, 5 cm, Guam (p. 120; aq. photo).

Plate 40. Cardinalfishes

A. *Apogon fuscus*, 8 cm, 25 m, Guam (p. 120).   B. *Apogon guamensis*, 6 cm, 1.5 m, Guam (p. 120).

C. *Apogon angustatus*, 6 cm, 16 m, Guam (p. 121).   D. *Apogon taeniophorus*, 7 cm, 1 m, Guam (p. 121).

E. *Apogon nigrofasciatus*, 7 cm, 1 m, Guam (p. 121).   F. *Apogon novemfasciatus*, 7 cm, 2 m, Guam (p. 121).

G. *Apogon compressus*, 7 cm, 6 m, Belau (p. 121).   H. *Apogon sealei*, 6 cm, 6 m, Belau (p. 121).

Plate 41. Cardinalfishes

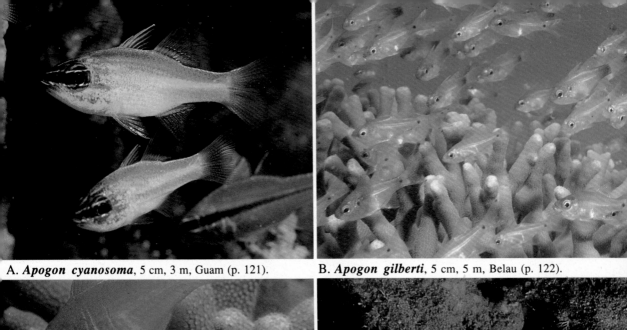

A. *Apogon cyanosoma*, 5 cm, 3 m, Guam (p. 121).

B. *Apogon gilberti*, 5 cm, 5 m, Belau (p. 122).

C. *Apogon leptacanthus*, 6 cm, 0.5 m, Belau (p. 122).

D. *Archamia biguttata*, 5 cm, 6 m, Guam (p. 122).

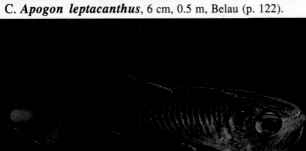

E. *Archamia fucata*, 6 cm, 12 m, Truk (p. 122).

F. *Archamia zosterophora*, 6 cm, 2 m, Belau (p. 122).

Plate 42. Cardinalfishes

A. *Sphaeramia nematoptera*, 6 cm, 1 m, Belau (p. 122).

B. *Sphaeramia orbicularis*, 7 cm, 0.5 m, Truk (p. 122).

C. *Cheilodipterus macrodon*, 12 cm, 1.5 m, Guam (p. 123).

D. *Cheilodipterus artus*, 7 cm, 18 m, Guam (p. 123).

E. *Cheilodipterus* sp. (*artus?*), 7 cm, 2 m, Belau.

F. *Cheilodipterus artus*, 11 cm, 17 m, Guam.

G. *Cheilodipterus quinquelineata*, 9 cm, 15 m, Guam (p. 123)

Plate 43. Cardinalfishes

A. *Kuhlia mugil*, 9.4 cm, Saipan (p. 125).

B. *Heteropriacanthus cruentatus*, 15 cm, 3 m, Guam (p. 126)

C. *Priacanthus hamrur*, 18 cm, 18 m, Guam (p. 126).

D. *Priacanthus hamrur*, the same individual as in C.

E. *Hoplolatilus starcki*, 10 cm, 37 m, Guam (p. 126).

F. *Malacanthus brevirostris*, 9 cm, 14 m, Hawaii (p. 126).

G. *Malacanthus latovittatus*, 7 cm, 12 m, Indonesia (p.126). H. *Echeneis naucrates*, 50 cm, Truk (p. 127).   M. Neubau

Plate 44. Flagtails, Bigeyes, Sand Tilefishes, and Remoras

A. *Decapterus maruadsi*, 15 cm FL, Guam (p. 128).　　B. *Alectis ciliaris*, 6 cm FL (p. 130; Waikiki Aq.).

C. *Gnathanodon speciosus*, 40 cm FL (p. 130; top) and
Caranx ignobilis, 25 cm FL (p. 131; Waikiki Aq.).　　D. *Carangoides ferdau*, 30 cm FL, 15 m, Belau (p. 130).

E. *Carangoides orthogrammus*, 20 cm FL, 4 m, Kosrae
(p.130).　　F. *Carangoides plagiotaenia*, 30 cm FL, 10 m, Belau (p. 130).

Plate 45. Jacks and Trevallys

A. *Caranx ignobilis*, 90 cm FL, (p. 131; Noumea Aq.).

B. *Caranx lugubris*, 40 cm FL, 24 m, Belau (p. 131).

C. *Caranx melampygus*, 50 cm FL, 15 m, Belau (p. 131).

D. *Caranx sexfasciatus*, 14 cm FL, Guam (p. 131).

E. *Caranx sexfasciatus*, 40 cm FL, 6 m, Enewetak (p. 131).

Plate 46. Jacks and Trevallys

A. *Scomberoides lysan*, 40 cm FL, Guam (p. 132).

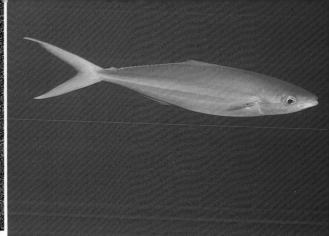

B. *Elagatis bipinnulatus*, 25 cm FL, Guam (p. 132).

C. *Seriola dumerili*, 60 cm FL, (p. 132; Waikiki Aq.). D. *Seriola rivoliana*, 60 cm FL, Wake Is. (p.132). M.Vanderlinden

E. *Trachinotus bailloni*, 40 cm FL, Enewetak (p. 132).   F. *Gerres argyreus*, 20 cm, 4 m, Guam (p. 133).

Plate 47. Jacks and Mojarras

A. *Aphareus furca*, 20 cm, 9 m, Guam (p. 135).

B. *Symphorichthys spilurus*, 30 cm (p. 135; Shedd Aq.).

C. *Aprion virescens*, 25 cm, 12 m, Oahu, Hawaii (p. 135).

D. *Macolor macularis*, 50 cm, 15 m, Belau (p. 135).

E. *Macolor macularis*, 8 cm, Indonesia.   M.Neubauer

F. *Macolor niger*, 3.5 cm, 5 m, Kosrae (p. 136).

G. *Macolor niger*, 28 cm, 18 m, Belau.

Plate 48. Snappers

A. *Lutjanus argentimaculatus*, 50 cm, 16 m, Indonesia (p.136). B. *Lutjanus bohar*, 15 cm, 15 m, Indonesia (p. 136).

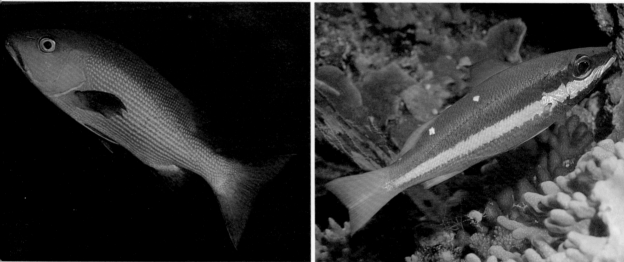

C. *Lutjanus bohar*, 60 cm, 15 m, Belau.   D. *Lutjanus biguttatus*, 20 cm, 15 m, Belau (p. 136).

E. *Lutjanus decussatus*, 25 cm, 12 m, Indonesia (p. 136).   F. *Lutjanus ehrenbergi*, 20 cm, 1 m, Pohnpei (p. 136).

Plate 49. Snappers

A. *Lutjanus fulvus*, 16 cm, 18 m, Guam (p. 137).

B. *Lutjanus gibbus*, 12 cm, 1 m, Saipan (p. 137).

C. *Lutjanus gibbus*, 25 cm, 3 m, Belau.

D. *Lutjanus kasmira*, 18 cm, 8 m, Belau (p. 137).

E. *Lutjanus monostigmus*, 30 cm, 4 m, Belau (p. 138).

F. *Lutjanus semicinctus*, 21.5 cm, Truk (p. 138).

Plate 50. Snappers

A. **_Caesio caerulaurea_**, 22 cm, 16 m, Guam (p. 138).

B. **_Caesio cuning_**, 24 cm, 5 m, Belau (p. 138).

C. **_Caesio lunaris_**, 24 cm, 16 m, Belau (p. 139).

D. **_Caesio teres_**, 20 cm, 16 m, Belau (p. 139).

E. **_Pterocaesio lativittata_**, 12 cm, 30 m, Belau (p. 139).

F. **_Pterocaesio marri_**, 14 cm (upper, lower left; p. 139) and **_Pterocaesio tile_**, 14 cm (lower right), 8 m, Enewetak (p.139)

G. **_Pterocaesio pisang_**, 16 cm, 12 m, Belau (p. 139).

H. **_Pterocaesio trilineata_**, 15 cm, 12 m, Belau (p. 139).

Plate 51. Fusiliers

A. *Diagramma pictum*, 9cm, 2m, New Caledonia (p.140). B. *Plectorhinchus celebecus*, Gr. Barrier Rf. (p.140). J.E.Rand

C. *Plectorhinchus albovittatus*, 9cm, Guam (p.140; aq. photo). D. *Plectorhinchus gaterinoides*, 25cm, 10m, Belau (p.14

E. *Plectorhinchus goldmanni*, 50 cm, 18 m, Indonesia (p. 140).

F. *Plectorhinchus obscurus*, Great Barrier Reef (p. 142). J. E. Randa

Plate 52. Sweetlips

A. *Plectorhinchus chaetodonoides*, 10 cm (Steinhart Aq.).

B. *P. chaetodonoides*, 45 cm, 15 m, Belau (right; p. 140).

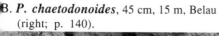

C. *Plectorhinchus orientalis*, 16 cm, 1 m, Guam.

D. *P. orientalis*, 35 cm, 20 m, Saipan (right; p. 142).

E. *Plectorhinchus picus*, 18 cm, 4 m, Guam.

F. *P. picus*, 45 cm, 18 m, Guam (p. 142).

Plate 53. Sweetlips

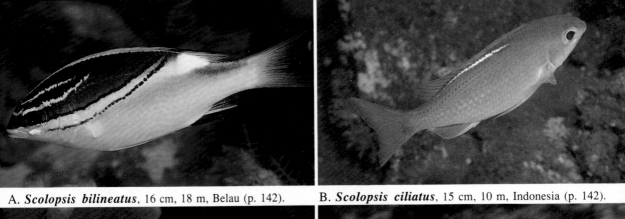

A. *Scolopsis bilineatus*, 16 cm, 18 m, Belau (p. 142).   B. *Scolopsis ciliatus*, 15 cm, 10 m, Indonesia (p. 142).

C. *Scolopsis lineatus*, 8 cm, 1 m, Guam (p. 142).   D. *Scolopsis lineatus*, 13 cm, 2 m, Guam (p. 142).

E. *Scolopsis margaritifer*, 18 cm, 5 m, Belau (p. 143).   F. *Scolopsis affinis*, 20 cm, 10 m, Indonesia (p. 143).

G. *Scolopsis trilineatus*, 14 cm, 4 m, Belau (p. 143).   H. *Pentapodus caninus*, 16 cm, 4 m, Belau (p. 143).

Plate 54. Spinecheeks

A. *Pentapodus macrurus*, 16 cm, 17 m, Guam (p. 143).

B. *Monotaxis grandoculus*, 7 cm, 10 m, Guam (p. 143).

C. *Monotaxis grandoculus*, 22 cm, 5 m, Belau (p. 143).

D. *Gnathodentex aurolineatus*, 15 cm, 16 m, Guam (p. 143).

E. *Lethrinus olivaceus*, 45 cm, 18 m, Indonesia (p. 146).

F. *Lethrinus harak*, 22 cm, 1.5 m, Guam (p. 146).

Plate 55. Spinecheeks and Emperors

A. *Lethrinus erythropterus*, 23 cm, 10 m, Belau (p. 146).   B. *Lethrinus erythracanthus*, 15 cm,. 18 m, Guam (p. 146).

C. *Lethrinus obsoletus*, 20 cm,. 18 m, Guam (p. 147).   D. *Lethrinus rubrioperculatus*, 18 cm, 12 m, Saipan (p. 147

E. *Lethrinus semicinctus*, 15 cm, 1.5 m, Saipan (p. 147).   F. *Lethrinus xanthochilus*, Maldives (p. 147).   J. E. Randa

Plate 56. Emperors

A. *Mulloides flavolineatus*, 10 cm, 3 m, Guam (p. 148).   B. *Mulloides vanicolensis*, 15 cm, 12 m, Guam (p. 148).

C. *Mulloides vanicolensis*, 16 cm, 15 m, Guam (p.148). D. *Parupeneus barberinoides*, 1 cm, Enewetak(p.149).   J.E.Randall

E. *Parupeneus barberinus*, 20 cm, 10 m, Belau (p. 149).   F. *Parupeneus barberinus*, 18 cm, 4 m, Guam (p. 149).

Plate 57. Goatfishes

A. *Parupeneus bifasciatus*, 18 cm, 5 m, Kosrae (p. 149).

B. *Parupeneus bifasciatus*, 20 cm, 17 m, Guam (p. 149).

C. *Parupeneus cyclostomus*, yellow and blue phases, 9 cm, 8 m, Guam (p. 149).

D. *Parupeneus cyclostomus*, 22 cm, 16 m, Guam (p. 149).

E. *Parupeneus ciliatus*, 18 cm, 27 m, Guam (p. 149).

F. *Parupeneus indicus*, 12 cm (top), and *P. ciliatus*, 1 m, New Caledonia (p. 150).

Plate 58. Goatfishes

A. *Parupeneus multifasciatus*, 16 cm (front; p. 150);
Parupeneus barberinus (rear; p. 149), 4 m, Guam.

B. *Parupeneus multifasciatus*, 18 cm, 8 m, Guam (p. 150).

C. *Parupeneus multifasciatus*, 18 cm, 18 m, Saipan (p.150).

D. *Parupeneus pleurostigma*, 13 cm, 3 m, Guam (p. 150).

E. *Upeneus tragula*, 16 cm, 2 m, Belau (p. 150).

F. *Parapriacanthus ransonneti*, 6 cm, 5 m, Belau (p. 151).

Plate 59. Goatfishes

A. *Pempheris oualensis*, 14 cm, 3 m, Saipan (p. 151).　　　B. *Kyphosus bigibbus*, 25 cm, (p. 151; Waikiki Aq.).

C. *Kyphosus cinerascens*, 15 cm, Guam (p. 151).　　　D. *Kyphosus cinerascens*, 30 cm, Indonesia (p. 151).

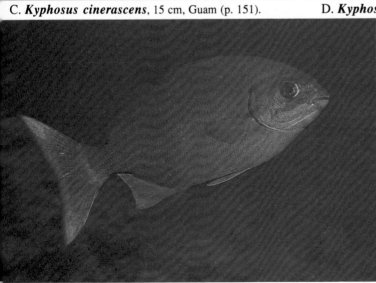

E. *Kyphosus vaigiensis*, 30 cm, 16 m, Saipan (p. 151).　　　F. *Monodactylus argenteus*, 12 cm, (p. 152; Shedd Aq

Plate 60. Sweepers, Rudderfishes, and Monos

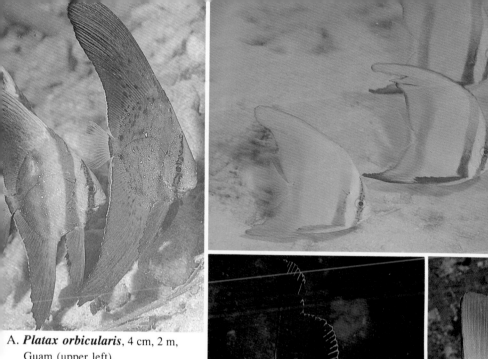

A. **Platax orbicularis**, 4 cm, 2 m, Guam (upper left).
B. **P. orbicularis**, 15 cm, 4 m, Guam.
C. **Platax pinnatus**, 12 cm, 4 m, Indonesia (near right).
D. **P. pinnatus**, 22 cm, 18 m, Belau.
E. **Platax teira**, 15 cm, 15 m, Belau (lower left).
F. **P. teira**, 35 cm (Shedd Aq.).

Plate 61. Batfishes (p. 152)

A. *Chaetodon auriga*, 10 cm, 17 m, Guam (p. 153).

B. *Chaetodon barronessa*, 8 cm, 4 m, Belau (p. 153).

C. *Chaetodon bennetti*, 9 cm, 16 m, Guam (p. 153).

D. *Chaetodon burgessi* (p. 153; aq. photo). R. Kosaki

E. *Chaetodon citrinellus*, 7 cm, 1 m, Guam (p. 154).

F. *Chaetodon ephippium*, 11 cm, 12 m, Guam (p. 154).

Plate 62. Butterflyfishes

A. *Chaetodon flavocoronatus*, 7.4 cm, Guam (p. 154; aq. photo). B. *Chaetodon kleinii*, 8 cm, 16 m, Guam (p. 154).

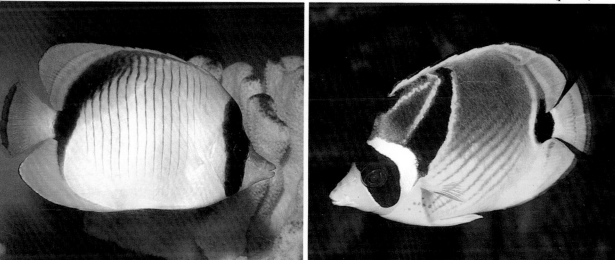

C. *Chaetodon lineolatus*, 10 cm, (p. 154; aq. photo). D. *Chaetodon lunula*, 9 cm, 18 m, Saipan (p. 154).

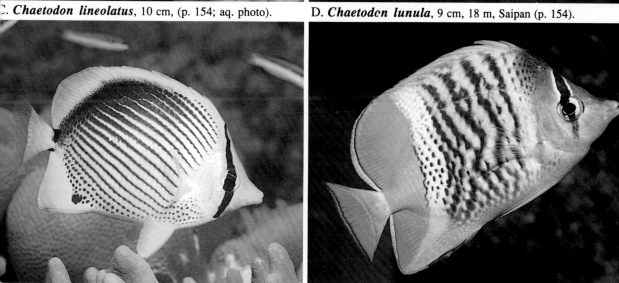

E. *Chaetodon melannotus*, 8 cm, 4 m, Belau (p. 154). F. *Chaetodon mertensii*, 8 cm, 18 m, Saipan (p. 154).

Plate 63. Butterflyfishes

A. *Chaetodon meyeri*, 3.5 cm, 15 m, Kosrae (p. 155).

B. *Chaetodon meyeri*, 8 cm, 5 m, Belau.

C. *Chaetodon octofasciatus*, 6 cm, 10 m, Belau (p. 155).

D. *Chaetodon ornatissimus*, 10 cm, 6 m, Guam (p. 155).

E. *Chaetodon oxycephalus*, 12 cm, 12 m, Indonesia (p.154).

F. *Chaetodon punctatofasciatus*, 7 cm, 18 m, Guam (p.15

Plate 64. Butterflyfishes

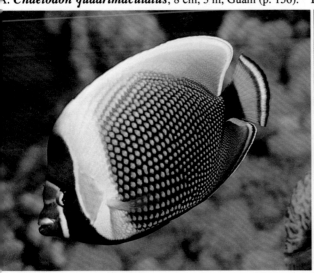

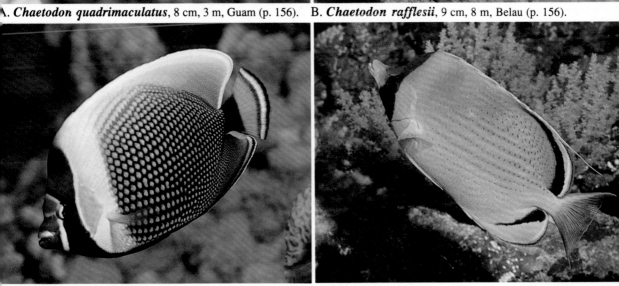

A. *Chaetodon quadrimaculatus*, 8 cm, 3 m, Guam (p. 156).   B. *Chaetodon rafflesii*, 9 cm, 8 m, Belau (p. 156).

C. *Chaetodon reticulatus*, 9 cm, 8 m, Guam (p. 156).   D. *Chaetodon semeion*, 10 cm, 8 m, Belau (p. 156).

E. *Chaetodon speculum*, 9 cm, 1 m, Belau (p. 156).   F. *Chaetodon tinkeri*, 10 cm (p. 156; Waikiki Aq.).

Plate 65. Butterflyfishes

A. *Chaetodon trifascialis*, 3.5 cm, 1 m, Guam (p. 156).

B. *Chaetodon trifascialis*, 8 cm, 1 m, Guam.

C. *Chaetodon trifasciatus*, 7 cm, 4 m, Guam (p. 156).

D. *Chaetodon ulietensis*, 9 cm, 16 m, Guam (p. 157).

E. *Chaetodon unimaculatus*, 8 cm, 6 m, Guam (p. 157).

F. *Chaetodon vagabundus*, 12 cm, 5 m, Belau (p. 157).

Plate 66. Butterflyfishes

A. *Coradion chrysozonus*, 9 cm, 12 m, Indonesia (p. 157).   B. *Forcipiger flavissimus*, 9 cm, 10 m, Guam (p. 157).

C. *Forcipiger longirostris*, 11 cm, 8 m, Guam (p. 157).   D. *Forcipiger longirostris*, 11 cm, Hawaii.   M. Vanderlinden

E. *Hemitaurichthys polylepis*, 8 cm, 15 m, Guam (p. 157).   F. *Hemitaurichthys thompsoni*, 8 cm, (p. 158; Waikiki Aq.).

Plate 67. Butterflyfishes

A. *Heniochus acuminatus*, 10 cm, 15 m, Guam (p. 158).

B. *Heniochus chrysostomus*, 6 cm, 14 m, Guam (p. 158).

C. *Heniochus chrysostomus*, 9 cm, 16 m, Guam.

D. *Heniochus monoceros*, 14 cm, 15 m, Guam (p. 158).

E. *Heniochus singularis*, 8 cm, 11 m, Guam (p. 159).

F. *Heniochus varius*, 12 cm, 10 m, Belau (p. 159).

Plate 68. Butterflyfishes

A. *Apolemichthys griffisi*, 11 cm (p. 159; Waikiki Aq.).   B. *Apolemichthys trimaculatus*, 12 cm, 25 m, Guam (p. 159)

C. *Apolemichthys xanthopunctatus*, 11cm (p. 159; Waikiki Aq.).   D. *Centropyge bicolor*, 8 cm, 10 m, Belau (p. 160).

E. *Centropyge bispinosus*, 8 cm, 18 m, Belau (p. 160).   F. *Centropyge colini*, 6 cm, Guam (p. 160; aq. photo).

Plate 69. Angelfishes

A. *Centropyge flavissimus*, 8 cm, 4 m Guam (p. 160).   B. *Centropyge heraldi*, 7 cm, 41 m Guam (p. 160).

C. *Centropyge loriculus*, 6cm, Pohnpei (p.160). M.Neubauer   D. *Centropyge multicolor*, 6cm, Kwaj. (p.160). J.E.Randal

E. *Centropyge multifasciatus*, 7 cm, 30 m Guam (p. 161).   F. *Centropyge nigriocellus* (p.161; aq. photo).   R. Pyle

Plate 70. Angelfishes

A. *Centropyge shepardi* male, 7 cm, 30 m, Guam (p. 161). B. *Centropyge shepardi* rare monochrome female, 21 m, Guam.

C. *Centropyge tibicen*, 8 cm, 8 m, Belau (p. 161). D. *Centropyge vrolikii*, 8 cm, 12 m, indonesia (p. 161).

E. *Genicanthus melanospilos* female, 8 cm, (Shedd Aq.). F. *Genicanthus melanospilos* male, 11 cm, (p.162; Shedd Aq.

Plate 71. Angelfishes

A. *Genicanthus watanabei* male, Coral Sea (p. 162). G.R.Allen B. *Pygoplites diacanthus*, 14 cm, 15 m, Belau (p. 162).

C. *Chaetodontoplus mesoleucus*, 5 cm, 2 m, Belau (p. 162).↑
D. *Pomacanthus navarchus*, 15 cm, 12 m, Belau (p. 163).

E. *Pomacanthus navarchus* x *xanthometapon* hybrid (Steinhart Aq.).↑
F. *Pomacanthus xanthometapon*, 30 cm, 7 m, Indonesia (p. 163).

Plate 72. Angelfishes

A. *Pomacanthus sexstriatus* juv. (p. 163; above; photo by R.E. Thresher).

B. *Pomacanthus sexstriatus* adult, 35 cm, 15 m, Belau.

. *Pomacanthus imperator* juv., 5 cm, 0.5 m, Guam (p. 163).

. *Pomacanthus imperator* adult, 25 cm, 16 m, Saipan (right).

. *Pomacanthus semicirculatus* juv. (p. 163; photo by R. E. Thresher)

Pomacanthus semicirculatus adult, 22 cm, 16m, Indonesia.

late 73. Angelfishes

A. *Amphiprion chrysopterus*, 8 cm, 18 m, Guam (p. 164).   B. *Amphiprion chrysopterus*, 9 cm, 16 m, Saipan.

C. *Amphiprion clarkii*, 9 cm, 30 m, Guam (p. 164).   D. *Amphiprion clarkii*, 8 cm, 15 m, Guam.

E. *Amphiprion melanopus*, 8 cm, 5 m, Guam (p. 164).   F. *Amphiprion perideraion*, 7 cm, 16 m, Guam (p. 165).

Plate 74. Damselfishes: Anemonefishes

A. *Chromis acares*, 4 cm, 16 m, Guam (p. 165).   B. *Chromis agilis*, 3.5 cm, 7 m, Guam (p. 165).

C. *Chromis agilis*, 6 cm, 14 m, Guam.   D. *Chromis alpha*, 7 cm, 16 m, Guam (p. 165).

E. *Chromis amboinensis*, 3 cm, 30 m, Guam (p. 165).   F. *Chromis amboinensis*, 5 cm, 15 m, Guam.

G. *Chromis analis*, 6 cm, 18 m, Belau (p. 165).   H. *Chromis atripectoralis*, 8 cm, 9 m, Guam (p. 166).

Plate 75. Damselfishes

A. *Chromis atripes*, 3.5 cm, 16 m, Belau (p. 166).   B. *Chromis caudalis*, 5 cm, 15 m, Belau (p. 166).

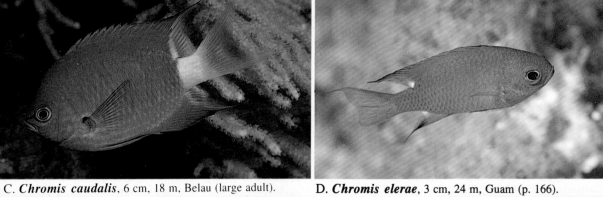

C. *Chromis caudalis*, 6 cm, 18 m, Belau (large adult).   D. *Chromis elerae*, 3 cm, 24 m, Guam (p. 166).

E. *Chromis lepidolepis*, 3.5 cm, 4 m, Kosrae (p. 166).   F. *Chromis margaritifer*, 5 cm, 10 m, Guam (p. 166).

G. *Chromis retrofasciata*, 3 cm, 18 m, Belau (p. 167).   H. *Chromis ternatensis*, 6 cm, 16 m, Guam (p. 167).

Plate 76. Damselfishes

A. *Chromis vanderbilti*, 4.5 cm, 7 m, Guam (p. 167).　　B. *Chromis viridis*, 5 cm, 9 m, Guam (p. 167).

Chromis viridis, nesting male, 6 cm, 1 m, Kosrae.　　D. *Chromis weberi*, 5 cm, 10 m, Indonesia (p. 167).

E. *Chromis xanthochir*, 7 cm, 10 m, Belau (p. 167).　　F. *Chromis xanthura*, 4 cm, 20 m, Guam (p. 167).

G. *Chromis xanthura*, 7 cm, 15 m, Guam.　　H. *Chromis xanthura*, 10 cm, 3 m, Belau.

Plate 77. Damselfishes

A. *Dascyllus aruanus*, 5 cm, 1.5 m, Guam (p. 167).

B. *Dascyllus melanurus*, 5 cm, 2 m, Kosrae (p. 167).

C. *Dascyllus trimaculatus*, 6 cm, 26 m, Guam (p. 168).

D. *Dascyllus trimaculatus*, 7 cm, 4 m, Guam (p. 168).

F. *Lepidozygus tapienosoma*, 6 cm, 6 m, Belau (p. 168).

E. *Dascyllus reticulatus*, 4.5 cm, 12 m, Saipan (p. 168).

G. *Cheiloprion labiatus*, 7 cm, 6 m, Belau (p. 168).

Plate 78. Damselfishes

A. *Abudefduf lorenzi*, 10 cm, 1.5 m, Belau (p. 168).

B. *Abudefduf notatus*, 12 cm, 1 m, Belau (p. 168).

C. *Abudefduf vaigiensis*, 12 cm, 6 m, Truk (p. 168).

D. *Abudefduf septemfasciatus*, 10 cm, 1 m, Guam (p. **169).**

E. *Abudefduf sexfasciatus*, 9 cm, 10 m, Guam (p. 169).

F. *Abudefduf sordidus*, 10 mm, 2 m, Guam (p. 169).

Plate 79. Damselfishes: Sergeants

A. *Amblyglyphidodon aureus*, 9 cm, 15 m, Belau (p. 169). B. *Amblyglyphidodon curacao*, 8 cm, Guam (p. 169).

C. *Amblyglyphidodon leucogaster*, 8 cm, 12 m, Belau (p.169). D. *Amblyglyphidodon ternatensis*, PNG (p.169). G.R.AI

E. *Chrysiptera biocellata*, 6 cm, 1 m, Guam (p. 169). F. *Chrysiptera caeruleolineata*, 3.5 cm, 24 m, Guam (p. 17

G. *Chrysiptera cyanea* female, 5 cm, 1 m, Belau (p. 170). H. *Chrysiptera cyanea* male, 6 cm, 1 m, Belau.

Plate 80. Damselfishes

A. *Chrysiptera glauca*, 5 cm, 1 m, Saipan (p. 170).   B. *Chrysiptera leucopoma*, 5 cm, 1 m, Guam (p. 170).

C. *Chrysiptera leucopoma*, *amabilis* ph., 5 cm, 4 m, Guam.   D. *Chrysiptera oxycephala*, 2 cm, 4 m, Belau (p. 170).

E. *Chrysiptera oxycephala*, 6 cm, 4 m, Belau.   F. *Chrysiptera rex*, 5 cm, 12 m, Belau (p. 170).

G. *Chrysiptera talboti*, 5 cm, 12 m, Belau (p. 170).   H. *Chrysiptera traceyi*, 4.5 cm, 5 m, Guam (p. 170).

Plate 81. Damselfishes

A. *Chrysiptera unimaculata*, 3.5 cm, 1 m, Belau (p. 171).

B. *Chrysiptera unimaculata*, 6 cm, 1 m, Belau.

C. *Dischistodus melanotus*, 3.5 cm, 1 m, Belau (p. 171).

D. *Dischistodus chrysopoecilus*, 7 cm, 1.5 m, Belau (p. 171).

E. *Dischistodus melanotus*, 10 cm, 4 m, Belau.

F. *Dischistodus perspicillatus*, 2.5 cm, 2 m, Belau (p. 171).

G. *Neopomacentrus nemurus*, 5 cm, 2 m, Belau (p. 171).

H. *Neopomacentrus violascens*, 3 cm, 29 m, Guam (p. 171).

I. *Dischistodus perspicillatus*, 10 cm, 2 m, Belau.

J. *Hemiglyphidodon plagiometapon*, 12 cm, 6 m, Belau (p. 171).

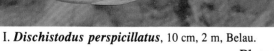

Plate 82. Damselfishes

A. *Neoglyphidodon melas* juv.,4 cm, 1m, Belau (p. 171).   B. *Neoglyphidodon melas*, 9 cm, 6 m, Belau.

C. *Neoglyphidodon nigroris* juv., 3 cm, 6 m, Indonesia.   D. *Neoglyphidodon nigroris*, 6 cm, 6 m, Belau (p. 172).

E. *Plectroglyphidodon dickii*, 6 cm, 1 m, Guam (p.172). F. *Plectroglyphidodon imparipennis*, 3.5 cm, 1 m, Guam (p.172).

G. *Plectroglyphidodon johnstonianus*, 6 cm, 8 m, Guam (p.172). H. *Plectroglyphidodon johnstonianus*, 5 cm, 3 m, Guam.

Plate 83. Damselfishes

A. *Plectroglyphidodon lacrymatus*, 7cm, 14m, Guam (p.172). B. *Plectroglyphidodon leucozona*, 7 cm, 1 m, Guam (p.172

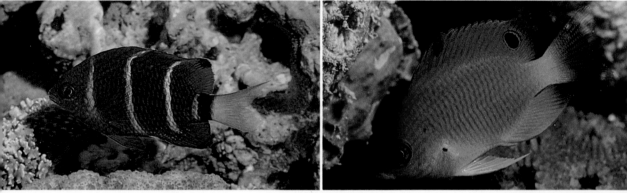

C. *Plectroglyphidodon phoenixensis*, 5 cm, 1 m, Guam (p.172). D. *Pomacentrus amboinensis*, 2 cm, 9 m, Guam (p. 172

E. *Pomacentrus amboinensis*, 7 cm, 17 m, Guam (p. 172). F. *Pomacentrus nagasakiensis*, 7cm (p.173), GBR. G.R.A|

G. *Pomacentrus bankanensis*, 6 cm, 1.5 m, Belau (p. 173). H. *Pomacentrus brachialis*, 6 cm, 12 m, Indonesia (p. 173)

Plate 84. Damselfishes

A. *Pomacentrus burroughi*, 6 cm, 2 m, Belau (p.173). B. *Pomacentrus chrysurus*, 7 cm, 1.5 m, GBR (p.173). G.R.Allen

C. *Pomacentrus coelestis*, 4 cm, 5 m, Belau (p. 173). D. *Pomacentrus coelestis*, 6 cm, 18 m, Belau.

E. *Pomacentrus emarginatus*, 7 cm, 16 m, Belau (p. 173). F. *Pomacentrus grammorhynchus*, 1.5 cm, 4 m, Belau (p. 173).

G. *Pomacentrus grammorhynchus*, 7 cm, 1 m, Belau. H. *Pomacentrus moluccensis*, 5 cm, 8 m, Belau (p. 174).

Plate 85. Damselfishes

A. *Pomacentrus nigromanus*, 4.5 cm, 5 m, Belau (p. 174).   B. *Pomacentrus pavo*, 6 cm, 11 m, Saipan (p. 174).

C. *Pomacentrus pavo*, 6 cm, 3 m, Truk.   D. *Pomacentrus philippinus*, 4.5 cm, 4 m, Kosrae (p. 174).

E. *Pomacentrus philippinus*, 6 cm, 5 m, Kosrae.   F. *Pomacentrus reidi*, 7 cm, 14 m, Belau (p. 174).

G. *Pomacentrus simsiang*, 7 cm, 1 m, Belau (p. 174).   H. *Pomacentrus* **sp.**, 4.5 cm, 2 m, Belau (p. 174).

Plate 86. Damselfishes

A. *Pomacentrus vaiuli*, 3.5 cm, 18 m, Guam (p. 174).   B. *Pomacentrus vaiuli*, 6 cm, 15 m, Guam.

C. *Pomachromis guamensis*, 5 cm, 4 m, Guam (p. 175).   D. *Stegastes albifasciatus*, 6 cm, 1.5 m, Guam (p. 175).

E. *Stegastes albifasciatus*, 7 cm, 1 m, Guam.   F. *Stegastes fasciolatus*, 7 cm, 11 m, Guam (p. 175).

G. *Stegastes lividus*, 7 cm, 2 m, Guam (p. 175).   H. *Stegastes nigricans*, 7 cm, 8 m, Guam (p. 175).

Plate 87. Damselfishes

A. ***Bodianus anthioides***, 12 cm, 18 m, Indonesia (p. 176).   B. ***Bodianus loxozonus***, Line Is. (p. 177).   J. E. Randal

C. ***Bodianus axillaris***, 5 cm, 18 m, Belau (p. 176).   D. ***Bodianus axillaris***, 12 cm, 9 m, Guam.

E. ***Bodianus diana***, 4 cm, 18 m, Belau (p. 176).   F. ***Bodianus diana***, 12 cm, 17 m, Belau.

G. ***Bodianus mesothorax***, 4 cm, 12 m, Belau (p. 177).   H. ***Bodianus mesothorax***, 10 cm, 15 m, Indonesia.

Plate 88. Wrasses

A. *Choerodon anchorago*, 13-15 cm, 1 m, Belau (p. 177).   B. *Pseudodax moluccanus*, 5 cm, 18 m, Belau (p. 177).

C. *Pseudodax moluccanus*, 13 cm, 20 m, Saipan (p. 177).   D. *Cheilinus arenatus*, 10 cm, 25 m, Guam (p. 177).

E. *Cheilinus bimaculatus*, 7.5 cm, 10 m, Hawaii (p. 177).   F. *Cheilinus celebecus*, 15 cm, 7 m, Belau (p. 178).

Plate 89. Wrasses

A. *Cheilinus chlorourus*, 13 cm, 16 m, Guam (p. 178).   B. *Cheilinus chlorourus*, 23 cm, 6 m, Enewetak (p. 178).

C. *Cheilinus digrammus*, 20 cm, 24 m, Guam (p. 178).   D. *Cheilinus fasciatus*, 20 cm, 6 m, Guam (p. 178).

E. *Cheilinus orientalis*, 8 cm, 16 m, Guam (p. 178).   F. *Cheilinus oxycephalus*, 11 cm (p. 178), with *Labroides dimidiatus* (p. 191) 10 m, Guam.

Plate 90. Wrasses

A. ***Cheilinus undulatus***, 7 cm,
   1 m, Belau (above).
B. ***Cheilinus undulatus***, 110 cm,
   Maldive Is., Indian Ocean.
                          J. E. Randall
R. Voorn

C. ***Cheilinus undulatus***, 160 cm, 10 m, Great Barrier Reef. D. ***Cheilinus trilobatus***, 16 cm, 18 m, Guam (p. 178).

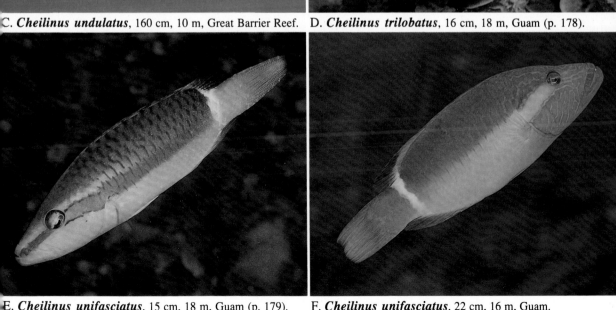

E. ***Cheilinus unifasciatus***, 15 cm, 18 m, Guam (p. 179).   F. ***Cheilinus unifasciatus***, 22 cm, 16 m, Guam.

Plate 91. Wrasses

A. *Epibulus insidiator*, 6 cm, 2 m, Kosrae (p. 180).

B. *Epibulus insidiator*, xanthic ph., 16 cm, 8 m, Guam.

C. *Epibulus insidiator*, 19 cm, 15 m, Guam.

D. *Epibulus insidiator*, 22 cm, 15 m, Enewetak.

E. *Cymolutes praetextatus*, 1 cm, 1 m, Guam (p. 180).

F. *Novaculichthys macrolepidotus*, 89 mm 2.5 m Saipan (p. 18

G. *Novaculichthys taeniourus*, 8 cm, 17 m, Hawaii (p.180). H. *Novaculichthys taeniourus*, 13 cm, 4 m, Guam (p. 180).

Plate 92. Wrasses

A. *Xyrichtys aneitensis*, 5 cm, 18 m, Guam (p. 180).

B. *Xyrichtys aneitensis*, 14 cm, 14 m, Guam (p. 180).

C. *Xyrichtys pavo*, 9 cm, 10 m, Guam (p. 181).

D. *Xyrichtys pavo*, 16 cm, 14 m, Guam.

E. *Cirrhilabrus cyanopleura*, 5 cm, 8 m, Belau (p. 181).

F. *Cirrhilabrus cyanopleura*, t.p., 6 cm, 8 m, Belau.

G. *Cirrhilabrus exquisitus*, i.p., 4.5 cm, 3 m, Belau (p.181).

H. *Cirrhilabrus exquisitus*, t.p., 6 cm, 4 m, Indonesia.

Plate 93. Wrasses

A. *Cirrhilabrus* **sp. 1**, i.p., 6 cm, 15 m, Guam (p. 181).　B. *Cirrhilabrus* **sp. 1**, t.p., 8 cm, 16 m, Guam.

C. *Cirrhilabrus luteovittatus*, t.p., 9cm (p.181;Waikiki Aq.).　D. *Pseudocheilinus evanidus*, 6 cm, 20 m, Guam (p. 182).

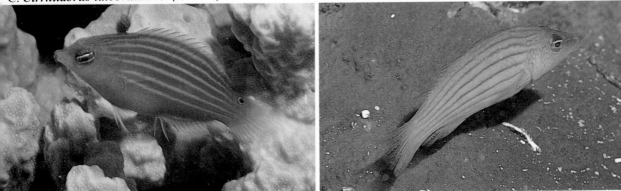

E. *Pseudocheilinus hexataenia*, 4 cm, 14 m, Guam (p. 182).　F. *Pseudocheilinus octotaenia*, 6 cm, 20 m, Guam (p. 182).

G. *Pseudocheilinus tetrataenia*, 4 cm, 15 m, Hawaii (lower fish; p. 182).　H. *Pterogogus cryptus*, 5 cm, 16 m, Guam (p. 182).

Plate 94. Wrasses

A. *Anampses caeruleopunctatus*, 4 cm, 3 m, Guam (p.182). B. *Anampses caeruleopunctatus*, i.p., 14 cm, 2 m, Enewetak.

C. *Anampses melanurus*, i.p., 8 cm, 12 m, Indonesia (p.183). D. *Anampses meleagrides*, i.p., 7 cm, 8 m, Guam (p.183).

E. *Anampses twisti*, 3.5 cm, 24 m, Guam (p. 184). F. *Anampses twisti*, 12 cm, 12 m, Belau.

G. *Cheilio inermis*, 30 cm, 7 m, Hawaii (p. 184). H. *Coris variegata*, 9 cm, 15 m, Enewetak (p. 184).

Plate 95. Wrasses

A. *Coris aygula*, 9 cm, 9 m, Guam (p.184).

B. *Coris aygula*, 23 cm, 8 m, Belau.

C. *Coris gaimard*, 6 cm, 12 m, Guam (p. 184).

D. *Coris gaimard*, 8 cm, 12 m, Guam.

E. *Coris gaimard*, 26 cm, Hawaii.   J. E. Randall

F. *Gomphosus varius*, 4 cm, 8 m, Guam (p.184).

G. *Gomphosus varius,* i.p., 11 cm, 10 m, Guam.

H. *Gomphosus varius*, t.p., 13 cm, 9 m, Guam.

Plate 96. Wrasses

A. *Halichoeres biocellatus*, 10 cm, 24 m, Guam (p. 185). B. *Halichoeres chloropterus*, 10 cm, 1 m, Belau (p. 185).

C. *Halichoeres hartzfeldii*, i.p., 8 cm, 11 m, Guam (p. 185). D. *Halichoeres hartzfeldii*, t.p., 12 cm, 18 m, Guam.

E. *Halichoeres hortulanus*, 6 cm, 10 m, Guam (p. 185). F. *Halichoeres hortulanus*, 17 cm, 12 m, Guam (p. 185).

G. *Halichoeres chrysus*, 7 cm, 10 m, Indonesia (p. 185). H. *Halichoeres margaritaceus*, 9 cm, 1 m, Guam (p. 185).

Plate 97. Wrasses

A. *Halichoeres marginatus*, i.p., 8 cm, 4 m, Belau (p. 186). B. *Halichoeres marginatus*, t.p., 12 cm, 5 m, Guam (p. 186

C. *Halichoeres melanurus*, i.p., 7 cm, 4 m, Belau (p. 186). D. *Halichoeres melanurus*, t.p., 9 cm, 4 m, Belau.

E. *Halichoeres melasmapomus*, t.p., 12 cm, (p.186). J.E.Randall F. *Halichoeres prosopeion*, 9 cm, 12 m, Belau (p.186

G. *Halichoeres* sp., 8 cm, 6 m, Belau (p. 186). H. *Halichoeres richmondi*, t.p., 12 cm, 6 m, Indonesia (p.18

Plate 98. Wrasses
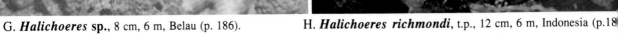

A. *Halichoeres scapularis*, i.p., 7 cm, 1 m, Indonesia (p.186). B. *Halichoeres scapularis*, t.p., 10 m, Philip.   J.E.Randall

C. *Halichoeres trimaculatus*, i.p., 9 cm, 3 m, Guam (p. 186). D. *Halichoeres trimaculatus*, t.p., 12 cm, 12 m, Guam.

E. *Hemigymnus fasciatus*, 5 cm, 18 m, Guam, with *Scarus gibbus*. F. *H. fasciatus*, 16 cm, 18 m, Guam (p. 187).

G. *Hemigymnus melapterus*, 5 cm, 3 m, Guam (p. 187). H. *Hemigymnus melapterus*, 16 cm, 5 m, Guam.

Plate 99. Wrasses

A. *Hologymnosus doliatus*, t.p., 22.7 cm, Guam (p. 187).

B. *Hologymnosus doliatus*, 2.5-4 cm, 12 m, Guam (p. 187).   C. *Hologymnosus doliatus*, t.p., Philippines.   J. E. Randa

D. *Macropharyngodon meleagris*, i.p., 8 cm, 11 m, Guam (p.187).   E. *Macropharyngodon meleagris*, t.p., 10 cm, 4 m, Guan

F. *Pseudocoris yamashiroi*, i.p. 8 cm, 6 m, Belau (p. 188).   G. *Pseudojuloides atavai*, i.p., Guam (p. 188).   J. E. Randa

Plate 100. Wrasses

A. *Pseudojuloides cerasinus*, i.p., 7 cm, 15 m, Hawaii (p.188). B. *Pseudojuloides cerasinus*, t.p., 11 cm, 15 m, Hawaii.

C. *Stethojulis bandanensis*, i.p., 7 cm, 9 m, Guam (p. 188). D. *Stethojulis bandanensis*, t.p., 9 cm, 16 m, Guam.

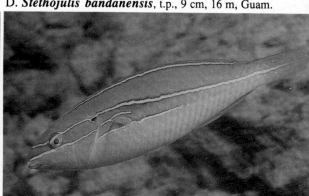

E. *Stethojulis strigiventer*, i.p., 8 cm, 7 m, Rota (p. 189). F. *Stethojulis strigiventer*, t.p., 12 cm, 3 m, Guam.

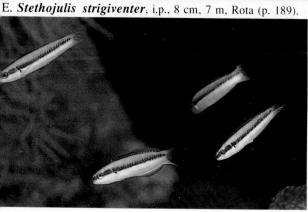

G. *Thalassoma amblycephalum*, i.p., 6 cm, 4 m, Belau (p. 189). H. *Thalassoma amblycephalum*, t.p., 11 cm, 12 m, Indonesia.

Plate 101. Wrasses

A. *Thalassoma hardwickii*, i.p., 8 cm, 1 m, Saipan (p.189). B. *Thalassoma hardwickii*, t.p., 15 cm, 1 m, Belau.

C. *Thalassoma janseni*, 12 cm, 1 m, Belau (p. 189). D. *Thalassoma lunare*, t.p., 13 cm, 5 m, Belau (p. 189).

E. *Thalassoma lutescens*, i.p., 9 cm, 12 m, Saipan (p.189). F. *Thalassoma lutescens*, t.p., 13 cm, 10 m, Guam.

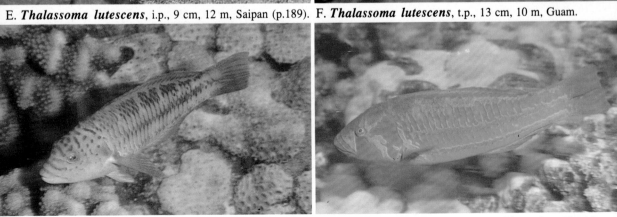

G. *Thalassoma purpureum*, i.p., 15 cm, 3 m, Hawaii (p.190). H. *Thalassoma purpureum*, t.p., 22 cm, 3 m, Hawaii.

Plate 102. Wrasses

A. *Thalassoma quinquevittatum*, t.p., 10 cm, 1 m, Guam (p. 190). B. *Thalassoma quinquevittatum*, t.p., 11 cm, 6 m, Guam.

C. *Thalassoma trilobatum*, i.p., 9 cm, Hawaii (aq. photo). D. *Thalassoma trilobatum*, t.p., 15 mm, 3 m, Hawaii.

E. *Diproctacanthus xanthurus*, 6 cm, 4 m, Belau (p. 190). F. *Labrichthys unilineatus*, 7 cm, 11 m, Truk (p. 190).

G. *Labrichthys unilineatus*, 11 cm, 5 m, Guam.   H. *Labroides bicolor*, 10 cm, 16 m, Guam (p. 191) with

Plate 103. Wrasses   *Parupeneus bifasciatus* (p. 149).

A. **Labroides dimidiatus**, 4 cm, 18 m, Guam (p. 191).

B. **Labroides dimidiatus**, 8 cm, 24 m, Guam.

C. **Labroides pectoralis**, 5 cm, 3 m, Belau (p. 191).

D. **Labropsis alleni**, 7 mm, 15 m, Indonesia (p. 191).

E. **Labropsis micronesica**, 26 mm, 24 m, Guam (p. 191).

F. **Labropsis micronesica**, 7 cm, 21 m, Guam.

G. **Labropsis xanthonota**, 4 cm, 16 m, Guam (p. 191).

H. **Labropsis xanthonota** male, 10 cm, 15 m, Guam.

Plate 104. Wrasses

A. *Calotomus carolinus*, i.p., 20 cm, 18 m, Hawaii (p.192).

B. *Calotomus carolinus*, t.p., 22 cm, 12 m, Guam.

C. *Leptoscarus vaigiensis*, Kenya (p. 193).   J. E. Randall

D. *Bolbometopon muricatum*, 110 cm, Wake Is. (p. 193).
M. Vanderlinden

E. *Cetoscarus bicolor*, juv. 6 cm, 25 m, Guam (p. 193).

F. *Cetoscarus bicolor*, i.p., 45 cm, 6 m, Belau.   G. *Cetoscarus bicolor*, t.p., 50 cm, 6 m, Belau.

Plate 105. Parrotfishes

A. *Hipposcarus longiceps*, 7.5 cm, 12 m, Guam (p. 193).

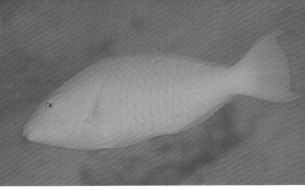

B. *Hipposcarus longiceps*, i.p., 30 cm, 18 m, Guam.

C. *Hipposcarus longiceps*, t.p., 50 cm, 18 m, Guam.

D. *Scarus altipinnis*, juv., 5 cm, 2 m, Enewetak (p. 194).

E. *Scarus altipinnis*, i.p., 20 cm, 16 m, Guam.

F. *Scarus altipinnis*, t.p., 35 cm, 6 m, Enewetak.

G. *Scarus atropectoralis*, i.p., 26 cm, 10 m, Belau (p. 194).

H. *Scarus atropectoralis*, t.p., 40 cm, 23 m, Belau.

Plate 106. Parrotfishes

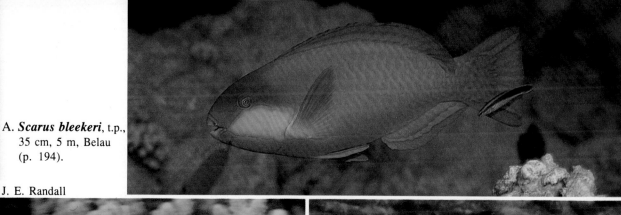

A. *Scarus bleekeri*, t.p., 35 cm, 5 m, Belau (p. 194).

J. E. Randall

B. *Scarus bowersi*, t.p., 17.5 cm, Belau (p. 194).

C. *Scarus chameleon*, t.p., 22 cm, 8 m, Belau (p. 194).

D. *Scarus dimidiatus*, i.p., 13 cm, 4 m, Belau (p. 194).

E. *Scarus dimidiatus*, t.p., 22 cm, 12 m, Belau.

F. *Scarus festivus*, t.p., 22 cm, 8 m, Belau (p. 194).

G. *Scarus flavipectoralis*, t.p., 28 cm, Great Barrier Reef (p. 194). J. E. Randall

Plate 107. Parrotfishes

A. *Scarus forsteni*, i.p., 18 cm, 9 m, Guam (p. 195).

B. *Scarus forsteni*, t.p., 40 cm, Enewetak.

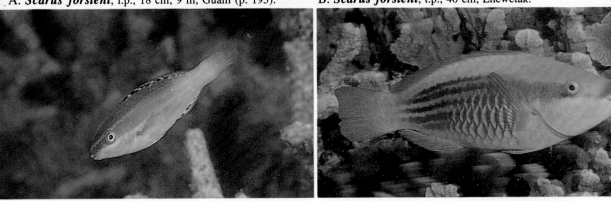

C. *Scarus frenatus*, juv., 10 cm, 1 m, Guam (p. 195).

D. *Scarus frenatus*, i.p., 18 cm, 8 m, Belau.

E. *Scarus frenatus*, t.p., 30 cm, 5 m, Belau.

F. *Scarus frontalis*, 30 cm, 16 m, Guam (p. 195).

G. *Scarus ghobban*, i.p., 25 cm, 18 m, Belau (p. 195).

H. *Scarus tricolor*, t.p., 35 cm, 12 m, Belau (p. 195).

Plate 108. Parrotfishes

A. *Scarus globiceps*, i.p., 15 cm, 6 m, Guam (p. 195).

B. *Scarus globiceps*, t.p., 21 cm, 8 m, Guam.

C. *Scarus microrhinos*, juv. 8 cm, 21 m, Guam (p. 195).

D. *Scarus microrhinos*, 20 cm, 16 m, Guam.

E. *Scarus microrhinos*, 50 cm, 6 m, Belau.

F. *Scarus hyselopterus*, t.p., Belau (p. 196).   J. E. Randall

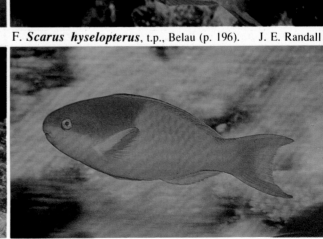

G. *Scarus oviceps*, i.p., 20 cm, 8 m, Belau (p. 196).

H. *Scarus oviceps*, t.p., 30 cm, 6 m, Belau.

Plate 109. Parrotfishes

A. *Scarus niger*, 20 cm, 14 m, Belau (p. 196).   B. *Scarus prasiognathos*, t.p., 35 cm, 10 m, Belau (p. 196)

C. *Scarus psittacus*, i.p., 16 cm, 8 m, Guam (p. 196). D. *Scarus psittacus*, t.p., 18 cm, at night, 1 m, Guam.

E. *Scarus quoyi*, t.p., 25 cm, 14 m, Belau (p. 197).   F. *Scarus rivulatus*, t.p., 26 cm, 6 m, Belau (p. 197).

G. *Scarus rubroviolaceus*, i.p., 35 cm, 16 m, Belau (p.197). H. *Scarus rubroviolaceus*, t.p., 40 cm, 15 m, Indonesia.

Plate 110. Parrotfishes

A. *Scarus schlegeli*, i.p., 20 cm, 18 m, Guam (p. 197).   B. *Scarus schlegeli*, t.p., 23 cm, 16 m, Guam.

C. *Scarus sordidus*, i.p., 18 cm, 4 m, Belau (p. 197).   D. *Scarus sordidus*, i.p., 18 cm, 8 m, Guam.

E. *Scarus sordidus*, t.p., 21 cm, 10 m, Guam.   F. *Scarus spinus*, t.p., 14 cm, 10 m, Belau (p. 197).

G. *Scarus* **sp.**, early t.p., 24 cm, 30 m, Guam (p. 198).   H. *Polydactylus sexfilis*, 18 cm (p. 200; Waikiki Aq.).

Plate 111. Parrotfishes and Threadfins

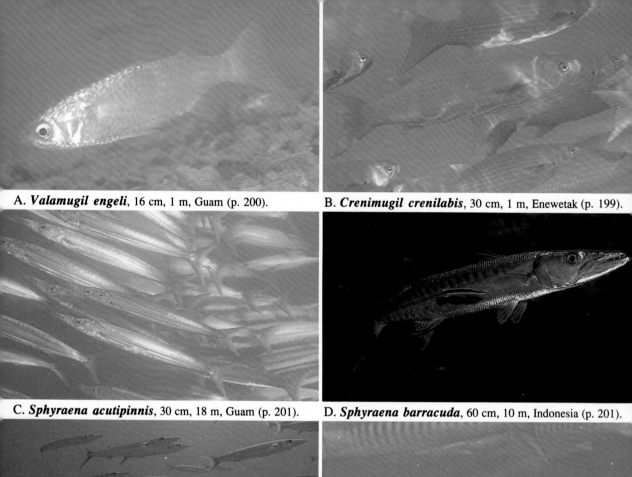

A. *Valamugil engeli*, 16 cm, 1 m, Guam (p. 200).   B. *Crenimugil crenilabis*, 30 cm, 1 m, Enewetak (p. 199).

C. *Sphyraena acutipinnis*, 30 cm, 18 m, Guam (p. 201).   D. *Sphyraena barracuda*, 60 cm, 10 m, Indonesia (p. 201).

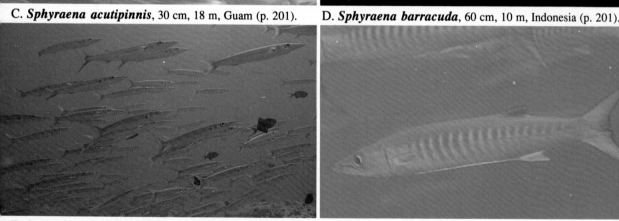

E. *Sphyraena forsteri*, 40 cm, 6 m, Belau (p. 201).   F. *Sphyraena genie*, 60 cm, 5 m, Belau (p. 201).

G. *Sphyraena novaehollandiae*, 20 cm, 1 m, Guam (p. 201).   H. *Sphyraena obtusata*, 30 cm, 1 m, New Caledonia (p. 201

Plate 112. Mullets and Barracudas

A. *Parapercis clathrata* female, 10 cm, 16 m, Guam (p. 202). B. *Parapercis clathrata* male, 11 cm, 18 m, Guam.

C. *Parapercis cylindrica*, 9 cm, 1 m, New Caledonia (p.202). D. *Parapercis millipunctata*, 10 cm, 1 m, Guam (p. 202).

E. *Parapercis xanthozona*, 9 cm, 1m, Indonesia (p. 202). F. *Trichonotus* sp. male, 12 cm, 15 m, Guam (p. 202).

G. *Trichonotus* sp. females, 8 cm, 15 m, Guam (p. 202)   H. Unid. tripterygiid 32 mm, 15 m, Guam (p. 203). I. Unid. tripterygiid 32 mm, 15 m, Guam (p. 203).

Plate 113. Sandperches, Sand-divers, and Triplefins

A. *Cirripectes polyzona*, 3.5 cm, 1.5 m, Guam (p. 206).

B. *C. polyzona* male, 8 cm, 1.5 m, Guam.

C. *Cirripectes variolosus*, 6 cr 5 m, Guam (p. 207).

D. *Exalias brevis*, 11 cm, 13 m, Hawaii (p. 208).

E. *Ecsenius bicolor*, bicolor ph., 6 cm, 6 m, Guam (p. 208

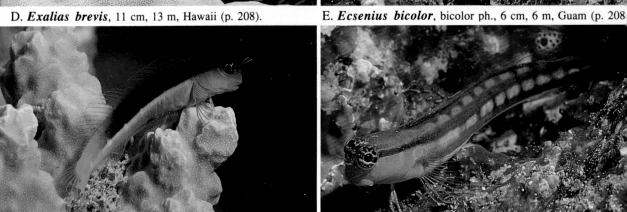

F. *Ecsenius bicolor*, lined ph., 6 cm, 8 m, Guam.

G. *Ecsenius opsifrontalis*, 4 cm, 9 m, Guam (p. 208).

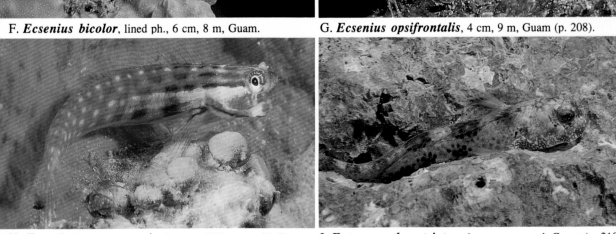

H. *Ecsenius yaeyamaensis*, 4 cm (p. 208).   M. Warner   I. *Entomacrodus striatus*, 6 cm, spray pool, Guam (p. 210)

Plate 114. Combtooth Blennies

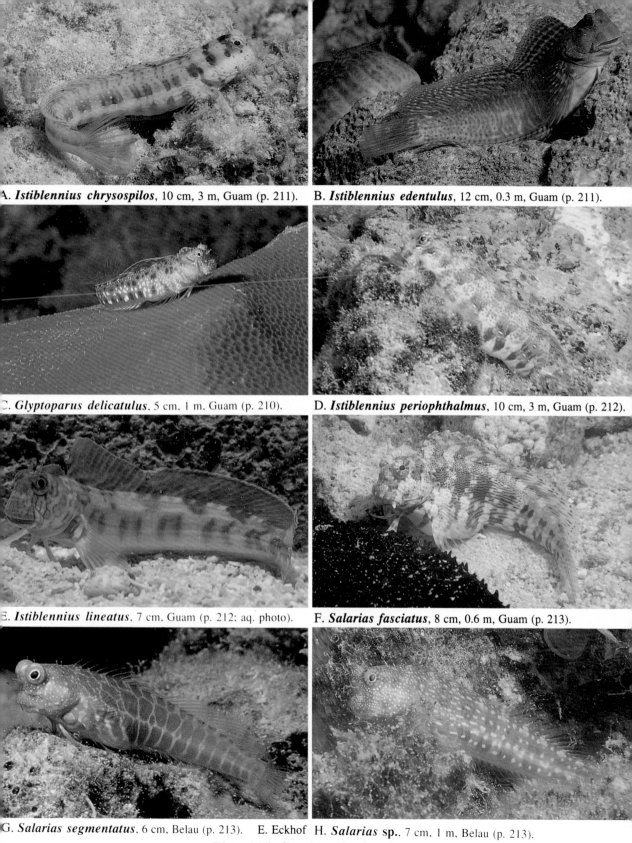

A. *Istiblennius chrysospilos*, 10 cm, 3 m, Guam (p. 211).   B. *Istiblennius edentulus*, 12 cm, 0.3 m, Guam (p. 211).

C. *Glyptoparus delicatulus*, 5 cm, 1 m, Guam (p. 210).   D. *Istiblennius periophthalmus*, 10 cm, 3 m, Guam (p. 212).

E. *Istiblennius lineatus*, 7 cm, Guam (p. 212; aq. photo).   F. *Salarias fasciatus*, 8 cm, 0.6 m, Guam (p. 213).

G. *Salarias segmentatus*, 6 cm, Belau (p. 213).   E. Eckhof   H. *Salarias* sp., 7 cm, 1 m, Belau (p. 213).

Plate 115. Combtooth Blennies

A. *Aspidontus taeniatus*, 7 cm, 3 m, Guam (p. 214).   B. *Meiacanthus atrodorsalis*, 6 cm, 14 m, Guam (p. 215).

C. *Meiacanthus grammistes*, 4 cm, 3 m, Belau (p. 215).   D. *Petroscirtes mitratus*, 4 cm, 1 m, Guam (p. 216).

E. *Petroscirtes xestus*, 4 cm, 3 m, Guam (p. 216).   F. *Plagiotremus laudandus*, 6.5 cm, 17 m, Guam (p. 215).

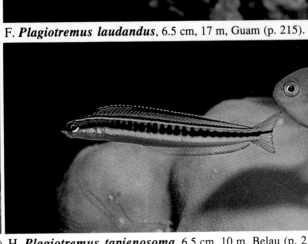

G. *Plagiotremus rhynorhynchus*, 7 cm, 3 m, Belau (p. 215). H. *Plagiotremus tapienosoma*, 6.5 cm, 10 m, Belau (p. 21

Plate 116. Sabretooth Blennies

A. *Callionymus simplicicornis* male, 5cm, 1m, Guam (p.218). B. *Synchiropus morrisoni* female, 3cm, 29m, Guam (p.218)

C. *Synchiropus splendidus*, 3 cm (p.218; Waikiki Aq.). K. Dummitt D. *Synchiropus* **sp.** male, 2 cm, 9 m, Rota (p.218).

E. *Gunnellichthys monostigma*, 10 cm, 18 m, Guam (p. 220). F. *Ptereleotris evides*, 3.5 cm, 5 m, Guam (p. 221).

G. *Ptereleotris evides*, 8.5 cm, 6 m, Guam (p. 221). H. *Ptereleotris hanae*, 9 cm, 12 m, Indonesia (p. 221).

Plate 117. Dragonets, Wormfishes, and Dartfishes

A. *Ptereleotris heteroptera*, 9 cm, 16 m, Guam (p. 221).

B. *Nemateleotris decora*, 6 cm (p. 221; aq. photo).

C. *Ptereleotris microlepis*, 7 cm, 8 m, Guam (p. 221).

D. *Nemateleotris helfrichi*, (p. 261; aq. photo by R. Kosaki)

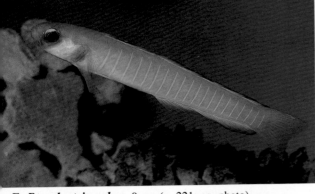

E. *Ptereleotris zebra*, 9 cm (p. 221; aq. photo).

F. *Parioglossus formosus*, 3 cm, 5 m, Belau (p. 222).

G. *Nemateleotris magnifica*, 6 cm, 9 m, Guam (p. 222).

Plate 118. Dartfishes

A. *Amblyeleotris fasciata*, 6.5 cm, 12 m, Guam (p. 226).　　B. *Amblyeleotris guttata*, 6 cm, 27 m, Guam (p. 226).

C. *Amblyeleotris wheeleri* (var.), 5cm, 12 m, Belau (p.226).　　D. *Amblyeleotris randalli*, 7 cm, 15 m, Belau (p. 226).

E. *Amblyeleotris steinitzi*, 5.5 cm, 27 m, Guam (p. 226).　　F. *Amblyeleotris wheeleri*, 6 cm, 10 m, Indonesia (p. 227).

G. *Cryptocentrus cinctus*, 5 cm, 1.5 m, Belau (p. 227).　　H. *Cryptocentrus cinctus*, yellow ph., 5 cm, 1.5 m, Belau.

Plate 119. Prawn-associated Gobies

A. *Cryptocentrus koumansi*, 5.5 cm, 1 m, Guam (p. 227).

B. *Cryptocentrus octafasciatus*, 5.5 cm, 1 m, Guam (p. 227).

C. *Cryptocentrus strigilliceps*, 6.5 cm, 6 m, Guam (p. 227).

D. *Cryptocentrus* **sp.**, 4.5 cm, 1.5 m, Belau (p. 227).

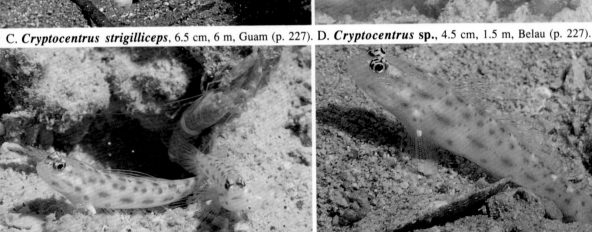

E. *Ctenogobiops feroculus*, 4.5 cm, 4 m, Guam (p. 228).

F. *Ctenogobiops pomastictus*, 4.5 cm, 9 m, Guam (p. 228).

G. *Ctenogobiops tangaroai*, 4.5 cm, 34 m, Guam (p. 228).

H. *Lotilia graciliosa*, 3.5 cm, 1.5 m, Guam (p. 229).

Plate 120. Prawn-associated Gobies

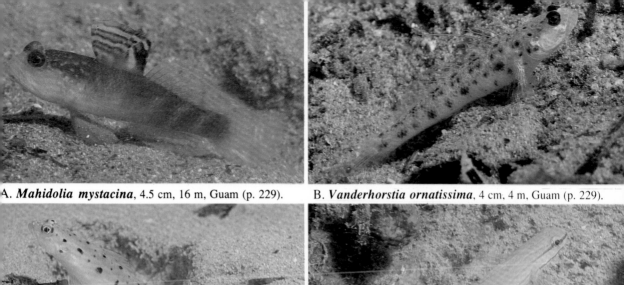

A. *Mahidolia mystacina*, 4.5 cm, 16 m, Guam (p. 229).　　B. *Vanderhorstia ornatissima*, 4 cm, 4 m, Guam (p. 229).

C. *Vanderhorstia ambonoro*, 6.5 cm, 11 m, Guam.　　D. *Amblygobius decussatus*, 5.5 cm, 2 m, Pohnpei (p. 229).

E. *Amblygobius nocturnus*, 5 cm, 10 m, Guam (p. 229).　　F. *Amblygobius phalaena*, 9 cm, 2 m, Guam (p. 230).

G. *Amblygobius rainfordi*, 6 cm, 1.5 m, Belau (p. 230).　　H. *Oplopomus oplopomus*, 6 cm, 10 m, Guam (p. 230).

Plate 121. Prawn-associated and other fossoral Gobies

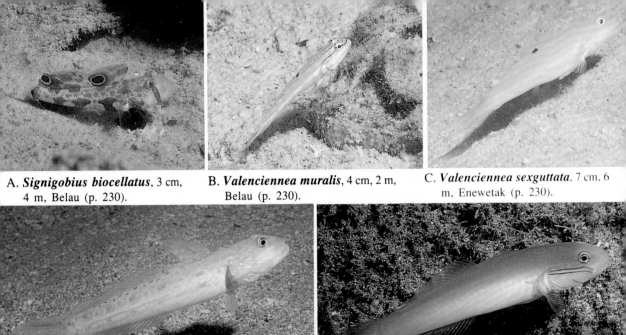

A. *Signigobius biocellatus*, 3 cm, 4 m, Belau (p. 230).

B. *Valenciennea muralis*, 4 cm, 2 m, Belau (p. 230).

C. *Valenciennea sexguttata*. 7 cm, 6 m, Enewetak (p. 230).

D. *Valenciennea puellaris*, 6.5 cm, 18 m, Guam (p. 230).

E. *Valenciennea strigata*. 8 cm, 8 m, Guam (p. 230).

F. *Valenciennea strigata*. 6.5 cm, 6 m, Guam.

G. *Asterropteryx semipunctatus*, 2.5 cm, 1 m, Guam (p. 231).

H. *Bathygobius fuscus*, 3 cm, 8 m, Guam (p. 231).

I. *Bryaninops amplus*, 2 cm, 17 m, Guam (p. 232).

J. *Bryaninops natans*, 2 cm, 14 m, Guam (p. 232).

K. *Bryaninops youngei*, 2 cm, 12 m, Belau (p. 232), with the shrimp *Dasycaris zanzibarica*.

Plate 122. Gobies

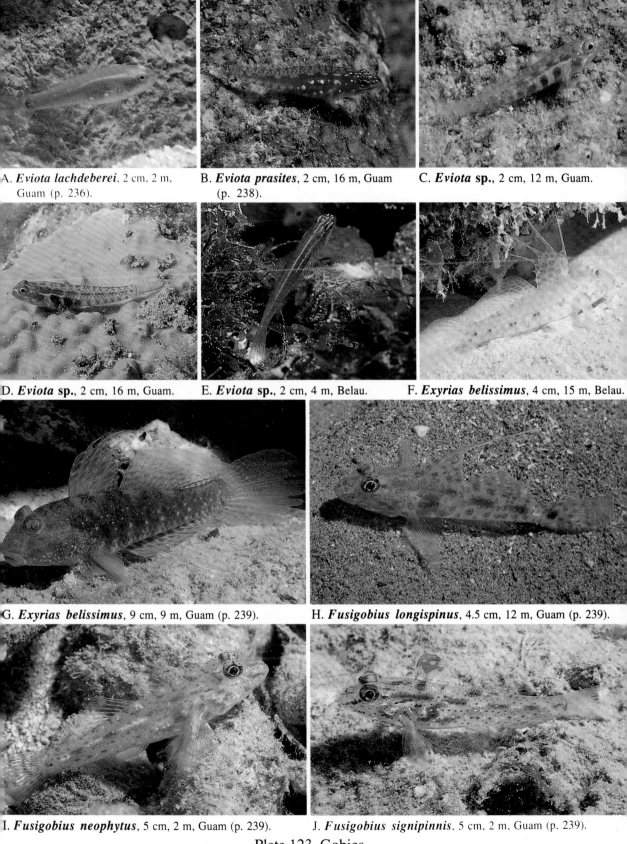

A. *Eviota lachdeberei*, 2 cm, 2 m, Guam (p. 236).

B. *Eviota prasites*, 2 cm, 16 m, Guam (p. 238).

C. *Eviota* sp., 2 cm, 12 m, Guam.

D. *Eviota* sp., 2 cm, 16 m, Guam.

E. *Eviota* sp., 2 cm, 4 m, Belau.

F. *Exyrias belissimus*, 4 cm, 15 m, Belau.

G. *Exyrias belissimus*, 9 cm, 9 m, Guam (p. 239).

H. *Fusigobius longispinus*, 4.5 cm, 12 m, Guam (p. 239).

I. *Fusigobius neophytus*, 5 cm, 2 m, Guam (p. 239).

J. *Fusigobius signipinnis*, 5 cm, 2 m, Guam (p. 239).

Plate 123. Gobies

A. *Gnatholepis cauerensis*, 4 cm, 1 m, Guam (p. 139).

B. *Gnatholepis scapulostigma*, 3 cm, 4 m, Guam (p. 239).

C. *Gnatholepis* sp., 3.5 cm, 18 m, Guam (p. 239).

D. *Gobiodon albofasciatus*, 2 cm, Belau (p. 239).　　　E. Eckhof

E. *Gobiodon citrinus*, 4 cm, Belau (p. 239; National. Aq.).

F. *Gobiodon okinawae*, 2 cm, 5 m, Belau (p. 239).

G. *Istigobius decoratus*, 5.5 cm, 10 m, Guam (p. 240).

H. *Istigobius ornatus*, 5 cm, 1 m, Guam (p. 240).

I. *Trimma caesiura*, 2 cm, 9 m, Guam (p. 242).

J. *Trimma tevegae*, 2 cm, 38 m, Guam (p. 243).

K. *Trimmatom* sp., 4 cm, 1 m, Guam (p. 139).

Plate 124. Gobies

A. *Acanthurus achilles*, 15 cm, 3 m, Hawaii (p. 244).
B. *Acanthurus bariene*, 22 cm, 12 m, Belau (p. 244).

C. *Acanthurus blochii*, 22 cm, 6 m, Hawaii (p. 244).
D. *Acanthurus dussumieri*, 20 cm, 4 m, Hawaii (p. 245).

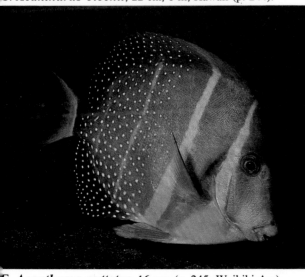

E. *Acanthurus guttatus*, 16 cm, (p. 245; Waikiki Aq.).
F. *Acanthurus leucocheilus*, 25 cm, 16 m, Belau (p. 245).

Plate 125. Surgeonfishes

A. *Acanthurus leucopareius*, 15 cm, 5 m, Hawaii (p. 245).   B. *Acanthurus lineatus*, 18 cm, 5 m, Indonesia (p. 245).

C. *Acanthurus maculiceps*, 15 cm, 1 m, Belau (p. 246).   D. *Acanthurus mata*, 18 cm, 12 m, Indonesia (p. 246).

E. *Acanthurus nigricans*, 15 cm, 18 m, Saipan (p. 246).   F. *Acanthurus nigricauda*, 20 cm, 20 m, Saipan (p. 246).

Plate 126. Surgeonfishes

A. *Acanthurus nigrofuscus*, 11 cm, 11 m, Hawaii (p. 246). B. *Acanthurus nigroris*, 15 cm, 5 m, Hawaii (p. 246).

C. *Acanthurus olivaceus*, 8 cm, 10 m, Hawaii (p. 246).

D. *Acanthurus pyroferus* juv., 6 cm, 9 m, Belau (p. 247), a mimic of *Centropyge vrolicki* (p. 161).

E. *Ctenochaetus strigosus* juv., 5 cm, 20 m, Guam (p. 248), a mimic of *Centropyge flavissimus*? (p. 161).

F. *Acanthurus olivaceus*, 18 cm, 20 m, Saipan. G. *Acanthurus pyroferus*, 18 cm, 12 m, Belau.

Plate 127. Surgeonfishes

A. *Acanthurus thompsoni*, 13 cm, 8 m, Belau (p. 247).   B. *Acanthurus triostegus*, 12 cm, 3 m, Guam (p. 247).

C. *Acanthurus xanthopterus*, 28 cm, 4 m, Hawaii (p. 247).

D. *Ctenochaetus binotatus*, 10 cm, 9 m, Guam (p. 247).

E. *Ctenochaetus marginatus*, Line Is. (p. 248).   J.E.Randall   F. *Ctenochaetus strigosus*, 11 cm, 16 m, Guam (p. 248).

Plate 128. Surgeonfishes

A. *Ctenochaetus hawaiiensis*, 16 cm, 10 m, Belau (p. 248).   B. *Ctenochaetus striatus*, 13 cm, 16 m, Guam (p. 248).

C. *Ctenochaetus binotatus*, 4.5 cm,   D. *Ctenochaetus hawaiiensis* juv., 5 cm,   E. *Ctenochaetus striatus* juv., 6 cm,
    10 m, Guam.   Hawaii (aq.photo).   15 m, Guam.

. *Ctenochaetus tominiensis*, 10 cm, 16 m, Indonesia (p. 248).   G. *Paracanthurus hepatus*, 10 cm (p. 248; Waikiki Aq.).

Plate 129. Surgeonfishes

A. *Zebrasoma flavescens*, 6 cm, 18 m, Guam (p. 249).　　B. *Zebrasoma scopas*, 9 cm, 8 m, Gaum (p. 249).

C. *Zebrasoma veliferum*, 15 cm, 18 m, Guam (p. 249).　　D. *Naso annulatus*, 16 cm, 16 m, Guam (p. 249).

E. *Naso annulatus*, 50 cm, Indonesia (p. 249). J.E.Randall　F. *Naso brevirostris*, 35 cm, 8 m, Belau (p. 250).

Plate 130. Surgeonfishes; Unicornfishes

A. *Naso hexacanthus*, 50 cm, 18 m, Belau (p. 250).　　B. *Naso lituratus*, 27 cm, 8 m, Hawaii (p. 250).

C. *Naso tuberosus*, 45 cm, Great Barrier Reef (p. 250).　J.E.Randall　D. *Naso unicornis*, 27 cm, 2 m, Hawaii (p. 250).

E. *Naso vlamingii* male 25 cm, 15 m, Indonesia (p. 250).

F. *Zanclus cornutus*, 9 cm, 17 m, Guam (p. 251).

Plate 131. Unicornfishes and Moorish idol

A. *Siganus (Lo) vulpinus*, 13 cm, 8 m, Belau (p. 251).

B. *Siganus argenteus*, 18 cm, 12 m, Belau.

C. *Siganus argenteus*, 20 cm, 1 m, Guam, at night (p. 251).

D. *Siganus canaliculatus*, 10 cm, 1 m, New Caledonia (p. 252), with *Scarus altipinnis* (juv., p. 194), *Stethojulis strigiventor* (p. 189), and *Parupeneus indicus* (p. 150).

E. *Siganus corallinus*, 18 cm, 10 m, Indonesia (p. 252).

F. *Siganus doliatus*, 14 cm, 4 m, Belau (p. 252).

Plate 132. Rabbitfishes

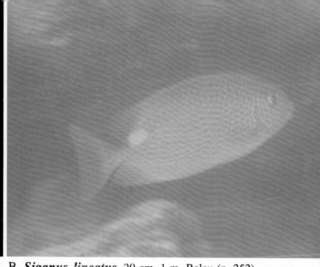

A. *Siganus guttatus*, 22 cm, 12 m, Indonesia,

B. *Siganus lineatus*, 20 cm, 1 m, Belau (p. 252).

C. *Siganus puellus*, 17 cm, 8 m, Belau (p. 252).

D. *Siganus punctatissimus*, 20 cm, 12 m, Belau (p. 252).

E. *Siganus punctatus*, 13 cm, 6 m, Belau (p. 253), with
   Labroides bicolor (p. 191).

F. *Siganus spinus*, 10 cm, 1.5 m, Saipan (p. 253).

Plate 133. Rabbitfishes

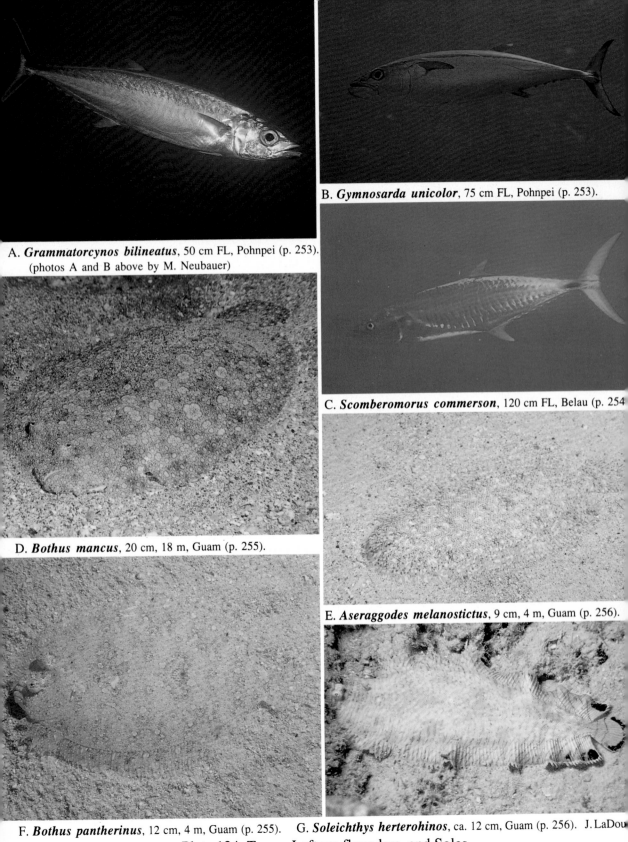

A. *Grammatorcynos bilineatus*, 50 cm FL, Pohnpei (p. 253).
(photos A and B above by M. Neubauer)

B. *Gymnosarda unicolor*, 75 cm FL, Pohnpei (p. 253).

C. *Scomberomorus commerson*, 120 cm FL, Belau (p. 254)

D. *Bothus mancus*, 20 cm, 18 m, Guam (p. 255).

E. *Aseraggodes melanostictus*, 9 cm, 4 m, Guam (p. 256).

F. *Bothus pantherinus*, 12 cm, 4 m, Guam (p. 255).   G. *Soleichthys herterohinos*, ca. 12 cm, Guam (p. 256).   J. LaDou

Plate 134. Tunas, Lefteye flounders, and Soles

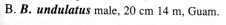

A. *Balistapus undulatus* female, 14 cm, 14
    m, Guam (p. 257; above).

B. *B. undulatus* male, 20 cm 14 m, Guam.

C. *Balistoides conspicillum*, juv., 7 cm,
    Guam (p. 257; aq. photo, above).

D. *B. conspicillum*, 20 cm, 4 m, Belau.

E. *Pseudobalistes flavimarginatus* juv.,6cm.

F. *Balistoides viridescens*, 50 cm, 8 m,
    Indonesia (p. 258; right).

Plate 135. Triggerfishes

A. *Melichthys niger*, 18 cm, 3 m, Hawaii (p. 258).

B. *Melichthys vidua*, 18 cm, 10 m, Guam (p. 258).

C. *Odonus niger*, 16 cm, 6 m, Belau (p. 258).

D. *Pseudobalistes flavimarginatus*, 35 cm, 10 m, Indonesia (p. 25

E. *Pseudobalistes fuscus* juv., 9 cm, Mauritius (p. 259).
J. E. Randall

F. *Pseudobalistes fuscus*, ca. 30 cm, Maldives. J. E. Rand

Plate 136. Triggerfishes

A. *Rhinecanthus aculeatus*, 15 cm, 4 m, Guam (p. 259). B. *Rhinecanthus rectangulus*, 14 cm, 4 m, Guam (p. 259).

C. *Rhinecanthus verrucosa*, 10 cm, 1 m, Indonesia (p. 259). D. *Sufflamen bursa*, 15 cm, 6 m, Hawaii (p. 259).

E. *Sufflamen chrysoptera*, 4 cm, 9 m, Guam (p. 260). F. *Sufflamen chrysoptera*, 14 cm, 6 m, Guam.

Plate 137. Triggerfishes

A. *Sufflamen freanatus* juv., 4.5 cm, 18 m, Guam (p. 260). B. *Sufflamen freanatus*, 15 cm, 18 m, Guam.

C. *Xanthichthys auromarginatus* female, 13 cm, 30 m, Guam. D. *X. auromarginatus* male, 13 cm, 30 m, Guam (p. 260).

E. *Alutera scriptus*, 25 cm, 17 m, Guam (p. 261). F. *Amanses scopas*, 13 cm, 18 m, Guam (p. 261).

Plate 138. Triggerfishes and Filefishes

A. *Cantherhines dumerilii*, 22 cm, 12 m, Hawaii (p. 261).   B. *Cantherhines pardalis*, 13 cm, 16 m, Saipan (p. 263).

C. *Oxymonacanthus longirostris*, 6 cm, 1 m, Guam (p. 263).   D. *Paraluteres prionurus*, 6 cm, 21 m, Guam (p. 263).

E. *Pervagor aspricaudus*, 6 cm, 15 mm, Hawaii (p. 263).   F. *Pervagor janthinosoma*, 6 cm, 8 m, Guam (p. 264).

Plate 139. Filefishes

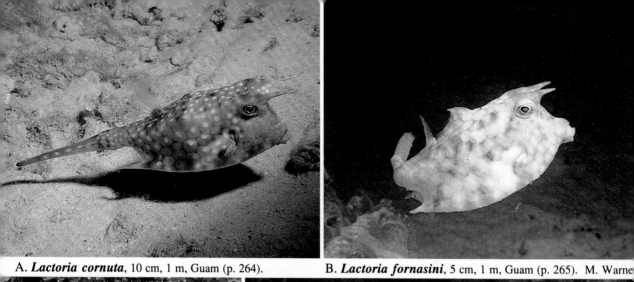

A. *Lactoria cornuta*, 10 cm, 1 m, Guam (p. 264).   B. *Lactoria fornasini*, 5 cm, 1 m, Guam (p. 265). M. Warne

C. *Ostracion cubicus*, 2 cm, 10 m, Indonesia
   (p. 265; above; photo by K. Dummitt).

D. *O. cubicus*, 20 cm, 3 m, Belau (right),
   with *Labroides bicolor* (p. 191).

E. *Ostracion meleagris* female, 4.5 cm, 10 m, Guam.   F. *Ostracion meleagris* male, 6 cm, 1 m, Guam (p. 265).

Plate 140. Cowfishes and Trunkfishes

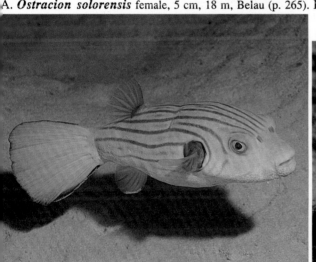

A. *Ostracion solorensis* female, 5 cm, 18 m, Belau (p. 265). B. *Ostracion solorensis* male, 6 cm, 4 m, Indonesia.

M. Neubauer

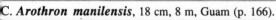

C. *Arothron manilensis*, 18 cm, 8 m, Guam (p. 166). D. *Arothron hispidus*, 30 cm, 3 m, Guam (p. 266).

E. *Arothron meleagris*, 18 cm, 10 m, Hawaii (p. 266). F. *Arothron meleagris*, xanthic ph., 12 cm, 1 m, Guam (aq. photo).

Plate 141. Trunkfishes and Puffers

A. *Arothron mappa*, 18 cm, Guam (p. 266).   A. Maben B. *Arothron nigropunctatus*, 15 cm, 4 m, Guam (p. 267).

C. *Arothron nigropunctatus*, 16 cm, 12 m, Indonesia.   D. *Arothron nigropunctatus*, 18 cm, 5 m, Indonesia.

E. *Arothron stellatus*, 12 cm, 1 m, Guam (p. 267).   F. *Arothron stellatus*, 50 cm, 3 m, Enewetak.

Plate 142. Puffers

A. *Canthigaster amboinensis*, 8 cm, 10, Hawaii (p. 267).

B. *Canthigaster bennetti*, 5 cm, 3 m, Guam (p. 267).

C. *Canthigaster compressa*, 6 cm, 4 m, Guam (p. 267).

D. *Canthigaster coronata*, 6 cm, 10 m, Guam (p. 267).

E. *Canthigaster epilampra*, 6 cm, 24 m, Guam (p. 267).

F. *Canthigaster janthinoptera*, 3 cm, 4 m, Guam (p. 267).

Plate 143. Tobies

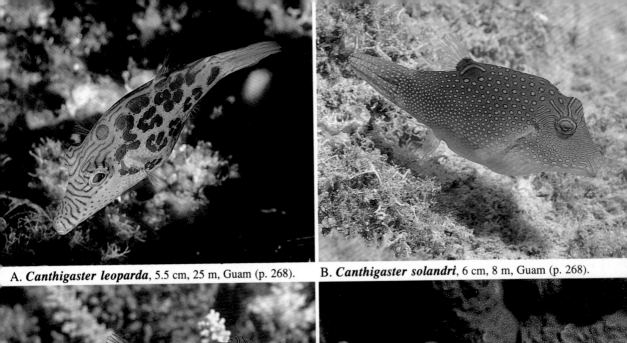

A. *Canthigaster leoparda*, 5.5 cm, 25 m, Guam (p. 268).

B. *Canthigaster solandri*, 6 cm, 8 m, Guam (p. 268).

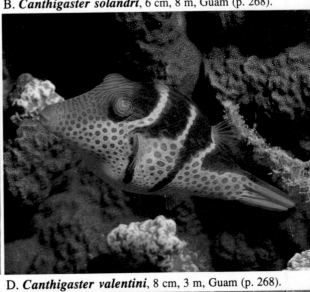

C. *Canthigaster solandri*, form *papua*, 7 cm, 5 m, Belau.

D. *Canthigaster valentini*, 8 cm, 3 m, Guam (p. 268).

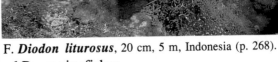

E. *Diodon hystrix*, 30 cm, 1 m, Guam (p. 268).

F. *Diodon liturosus*, 20 cm, 5 m, Indonesia (p. 268).

Plate 144. Tobies and Porcupinefishes

West-central Pacific: Philippines to the Tuamotus, n. to the Ryukyus, s. to Lord Howe and Rapa Is.; throughout Micronesia.

Chaetodon meyeri Schneider, 1801   Pl. 64A,B
Meyer's butterflyfish

SL: to 138 mm (5.4 in); D (XII)-XIII, 23-25(23-24); A III, 18-20(19-20); P 16-(17); LL 47-55; LP 37-49(40-47); GR 21-29.

This gorgeous species inhabits areas of rich coral growth of clear lagoon and seaward reefs at depths of 5 to 25 m. Adults usually occur in pairs and are home-ranging. Juveniles remain near the shelter of branching corals. It feeds exclusively on coral polyps.

Indo-Pacific: E. Africa to the Line Is., n. to the Ryukyus, s. to the Great Barrier Reef; Belau to the e. Carolines and s. Marshalls in Micronesia.

Chaetodon ocellicaudus Cuvier, 1831   Fig. 1b
Spot-tail butterflyfish

SL: to 118 mm (4.6 in); D XII, 19-12; A III, 17-18; P (14)-15; LL 29-30; GR 12-15.

This species is nearly identical to *C. melannotus* differing only in the shape of the black mark on the caudal peduncle, in lacking a black mark on the chest, and in having 14 rather than 15 modal pectoral rays. Its ecology and behavior are presumably similar to that of *C. melannotus*. The soft corals in its diet include *Litophyton viridis* and species of the genera *Sarcophyton*, *Nephthia*, and *Clavularia*. It has recently been reported from Belau.

Indo-Australian: (E. Africa?) Malaysia to New Guinea, n. to the Philippines; Belau in Micronesia.

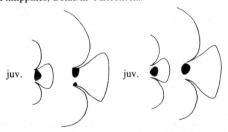

a. *C. melannotus*   b. *C. ocellicaudus*
Fig. 1. Caudal base markings of two species of *Chaetodon*.

Chaetodon octofasciatus Bloch, 1787   Pl. 64C
Eight-banded butterflyfish

SL: to 79 mm (3.1 in); D X-XII(XI), 17-19(18-19); A (III)-IV, 14-17(15-16); P 13-15(14-15); LL 36-42(39-40); LP 27-38; GR 11-19(14-16).

The eight-banded butterflyfish inhabits coral rich areas of sheltered lagoon and inshore reefs at depths of 3 to 20 m. Juveniles occur in groups among tightly branching *Acropora* corals; adults occur in pairs. It feeds exclusively on coral polyps. It is occasionally encountered among Belau's Rock Islands.

Indo-west Pacific: Maldives to the Solomon Is., n. to the Ryukyus, s. to the Great Barrier Reef; Belau in Micronesia.

Chaetodon ornatissimus Solander *in* Cuvier, 1831
Ornate butterflyfish   Pl. 64D

SL: to 148 mm (5.8 in); D (XII)-XIII, 24-28(26-28); A III, 20-23(21-23); P 16-18(16-17); LL 47-52; LP 36-51; GR 21-23.

The ornate butterflyfish inhabits areas of clear water and rich coral growth of lagoon and seaward reefs at depths of 1 to 36 m. It is relatively common on seaward reefs, but uncommon in lagoons. Juveniles are solitary and live among branching corals; adults are almost always paired and are home-ranging. They feed exclusively on coral tissue, particularly on damaged areas that exude large quantities of mucus.

Indo-Pacific: Sri Lanka to the Hawaiian, Marquesan, and Ducie Is., n. to s. Japan, s. to Lord Howe and Rapa Is.; throughout Micronesia.

Chaetodon oxycephalus Bleeker, 1853
Spot-nape butterflyfish   Pl. 64E; Fig. 2b

SL: to 171 mm (6.7 in); D XI-(XII), 22-24(23-24); A III, 18-20(19); P 15-17(16); LL 26-34; LP 24-30; GR 13-(15).

This species closely resembles *C. lineolatus*, but differs by having an interrupted ocular band leaving an isolated spot on the nape, and by having fewer soft dorsal, soft anal, and pectoral rays. It inhabits areas of rich coral growth of coastal reefs at depths of 10 to 40 m. It feeds primarily on corals and usually occurs in pairs. It is relatively uncommon in Palau where it co-occurs with *C. lineolatus*.

Indo-west Pacific: Sri Lanka to Papua New Guinea, n. to the Philippines; Belau in Micronesia.

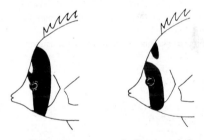

a. *C. lineolatus*   b. *C. oxycephalus*
Fig. 2. Head markings of two species of *Chaetodon*.

Chaetodon punctatofasciatus Cuvier, 1839
Spot-banded butterflyfish   Pl. 64F

SL: to 96 mm (3.8 in); D (XIII)-XIV, 22-25(23-24); A III, 17-18; P 14-15; LL 37-44(39-42); LP 34-42; GR 15-19(17).

This butterflyfish is a common inhabitant of areas of rich coral growth and clear water on both lagoon and seaward reefs at depths of 6 to 45 m. It occasionally occurs on outer subtidal reef flats. It usually occurs in pairs and feeds on a wide variety of benthic invertebrates, corals, and filamentous algae.

West-central Pacific: Christmas Is., Indian Ocean, to the Line Is., n. to the Ryukyus, s. to Rowley Shoals and the n. Great Barrier Reef and Line Is.; throughout Micronesia.

Chaetodon quadrimaculatus Gray, 1833   Pl. 65A
Fourspot butterflyfish

SL: to 126 mm (5.0 in); D XIII-(XIV), 20-23; A III, 16-18; P (15)-17; LL 38-45; LP 38-43; GR 15-19.

The fourspot butterflyfish occurs almost exclusively on exposed seaward reefs at depths of 2 to 15 m. It occurs singly or in pairs and feeds primarily on the polyps of *Pocillopora* corals.

Pacific Plate: Taiwan to the Hawaiian, Marquesan, and Pitcairn Is., n. to the Ryukyu and Bonin Is., s. to the Samoan and Austral Is.; Marianas and Marshalls in Micronesia.

Chaetodon rafflesii Bennett, 1830   Pl. 65B
Latticed butterflyfish

SL: to 114 mm (4.5 in); D XII-(XIII), 21-23; A III, 18-20; P 15-16; LL 30-37(33-35); LP 25-35(27-32); GR 15-19.

The latticed butterflyfish is an uncommon inhabitant of areas of rich coral growth of lagoon and protected reef flats and seaward reefs to a depth of 15 m. It feeds on sea anemones, polychaetes, and octocorallian and scleractinian coral polyps.

Indo-Pacific: Sri Lanka to the Tuamotus, n. to s. Japan, s. to the Great Barrier Reef; Belau to the e. Carolines in Micronesia.

Chaetodon reticulatus Cuvier, 1831   Pl. 65C
Reticulated butterflyfish

SL: to 132 mm (5.2 in); D (XII)-XIII, 26-29(27-28); A III, 20-22(21); P 16-18(17); LL 45-48; LP 40-46; GR 18-28.

This species is relatively common on exposed seaward reefs at depths of 1 to at least 30 m. It occasionally occurs on shallow lagoon reefs in areas of rich coral growth and clear water. It often occurs in pairs and feeds primarily on scleractinian coral polyps.

West-central Pacific: Philippines and Taiwan to the Hawaiian, Marquesan, and Ducie Is., n. to the Ryukyu and Bonin Is., s. to the s. Great Barrier Reef, New Caledonia, and the Austral Is.; throughout Micronesia.

Chaetodon semeion Bleeker, 1855   Pl. 65D
Dotted butterflyfish

SL: to 192 mm (7.6 in); D XIII-(XIV), 23-26(24-25); A III, 19-22(21); P 15-16; LL 33-39; LP 28-35; GR 12-17(16-17).

This species inhabits areas of rich coral growth and clear water of outer lagoon and semi-protected seaward reefs to a depth of 25 m. It usually occurs in pairs or small groups. It is known from Guam on the basis of a single reliable observation, is rare in the Marshall Islands, and uncommon in the rest of Micronesia.

Indo-Pacific: Maldives to the Tuamotus, n. to the Ryukyus, s. to the Great Barrier Reef; throughout Micronesia.

Chaetodon speculum
   (Kuhl & Van Hasselt *in* Cuvier, 1831)   Pl. 65E
Oval-spot butterflyfish

SL: to 132 mm (5.2 in); D XIV, (17)-18; A III, 15-(16); P 14-16(15); LL 37-42(39-40); LP 33-39; GR 17-21.

In Belau, the oval-spot butterflyfish occurs in clearwater, coral-rich areas of outer lagoon and seaward reefs at depths of 3 to 20 m. It is generally solitary and relatively uncommon. It feeds on invertebrates as well as coral polyps and is reported to adapt fairly well to the aquarium.

West Pacific: Christmas Is., Indian Ocean, to Tonga, n. to s. Japan, s. to Rowley Shoals and Lord Howe Is.; Belau and Yap in Micronesia.

Chaetodon tinkeri Schultz, 1951   Pl. 65F
Tinker's butterflyfish

SL: to 114 mm (4.5 in); D (XIII)-XIV, 18-22; A III, (16)-17; P (15)-16; LL 36-40; LP 36-41; GR 16-19 (counts based on Hawaiian specimens).

This species differs from *C. flavocoronatus* by lacking a broad yellow band on the nape. It is known from Enewetak on the basis of a single collection and handfull of observations made from a submersible in the depth range of 56 to 135 m, and observations by divers at Kwajalein, all along steep dropoffs. The single Enewetak specimen differs from Hawaiian individuals by having a broader submarginal region of orange-yellow on the dorsal fin. Further study is needed to determine if it represents a link between *C. tinkeri* and *C. declivis* from the Line and Marquesan Islands. *C. declivis*, is yellowish-brown rather than black posteriordorsally. Although confined to deep water, *C. tinkeri* does well in the aquarium because it feeds on a wide variety of benthic and planktonic invertebrates. It is a high-priced aquarium export from the Hawaiian Islands.

Pacific Plate: Marshall, Johnston, and Hawaiian Is.

Chaetodon trifascialis (Quoy & Gaimard, 1825)
Chevroned butterflyfish   Pl. 66A,B

(*Megaprotodon trifascialis*; *Megaprotodon strigangulus*)

SL: to 134 mm (5.3 in); D XIII-XV(XIV), 14-16(15); A III, (IV)-V, 13-15(15); P 14-16(15); LL 22-29(24-26); LP 20-29(20-25); GR 23-27(23-24).

The chevron butterflyfish is relatively common in certain coral-rich areas of shallow lagoon and semi-protected seaward reefs to a depth of 30 m. It is closely associated with tabletop and staghorn *Acropora* corals and feeds exclusively on their polyps and mucus. It occurs singly or in pairs and is highly territorial. Juveniles have a mostly yellow tail and a broad black band extending from the rear of the dorsal fin to the rear of the anal fin.

Indo-Pacific: Red Sea to the Hawaiian, Line, and Society Is., n. to s. Japan, s. to Lord Howe and Rapa Is.; throughout Micronesia.

Chaetodon trifasciatus Park, 1797   Pl. 66C
Redfin butterflyfish

SL: to 118 mm (4.6 in); D XIII-XIV, 20-22(21); A III, 18-21(19); P 14-16(15); LL 30-39(34-39); LP 27-36(30-32); GR 15-23.

The redfin butterflyfish is a common inhabitant of coral-rich areas of lagoon and semi-protected seaward reefs to a depth of 20 m. Adults are usually paired. This species is home-ranging and feeds almost exclusively on coral polyps.

Indo-Pacific: E. Africa to the Hawaiian, Line, and Tuamotu Is., n. s. Japan, s. to Lord Howe and Rapa Is.; throughout Micronesia.

Chaetodon ulietensis Cuvier, 1831 Pl. 66D
Pacific double-saddle butterflyfish
(*C. falcula* Woods in Schultz et al., 1953)
SL: to 127 mm (5.0 in); D XII, 23-25(24-25); A (III)-IV, (19)-21; P 15-17(15-16); LL 32-37; LP 23-30; GR 14-20.
This is a relatively common inhabitant of lagoon reefs in areas of rich coral growth. It is less common on seaward reefs at depths of 9 to 30 m. It occurs singly, in pairs, or occasionally in groups. It feeds on a wide variety of plant and animal material and does relatively well in the aquarium.
West-central Pacific: Indonesia and Philippines to the Tuamotus, n. to s. Japan, s. to Rowley Shoals, New Caledonia, and Tonga; throughout Micronesia; closely related to *C. falcula* from the Indian Ocean.

Chaetodon unimaculatus Bloch, 1787 Pl. 66E
Teardrop butterflyfish
SL: to 164 mm (6.5 in); D XII-(XIII), 19-23; A III, 18-20; P 14-17(15-16); LL 38-47(41-45); LP 37-44(38-42); GR 17-21.
The teardrop butterflyfish occurs on reef flats and clear lagoon and seaward reefs to a depth of 60 m. It is common on shallow seaward and certain lagoon reef areas where there is an abundance of *Sinularia* and *Sarcophyton* soft corals. It feeds primarily on a wide variety of soft and hard corals, as well as on polychaetes, small crustaceans, and filamentous algae.
Indo-Pacific: E. Africa to the Hawaiian, Marquesan, and Ducie Is., n. to s. Japan, s. to Lord Howe and Rapa Is.; throughout Micronesia.

Chaetodon vagabundus Linnaeus, 1758 Pl. 66F
Vagabond butterflyfish
SL: to 156 mm (6.1 in); D XIII, 22-25(23-25); A II-(III), 19-22(19-20); P 15-17(16); LL 34-40; LP 30-37; GR 15-18.
This species occurs on reef flats and lagoon and shallow seaward reefs to a depth of 30 m. It sometimes occurs in turbid areas subject to freshwater runoff, but is not particularly common anywhere. It is often paired and feeds primarily on sea anemones, coral polyps, polychaetes, and algae.
Indo-Pacific: E. Africa to the Line and Tuamotu Is., n. to s. Japan, s. to Lord Howe and the Austral Is.; throughout Micronesia.

Coradion chrysozonus (Cuvier, 1831) Pl. 67A
Orange-banded coralfish
SL: to 115 mm (4.5 in); D IX, 28-30(28-29); A III, 19-21 (20); P (16)-17; LL 48-52; GR 9.
Species of *Coradion* differ from those of *Chaetodon* by having fewer dorsal spines (8-10 vs 11-16) that progressively increase in length from front to back, and a complete lateral line with 43-52 scales (lateral line incomplete with 22-55 scales in *Chaetodon*). In addition to the features just mentioned, all three species of *Coradion* have somewhat elevated soft dorsal and anal fins, giving them a "high-bodied" appearance, and a similar color pattern of four broad orange to bronze bands. All three are confined to the Indo-Australian region where they inhabit coastal reefs, often in areas of poor coral development. This species is known from the

depth range of 3 to 60 m. In Micronesia, it is known only from Belau where it appears to be uncommon.
West Pacific: Malaysia to the Solomon Is., n. to the Bonin Is., s. to nw. Australia and the Great Barrier Reef; Belau in Micronesia.

Forcipiger flavissimus Jordan & McGregor, 1898
Long-nosed butterflyfish Pl. 67B; Fig. 3a
SL: to 175 mm (6.9 in); D (XII)-XIII, 19-25(22-24); A III, 17-19; P 15-17(16); LL 74-80; GR 12-16; snout 3.6-4.5 in SL.
The unique color pattern separates species of *Forcipiger* from all other chaetodontids. The relatively shorter snout with a larger mouth, higher dorsal spine count, and absence of dark-centered scales on the thorax separate *F. flavissimus* from *F. longirostris*. *F. flavissimus* is a common inhabitant of exposed seaward reefs from as little as 2 to 114 m. It is less common on lagoon reefs. It occurs singly or in small groups and prefers areas with ledges and small caves. It feeds on a wide variety of animal prey including hydroids, fish eggs, and small crustaceans, but seems to have a prediliction for pieces of larger prey such as the tubed feet of echinoderms, pediciliaria of sea urchins, and polychaete tentacles. Despite its relative difficulty as an aquarium fish, the long-nosed butterflyfish is the second most important export in Hawaii's tropical fish trade.
Indo-pan-Pacific: Red Sea to Mexico, n. to s. Japan and the Hawaiian Is., s. to Lord Howe and Easter Is.; throughout Micronesia.

a. *F. flavissimus*   b. *F. longirostris*
Fig. 3. Head and snout morphology of *Forcipiger*.

Forcipiger longirostris (Broussonet, 1782)
Big long-nosed butterflyfish Pl. 67C,D; Fig. 3b
SL: to 179 mm (7.0 in); D X-(XI), 24-28(24-26); A III, 17-20(18-20); P 15-17(15-16); LL 66-75; GR 15-18; snout 2.6-3.0 in SL.
In addition to the features mentioned under *F. flavissimus*, this species has a rare uniformly black color phase. It occurs on seaward reefs at depths of 5 to at least 60 m but is relatively uncommon throughout its range. Unlike *F. flavissimus*, it feeds primarily on whole organisms, particularly small crustaceans.
Indo-Pacific: E. Africa to the Hawaiian, Marquesan, and Pitcairn Is., n. to the Bonin Is., s. to New Caledonia and the Australs; throughout Micronesia.

Hemitaurichthys polylepis (Bleeker, 1857)
Pyramid butterflyfish Pl. 67E
SL: to 127 mm (5.0 in); D XII, 23-26(24-25); A III, 19-21;

P 17-19(18); LL 68-74; GR 15-17.

Species of *Hemitaurichthys* differ from those of *Chaetodon* by having complete lateral lines with 70-90 scales. They are planktivores that aggregate in the water column. The pyramid butterflyfish occurs in large aggregations that may extend several meters above the edges of steep current-swept outer reef slopes at depths of 3 to over 40 m. It is relatively hardy in the aquarium.

West-central Pacific: Christmas Is., Indian Ocean, and Indonesia to the Hawaiian, Line, and Pitcairn Is., n. to s. Japan, s. to Rowley Shoals and New Caledonia; throughout Micronesia.

Hemitaurichthys thompsoni Fowler, 1923   Pl. 67F
Thompson's butterflyfish

SL: to 185 mm (7.3 in); D XII, 25-27(26); A III, 20-21; P 18-(19); LL 76-87; GR 14-17.

This is the only Micronesian butterflyfish that is always uniformly dark gray to black. It is known from a few scattered localities across the Pacific Plate. It usually occurs in aggregations above steep outer reef slopes at depths below 10 to 300 m, but is occasionally found above clear lagoon reefs as shallow as 4 m. It is considerably less common than *H. polylepis*, and highly localized in distribution.

Pacific Plate: Mariana, Samoan, Johnston, Hawaiian, and Tuamotu Is.

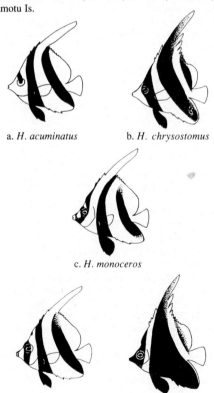

a. *H. acuminatus*   b. *H. chrysostomus*

c. *H. monoceros*

d. *H. singularis*   e. *H. varius*

Fig. 4. Banding patterns in juvenile *Heniochus*.

Heniochus acuminatus (Linnaeus, 1858)
Long-fin bannerfish   Pl. 68A; Fig. 4a

SL: to 196 mm (7.7 in); D (XI)-XII, 24-27; A III 17-19; P 15-18; LP 47-54.

The bannerfishes of the genus *Heniochus* get their common name from the elongate 4th dorsal spine which is usually produced into a wide filament. They are further characterized by an incomplete lateral line with 40-50 scales, and a color pattern consisting of two or more oblique white bands. Most species with exception of *H. chrysostomus* do reasonably well in the aquarium. The elongate dorsal filament reaches its greatest development in this species and the closely related *H. diphreutes*. *H. acuminatus* is a moderately common inhabitant of deep, protected lagoons and channels, and the deeper portions of outer reef slopes. In protected areas, it may occur as shallow as 2 m; on seaward reefs it usually occurs from below 20 m to at least 75 m. Juveniles are usually solitary, adults are often paired. It is a planktivore that generally remains within a few meters of the reef. It is uncertain whether or not the closely related *H. diphreutes* occurs in Micronesia. That species has an identical color pattern, but may be distinguished by its different modal dorsal fin count (D XII (rarely XIII), 23-25), less protruding snout, longer pelvic fins, and shorter anal fin. Unlike *H. acuminatus*, it is a schooling species that forms large aggregations high in the water clolumn. *H. diphreutes* occurs primarily along outer reef slopes at depths of 15 to 210 m, and in the deep tropics tends to occur where there is cooler upwelling water. A single collection of over 10 juveniles trapped in deep water off the Marianas, but unfortunately discarded when they died, may have consisted of *H. diphreutes*.

Indo-Pacific: E. Africa and Persian Gulf to the Society Is., n. to s. Japan, s. to Lord Howe Is.; throughout Micronesia; *H. diphreutes* ranges from the Red Sea and South Africa to warm-temperate Australia and the Hawaiian Is.

Heniochus chrysostomus Cuvier, 1831
Pennant bannerfish   Pl. 68B,C; Fig. 4b
(*H. permutatus*)

SL: to 125 mm (4.9 in); D (XI-I)-XII-I, 21-22; A 17-18; P 17; LL 57-61; GR 22-26.

The pennant bannerfish is a common inhabitant of areas of rich coral growth of subtidal reef flats and lagoon and seaward reefs to a depth of over 40 m. Juveniles have a longer, narrower "pennant" than adults as well as a double ocellus in the black portion of the anal fin. They are solitary and prefer shallow, protected areas. This species feeds primarily on coral polyps.

Indo-Pacific: w. India to Pitcairn Is., n. to s. Japan, s. to Rowley Shoals, s. Queensland, and New Caledonia; throughout Micronesia.

Heniochus monoceros Cuvier, 1831
Masked bannerfish   Pl. 68D; Fig. 4c

SL: to 181 mm (7.1 in); D XII, 24-27(25)A III, 17-19(18-19); P 17-(18); LL 58-64; LP 55-61; GR 13-19.

This somewhat uncommon bannerfish inhabits lagoon and seaward reefs at depths of 2 to over 20 m. It prefers areas of rich coral growth, but is occasionally found in relatively "dead" reef areas. Juveniles are solitary; adults are frequently paired and sometimes found hovering side by side under tabular corals. Adults develop a small hump on the forehead and a short horn above each eye. Juveniles of this species and *H. singularis* closely resemble one another. They differ in the position of the the middle black band which passes behind the white pennant in *H. monoceros* and in front of it in *H. singularis*.

Indo-Pacific: E. Africa to the Tuamotu Is., n. to s. Japan, s. to New South Wales and Tonga; throughout Micronesia.

Heniochus singularis Smith & Radcliffe, 1911
Singular bannerfish   Pl. 68E; Fig. 4d

SL: to 237 mm (9.3 in); D XI-XII, 25-27(25); A III, 17-18; P 17-(18); LL 53-64; LP 51-60; GR 13-14.

This is the only bannerfish in which adults have black-centered scales in the main white band. Juveniles closely resemble juvenile *H. monoceros* and *H. acuminatus*. The white ring around the mouth and complete ocular bar distinguish this species from *H. acuminatus* at all sizes. The singular bannerfish is an uncommon inhabitant of deep lagoon and seaward reefs. Solitary juveniles occur in the depth range of 2 to 36 m. Adults occur singly or in small groups and prefer areas of rich coral growth and high vertical relief at depths of about 12 to over 40 m.

West-central Pacific: Andaman Is. to Samoa, n. to s. Japan, s. to Rowley Shoals and New Caledonia; throughout Micronesia.

Heniochus varius (Cuvier, 1829)   Pl. 68F; Fig. 4e
Humphead bannerfish

SL: to 152 mm (6.0 in); D XI, 22-25(23-24); A III, 17-18; P 15-16; LL 52-65; LP 52-62; GR 15-22.

Adults of this species develop a prominent hump on the forehead and a curved horn above each eye, and lose the elongate dorsal filament. The humphead bannerfish is a relatively uncommon inhabitant of deep lagoons and steep outer reef slopes at depths of 2 to over 20 m. It prefers high-relief areas of rich coral growth with an abundance of small caves. It occurs singly or in small aggregations.

West-central Pacific: Indonesia to the Society Is., n. to s. Japan, s. to Rowley Shoals and New Caledonia; throughout Micronesia.

POMACANTHIDAE (ANGELFISHES)

Angelfishes superficially resemble butterflyfishes and at one time were classified in the same family. They share certain chaetodontid characteristics such as a deep compressed body with small ctenoid scales extending on to the median fins, a small mouth with brush-like teeth, and a single unnotched dorsal fin. They differ by possessing a prominent spine at the corner of the preopercle as well as lesser spines on the preopercle, interopercle and preorbital, by having more strongly ctenoid scales and auxillary scales on adults, and in lacking the distinctive chaetodontid *tholichthys* postlarval stage. All species studied to date are protogynous hermaphrodites with haremic social systems. Each male defends a territory containing two to five females. Territory size ranges from a few square meters for some species of *Centropyge* to well over 1,000 square meters for large species of *Pomacanthus*. Spawning is paired, typically occuring around sunset, at the apex of an upward rush following courtship displays and nuzzling by the male. Hatching occurs within 24 hours and the pelagic larval stage lasts about three to four weeks. Species of *Centropyge* feed primarily on filamentous algae and species of *Genicanthus* feed primarily on zooplankton as well as small amounts of benthic invertebrates and algae. Most others feed primarily on sponges and to a lesser extent on soft-bodied invertebrates, algae, and fish eggs. At least 26 species in 6 genera occur in Micronesia. (Lit.: Burgess, 1973; Randall, 1975; Randall and Yasuda, 1979; Randall and Wass, 1974; Myers, 1980; Smith-Vaniz and Randall, 1974)

Subfamily Holacanthinae: characterized by relatively large scales (LR 42-54) and an incomplete lateral line ending at end of soft dorsal fin (LP counts apply to upper series only in cases where an additional series of small small pores are on the caudal peduncle).

Apolemichthys griffisi (Carlson & Taylor, 1981)
Griffis angelfish   Pl. 69A

SL: to 157 mm (6.2 in).
D XIV, 18; A III, 18; P 17-18; LR 46-47; LP 38-47+5-6; GR 3-6+12-13.

This distinctive angelfish has recently been photographed at a depth of 60 m off a steep dropoff at Ant Atoll (11 km w. of Pohnpei). At atolls east of Micronesia, it has been reported from outer reef slopes at depths of 10 to 33 m.

Tropical w. Pacific: Ant Atoll, Nauru (sight record), Gilbert, Phoenix, and Line Islands.

Apolemichthys trimaculatus
(Lacepède in Cuvier, 1831)   Pl. 69B
Three-spot angelfish; Flagfin angelfish

SL: to 260 mm (10.2 in); D XIV, 16-18; A III, 17-19; P 17; LR 46-47, LP 38-47+4-6; GR 3-6+12-14.

This angelfish inhabits outer reef slopes and clear lagoon reefs at depths of 3 to over 40 m. It prefers areas of relatively high vertical relief and feeds primarily on sponges and tunicates.

Indo-west Pacific: E. Africa to Samoa, n. to s. Japan, s. to New Caledonia; Belau to e. Carolines and Marianas in Micronesia.

Apolemichthys xanthopunctatus Burgess, 1973
Golden spotted angelfish   Pl. 69C

SL: to 174 mm (6.9 in); D XIV, 17-18; A III, 17-19(17-18); P 16; LR 45-46, GR 15-19.

This spectacular angelfish occurs in Micronesia only at the isolated outpost of Kapingamarangi Atoll. One specimen was collected in a wooden trap set at a depth of 3 m on a mixed sand and coral lagoon slope. Others have been observed in channels and on outer reef slopes.

Pacific Plate: Kapingamarangi, Nauru, Canton (Phoenix Is.), Howland, Baker, and Fanning (Line Is.) Atolls.

Centropyge bicolor (Bloch, 1787)   Pl. 69D
Bicolor angelfish
SL: to 144 mm (5.7 in); D XV, 15-17; A III, 17-18; P 16-17; LR 46-48; GR 5+12-14.

Centropyge is the largest pomacanthid genus with 26 species in the Indo-Pacific, 13 of which occur in Micronesia. All species are relatively small. The bicolor angelfish occurs among small patches of rubble on lagoon, channel, or protected seaward reef slopes at depths of 3 to over 20 m. It remains close to the substrate, never far from shelter. It is among the least common species of *Centropyge* from Belau to the e. Carolines, and extremely rare in the Marianas and Marshalls.

Indo-Pacific: E. Africa to the Samoan and Phoenix Is., n. to s. Japan, s. to New Caledonia; throughout Micronesia.

Centropyge bispinosus (Günther, 1860)   Pl. 69E
Two-spined angelfish; Dusky angelfish
SL: to 97 mm (3.8 in); D XIV, 16-18; A III, 17-19; P 15-17(16); LR 42-45; GR 6-8+16-17.

This gorgeous little angelfish is highly variable in coloration with some individuals predominately light orange with the barring broken into a series of spots, and others almost entirely purple with prominent barring and very little orange. It inhabits lagoon and seaward reef slopes in areas of rich coral growth at depths of 9 to at least 45 m. It is relatively common on lagoon pinnacles in the Marshalls and on outer reef slopes from Belau to the e. Carolines, but rare in the Marianas. At Guam a lone female has been observed to spawn with a male *C. shepardi*, the dominant species of the genus there on outer reef slopes below 18 m.

Indo-Pacific: E. Africa to the Tuamotus, n. to the Izus, s. to Lord Howe Is.; throughout Micronesia.

Centropyge colini Smith-Vaniz & Randall, 1974
Colin's angelfish   Pl. 69F
SL: to 70 mm (2.8 in); D XIV, 16-17; A III, 17; P 15-16; LP 32-42; GR 4-6+11-12=16-18.

This rare species is a secretive dweller of crevices and clefts in caves of outer reef dropoffs at depths of 24 to 75 m. It is known in Micronesia on the basis of a few individuals collected at Guam's "Blue Hole" and the walls of Belau.

West Pacific: Cocos-Keeling Atoll, Belau, Fiji, and Guam.

Centropyge flavicauda Fraser-Brunner, 1933
White-tail angelfish   Fig. 1
SL: to 57 mm (2.3 in); D XIV, 15; A III, 17.

This diminuitive angelfish has a dark body and a cream colored tail. Body color ranges from a greenish to blueish brown with a blue margin on the dorsal and anal fins of males. The whitetail angelfish occurs on rubble bottoms of

channel or outer reef slopes at depths of 10 to 60 m.

Indo-Pacific: E. Africa to the Tuamotus, n. to s. Japan, s. to the Great Barrier Reef; Belau and the Marshalls in Micronesia.

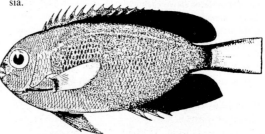

Fig. 1. *C. flavicauda* 37mm SL (after Frazer-Brunner,1933).

Centropyge flavissimus (Cuvier, 1831)   Pl. 70A
Lemonpeel angelfish
SL: to 78 mm (3.1 in); D XIV, 15-16; A III, 16; P 16-17; LR 44-50.

Juveniles have a characteristic blue-edged black ocellus in the middle of each side. The lemonpeel angelish inhabits areas of rich coral growth of shallow lagoon and exposed seaward reefs from the lower surge zone to a depth of 25 m or more. It is the most common *Centropyge* in less than 20 m in the Marianas and Marshalls, but is relatively rare in the Carolines and has not yet been recorded from Belau. Juveniles are much more secretive than adults. Hybrids of this and *Centropyge vrolicki* that have an intermediate color pattern are occasionally seen.

West-central Pacific: Cocos-Keeling Atoll to the Line, Marquesan and Ducie Is., straying to Easter Is., n. to the Ryukyus, s. to New Caledonia and Rapa; throughout Micronesia except for Belau and Yap (?).

Centropyge heraldi Woods & Schultz, 1953
Herald's angelfish   Pl. 70B
SL: to 80 mm (3.1 in); D XV, 15; A III, 17; P 14-17; LR 46-48.

Herald's angelfish lacks the blue trim of the lemonpeel angelfish. Large males develop somewhat angular dorsal and anal fins and a dusky patch behind each eye. This is a moderately common species of steep outer reef slopes at depths of 15 to over 40 m that occasionally occurs on lagoon reefs or as shallow as 5 m.

West-central Pacific: Taiwan to the Tuamotus, n. to s. Japan, s. to the Great Barrier Reef; throughout Micronesia, except possibly Belau and Yap.

Centropyge loriculus (Günther, 1860)   Pl. 70C
Flame angelfish
(*C. flammeus* Schultz, 1953)
SL: to 93 cm (3.7 in); D XIV, 16-18; A III, 17-18; P (17)-18; LR 44-49; GR 6-7+16-17.

The spectacular flame angelfish inhabits areas of rich coral growth of clear lagoon and seaward reefs from the lower surge zone to a depth of 57 m. It is common from Belau to the e. Carolines and s. Marshalls, but rare in the Marianas and n. Marshalls. It is fairly secretive and stays very near shelter. A brilliant blue trim begins to appear on the soft dorsal and anal fins of large females and becomes highly developed on males. The flame angelfish is regularly exported from Majuro for the aquarium trade and does well in the aquarium if given a sunlit tank with ample algal growth.

Pacific Plate: Belau to the Hawaiian, Marquesan, and Ducie Is., sw. to Egum Atoll and Samoa; throughout Micronesia.

Centropyge multicolor Randall & Wass, 1974
Multicolor angelfish   Pl. 70D

SL: to 49 mm (1.9 in); D XIV, (16)-17; A III, 17; P 16-17; LR 44-46; GR 6-7+16.

This colorful little angelfish inhabits steep outer reef slopes at depths of 20 to 90 m. It typically occurs in small tracks of rubble between areas of rich coral growth and is secretive, remaining close among the rubble. It is reported to be abundant in certain areas of Pohnpei.

Pacific Plate: e. Caroline (Pohnpei, Kosrae), Marshall, Society, and Hawaiian Is.(1 specimen).

Centropyge multifasciatus
  (Smith & Radcliffe, 1911)   Pl. 70E
Multibarred angelfish

SL: to 93 mm (3.7 in); D XIII, 17-19; A III, 17-18; P 15-(16); LR 45-47; GR 5-6+12-13.

This is the only conspicuously barred *Centropyge*. It is a common inhabitant of caves and crevices of steep outer reef slopes at depths of 20 to 70 m. Occasionally it occurs on clear lagoon reefs. It is secretive and rarely ventures more than a few centimeters from an escape hole.

West-central Pacific: Cocos-Keeling Atoll to the Society Is., n. to the Yaeyamas, s. to the Great Barrier Reef; throughout Micronesia.

Centropyge nigriocellus Woods & Schultz, 1953
Black-spot angelfish   Pl. 70F; Fig. 2

SL: to 43 mm (1.7 in); D XIII, 15; A III, 15; P 17; LR 44.

This small species inhabits dead coral rubble of clear lagoon and exposed seaward reefs at depths of 4 to 15. It is quite secretive; the few known specimens have been collected with the aid of ichthyocides. The only known Micronesian specimen was collected at Tinian.

Pacific Plate: Mariana, Admiralty, Samoan, Society, Line, and Johnston Is.

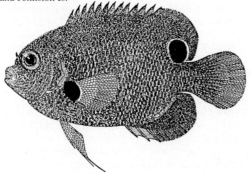

Fig. 2. *C. nigriocellus*, 38 mm SL (after A. M. Awl *in* Schultz et al., 1953).

Centropyge shepardi Randall & Yasuda, 1979
Shepard's angelfish   Pl. 71A,B

SL: to 70 mm (2.8 in); D XIV, 16-18; A III 17-18; P 16-(17); LP 34-38; GR 7-8+17-19.

In the Marianas, Shepard's angelfish is the dominant *Centropyge* of exposed outer reef slopes at depths of 18 to 56 m. On rare occasions it may occur on clear lagoon reefs as shallow as 1m. It prefers areas of mixed dead and living coral with numerous shelter holes and passages. It is quite variable in color: the ground color may range from an almost red to a light apricot and the barring can be reduced to a small patch behind the operculum, or in rare cases, be entirely absent. Like *C. loriculus*, the blue trim on the soft dorsal and anal fins is absent or reduced in females and highly developed in males. Shepard's angelfish is available to the U. S. aquarium trade only through occasional shipments from Guam and commands a high price (about $50-75).

Marianas and Bonins: straying to the Izus.

Centropyge nox (Bleeker, 1853)
Midnight angelfish

SL: to 78 mm (3.7in); D XIV-XV, 16-17; A III, 16-17.

This is the only angelfish that is uniformly black. It is a secretive inhabitant of rubble in coral-rich areas of clear lagoon and seaward reefs. At Belau, it has been observed at a depth of 10 m in channels and at a depth of 70 m along steep dropoffs. It has also been collected from a coral head at a depth of 10 m in Kapingamarangi lagoon.

West Pacific: Indonesia to New Caledonia, n. to the Ryukyus; Belau and Kapingamarangi in Micronesia.

Centropyge tibicen (Cuvier, 1831)   Pl. 71C
Keyhole angelfish

SL: to 149 mm (5.9 in); D XIV, 15-16; A III, 16-17.

This species is a relatively uncommon inhabitant of areas of mixed coral and rubble of lagoon and seaward reefs at depths of 4 to 30 m.

West Pacific: Christmas Is. (e. Indian Ocean) to Vanuatu and New Caledonia, n. to s. Japan, s. to Scott Reef and Lord Howe Is.; Belau, Yap, and Ifaluk in Micronesia.

Centropyge vrolikii (Bleeker, 1853)   Pl. 71D
Pearlscale angelfish

SL: to 75 mm (3.0 in); D XIV, 15-16; A III, 16-17; P 16-17; LR 46-47.

The pearlscale angelfish occurs on lagoon and seaward reefs, primarily in areas of rich coral growth at depths of 3 to 25 m. It is relatively common from Belau to the e. Carolines. In the westernmost Carolines it replaces the lemonpeel angelfish. In the Marianas it is relatively rare and readily hybridizes with the lemonpeel angelfish.

Indo-Pacific: E. Africa to the Marshalls and Vanuatu, n. to s. Japan, s. to Lord Howe Is.; throughout Micronesia.

Genicanthus bellus Randall, 1975   Fig. 4a
Ornate angelfish

SL: to 106 mm (4.2 in); D XV, 15-16; A III, 16-17; P 16-17; LR 46-48; GR 4-5+12-14=16-17.

Genicanthus is the only angelfish genus in which the spe-

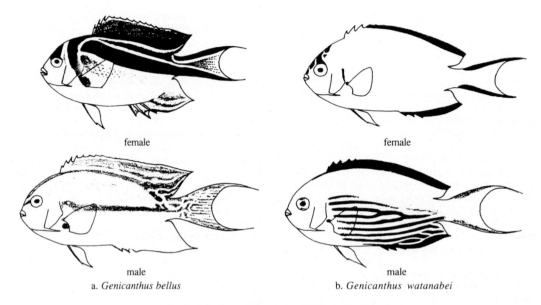

female

female

male

male

a. *Genicanthus bellus*

b. *Genicanthus watanabei*

Fig. 4. Micronesian species of *Genicanthus*.

cies are strikingly sexually dimorphic, have an emarginate to lunate tail, and are planktivorous. Like many planktivores, they venture up to several meters out into the water to feed, but quickly seek shelter when approached. They do well in the aquarium but many of the species are rare and deep-dwelling. *G. bellus* typically occurs in small aggregations along steep current-swept outer reef dropoffs at depths of 45 to at least 97 m. On rare occasions it has been collected in as little as 24 m. It is known from Micronesia on the basis of three specimens and a handful of sightings made at Guam and Enewetak Atoll.

West-central Pacific: Cocos-Keeling Atoll, Philippines, Guam, Marshalls, and Tahiti.

Genicanthus melanospilos (Bleeker, 1857)
Black-spot angelfish   Pl. 71E,F

SL: to 149 mm (5.9 in); D XV, 15-17(16); A III, 17-(18); P 15-17(16); LR 46-48; GR 3-(4)+(12)-13=16.

This species is reported from areas of rich coral growth interspersed with sand at depths below 20 m. It generally occurs in pairs.

West Pacific: s. China Sea and Indonesia to Fiji, n. to the Ryukyus, s. to Rowley Shoals and New Caledonia; Belau in Micronesia.

Genicanthus watanabei (Yasuda &Tominaga,1970)
Watanabe's angelfish   Pl. 72A; Fig. 4b

SL: to 138 mm (5.4 in); D (XV)-XVI, 15-(16); A III, 17; P 16; LR 45-48; GR 4-5+12-(13).

Watanabe's angelfish inhabits current-swept outer reef slopes and dropoffs. It is rare and deep-dwelling in Micronesia. At Guam, it has been observed in small groups at a depth of 45 m off Cocos Island and photographed at 25 m off Uruno Pt.

At Enewetak it has been observed from a submersible at 81 m.

West-central Pacific: Taiwan to the Tuamotus, n. to the Ryukyus, s. to New Caledonia and the Australs; Marianas and Marshalls in Micronesia.

Pygoplites diacanthus (Boddaert, 1772)   Pl. 72B
Regal angelfish

SL: To 209 mm (8.2 in); D XIV, 17-19; A III, 17-19; P 16-(17); LL 47-50; GR 5-6+12-13.

This spectacular angelfish inhabits areas of rich coral growth of clear lagoon and seaward reefs at depths of 3 to at least 48 m. It often occurs in the vicinity of caves and feeds on sponges and tunicates. It is moderately common throughout Micronesia and often seen singly or in pairs. Juveniles are secretive and resemble adults but have a large ocellus and less blue on the soft dorsal fin. The regal angelfish is a highly prized aquarium fish but difficult to keep alive for a great length of time.

Indo-Pacific: Red Sea to the Tuamotus, n. to the Ryukyus, s. to New Caledonia; throughout Micronesia.

Subfamily Pomacanthinae: characterized by relatively small scales (LL 46-115) and absence of preorbital and interopercular spines.

Chaetodontoplus mesoleucus (Bloch, 1787)
Vermiculated angelfish   Pl. 72C

SL: to 151 mm (5.6 in); D XII, 17-18; A III, 17-18; LL 61-72; GR 4+12.

Species of *Chaetodontoplus* have an incomplete lateral line and smaller scales than other angelfishes, except for some species of *Pomacanthus* subgenus *Pomacanthodes*. This an-

gelfish more closely resembles a butterflyfish in body shape, but is easily identified as an angelfish by its strong opercular spine. It inhabits coral rich areas of lagoon reefs in and around Belau's Rock Islands. It feeds on attached organisms such as sponges and tunicates as well as filamentous algae.
West Pacific: Malaysia to the Solomon Is., n. to the Ryukyus, s. to Indonesia; Belau in Micronesia.

Pomacanthus navarchus (Cuvier, 1831)   Pl. 72D
Blue-girdled angelfish
(*Euxiphipops navarchus*)
SL: to 203 mm (8.0 in); D XIII- XIV, 17-18; A III, 18; LL 45-48; GR 6+12.
Species of *Pomacanthus* have a complete lateral line. Those in the subgenus *Euxiphipops* (*navarchus*, *sexstriatus*, and *xanthometopon*) have larger scales (LR 45-52) than the those in the subgenus *Pomacanthodes* (all other Indo-Pacific species; LR ≥ 65). Juveniles of both subgenera are strikingly different from adults, but similar to each other. Juveniles of the subgenus *Euxiphipops* have straight vertical bars. *P. navarchus* is the only one in which the bars are entirely bluish-white and the tail is clear over most of its length. Transformation to the adult pattern begins with the hint of an orange dorsal fin at the small size of 3 cm and is complete by the size of about 8 cm. Juveniles occur in protected areas. The stunning adults inhabit areas of rich coral growth of clear lagoons, channels, and protected outer reef slopes at depths of 3 to 30 m. They are usually solitary and relatively shy. All species of *Pomacanthus* feed primarily on sponges and tunicates and many make a curious grunting noise when disturbed. In Micronesia, this species is only known from Belau where it is relatively rare. It is a highly prized aquarium export from the Philippines, but is difficult to maintain.
Indo-Australian: Indonesia to Papua New Guinea, n. to the Philippines, s. to Rowley Shoals and the s. Great Brrier Reef; Belau and Yap in Micronesia.

Pomacanthus sexstriatus (Kuhl &Van Hasselt *in* Cuvier, 1831)
Six-banded angelfish   Pl. 73A,B
(*Euxiphipops sexstriatus*)
SL: to 375 mm (14.7in), possibly to 415 mm (16.3 in); DXIV, 18-23; A III, 18-19; P 18; LR 48; GR 5+13.
This is the largest Micronesian pomacanthid. Small juveniles are nearly identical to those of *P. xanthometopon*, but the dorsal and anal fins are slightly less elevated. Transformation to the adult color pattern occurs over the size range of about 8 to 15 cm. Juveniles prefer sheltered inner reefs and are secretive. Adults occur in pairs and prefer areas of rich coral growth and high vertical relief of lagoon and seaward reefs at depths of 3 to 50 m. This species has a large home-range and is less common than *P. imperator* or *Pygoplites diacanthus*. No more than one or two pairs could be expected to be encountered on a given dive on the dropoffs or channels of Belau.
West Pacific: Malaysia to the Solomons, n. to the Ryukyus, s. to Rowley Shoals and New Caledonia; Belau and Yap in Micronesia.

Pomacanthus xanthometopon (Bleeker, 1853)
Yellow-faced angelfish; Blue-faced angelfish
(*Euxiphipops xanthometapon*)   Pl. 72E
SL: to 320 mm (12.6 in); D XIII-XIV, 16-18; A III, 16-18, LR 50-52; LP 46-47; GR 5+11-12.
The differences between the juveniles of this species and *P. navarchus* and *P. sexstriatus* are given in their accounts, but to add to the confusion, this species is known to hybridize with both of the others (Pl. 72F). Hints of the adult ground color begin to show at a size of 7 cm and transformation is complete at a size of about 12 cm. Adults inhabit areas of rich coral growth of lagoons, channels, and outer reef slopes at depths of 5 to over 25 m. The blue-faced angelfish is relatively uncommon at Belau and Kosrae, but common at Pohnpei where it is speared for food. Small specimens command a high price in the aquarium trade, but are difficult to maintain.
Indo-west Pacific: Maldives to Vanuatu, n. to the Yaeyamas, s. to Rowley Shoals and the Great Barrier Reef; Belau to Kosrae in Micronesia.

Pomacanthus imperator (Bloch, 1787)   Pl. 73C,D
Emperor angelfish
SL: to 305 mm (12.0 in); D XIII-(XIV), 18-21; A III, 18-21; P 19-(20); LR 90-103; GR 6-7+13-14.
The juvenile of *P. imperator* is the only *Pomacanthus* with concentric white circles. Transformation to the adult color pattern occurs over the size range of about 8 to 12 cm. Juveniles are solitary and occur under ledges or in holes of outer lagoon patch reefs or semi-protected areas of exposed channels and outer reef flats. They move out to reef front holes and surge channels as subadults. Large adults occur near ledges and caves in areas of rich coral growth on clear lagoon, channel, or seaward reefs at depths of 3 to 70 m. Although haremic, they are usually encountered singly or in pairs, and are not particularly common. Juveniles are highly sought after aquarium fishes. This species has been known to live up to five years or more in captivity.
Indo-Pacific: Red Sea to the Hawaiian (2 cases), Line, and Tuamotu Is., n. to s. Japan, s. to New Caledonia and the Australs; throughout Micronesia.

Pomacanthus semicirculatus (Cuvier, 1831)
Semicircle angelfish   Pl. 73E,F
SL: to 290 mm (11.4 in); D XIII, 20-23; A III, 18-22; P 19-21; LL 65-70; GR 4-5+12-13.
This is the only Micronesian *Pomacanthus* in which the posteriormost bars of juveniles are curved into distinctive semicircles. Transformation occurs over the size range of about 8 to 16 cm. Juveniles occur on shallow protected reefs in areas of mixed sand and coral and when very small, remain hidden in holes and crevices. Adults occur on coastal reefs in areas of heavy coral growth with well-encrusted caves or in wrecks. This species is generally solitary and is reported from Micronesia only at Belau where it appears to be rare.
Indo-west Pacific: E. Africa to Fiji, n. to s. Japan, s. to Lord Howe Is.; Belau in Micronesia.

POMACENTRIDAE (DAMSELFISHES)

Damselfishes are a large family of small, often colorful, fishes associated with coral or rocky reefs in tropical or warm-temperate waters. They are characterized by a moderately deep and compressed body with moderately large ctenoid scales that extend to the basal portion of the median fins, a small terminal mouth with conical or incisiform teeth, a single pair of nostrils (a minute second posterior pair is present in some species), a single continuous dorsal fin, an anal fin with II spines, an emarginate or forked tail, and an interrupted lateral line in which the first part ends beneath the dorsal fin. Damselfishes are a conspicuous and numerous element of virtually every coral reef, occuring wherever there is shelter. The species of *Chromis*, *Dascyllus*, *Lepidozygus*, *Amblyglyphidodon*, *Neopomacentrus*, and *Pomachromis* are aggregating planktivores that often occur in large clouds above the reef. Most species of *Abudefduf*, *Chrysiptera*, and *Pomacentrus* are omnivores that feed on a combination of benthic algae, small invertbrates, or zooplankton. The species of *Plectroglyphidodon* and *Stegastes* are pugnacious, highly territorial herbivores. Damselfishes lay elliptical demersal eggs that are guarded by the male. Spawning generally occurs in the morning. In many species reproductive activity peaks on a lunar cycle, and in many tropical areas seems to occur more frequently in the early summer. Although not normally sexually dimorphic, males of many species develop a distinctive, often darkened courtship coloration. Damselfishes are among the hardiest of aquarium fishes, but the aggressive nature of many species makes them ill-suited for the community aquarium. With at least 89 species in 16 genera, the Pomacentridae is Micronesia's third largest family of fishes. (In the following species accounts lateral line pore counts are given only for the upper series.) (Lit.: Allen, 1972, 1975, 1978, *in* Smith & Heemstra, 1986; Allen and Emery, 1985; Allen and Larson, 1975; Allen and Randall, 1980; Donaldson, 1984; Marliave, 1985; Randall (H. A.) and Allen, 1977; Randall et al., 1980, 1985; Randall and Swerdloff, 1973; Shepard and Moyer, 1980; Yoshino, 1982)

Subfamily Amphiprioninae (Anemonefishes)

Members of this subfamily, popularly known as anemonefishes or clownfishes, live in close association with large sea anemones. Each species has a preferred anemone host, although most occasionally occur in a number of other anemone species, and individual anemones occasionally host more than one species of anemonefish. They never live without an anemone, but it is not uncommon to find suitable anemones without anemonefish. Large anemones often host a semipermanent monogamous pair of adult anemonefishes and several small juveniles. Anemonefish are protandrous hermaphrodites, that is all individuals mature as males, and all females are sex-reversed males. Sex and growth are socially controlled by a dominant female. In the absence of a female, the largest male will turn into a female and the largest juvenile will rapidly mature into a male. The growth of the remaining juveniles is stunted by the adult pair. Spawning usually takes place around the full moon, all year round in the tropics, but only during the warmer months in warm-temperate areas. Typically, several hundred adhesive eggs are laid in a patch of cleared rock near the base of the anemone and cared for by the male. Hatching occurs at night after about a week, and the larvae drift in the plankton for 16 days or more before settling and seeking an anemone host. Anemonefishes feed primarily on zooplankton, primarily copepods, and filamentous algae. Aside from their characteristic coloration and ecology, members of this subfamily are the only pomacentrids that have serrated edges on all the opercles and more than 50 scales in a longitudinal series (vs <45).

Amphiprion chrysopterus Cuvier, 1830 Pl. 74A,B
Orange-fin anemonefish

(*A. bicinctus* Woods and Schultz, 1960)

SL: to 123 mm (4.8 in); D (X)-XI, 15-17; A II, 13-14; P 20-21; LP 35-42; GR 19-21.

Juveniles are a dull orange; adults are variable but usually become a dark brown with bright orange fins, and may have a white or yellow-orange tail. The light bands range from white to a dazzling light blue. Blue-banded individuals are rare in the Marianas but common from Belau to the eastern Carolines. This species is the most common anemonefish of seaward reefs from the lower surge zone to a depth of 30 m or more. Occasionally it occurs on lagoon reefs. Its usual host is the anemone *Heteractis crispa*, but it also occurs in the carpet anemone *Stichodactyla mertensii* or the colorful *H. aurora*, sometimes with juvenile *Dascyllus trimaculatus*.
West-central Pacific: New Guinea and Vanuatu to the Tuamotus, n. to the Marianas; throughout Micronesia.

Amphiprion clarkii (Bennett, 1830) Pl. 74C,D
Clark's anemonefish

SL: to 95 mm (3.7 in); D X, 15-16; A II, 13-14; P 19-20; LP 36-40; GR 18-20.

This is the least common anemonefish throughout most of Micronesia. It is known from the depth range of 1 to 55 m, and is more apt to occur on outer reef slopes than in lagoons. It inhabits the anemones *Stichodactyla mertensii*, *H. crispa*, and *H. aurora*.
Indo-west Pacific: Persian Gulf to Vanuatu, n. to s. Japan, s. to Rowley Shoals and New Caledonia; Belau to the e. Carolines and Marianas in Micronesia.

Amphiprion melanopus Bleeker, 1852 Pl. 74E
Dusky anemonefish

SL: to 88 mm (3.5 in); *frenatus* to 100 mm (3.9 in); D X, 16-18; A II, 13-14; P 18-19; LP 34-42; GR 17-19.

A recent series of breeding experiments conducted at the Vancouver Aquarium strongly suggests that *A. frenatus*, *A.*

melanopus, A. rubrocinctus, and possibly *A. ephippium* are actually stable polymorphs of the same species. Positive assortative mating (mating only with ones own color morph) as well as unknown environmental factors may determine the geographic distribution of each morph. If they are truly conspecific, then the oldest name, *A. ephippium* (Bloch, 1790) has priority. *A. melanopus* is the only form that occurs in Micronesia. I retain that name pending resolution of this intriguing problem. Small juveniles are red with one to two additional white bars on the body. This is the most common anemonefish in the Marianas where it is the only species that normally occurs on reef flats. It also occurs on lagoon reefs to a depth of 18 m. It lives exclusively in the cluster anemone *Entacmaea quadricolor*.

West-central Pacific: Moluccas to Samoa, n. to the Marianas, s. to the Great Barrier Reef; throughout Micronesia (*A. ephipium*: Andamans to Moluccas; *A. frenatus*: S. Africa to New Guinea, n. to the Ryukyus; *A. rubrocinctus*: nw. Australia to Samoa and Tonga).

Amphiprion perideraion Bleeker, 1855   Pl. 74F
Pink anemonefish
SL: to 72 mm (2.8 in); D X, 16-17; A II, 12-13; P 16-18; LP 32-43; GR 17-20.
This small anemonefish inhabits lagoon reefs below 3 m and seaward reefs from 15 to at least 30 m. It occurs exclusively in the large colorful anemone *Heteractis magnifica*.

West-central Pacific: Malaysia to Samoa, s. to Rowley Shoals and New Caledonia, n. to the Ryukyus; throughout Micronesia.

Amphiprion tricinctus Schultz & Welander, 1960
Three-banded anemonefish   Fig. 1
(*A. chrysogaster* Woods and Schultz, 1960)
SL: to 97 mm (3.8 in); D (X)-XI, 15-16; A II, 13-14; P 19-20; LP 38-43; GR 20-21.
This Marshall Islands endemic inhabits lagoon and seaward reefs at depths of 3 to 38 m. It occurs in two basic color phases. The cause appears to be environmental; those occurring in the anemone *Stichodactyla mertensii* are black while those in *H. aurora* are orange. It rarely associates with *Entacmaea quadricolor*.
Marshall Is.

.normal   dark
Fig. 1. Two color phases of *Amphiprion tricinctus*.

Subfamily Chrominae

Members of this subfamily are typically aggregating planktivores that are closely tied to a particular patch of coral. They have two to three projecting spiniform procurrent rays on the upper and lower edge of the caudal base and conical jaw teeth, usually with an outer row of large teeth followed by one or more secondary rows.

Chromis acares Randall & Swerdloff, 1973
Midget chromis   Pl. 75A
SL: to 35 mm (1.4 in); D (XII)-XIII, 11; A II, 10-(11); P 16-18(17); LP 15-17; GR 5-6+16-19.
This colorful little *Chromis* is a relatively uncommon inhabitant of exposed seaward reefs at depths of 2 to 37 m. It occasionally occurs in clear lagoons or channels. It aggregates a short distance above prominent coral heads.
Pacific Plate: Marianas to the Hawaiian and Society Is., s. to Vanuatu and the Austral Is.; Marianas, e. Carolines, and Marshalls in Micronesia; possibly also at Rowley Shoals.

Chromis agilis Smith, 1960   Pl. 75B,C
Bronze reef chromis
(*C. leucurus* Schultz et al., 1960)
SL: to 78 mm (3.1 in); D XII, 12-14(13); A II, 12-14(13); P 16-18(17); LP 15-17(16); GR 8-9+20-23=27-30.
This species inhabits clear lagoon and seaward reefs at depths of 6 to 65 m. It generally occurs in loose aggregations, often near caves or ledges, and is relatively common throughout Micronesia.
Indo-Pacific: E. Africa to the Hawaiian and Pitcairn Is., n. to the Marianas, s. to New Caledonia and Rapa; Marianas and Marshalls in Micronesia; primarily around oceanic islands.

Chromis alpha Randall, 1987   Pl. 75D
Yellow-speckled chromis
(*Chromis* sp. A Allen, 1975)
SL: to 90 mm (3.5 in); D XIII, 12-13; A II, 12-13; P 17-18; LP 14-15; GR 27-28.
This rather drab species aggregates a few meters above steep outer reef slopes at depths of 15 to 95 m. In the Marianas, it is abundant in certain areas. It nests in patches of loose sand.
West-central Pacific: Christmas Is., Indian Ocean, to the Society Is., n. to the Marianas, s. to New Caledonia; throughout Micronesia.

Chromis amboinensis (Bleeker, 1873)   Pl. 75E,F
Ambon chromis
SL: to 60 mm (2.4 in); D XII, 12-13; A II, 12-13; P 16; LP (13)-14; GR 26-29.
Juveniles have more blue around the eyes and the margins of the dorsal and anal fins, as well as greatly elongate outermost caudal rays. In the Marianas, this is one of the most abundant damselfishes of coral rich areas of steep outer reef slopes below 24 m. Elsewhere it occurs in passes or clear lagoons at depths of 5 to 70 m. It generally occurs in aggregations that remain near the substrate.
West-central Pacific: Christmas Is., Indian Ocean, to Samoa, n. to the Marianas, s. to Rowley Shoals and New Caledonia; throughout Micronesia.

Chromis analis (Cuvier, 1830)   Pl. 75G
Yellow chromis
SL: to 141 mm (5.6 in); D XIII, 11-13(11-12); A II, 11-12;

P 18-20; LP 16-19(16-18); GR 6-7+16-19.

This species ranges from solid yellow to chocolate brown with yellow median fins and eyes (Marianas specimens). It occurs singly or in small aggregations along outer reef slope walls below 10 m. In the Marianas, it has been taken only once, at a depth of 144 m off Guam.

West Pacific: Indonesia to Fiji, n. to s. Japan, s. to Rowley Shoals and New Caledonia; Belau to Pohnpei and the Marianas in Micronesia.

Chromis atripectoralis Welander & Schultz, 1951
Black-axil chromis   Pl. 75H

SL: to 84 mm (3.3 in); D XII, 9-(10); A II, 9-10; P 18-20 (19-20); LP 15-16; GR 8-10+21-23.

This species differs from the smaller blue-green chromis, *C. viridis*, by possessing a distinct black blotch on the inner pectoral axil. It is a common inhabitant of clear lagoon and protected seaward reefs at depths of 1 to at least 18 m. It occurs in loose aggregations associated with branching corals, particularly staghorn *Acropora*, and wanders several meters above the bottom. Spawning takes place on dead coral branches. Egg-guarding males assume a blotchy coloration.

Indo-Pacific: Seychelles to the Line and Tuamotu Is., n. to the Ryukyus, s. to Lord Howe and Rapa Is.; throughout Micronesia.

Chromis atripes Fowler & Bean, 1928   Pl. 76A
Dark-fin chromis

SL: to 51 mm (2.0 in); D XII, 12; A II, 12; P 15-17(16-17); LP 14-16; GR 6-9+18-22.

This small species occurs in coral rich areas of outer reef passes and slopes at depths of 2 to 40 m. It is typically solitary and closely tied to the bottom.

West-central Pacific: Christmas Is., Indian Ocean, to Kiribati, n. to the Izus, s. to Rowley shoals and New Caledonia; Belau to the e. Carolines and s. Marshalls in Micronesia.

Chromis caudalis Randall, 1987   Pl. 76B,C
Blue-axil chromis

SL: to 75 mm (3.0 in); D XII, 12-14(12-13); A II, 12-(13); P 16-18(17); LP13-15(14); GR 7-9+19-22.

This is the only Micronesian chromis with a deep blue inner pectoral axil. It is common around ledges and the bases of small caves of steep outer reef slopes at depths of 15 to 55 m. It typically occurs in small groups that remain close to shelter.

West-Pacific: Indonesia to the Solomon Is., n. to the Philippines, s. to Christmas Is.; Belau to Pohnpei in Micronesia.

Chromis delta Randall, 1987
Deep reef chromis

SL: to 49 mm (2.0 in); D XII, (13)-14; A II, (13)-14; P 15-17(16); LP 12-14; GR 6-9+18-21.

This small chromis is dark grey with a slightly darker bar in front of a white caudal peduncle and a round black spot on the pectoral axil. It inhabits steep outer reef slopes at depths of 20 to 80 m. At Belau, it is the most abundant pomacentrid at depths of 60-70 m, but is rare in less than 30 m. It occurs solitarily or in groups and remains close to shelter.

Indo-Australian: Christmas Is. and Indonesia to Fiji, n. to Taiwan, s. to the n. Great Barrier Reef; Belau in Micronesia.

Chromis elerae Fowler & Bean, 1928   Pl. 76D
Twin-spot chromis

SL: to 51 mm (2.0 in); D XII, (11)-12; A II, (10)-11; P 17-19; LP 15-17; GR 7-9+19-22.

This little *Chromis* occurs in small aggregations in the entrances to caves and crevices of steep outer reef slopes at depths of 18 to 70 m.

Indo-Pacific: Maldives to the Marshalls and Fiji, n. to Taiwan, s. Fiji; throughout Micronesia, except the n. Marshalls.

Chromis lepidolepis Bleeker, 1877   Pl. 76E
Scaly chromis

SL: to 59 mm (2.3 in); D XII, 11-13(12); A II, (11)-12; P 17-19(18); LP 15-18; GR 8-10+20-22=27-31.

The intense black spot at the tip of each caudal lobe is distinctive. This small species inhabits coral-rich areas of lagoon and seaward reefs at depths of 5 to at least 40 m. It occurs in aggregations close to shelter and feeds on zooplankton. It is quite rare in the Marianas, but fairly common elsewhere in Micronesia.

Indo-Pacific: Chagos Is. to the Line Is., n. to the Izu Is., s. to Rowley Shoals and New Caledonia; throughout Micronesia.

Chromis lineata Fowler & Bean, 1928   Fig. 2
Lined chromis

SL: to 40 mm (1.6 in); D XII, 11-12; A II, 11-12; P 17; LP 14-15; GR 22-24.

This species differs from the very similar *C. vanderbilti* by having a pale lower caudal lobe and fewer tubed lateral line scales. It occurs in aggregations above the upper edges of outer reef slopes at depths of 2 to 10 m.

Indo-Australian: Christmas Is., Indian Ocean, to the Solomons; Belau in Micronesia; closely related to *C. nigrurus* from the Indian Ocean.

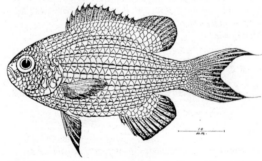

Fig. 2. *C. lineata*, ca. 39 mm (after Fowler and Bean, 1928).

Chromis margaritifer Fowler, 1946   Pl. 76F
Bicolor chromis
(*C. dimidiatus* Schultz et al., 1960)

SL: to 62 mm (2.4 in); D XII, (12)-13; A II, 11-(12); P 16-18(17); LP 16-18; GR 7-10+19-21.

This distinctive species is common on exposed seaward reefs at depths of 3 to 20 m, but is less abundant in lagoons and channels. It occurs singly or in small aggregations and feeds on zooplankton.

West-central Pacific: Christmas Is., Indian Ocean, to the Line and Tuamotu Is., n. to the Izus, s. to Rowley Shoals and Lord Howe Is.; throughout Micronesia.

Chromis retrofasciata Weber, 1913   Pl. 76G
Black-bar chromis

SL: to 40 mm (1.6 in); D XII, 12-13; A II, 12-13; P 15-16; LP 12; GR 24-26.

This exquisite little chromis inhabits clear lagoon and seaward reefs in areas of rich coral growth at depths of 5 to 65 m. It occurs singly or in small groups and remains close to shelter.

West Pacific: Indonesia to Fiji, n. to the Ryukyus, s. to New Caledonia; Belau in Micronesia.

Chromis ternatensis (Bleeker, 1856)   Pl. 76H
Ternate chromis

SL: to 74 mm (2.9 in); D (XII)-XIII, 10-12(11-12); A II, 10-12; P 17-19(18); LP 14-17; GR 7-9+21-23=28-33.

This species occurs in large aggregations above branching corals along the upper margins of clear lagoon and outer reef slopes at depths of 2 to at least 18 m. It is common through most of Micronesia, but rare in the Marianas where it has been photographed in Apra Harbor.

Indo-Pacific: E. Africa to Samoa, n. to the Ryukyus, s. to New Caledonia; throughout Micronesia.

Chromis vanderbilti (Fowler, 1941)   Pl. 77A
Vanderbilt's chromis

SL: to 48 mm (1.9 in); D XII, 10-12(10-11); A II. 10-12 (11); P 16-18(17); LP 16-18; GR 6-8+18-20.

This small striped chromis occurs on exposed seaward reefs at depths of 2 to 20 m. It is uncommon through most of Micronesia, but where found, tends to occur in aggregations above prominent coral heads.

West-central Pacific: Taiwan to the Hawaiian and Pitcairn Is., n. to the Izus, s. to Rowley Shoals and Lord Howe and Rapa Is.; throughout Micronesia.

Chromis viridis (Cuvier, 1830)   Pl. 77B,C
Blue-green chromis

(*C. caerulea*)

SL: to 68 mm (2.7 in); D XII, (9)-11; A II, 9-11; P 17-18; LP 15-17; GR 8-10+20-24=28-30.

Huge aggregations of this brilliant little chromis often occur above thickets of branching corals in sheltered areas such as subtidal reef flats and lagoons to a depth of 12 m. Swarms of juveniles occur above smaller isolated coral heads. Courting males develop blackish dorsal fin and upper pectoral rays and in some areas (e.g. Kosrae) may become mostly yellow posteriorly.

Indo-Pacific: Red Sea to Line, Marquesan , and Tuamotu Is., n. to the Ryukyus, s. to New Caledonia; throughout Micronesia.

Chromis weberi Fowler & Bean, 1928   Pl. 77D
Weber's chromis

SL: to 94 mm (3.7 in); D XII-XIII, 11-12; A II, 11-12; P 18-20(19-20); LP 17-19; GR 8-9+19-22=28-32.

Weber's chromis inhabits passes and steep outer reef slopes at depths of 3 to 25 m. It occurs singly or in small groups and is relatively uncommon in Belau.

Indo-Pacific: Red Sea to the Line and Samoan Is., n. to s. Japan, s. to New Caledonia; Belau in Micronesia.

Chromis xanthochir (Bleeker, 1851)   Pl. 77E
Yellow-axil chromis

SL: to 100 mm (3.9 in); D XIII, 11; A II, 11-12; P 19; LP 16-17; GR 30-32.

This species differs from the similar *C. weberi* by having a thin black preopercular bar and lacking black tips on its caudal lobes. At Belau, it is a relatively uncommon inhabitant of steep outer reef slopes in 10 to 48 m that occurs singly or in small groups.

Indo-Australian: Indonesia to the Solomons, n. to the Philippines; Belau in Micronesia.

Chromis xanthura (Bleeker, 1854)   Pl. 77F,G,H
Black chromis

SL: to 117 mm (4.6 in); D XIII, 10-11; A II, 9-10; P 18-20(18-19); LP 16-19; GR 6-8+19-22.

This large chromis undergoes dramatic changes in coloration with growth and occurs in two or more geographic variations. Juveniles are a slate gray to a brilliant metallic blue with a bright orange-yellow tail; adults are dark gray to black, and in most areas have a white tail. Those in the Marianas have a black tail. *C. xanthura* typically occurs in loose aggregations that may extend several meters above steep outer reef slopes to a depth of over 40 m. Along relatively sheltered dropoffs it may occur in as little as 4 m, but in the Marianas is usually found below 15 m. It nests in small patches of loose sand at the base of coral slopes or under overhangs.

West-central Pacific: Christmas Is., Indian Ocean, to the Line, Marquesan, and Pitcairn Is., n. to the Izus, s. to Rowley Shoals and New Caledonia; throughout Micronesia; *C. opercularis* of the w. Indian Ocean may be the same species.

Dascyllus aruanus (Linnaeus, 1758)   Pl. 78A
Humbug dascyllus

SL: to 65 mm (2.6 in); D XII, 11-13(12); A II, 11-13(12); P 17-19(17-18); LP 15-19(17-18); GR 5-8(6-7)+15-19(16-17).

This is one of the most abundant fishes of shallow lagoon and subtidal reef flats. It typically occurs in large aggregations above staghorn *Acropora* thickets or in smaller groups above isolated coral heads. It is closely tied to its "home" coral head and will often remain wedged among the branches after the coral is removed from the water. Species of *Dascyllus* feed on zooplankton, benthic invertebrates, and algae.

Indo-Pacific: Red Sea to Line, Marquesan, and Tuamotu Is., n. to the Ryukyus, s. to Lord Howe and Rapa Is.; throughout Micronesia.

Dascyllus melanurus Bleeker, 1854   Pl. 78B
Black-tail dascyllus

SL: to 61 mm (2.4 in); D XII, 12-13; A II, 12-13; P 18-19; LP 15-19(16-17); GR 6-8+16-19.

This species differs from the similar *D. aruanus* by having a large black area over the outer two-thirds of its tail. It also occurs in aggregations associated with shallow lagoon branching corals, but is considerably less common than *D. aruanus* and often occurs with it.

West Pacific: Sumatra to Vanuatu, n. to the Ryukyus, s. to New Caledonia; Belau to Kosrae in Micronesia.

Dascyllus reticulatus (Richardson, 1846)   Pl. 78E
Reticulated dascyllus

SL: to 63 mm (2.5 in); D XII, 14-16(14-15); A II, 12-14 (13); P 19-21(20); LP 17-19(18); GR 6-8(7)+18-22(19-21).

This species inhabits outer lagoon and seaward reefs at depths of 1 to 50 m. It occurs in colonies associated with heads of branching corals, particularly *Pocillopora eydouxi*, and is one of the most common pomacentrids of exposed seaward reefs. It is somewhat less common in deep lagoons. Juveniles rarely occur in sheltered shallow lagoon areas, but never seem to survive there for long.

West-central Pacific: Cocos-Keeling Is. to Samoa and the Line Is., n. to s. Japan, s. to Rowley Shoals and Lord Howe Is.; throughout Micronesia.

Dascyllus trimaculatus (Rüppell, 1828)   Pl. 78C,D
Three-spot dascyllus

SL: to 110 mm (4.3 in); DXII, 14-16(14-15); A II, (14)-15; P19-21(19-20); LP17-20(18-19); GR6-8(6-7)+16-19(17-18).

The three-spot dascyllus inhabits lagoon and seaward reefs at depths of 1 to at least 55 m. It is much less common than *D. aruanus* and *D. reticulatus*. Juveniles are associated with large sea anemones which they share with species of *Amphiprion*. They possess the same ability to swim among the tentacles with impunity. Adults lose the white spots of the juveniles as well as their association with anemones. They typically occur in small groups around prominent coral mounds or isolated large rocks.

Indo-Pacific: Red Sea to the Line and Pitcairn Is., n. to s. Japan, s. to Lord Howe Is.; throughout Micronesia.

Subfamily Lepidozyginae

This subfamily contains a single species, a somewhat elongate aggregating planktivore with uniseral dentition and small papilla-like structures on the inner edge of the posterior circumorbitals.

Lepidozygus tapienosoma (Bleeker, 1856)   Pl. 78F
Fusilier damsel

SL: to 71 mm (2.8 in); D XII, 14-15; A II, 15-16; P 21-23; LP 19-20; GR 26-28.

This small elongate damselfish typically occurs in aggregations, often with *Anthias* species, above the upper edges of current-swept seaward reefs at depths of 1 to at least 18 m. Occasionally it occurs around lagoon patch reefs. It is not particularly common and often localized in distribution. In the Marianas, it seems to prefer offshore banks and is rare around the main islands.

Indo-Pacific: E. Africa to the Line, Marquesan, and Tuamotu Is., n. to the Ryukyus, s. to New Caledonia; throughout Micronesia.

Subfamily Pomacentrinae

This diverse subfamily contains the bulk of pomacentrid genera and species. They are orbiculate to elongate, possess conical or incisiform teeth in one or two rows, have smooth to serrated preopercles, and lack projecting spiniform rays on the upper and lower edges of the caudal base.

Cheiloprion labiatus (Day, 1877)   Pl. 78G
Big-lip damsel, Minstrel fish

SL: to 60 mm (2.4 in); D XIII, 13-14; A II, 13-14; P 17; LP 18; GR 16-17.

The white enlarged and curled back lips are distinctive, particularly in large individuals. Juveniles are dull orange while adults are dark brown. The unusual lips may be an adaptation to feeding on live coral polyps. This species is always found among beds of branching corals in shallow lagoon waters. The eggs which are attached to a dead coral branch are agggressively guarded.

Indo-west Pacific: Sri Lanka to the Solomons, n. to the Philippines, s. to Vanuatu and n. Australia; Belau in Micronesia.

Abudefduf lorenzi Hensley & Allen, 1977   Pl. 79A
Black-tail sergeant
(*Abudefduf* sp. Allen, 1975)

SL: to 150 mm (5.9 in); D XIII, 12-13; A II, 12-13; P 18; LP 20-22; GR 22-24.

The black blotch in the middle of the caudal fin base separates this from all other Micronesian *Abudefduf*. At Belau, this species is common along sheltered rocky shorelines of the rock islands as well as docks and piers to a depth of 6 m.

Indo-Australian: Philippines and Moluccas to the Solomons; Belau in Micronesia; the closely related *A. bengalensis* frome w. India and Taiwan to ne. Australia.

Abudefduf notatus (Day, 1869)   Pl. 79B
Yellow-tail sergeant

SL: to 130 mm (5.1 in); D XIII, 13-14; A II, 13-14; P 18; LP 19-21; GR 26-27.

This distinctive sergeant occurs in small groups along the upper edges of sheltered shear dropoffs. At Belau, a single tightly-knit group was observed over a three year span at Turtle Cove, south of the Ngemelis group. The group ranged widely along the reef margin at depths of .5 to 4 m and was difficult to approach.

Indo-west Pacific: E. Africa to New Britain, n. to s. Japan; Belau in Micronesia.

Abudefduf vaigiensis (Quoy & Gaimard, 1825)
Sergeant-major   Pl. 79C

(*A. saxatilis* (non-Linnaeus) of recent use in Indo-Pacific)

SL: to ca. 148 mm (5.8 in); D XIII, 11-13; A II, 11-13; P

18-19; LP 21-22; GR 8-9+18-21=25-28.

The sergeant-major occurs in aggregations in a variety of habitats ranging from rocky lagoon shorelines to reef flats, lagoon reef margins, and seaward reefs to a depth of 12 m. Juveniles often occur in tidepools. The sergeant-major is not particularly common and tends to be localized in distribution. It feeds on zooplankton, benthic algae, and small invertebrates.

Indo-Pacific: Red Sea to Samoa and the Marquesas (absent from the rest of Polynesia), n. to s. Japan, s. to Lord Howe Is.; throughout Micronesia.

Abudefduf septemfasciatus (Cuvier, 1830) Pl. 79D
Banded sergeant
SL: to ca. 170 mm (6.7 in); D XIII, 12-13; A II, 12-13; P 18-20; LP 20-22; GR 23-25.

This species lacks the black blotch on the top of the caudal peduncle of *S. sordidus*. Both species inhabit rocky lagoon and reef flat shorelines and piers in shallow areas exposed to mild surge. They feed on benthic algae and associated small invertebrates and are aggressively territorial.

Indo-Pacific: E. Africa to the Line and Tuamotu Is., n. to s. Japan, s. to the s. Great Barrier Reef; throughout Micronesia.

Abudefduf sexfasciatus (Lacepède, 1801) Pl. 79E
Scissor-tail sergeant
(*A. coelestinus*)
SL: to ca. 125 mm (4.9 in); D XIII, 12-14; A II, 12-14; P 17-19; LP 20-22; GR 7-9+18-19=22-27.

This is the only Micronesian sergeant with a dark longitudinal band on each caudal lobe. It is moderately common in coral rich areas along the upper portions of lagoon and seaward slopes to a depth of 12 m. It feeds on zooplankton and algae and aggregates high in the water column.

Indo-Pacific: Red Sea to the Tuamotus, n. to s. Japan, s. to Lord Howe and Rapa Is.; throughout Micronesia.

Abudefduf sordidus (Forsskål, 1775) Pl. 79F
Black-spot sergeant
SL: to ca. 170 mm (6.7 in); D XIII, 14-16; A II, 14-15; P 19-20; LP 20-23; GR 9-11+14-15=26-28.

Like *A. septemfasciatus*, this species inhabits rocky lagoon and reef flat shorelines and piers subject to mild surge. Juveniles are common in tidepools.

Indo-Pacific: Red Sea to the Hawaiian, Line, Marquesan, and Pitcairn Is., n. to s. Japan, s. to Lord Howe and Rapa Is.; throughout Micronesia.

Amblyglyphidodon aureus (Cuvier, 1830) Pl. 80A
Golden damsel
(*Abudefduf aureus*)
SL: to 100 cm (3.9 in); D XIII, 12-14; A II, 14-15; P 17; LP 16; GR 25-29.

The golden damsel typically inhabits steep outer reef slopes at depths of 15 to 45 m. Occasionally it occurs in deep lagoons and along channel walls. It is common along the precipitous dropoffs of southwestern Belau and may occur in as little as 3 m. It is rare in the Marianas. It generally occurs

in small loosely-knit aggregations that feed on zooplankton a few meters from the substrate. Juveniles often settle among large sea fans or black corals.

West-central Pacific: Christmas Is., Indian Ocean, to Fiji, n. to the Ryukyus, s. to Rowley Shoals and New Caledonia; throughout Micronesia.

Amblyglyphidodon curacao (Bloch, 1787) Pl. 80B
Staghorn damsel
(*Abudefduf curacao*)
SL: to 90 mm (3.5 in); D XIII, 12-13; A II, 13-15; P 17-18; LP 16-17; GR 25-27.

This is one of the most abundant pomacentrids of coral-rich areas of lagoons and sheltered bays at depths of 1 to 40 m. Juveniles often occur among *Sarcophyton* and *Sinularia* soft corals. Adults occur in large zooplankton-feeding aggregations that range high above the corals. They also feed on filamentous algae and its associated microfauna.

West-central Pacific: Malaysia to Samoa, n. to the Ryukyus, s. to Rowley Shoals and the s. Great Barrier Reef; throughout Micronesia.

Amblyglyphidodon leucogaster (Bleeker, 1847)
White-belly damsel Pl. 80C
SL: to >107 mm (4.2 in); D XIII, 12-13; A II, 12-14; P 16-18; LP 14-17; GR 7-9+17-20.

This species typically occurs singly or in small groups in coral rich areas of deep clear lagoons and seaward reefs at depths of 9 to 34 m.

Indo-Pacific: Red Sea to Samoa, n. to the Ryukyus, s. to the Great Barrier Reef; Belau, Carolines, and Marshalls in Micronesia.

Amblyglyphidodon ternatensis (Bleeker, 1853)
Ternate damsel Pl. 80D
SL: to 100 mm (3.9 in); D XIII, 11-12; A II, 12-13; P 15-16; LP 13-14; GR 27-30.

This species closely resembles subadult *A. curacao* with obscure stripes, but has a dusky upper caudal peduncle, a series of four light blotches along the base of the dorsal fin, and lower lateral line and pectoral ray counts. In Belau, it is common among the sheltered coastal reefs of the rock islands where it aggregates with *A. curacao*.

West Pacific: Indonesia to the Solomons, n. to the Ryukyus; Belau in Micronesia.

Chrysiptera biocellata (Quoy & Gaimard, 1824)
Two-spot demoiselle Pl. 80E
(*Abudefduf biocellatus*; *Glyphididontops biocellatus*)
SL: to 75 mm (3.0 in); D XIII, 12-14; A II, 13-14; P 17-19; LP 17; GR 23-25.

This drab damselfish inhabits protected inner reef flats and shallow lagoons and channels to a depth of 4 m. It is common among rubble and coral patch reefs of sandy areas. It is territorial and feeds mainly on filamentous algae.

Indo-Pacific: Chagos Is. to the Line Is., n. to the Ryukyus., s. to Rowley Shoals and New Caledonia; throughout Micronesia.

Chrysiptera caeruleolineata (Allen, 1973) Pl. 80F
Blue-line demoiselle

(*Glyphidodontops caeruleolineatus*)

SL: to 40 mm (1.6 in); D XIV., 11-13; A II, 13-14; P 15-16; LP 12-15; GR 20-23.

This striking little damselfish closely resembles the blue phase of *C. leucopoma*, but differs in several counts as well as details of coloration. It also occurs in much deeper water, exclusively along steep outer reef slopes at depths of 24 to 62 m. It occurs singly or in small groups in patches of rubble or near sand channels and feeds primarily on copepods.

West-central Pacific: Ryukyus and Rowley Shoals to Samoa; Guam and the Marshalls in Micronesia; absent from most Indo-Australian coastal reefs.

Chrysiptera cyanea (Quoy & Gaimard, 1825)
Blue devil Pl. 80G,H

(*Glyphidodontops cyaneus*)

SL: to 60 mm (2.4 in); D XIII, 12-13; A II, 13-14; P 16-17; LP 16-17; GR 17-19.

The stunning electric blue makes this among the most spectacular of reef fishes! It is one of the few damselfishes to display sexual dichromatism: juveniles and females usually possess a small black spot at the rear base of the dorsal fin and (at least in Micronesia) lack yellow; males have a bright yellow tail and lack the black spot. The blue devil is common among rubble and coral of clear sheltered lagoons and reef flats to a depth of 3 m, occasionally to 10 m. It occurs in groups of a male and several females or juveniles and feeds on algae, pelagic tunicates, and planktonic crustaceans. Males of the Philippine and Ryukyu populations lack the yellow tail.

West Pacific: Indonesia to Vanuatu, n. to the Ryukyus, s. to Rowley Shoals and New Caledonia; Belau and Yap in Micronesia; replaced by *C. taupou* in Fiji and Samoa.

Chrysiptera glauca (Cuvier, 1830) Pl. 81A
Gray demoiselle

(*Abudefduf glaucus*; *Glyphidodontops glaucus*)

SL: to 75 cm (3.0 in); D XIII, 12-13; A II, 11-13; P 18; LP 15-19; GR 21-24.

Juveniles are a brilliant blue, but are lighter in coloration and not nearly as spectacular as *C. cyaneus*. The blue gives way to a dull blueish-grey with growth. This species is common among rubble or consolidated reef rock of exposed intertidal reef flats and sandy beaches that are subject to mild surge. It occurs in small groups and feeds primarily on benthic algae.

Indo-Pacific: E. Africa to the Line and Pitcairn Is., n. to s. Japan, s. to ; throughout Micronesia.

Chrysiptera leucopoma (Lesson, 1830) Pl. 81B,C
Surge demoiselle

(*Abudefduf amabilis*; *A. leucopomus*; *Glyphidodontops leucopomus*)

SL: to 60 mm (2.4 in); D XIII, 12-13; A II, 11-13; P 17-19; LP 17-19; GR 17-21.

This species occurs in two basic color phases: a blue-backed (*leucopomus*) phase and a gray to black (*amabilis*) phase

usually with two light bars, but occasionally lacking all markings except a yellowish opercular patch. Intermediates are uncommon. The basis for this dichromatism remains unknown; it does not seem to be related to size or habitat. In the Marianas and Marshalls, the surge demoiselle is perhaps the most abundant fish of rubble-strewn surge channels, the outermost reaches of exposed reef flats, and the upper submarine terrace to a depth of 12 m. It is territorial but generally occurs in groups, and remains close to shelter and feeds primarily on benthic algae and small crustaceans.

Indo-Pacific: E. Africa to the Marquesan, Society, and Austral Is., n. to s. Japan, s. to New Caledonia; throughout Micronesia.

Chrysiptera oxycephala (Bleeker, 1877) Pl. 81D,E
Blue-spot demoiselle

(*Glyphidodontops azurepunctatus*)

SL: to 65 mm (2.6 in); D XIII, 11-12; A II, 12-13; P 15; LP 14-15; GR 30-34.

This species occurs among live coral of sheltered lagoon and inshore reefs at depths of 1 to 16 m. It aggregates a short distance above the coral to feed on zooplankton and is abundant among the rock islands of Belau.

Indo-Australian: Borneo, Philippines, New Guinea, and Belau.

Chrysiptera rex (Snyder, 1909) Pl. 81F
King demoiselle

(*Glyphidodontops rex*)

SL: to 55 mm (2.2 in); D XIII, 13-14; A II, 13-14; P 16-17; LP 16-17; GR 17-19.

At Belau, this somewhat drab demoiselle is an uncommon inhabitant of semi-protected areas of reef margins and upper edges of outer reef slopes to a depth of 6 m. It occurs singly or in small groups and feeds primarily on algae.

West Pacific: n. to the Izus, s. to Scott Reef and New Caledonia; Belau in Micronesia.

Chrysiptera talboti (Allen. 1973) Pl. 81G
Talbot's demoiselle

(*Glyphidodontops talboti*)

SL: to 45 mm (1.8 in); D XIII, 11-12; A II, 11-13; P 15-16; LP 14-16; GR 18-20.

This species is reported from outer reef slopes at depths of 6 to 35 m. It occurs singly or in small groups and feeds on zooplankton. It is known from Micronesia on the basis of the photograph herein which was taken in an area of rich coral growth along a steep outer reef slope.

West Pacific: Moluccas to Fiji, n. to Belau and New Britain, s. to the s. Great Barrier Reef; Belau in Micronesia.

Chrysiptera traceyi (Woods & Schultz, 1960)
Tracey's demoiselle Pl. 81H

(*Pomacentrus traceyi*; *Glyphidodontops traceyi*)

SL: to 45 mm (1.8 in); D XIII, 10-12; A II, 11-12; P 15-16; LP 14-16; GR 20-22.

In the Marianas this species is abundant in coral, rock, or rubble habitats of both lagoon and seaward reefs from below the effects of surge to a depth of 40 m. It is rare elsewhere in Micronesia. It occurs singly or in small groups that remain close to the bottom and probably feeds on algae and zooplankton.

Micronesia: all major island groups.

Chrysiptera unimaculata (Cuvier, 1830) Pl. 82A,B
One-spot demoiselle

SL: to 62 mm (2.4 in); D XIII, 13-14; A II, 12-14; P 18-19; LP 16-18; GR 22-23.

This species may resemble *C. biocellata* but never has a pale bar on its side and usually has more (19 vs 18) pectoral rays and more pored lateral line scales (18 vs 17 in upper series). It occurs singly or in small groups among rubble or over open beach-rock of reef flats exposed to moderate surge. It feeds primarily on benthic algae.

Indo-west Pacific: Red Sea to Fiji, n. to the Ryukyus, s. to the s. Great Barrier Reef; Belau in Micronesia.

Dischistodus chrysopoecilus
(Schlegel & Müller, 1839) Pl. 82D
White-spot damsel

SL: to 120 mm (4.7 in); D XIII, 14-15; A II, 13-14; P 17; LP 17; GR 22-24.

This rather drab species occurs among coral in silty areas of lagoon and coastal reefs at depths of 1.5 to 5 m.

Indo-Australian: Indonesia to the Solomons, n. to the Philippines; Belau and Yap in Micronesia.

Dischistodus melanotus (Bleeker,1858) Pl. 82C,E
Black-vent damsel

(*D. notophthalmus*)

SL: to 130 mm (5.1 in); D XIII, 13-15; A II, 13-14; P 17; LR 26; LP 15-17; GR 21-23.

This colorful "farmer fish" inhabits lagoon reefs at depths of 1 to 10 m (see *Stegastes* spp., p. 175). It generally occurs around small patch reefs on on sand or rubble and aggessively guards its territory against other herbivorous fishes.

West Pacific: Indonesia to the Solomons, n. to the Yaeyamas, s. to the Great Barrier Reef; Belau and Yap in Micronesia.

Dischistodus perspicillatus (Cuvier, 1830)
White damsel Pl. 82F,I

(*Pomacentrus bifasciatus*)

SL: to 160 mm (6.3 in); D XIII, 14-15; A II, 14-15; P 17-18; LP 17-18; GR 33-35.

This drab "farmer fish" inhabits small patch reefs of shallow lagoons to a depth of 10 m. Its behavior is similar to that of *D. melanotus*.

Indo-Australian: Andamans to the Solomons and Vanuatu, n. to s. China, s. to Rowley Shoals and the Great Barrier Reef; Belau and Yap in Micronesia.

Hemiglyphidodon plagiometopon (Bleeker, 1852)
Giant farmer fish Pl. 82J

SL: to 150 mm (5.9 in); D XIII, 14-15; A II, 14-15; P 16-17; LP 14-16; Gr 65-85.

Juveniles are orange-yellow posterioventrally and brown anterodorsally with numerous blue lines and spots on the face

and back. This large "farmer fish" inhabits protected lagoon and coastal reefs at depths of 1.5 to 20 m. It occurs among patches of large branching corals with dead algal-covered bases. Like certain species of *Stegastes* (p. 175), it is a territorial herbivore that "farms" algae by "weeding" out undesired species to promote the growth of desired ones.

Indo-Australian: Malaysia to the Solomons and Vanuatu, n. to s. China, s. to the Dampier Is. and Great Barrier Reef; Belau and Yap in Micronesia.

Neopomacentrus nemurus (Bleeker, 1857) Pl. 82G
Coral demoiselle

(*Neopomacentrus* sp. Allen, 1975)

SL: to 55 mm (2.2 in); D XIII, 11-12; A II, 11-12; P 16-17; LP 16-17; GR 21-22.

The genus *Neopomacentrus* is restricted to continental shorelines and nearby islands. This species inhabits silty areas of lagoon and coastal reefs at depths of 1 to 10 m where it aggregates above coral outcrops to feed on zooplankton.

Indo-Australian: Indonesia to the Solomons, n. to the Philippines and New Britain, s. to n. Australia and Vanuatu; Belau in Micronesia.

Neopomacentrus taeniurus (Bleeker, 1856)
Fresh-water demoiselle

SL: to 60 mm (2.4 in); D XIII, 11-12; A II, 11-12; P 16-17; LP 16-17; GR 21-23.

This species inhabits fresh and brackish water streams.

Indo-Australian: Indonesia to the Solomons, n. to the Philippines, s. to Vanuatu; Belau in Micronesia.

Neopomacentrus violascens (Bleeker, 1848)
Violet demoiselle Pl. 82H

SL: to 50 mm (2.0 in); D XIII, 11-12; A II, 10-11; P 17-18; LP 16-17; GR 20-22.

This species is actually more black than violet. In Micronesia it is known only from Apra Harbor, Guam where it was likely introduced by way of fouling on the hulls of naval barges towed from the Philippines. It is abundant around sponge-encrusted mooring bouys and their anchor lines to a depth of 30 m and occurs in smaller colonies around rocks and refuse.

Indo-Australian: Indonesia to the Solomons, n. to s. China, s. to n. Australia and Vanuatu; introduced to Guam in Micronesia.

Neoglyphidodon melas (Cuvier, 1830) Pl. 83A,B
Royal damsel (juv.); **Black damsel** (adult)

(*Paraglyphidodon melanopus* (juv.); *Paraglyphidodon melas*)

SL: to >131 mm (5.2 in); D XIII, 13-15; A II, 12-15(13-14); P 17-19; LP 15-18; GR 5-8+14-16=19-21.

Transformation from the colorful juvenile to the uniformly black adult stage occurs at a size of 50 to 65 mm. This species inhabits coral-rich areas of lagoon and seaward reefs to a depth of about 12 m. It occurs singly or in pairs and is usually associated with soft corals on which it feeds. It is not particularly common, and juveniles are more apt to be encountered around staghorn *Acropora* corals on lagoon reefs.

Indo-west Pacific: Red Sea to Vanuatu, n. to s. Japan, s. to

Scott Reef and the s. Great Barrier Reef; Belau and Yap in Micronesia.

Neoglyphidodon nigroris (Cuvier, 1830) Pl. 83C,D
Yellowfin damsel (adult)

(*Paraglyphidodon behni* (juv.); *Paraglyphidodon nigroris*)
SL: to 100 mm (3.9 in); D XIII, 14-16; A II, 13-15; P 17; LP 17; GR 24-16.
Transformation from the juvenile to the adult coloration occurs at about 40 mm. The yellowfin damsel inhabits coral-rich areas of lagoon and seaward reefs at depths of 2 to 23 m. It is usually solitary and feeds on algae, pelagic tunicates, salps, and crustaceans. At Belau it is relatively uncommon around the rock islands and windward outer reef slopes.
West Pacific: Java to Vanuatu, n. to the Ryukyus, s. to Scott Reef and the Great Barrier Reef; Belau in Micronesia.

Plectroglyphidodon dickii (Liénard, 1839) Pl. 83E
Dick's damsel

(*Abudefduf dickii*)
SL: to 85 mm (3.3 in); D XII, 16-18; A II, 14-16; P 18-19; LP 20-26; GR 16-19.
This species is a common in coral-rich, often surgy areas of clear lagoon and seaward reefs at depths of 1 to 12 m. It is a solitary territorial inhabitant of robustly branching *Pocillopora* or *Acropora* corals. It feeds on filamentous algae, small benthic invertebrates, and occasionally on small fishes.
Indo-Pacific: E. Africa to the Line, Marquesan, and Tuamotu Is., n. to s. Japan, s. to Lord Howe Is.; throughout Micronesia.

Plectroglyphidodon imparipennis
(Vaillant & Sauvage, 1875) Pl. 83F
Bright-eye damsel

(*Abudefduf imparipennis*)
SL: to 45 mm (1.8 in); D XII, 14-15; A II, 11-12; P 20; LP 19-22; GR 10-12.
This skittish little fish occurs exclusively in the surge zone of seaward reefs to a depth of about 6 m. It is a territorial omnivore of benthic algae and small invertebrates. It always remains close to the shelter of small holes or sea urchin furrows in bare rock.
Indo-Pacific: E. Africa to the Hawaiian, Marquesan, and Pitcairn Is., n. to the Ryukyu and Bonin Is., s. to New Caledonia and Rapa; throughout Micronesia.

Plectroglyphidodon johnstonianus
Fowler & Ball, 1924 Pl. 83G,H
Johnston Island damsel

(*Abudefduf johnstonianus*)
SL: to 70 mm (2.8 in); D XII, 17-19; A II, 16-18; P 19; LP 21-22; GR 11-14.
In addition to the normal color phase, an uncommon light phase which lacks the dark area posteriorly occurs in Micronesia. This species is fairly common on shallow exposed seaward reefs to a depth of 18 m. It is solitary and territorial, with each territory encompassing a few closely spaced *Acropora*, *Pocillopora*, or *Stylophora* coral heads, or a single

large head of *Pocillopora eydouxi*. It feeds on benthic algae and probably on coral polyps.
Indo-Pacific: E. Africa to the Hawaiian, Marquesan, and Pitcairn Is., n. to the Ryukyu and Bonin Is., s. to Lord Howe and Rapa Is.; throughout Micronesia.

Plectroglyphidodon lacrymatus
(Quoy & Gaimard, 1825) Pl. 84A
Jewel damsel

(*Abudefduf lacrymatus*)
SL: to 85 mm (3.3 in); D XII, 16-18; A II, 13-14, P 18-20; LP 17-21; GR 8-11+12-14=20-23.
Juveniles have brighter and more numerous blue spots. The jewel damsel is a common inhabitant of areas of mixed coral and rubble or dead coral rock of clear lagoon and seaward reefs at depths of 1 to 40 m. It is a somewhat pugnacious territorial omnivore that occupies algae-covered substrates between coral heads and feeds primarily on benthic algae and associated small invertebrates and fish eggs.
Indo-Pacific: Red Sea to the Marquesan, Society, and Austral Is., n. to the Ryukyus., s. to Lord Howe Is.; throughout Micronesia.

Plectroglyphidodon leucozonus leucozonus
(Bleeker, 1859) Pl. 84B
White-band damsel

(*Abudefduf leucozona*)
SL: to 90 mm (3.5 in); D XII, 15-17; A II, 12-13; P 19-21; LP 20-21; GR 15-18.
Juveniles have a conspicuous dorsal ocellus behind a wide white band; large adults are uniformly dirty bronze. This active damselfish is a common inhabitant of surge-swept shorelines and seaward reef margins to a depth of 3 m. Juveniles often occur in pockets of the intertidal reef crest while adults occupy the ridges between surge channels. They are territorial herbivores of benthic algae.
Indo-Pacific: E. Africa to the Marquesan and Pitcairn Is., n. to s. Japan; s. to Lord Howe and Rapa Is.; throughout Micronesia; the subspecies *P. l. cingulum* from the Red Sea.

Plectroglyphidodon phoenixensis (Schultz, 1943)
Phoenix Islands damsel Pl. 84C

(*Abudefduf phoenixensis*)
SL: to 70 mm (2.8 in); D XII, 16-17; A II, 13-14; P 20-21; LP 21-22; GR 14-16.
This damselfish occurs exclusively in the surge zone of seaward reef margins to a depth of 3 m, but is not as common as *P. leucozonus*. It is a solitary territorial herbivore that remains in or near patches of *Acropora* or *Pocillopora* corals.
Indo-Pacific: Mauritius to the Line and Tuamotu Is., n. to the Ryukyus; Marianas and Marshalls in Micronesia; strays to main Hawaiian Is.; absent from continental shelf reefs.

Pomacentrus amboinensis Bleeker, 1868 Pl. 84D,E
Ambon damsel

SL: to 80 mm (3.1 in); D XIII, 14-16; A II, 14-16; P 17; LP 16-17; GR 22-24.
The Ambon damselfish ranges in color from a light tan or lavender-yellow to a dark chocolate brown. In the Marianas,

the Ambon damsel is relatively common on sheltered lagoon reefs at depths of 3 to 40 m, and occasionally occurs on seaward reefs at depths of 20 to over 40 m. It typically occurs in aggregations a short distance above isolated patch reefs or reefs bordering open sand.

West-central Pacific: Indonesia to Vanuatu, n. to the Ryukyus, s. to Scott Reef and New Caledonia; throughout Micronesia.

Pomacentrus nagasakiensis Tanaka, 1917   Pl. 84F
Speckled-fin damsel; Nagasaki damsel
(*Pomacentrus* species Allen, 1975; *P. arenarius*)
SL: to 80 mm (3.1 in); D XIII, 15-16; A II, 15-16; P 18-19; LP 17-19; GR 19-21.

This dark brown to black species usually has several rows of pale spots on the soft dorsal, anal, and caudal fins and a pale tail. It is reported from sandy areas of both lagoon and seaward reefs at depths of 3 to 35 m and feeds primarily on zooplankton well above the bottom.

Indo-west Pacific: Sri Lanka to Vanuatu, n. to s. Japan; s. to nw Australia and New Caledonia; Belau in Micronesia.

Pomacentrus bankanensis Bleeker, 1853   Pl. 84G
Speckled damsel
SL: to 70 mm (2.8 in); D XIII, 15-16; A II, 15-16; P 18; LP 17-19; GR 20-22.

This species closely resembles *P. vaiuli*, but differs by having an abruptly white tail, a blueish mid-dorsal stripe on the snout, interorbital and forehead, and in having a generally more reddish ground color. At Belau, it is relatively common among patches of rubble with scattered live corals on clear lagoon and semi-protected seaward reefs at depths of 1 to 12 m. It occurs in small groups and feeds primarily on algae and to a lesser extent on planktonic crustaceans and pelagic tunicates.

West Pacific: Christmas Is., Indian Ocean, to Fiji, n. to s. Japan, s. to Rowley Shoals and New Caledonia; Belau and Yap in Micronesia.

Pomacentrus brachialis (Cuvier, 1830)
Charcoal damsel   Pl. 84H; Fig. 3
(*P. melanopterus*)
SL: to 80 mm (3.1 in); D XIII, 13-15; A II, 14-15; P 16-17; LP 16-17; GR 19-21.

This species is reported from passages and outer reef slopes at depths of 6 to 40 m. It occurs singly or in groups and feeds on zooplankton and benthic algae.

West-central Pacific: Indonesia to Fiji, n. to the Ryukyus, s. to New Caledonia; Kapingamarangi and Marshalls in Micronesia.

Fig. 3. Anterior region of *P. brachialis* showing black pectoral fin base.

Pomacentrus burroughi Fowler, 1918   Pl. 85A
Burrough's damsel
SL: to 65 mm (2.6 in); D XIII, 15-16; A II, 15-16; P 16-17; LP 14-16; GR 24-25.

This drab damsel inhabits lagoon and coastal reefs at depths of 2 to 16 m. It occurs singly or in small groups and feeds primarily on benthic algae.

Indo-Australian: Philippines, New Guinea, Solomon Is., and Belau.

Pomacentrus coelestis Jordan & Starks, 1901
Neon damsel   Pl. 85C,D
SL: to 70 mm (2.8 in); D XIII, 13-15; A II, 14-15; P 17-18; LP 17-18; GR 20-22.

This brilliant blue damsel has more yellow ventrally than *P. pavo* and occurs in a different habitat. It typically aggregates close to the bottom among rubble beds of lagoon and seaward reefs at depths of 1 to 12 m. It feeds primarily on zooplankton and to a lesser extent on benthic algae.

West-central Pacific: Christmas Is., Indian Ocean, to the Line and Tuamotu Is., n. to s. Japan, s. to Rowley Shoals and Lord Howe Is.; Belau to the e. Carolines and Marshalls in Micronesia.

Pomacentrus chrysurus Cuvier, 1830   Pl. 85B
White-tail damsel
(*P. rhodonotus*; *P. flavicauda*?)
SL: to 65 mm (2.6 in); D XIII, 14-16; A II, 15-16; P 18; LP 18-19; GR 18-19.

This species inhabits reef flats and shallow lagoons to a depths of 3 m. It typically occurs singly or in small groups around rocky outcrops surrounded by sand and feeds primarily on algae.

West Pacific: Christmas Is., Indian Ocean, to the Solomons, n. to the Ryukyus, s. to New Caledonia; Belau in Micronesia.

Pomacentrus emarginatus Cuvier, 1830   Pl. 85E
Outer-reef damsel
SL: to 75 mm (3.0 in); D XIII, 14; A II, 13-14; P 18; LP 17-18; GR 23-24.

This somber damsel inhabits the upper edges of steep outer reef slopes at depths of 4 to 12 m. It is not uncommon along the leeward dropoffs of Belau. It occurs singly or in small groups and feeds on zooplankton and algae.

Indo-Australian: Waigeo (off w. New Guinea) and Belau.

Pomacentrus grammorhynchus Fowler, 1918
Blue-spot damsel   Pl. 85F,G
SL: to 80 mm (3.1 in); D XIII, 14-15; A II, 14-15; P 17-18; LP 16-17; GR 26-30.

The blue spot on top of the caudal peduncle is distinctive. Juveniles closely resemble juveniles of *P. simsiang*, but that species lacks the blue spot. This damselfish typically lives among branching corals in lagoons and passages at depths of 2 to 12 m. It occurs singly or in small groups and feeds primarily on benthic algae.

Indo-Australian: Philippines, New Guinea, Rowley Shoals,

Great Barrier Reef, and Belau, Truk, and Pohnpei in Micronesia.

Pomacentrus moluccensis Bleeker, 1853   Pl. 85H
Lemon damsel
(*P. popei*, Allen, 1974)
SL: to 55 mm (2.2 in); D XIII, 14-15; A II, 14-15; P 17; LP 17-18; GR 23-24.
This uniformly yellow *Pomacentrus* typically occurs in small groups among branching corals of clear lagoons and seaward reefs at depths of 1 to 14 m. It feeds primarily on algae and planktonic crustaceans.
West Pacific: Indonesia to Fiji, n. to the Ryukyus, s. to Rowley Shoals and New Caledonia; Belau and Yap in Micronesia.

Pomacentrus nigromanus Weber, 1913   Pl. 86A
Black-axil damsel
(*P. alexanderae* Allen, 1975)
SL: to 70 mm (2.8 in); D XIII, 13-14; A II, 14-15; P 17; LP 16-17; GR 20-22.
This species is reported from both lagoon and seaward reefs at depths of 6 to 60 m. At Belau, it is relatively common among the rock islands where it aggregates in small groups above hard or soft coral-encrusted slopes. It feeds on planktonic crustaceans, fish eggs, algae, and small invertebrates.
Indo-Australian: Indonesia to the Solomons, s. to n. Australia and Vanuatu; Belau in Micronesia; the closely related *P. alexanderae* from the Philippines and Ryukyus.

Pomacentrus pavo (Bloch, 1787)   Pl. 86B,C
Sapphire damsel
SL: to 85 mm (3.3 in); D XIII, 13-14; A II, 12-14; P 17; LP 16-17; GR 23-24.
This deep blue damselfish is a common inhabitant of sandy areas of lagoon reefs at depths of 1.5 to at least 12 m. It typically occurs in aggregations around isolated patch reefs, coral heads, or rubble. It generally remains close to shelter and feeds on zooplankton and filamentous algae. It is abundant around the shallower wrecks of Truk Lagoon. There large males are an unusually deep blue with intense yellow pectoral fins and no yellow on the tail.
Indo-Pacific: E. Africa to the Tuamotus, n. to the Marianas and Marshalls, s. to Lord Howe Is.; throughout Micronesia.

Pomacentrus philippinus Evermann & Seale, 1907
Philippine damsel   Pl. 86D,E
SL: to 80 mm SL (3.1 in); D XIII, 14-15; A II, 14-16; P 18-19; LP 17-18; GR 23-24.
Juveniles have yellow vertical fins and a purplish cast on the body. This damselfish inhabits lagoons, steep-sided channels, and seaward reefs at depths of 2 to over 12 m. It typically occurs in loose aggregations off the sides of vertical drops and overhanging ledges. It is relatively common at Pohnpei and Kosrae but is not known elsewhere in Micronesia.
West Pacific: Philippines to Fiji, n. to the Ryukyus, s. to Rowley Shoals and New Caledonia; Pohnpei and Kosrae in Micronesia.

Pomacentrus reidi Fowler & Bean, 1928   Pl. 86F
Reid's damsel
SL: to 90 mm 3.5 in); D XIII, 13-15; A II, 15-16; P 17-18; LP 16-17; GR 19-21.
This relatively deep-bodied *Pomacentrus* inhabits steep outer reef slopes at depths of 12 to 70 m. It is generally solitary, but common along the steep dropoffs of leeward Belau.
Indo-Australian: Philippines and Celebes to the Solomons and Vanuatu, s. to Rowley Shoals (?) and the Great Barrier Reef; Belau in Micronesia.

Pomacentrus simsiang Bleeker, 1856   Pl. 86G
Blueback damsel
(*P. moluccensis* Allen, 1975)
SL: to 70 mm (2.8 in); D XIII, 14-16; A II, 14-15; P 17; LP 16-17; GR 21-23.
This species lacks the distinctive blue spot on ther upper caudal peduncle of the very similar *P. grammorhynchus*. The brilliant blue dorsal markings of juveniles become thinner and less intense with growth. This species inhabits somewhat turbid areas of lagoon and coastal reefs to a depth of 10 m. It occurs singly or in small groups and feeds primarily on benthic algae.
West Pacific: Philippines and Moluccas to the Solomons, n. to the Ryukyus, s. to Vanuatu; Belau to Truk in Micronesia.

Pomacentrus sp. 1   Pl. 86H
Dusky damsel
(*P. taeniometopon* Allen, 1975)
SL: to 60 mm (2.4 in); D XIII, 15-16; A II, 14-15; P 17; LP 17; GR 21-22.
This damselfish is reported from lagoon and seaward reefs at depths of 2 to 8 m. It occurs singly or in small groups among branching corals or alcyonarians and feeds primarily on benthic algae. At Belau, it was occasionally observed on shallow reefs among the rock islands.
Indo-Australian: Indonesia to Vanuatu, s. to New Caledonia; Belau in Micronesia.

Pomacentrus vaiuli Jordan & Seale, 1906 Pl. 87A,B
Princess damsel
SL: to 70 mm (2.8 in); D XIII, 15-16; A II, 15-16; P 17-18; LP 17-18; GR 20-21.
The background color of this species is quite variable ranging from a light tan to a deep blue or dark brownish purple. In the Mariana and Marshall Islands, it is one of the most ubiquitous and common damselfishes. It occurs on both lagoon and seaward reefs from the lower surge zone to a depth of 40 m. It is generally a solitary inhabitant of areas of mixed coral and rubble that feeds on filamentous algae and small invertebrates.
West-central Pacific: Moluccas to Samoa, n. to the Izus, s. to Rowley Shoals and New Caledonia; throughout Micronesia.

Pomachromis exilis (Allen & Emery, 1972) Fig. 4
Slender reef-damsel

SL: to 60 mm (2.4 in); D XIV, 12-13; A II, 12-13; P 19; LP 17-18; GR 22-24.

This species is light green with a distinctive elongate dark blotch on the upper caudal peduncle and large black spot on the upper pectoral axil. It is an aggregating planktivore of lagoon and seaward reefs at depths of 8 to 12 m.
Truk and Enewetak.

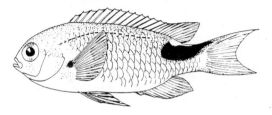

Fig. 4. *Pomacentrus exilis.*

Pomachromis guamensis Allen & Larson, 1975
Guam damsel   Pl. 87C
SL: to 60 mm (2.4 in).see UG collection; D XIV, 12-13; A II, 13; P 18-19; LP 17; GR 21.

The Guam damsel is one of the few fish species endemic to the Marianas. It inhabits exposed seaward reefs at depths of 3 to 33 m. Throughout the chain, it is one of the most abundant fishes on relatively barren gently sloping terraces with scattered low-profile corals. It is a zooplanktivore that occurs in large aggregations one to two meters above the substrate.
Marianas

Stegastes albifasciatus (Schlegel & Müller, 1839)
White-bar gregory   Pl. 87D,E
(*Pomacentrus albofasciatus*; *Eupomacentrus albofasciatus*)
SL: to 88 mm 3.5 in); D XII, 15-16; A II, 12-13; P 19-20; LP 18-20; GR +11-15=19-26.

Most Micronesian *Stegastes* are rather drab but variable in coloration and superficially resemble one another. *Stegastes albifasciatus* is the only one with blue-centered scales on the body. Juveniles have a blue-ridged white bar in front of a black spot at the posterior base of the dorsal fin. Subadults and adults often bear two wide pale bands on the sides. *S. albifasciatus* inhabits reef flats, shallow lagoons, and semi-sheltered reef margins to a depth of 4 m. It is common around patches of rubble or porous reef rock surrounded by live coral, particularly in areas of mild surge. It is a territorial herbivore, but is not as aggressive as *S. lividus* or *nigricans*, and does not seem to actively "farm" algae.
Indo-Pacific: Seychelles and Reunion to the Line and Tuamotu Is., n. to the Ryukyus; s. to New Caledonia; throughout Micronesia.

Stegastes fasciolatus (Ogilby, 1889)   Pl. 87F
Pacific gregory
(*Pomacentrus jenkinsi*; *Eupomacentrus fasciolatus*)
SL: to 121 mm (4.8 in); D XIII, 15-17; A II, 12-14(12-13); P 19-21; LP 19-21(20); GR +10-13=15-19.

This is the only Micronesian species of *Stegastes* with XIII dorsal spines. Juveniles usually have blue-bordered dorsal and anal fins. This species is common on shallow seaward reefs exposed to mild to moderate surge at depths of 0.5 to 10 m. Its feeding territory consists of a patch of filamentous algae-covered reef rock with suitable shelter in the form of holes or coral. It is not known whether or not it actively "farms" algae.
Indo-Pacific: E. Africa to Easter Is., n. to the Ryukyu and Hawaiian Is., s. to Lord Howe Is.; throughout Micronesia.

Stegastes lividus (Bloch & Schneider, 1801)
Blunt snout gregory; Farmerfish   Pl. 87G
(*Pomacentrus lividus*;*Eupomacentrus lividus*)
SL: to 127mm (5.0 in); D XII, 14-16(15-16); A II, 12-14 (12-13); P 18-19; LP 17-20; GR +15-19=23-29.

Juveniles are brown with a diffuse black blotch with lavender speckles on the rear base of the dorsal fin; adults loose the lavender speckles and range from a light grayish brown to black in color. This is the largest and most pugnacious Micronesian species of *Stegastes*. It is common on reef flats and shallow lagoons, wherever staghorn *Acropora* corals occur. Occasionally, it occurs among piles of rocks. Juveniles inhabit small isolated coral patches or the fringes of larger patches and feed heavily on small invertebrates as well as filamentous algae. Adults typically occur in groups in larger thickets of coral in which the innermost and lower bases of the branches have died and are covered with a luxuriant growth of filamentous algae. Each fish "farms" its patch of algae by "weeding", that is, removing, undesired species and aggressively defending the area from all intruders of any size. It is even known to charge and nip humans!
Indo-Pacific: Red Sea to the Line and Society Is., n. to the Ryukyu and Bonin Is., s. to New Caledonia and Tonga; throughout Micronesia.

Stegastes nigricans (Lacepède, 1803)   Pl. 87H
Dusky farmerfish
(*Pomacentrus nigricans*; *Eupomacentrus nigricans*)
SL: to 115 mm (4.5 in); D XII, 14-17(15-17); A II, 12-14 (13); P 18-20; LP 18-20; GR +10-15=21-25.

This species closely resembles *S. lividus*, but always has a well-defined rather than diffuse black blotch at the rear base of the dorsal fin. It also ranges from a light gray or brown to black in color. It is common on reef flats and lagoon reefs to a depth of 10 m. It is also an extremely pugnacious territorial "farmer fish". It's territories occur within patches of a variety of branching corals such as *Porites rus* as well as within staghorn *Acropora*.
Indo-Pacific: Red Sea to the Line, Marquesan, and Tuamotu Is., n. to the Ryukyu and Bonin Is., s. to New Caledonia and Tonga; throughout Micronesia.

LABRIDAE (WRASSES)

Wrasses are perhaps the most diverse of reef fishes in terms of size and form. They are also the second most speciose family of Indo-Pacific fishes, exceeded only by the gobies. Wrasses have a terminal mouth usually with somewhat thickened lips and one or more pairs of protruding canine teeth, nodular pharyngeal teeth (located in the throat in the gill region), moderately to greatly elongate bodies with cycloid scales, a continuous or interrupted lateral line, a single unnotched dorsal fin with VIII to XIV spines, and anal fin with II (rarely) to III spines. Most species have complex and often brilliant color patterns that change with growth or sex. Sex-reversal appears to be universal. All of the genera and species thus far studied are protogynous hermaphrodites in which females have the capacity to turn into males. Most species have an initial phase consisting either entirely of females or of both females and non-sex-reversing males, and a brightly colored terminal phase consisting of males that were once females. Wrasses are pelagic spawners: initial phase males spawn in large groups, terminal males are usually territorial and successively pair spawn with females of their choice. Most wrasses are carnivores of benthic invertebrates or fishes, but some are planktivores, corallivores, or cleaners that feed on the ectoparasites of other fishes. All wrasses are inactive at night; most of the smaller species sleep beneath the sand. The 96 known species of Micronesian labrids belong to three subfamilies and two suprageneric groups of unresolved status. (Lit.: Allen, 1973; Kuiter and Randall, 1981; Lobel, 1981; Randall, 1972a, 1974a, 1976, 1978, 1980c, 1981a, 1981e, 1982, 1983a; Randall and Edwards, 1984; Randall and Helfman, 1972; Randall and Smith, 1982; Randall and Springer, 1973, 1975)

Subfamily Bodianinae

Members of this subfamily share the following characteristics: XI-XIV, 6-11 dorsal rays; A III, 8-13 anal rays; 15-21 pectoral rays; lateral line continuous, smoothly curved with 24-57 scales; at least one pair of canines in front of each jaw; preopercular edge finely serrated. Most species undergo major changes in color with age and sex. All are carnivores of benthic invertebrates. Two species not covered, *Bodianus tanyokidus* and *Polylepion russelli*, occur at depths of over 100 m.

Bodianus anthioides (Bennett, 1831) Pl. 88A
Lyretail hogfish
SL: to ca. 240 mm (9.4 in), os to 152 mm (6.0 in); D XII, 9-(10); A III, 10-(12); P 15-17; LL 29-31(+2 on c); GR 4+12; depth 2.65-2.9.
This spectacular wrasse has an unusually large tail and undergoes relatively minor changes in color with growth. It is rare throughout Micronesia and is usually found along steep outer reef slopes deeper than 25 m. Elsewhere, it inhabits seaward reefs at depths of 6 to 60 m.
Indo-Pacific: Red Sea to the Line and Tuamotu Is., n. to s. Japan, s. to New Caledonia and the Australs; e. Carolines, Marianas, and Marshalls in Micronesia.

Bodianus axillaris (Bennett, 1831) Pl. 88C,D
Axilspot hogfish
SL: to 157 mm (6.2 in); D XII, 9-10; A III, (12)-13; P 15-17; LL 29-31; GR 5+12=15-18; depth 2.9-3.25.
This small hogfish undergoes a dramatic change in color with growth, but the sexes remain similar. Juveniles closely resemble juvenile *B. mesothorax*, but have white rather than yellow spots. The axilspot hogfish is a solitary inhabitant of clear lagoon and seaward reefs at depths of 2 to 40 m. Juveniles are usually found in caves or under ledges and sometimes act as cleaners, picking at the bodies and fins of other fishes.

Indo-Pacific: Red Sea to the Line, Marquesan, and Pitcairn Is., n. to s. Japan, s. to Lord Howe and Rapa; throughout Micronesia.

Bodianus bimaculatus Allen, 1973 Fig. 1
Two-spot slender hogfish
SL: to 50 mm (2.0 in); D XII, 9-10; A III, 12; P 14-16; LL 30-32 (+2 on c); GR 14-16; depth 3.6-3.9.
This small hogfish inhabits steep outer reef slopes at depths of 30 to 60 m.
West Pacific: New Guinea, New Britain, s. Japan, and Belau.

Fig. 1. *Bodianus bimaculatus*, ca. 50 mm.

Bodianus diana (Lacepède, 1801) Pl. 88E,F
Diana's hogfish
SL: to 210 mm (8.3 in), rarely >150 mm; D XII, 9-10; A III, 10-12; P 15-17; LL 30-31; GR 5+10=15-18; depth 3.1-3.3.
This hogfish inhabits coral-rich areas of seaward reefs at depths of 6 to 25 m. It is relatively common along steep outer reef slopes of Belau, but becomes extremely rare further east. Juveniles often shelter near black corals and gorgonians.
Indo-Pacific: Red Sea to Samoa, n. to s. Japan, s. to New Caledonia and Tonga; Belau and Kwajalein in Micronesia; replaced by the longer snouted *B. prognathus* in the Line Is. and by *B. nielli* in Sri Lanka and the w. Indian Ocean.

Bodianus loxozonus loxozonus (Snyder, 1908)
Blackfin hogfish Pl. 88B; Fig. 2
SL: to 385 SL (15.2 in); D XII, 9-11; A III, 12; P 16-17;

LL 31-32; GR 6-7+12-14; depth 2.65-2.9.

This large hogfish is a rarely encountered inhabitant of clear lagoon and seaward reefs at depths of 3 to over 40 m. It is known from the Marianas on the basis of a single male specimen taken from the edge of Galvez Banks.

West-central Pacific: Vietnam to Tonga, n. to the Ryukyu and Bonin Is.; Marianas and Marshalls in Micronesia; replaced by the subspecies *trotteri* in the Line, Marquesan, Society, Tuamotu, and Rapa Is.; closely related to *B. bilunulatus* and *B. macrourus*.

Fig. 2. *Bodianus loxozonus*, male, mm, Guam.

Bodianus mesothorax (Schneider, 1801) Pl. 88G,H
Mesothorax hogfish

SL: to ca. 160 mm (6.3 in); D XII, 9-10; A III, 11-12; P 16; LL 30-32; GR 4+12.

Both the juvenile and adult phases of this species resemble their counterparts of *B. axillaris*, but juveniles are yellow-spotted rather than white-spotted and adults have a well-defined black band separating the dark and light portions of the body above the pectoral axil and a light throat, and lack ocelli on the dorsal and anal fins. At Belau, this species occurs along coral-rich steep outer reef slopes at depths of 5 to over 20 m, particularly in the vicinity of caves, but is much less common than *B. axillaris*.

West Pacific: Christmas Is., Indian Ocean, Indonesia, Philippines, n. to s. Japan, s. to the Great Barrier Reef; Belau in Micronesia.

Choerodon anchorago (Bloch, 1791) Pl. 89A;
Yellow-cheeked tuskfish Fig. 2

SL: to 300 mm (11.8 in); D XII-XIII, 7; A III, 7-9; P 15-16; LL 26-30; GR 5-6+9=14-15.

Species of *Choerodon*, popularly known as tuskfishes, have relativley deep bodies with a steep head profile and a pair of greatly enlarged canine teeth in the front of the jaws (Fig. 3). Unlike most species of *Bodianus*, their color does not change greatly with age or sex. Most species are confined to the greater Indo-Australian region and only *C. anchorago* penetrates western Micronesia. Tuskfishes typically occur around rubbly or sandy areas and use their large teeth for picking up rocks as they search for prey. They feed primarily on benthic crustaceans. *C. anchorago* inhabits seagrass beds and areas of mixed coral, rubble, and sand of reef flats, channels, and lagoons to a depth of 25 m. At Belau, it aggregates to spawn along the outer edge of fringing reefs around the new and full moons of January to March.

Indo-west Pacific: Sri Lanka to New Guinea, n. to the Ryukyus, s. to New Caledonia; Belau and Yap in Micronesia.

Fig. 3. Dentition of *Choerodon*.

Subfamily Pseudodacinae

The single species comprising this subfamily has unique dentition in which the anterior teeth in each jaw are coalesced into a pair of chisel-like incisors and the teeth in the sides of the jaws are coalesced into a bony ridge.

Pseudodax moluccanus (Valenciennes, 1839)
Chiseltooth wrasse Pl. 89B,C

SL: to 204 mm (8.0 in); D XI, 12; A III, 14; P 15; LL continuous, 30-31 (+2 on c); GR 16-19; depth 2.5-2.7.

Pseudodax is relatively rare in Micronesia, where it occurs primarily in coral-rich areas of outer lagoon channels and seaward reefs at depths of 3 to 40 m. The distinctive juveniles seem to prefer somewhat deeper water and were observed only along the steep outer walls of leeward Belau below 18 m.

Indo-Pacific: Red Sea to the Society, Marquesan, and Tuamotu Is., n. to s. Japan; throughout Micronesia except n. Marshalls.

Subfamily Cheilininae

Members of this subfamily have an interrupted lateral line with the anterior section running dorsally and the posterior section along the axis of the caudal peduncle. Its members range in size from the tiny *Wetmorella albofasciata* (4.6 cm) to the enormous *Cheilinus undulatus* (229 cm). Most species feed on benthic invertebrates; species of *Cirrhilabrus* and *Paracheilinus* are planktivores.

Cheilinus arenatus Valenciennes, 1840 Pl. 89D
Arenatus wrasse

SL: to 158 mm (6.2 in); D IX, 10; A III, 8; P 12; LP 16+6(+ 2 on c); GR 12; depth 2.8.

Species of *Cheilinus* have relatively large scales, large canine teeth in the front of the jaws, and do not change greatly in color with growth or sex. This slender *Cheilinus* inhabits caves of steep outer reef dropoffs at depths of 25 to over 46 m. In the Marianas it has only been observed inside Guam's "Blue Hole" off Orote Peninsula.

Indo-Pacific: Red Sea to Samoa, n. to the Philippines; throughout Micronesia.

Cheilinus bimaculatus Valenciennes, 1840 Pl. 89E
Twospot wrasse

SL: to 117 mm (4.6 in), ♂ ≥53 mm; D IX, 9-11; A III, 8; P (12)-13; LL 14-16+5-7; GR 12-16; depth 2.6-3.1.

This small *Cheilinus* occurs among rubble or clumps of algae in relatively "dead" areas of outer reef slopes or deep, clear lagoons. It has been recorded from the depths of 2 to 110 m, but is rare in less than 15 m, and rare in Micronesia.

Indo-Pacific: E. Africa to the Hawaiian and Marquesan Is., n. to s. Japan, s. to Vanuatu; throughout Micronesia.

Cheilinus celebecus Bleeker, 1853   Pl. 88F
Celebes wrasse

SL: to ca. 200 mm (7.9 in); D IX, 10; A III, 8; P 12; LL 14-15+7-8; GR 3-4+8=11-12.

The concave head profile of this species is similar to that of *C. oxycephalus*, but its coloration is distinctive. In Micronesia, it is a rare inhabitant of coral-rich areas of protected lagoon reefs.

West-central Pacific: Moluccas to the Solomons, n. to s. Japan, s. to Rowley Shoals; Belau to e. Carolines and Marshalls in Micronesia.

Cheilinus chlorourus (Bloch, 1791)   Fig. 90A,B
Floral wrasse

SL: to ca. 230 mm (9.1 in); D X, 8-9; A III, 8; P 12; LL 14-16+5-9; GR 5-7+6-7=11-13; depth 2.3-2.8.

This is the only *Cheilinus* that normally has X dorsal spines. It is similar in coloration to *C. trilobatus*. Both are highly variable in shade and intensity and may possess light and dark blotches, but *C. chlorourus* always has black and white specks on its body and a dusting of white specks on its pelvic, anal, and caudal fins, while *C. trilobatus* has vertical red, white, and black streaks on its body scales. Large adults of both species have numerous red spots and streaks on the head and a trilobed tail. *C. chlorourus* is moderately common in areas of mixed sand, rubble, and coral of lagoon reefs at depths of 2 to at least 30 m. It feeds on benthic invertebrates including molluscs, crustaceans, polychaetes, and sea urchins.

Indo-Pacific: E. Africa to the Marquesan, and Tuamotu Is., n. to the Ryukyus, s. to New Caledonia and Rapa; throughout Micronesia.

Cheilinus digrammus (Lacepède, 1801)   Pl. 90C
Bandcheek wrasse

SL: to 255 mm (10.0 in); D IX, 10; A III, 8; P 12; LL 14-16+7-9; GR 5-7+9-10=15-16; depth 2.8-3.3.

This species differs from the very similar *C. unifasciatus* by always lacking the white bar in front of the caudal base as well as the area clear of red streaks extending from the eye to just above the pectoral axil (Fig. 4). *C. digrammus* inhabits coral-rich areas of lagoon and sheltered seaward reefs at depths of 3 to possibly 120 m. It is common from Belau to the e. Carolines, but rare in the Marianas.

Indo-Pacific: Red Sea to Samoa, n. to the Ryukyus, s. to New Caledonia; throughout Micronesia.

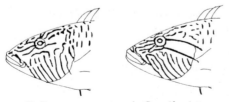

a. *C. digrammus*   b. *C. unifasciatus*
Fig. 4. Pattern of facial streaks in two species of *Cheilinus*.

Cheilinus fasciatus (Bloch, 1791)   Pl. 90D
Red-breasted wrasse

SL: to 275 mm (10.8 in); D IX, 10; A III, 8; P 12; LL 14-16+8-11; GR 5-7+7-9=13-15; depth 2.3-2.6.

This colorful *Cheilinus* inhabits lagoon and seaward reefs at depths of 4 to at least 40 m. It is particularly common in areas of mixed coral and rubble of lagoon patch reefs. It feeds on sand- and rubble-dwelling invertebrates and will often station itself close to a diver's fins in order to prey on small animals that may become exposed.

Indo-Pacific: Red Sea to Samoa, n. to the Ryukyus, s. to New Caledonia; throughout Micronesia.

Cheilinus orientalis Günther, 1862   Pl. 90E
Oriental wrasse

(*C. celebecus* Masuda et al., 1975)

SL: to 102 mm (4.0 in); D IX, 10; A III, 8; P 12; LL 13-14+7-8(14+7); GR 12-16; depth 3.3-4.0.

This small species resembles subadults of *C. digrammus* and *C. unifasciatus*. It occurs among corals or dense beds of algae in lagoons at depths of 18 to 70 m and is relatively rare in Micronesia.

West-central Pacific: Moluccas to Samoa, n. to the Ryukyus; Carolines, Marshalls, and Marianas in Micronesia; replaced by *C. mentalis* in the w. Indian Ocean.

Cheilinus oxycephalus Bleeker, 1853   Pl. 90F
Snooty wrasse

SL: to ca. 140 mm (5.6 in); D (IX)-X, 9-(10); A III, 8; P 12; LL 15-16+6-7; depth 2.4-3.0.

This small *Cheilinus* is moderately common in coral-rich areas of lagoon and seaward reefs at depths of 1 to over 40 m. It is perhaps the most secretive species in the genus and rarely travels more than a few centimeters from shelter.

Indo-Pacific: E. Africa to the Marquesan and Society Is., n. to Taiwan, s. to the s. Great Barrier Reef and the Australs; Marianas and Marshalls in Micronesia.

Cheilinus trilobatus Lacepède, 1801   Pl. 91D
Tripletail wrasse

SL: to 277 mm (10.9 in), TL: to 398 mm (15.7 in); D IX, 10; A III, 8; P 12; LL 14-17+7-9; GR 4-5+5-7=10-12; depth 2.3 -2.6.

The tripletail wrasse gets its name from the tri-lobed tail that develops in large adults (Fig. 6). It inhabits lagoon as well as seaward reefs at depths of 1 to over 30 m. It is relatively common along shallow reef margins or shallow, clear lagoon reefs with good coral cover and numerous holes and cuts. It feeds primarily on shelled benthic invertebrates such as crustaceans and mollusks, but occasionally takes fishes. It is a wary fish that is adept at slinking around corners or hiding under ledges and is difficult to photograph.

Indo-Pacific: E. Africa to the Tuamotu and Austral Is., n. to the Ryukyus, s. to New Caledonia; throughout Micronesia.

Fig. 5. Tail of large adult
     C. trilobatus.

Cheilinus undulatus Rüppell, 1835   Pl. 91A,B,C
Humphead wrasse; Napoleonfish

SL: to 180 cm (5.9 ft); TL: to 229 cm (7.5 ft); Wt.: to 190.5 kg (420 lb); D IX, 10; A III, 8; P 12; LL 14-16+7-8; GR 6-7+13-14=19-21; depth 2.2-2.7, increasing with age.

The humphead wrasse is among the largest of reef fishes. Adults develop a prominent bulbous hump on the forehead and amazingly thick fleshy lips. Adults occur along steep outer reef slopes, channel slopes, and occasionally on lagoon reefs, at depths of 2 to at least 60 m. They often have a "home" cave or crevice within which they sleep or enter when pursued. Juveniles occur in coral-rich areas of lagoon reefs, particularly among thickets of staghorn *Acropora* corals. The humphead wrasse is usually solitary, but occasionally occurs in pairs. It feeds primarily on mollusks and a wide variety of other well-armored invertebrates including crustaceans, echinoids, brittle stars, and starfish, as well as on fishes. It is one of the few predators of toxic animals such as the crown-of-thorns starfish, boxfishes, and sea hares. The thick fleshy lips appear to absorb sea urchin spines, and the pharyngeal teeth easily crush heavy-shelled gastropods like *Trochus* and *Turbo*. Much of its prey comes from sand or rubble. In certain areas the humphead wrasse may by ciguatoxic. Despite its size, it is among the wariest of fishes and extremely difficult to approach. The only places one stands a chance of a prolonged close encounter with this wrasse is in underwater parks where spearfishing is banned.

Indo-Pacific: Red Sea to the Tuamotus, n. to the Ryukyus, s. to New Caledonia; throughout Micronesia.

Cheilinus unifasciatus Streets, 1877   Pl. 91E,F
Ringtail wrasse

(*C. rhodochrous* Schultz, 1960)

SL: to 375 mm (14.8 in), but rarely >240 mm; Wt.: to 1.4 kg (3.1 lb); D IX, 10; A III, 8; P 12; LL 15-16+6-9; GR 4-5+9-10=13-15; depth 2.55-3.2.

This species differs from other narrow-bodied *Cheilinus* by always having a red-bordered area lacking red streaks extending from the eye to the tip of the operculum (Fig. 4b). Like many *Cheilinus*, it is capable of some amazingly rapid color changes. On one occasion, I observed an individual switch from a dark-backed white-bellied phase to a uniformly light gray to a dark ruddy-green within a span of a few minutes, each switch taking just seconds! This species also undergoes slight changes in color with growth; large adults develop a distinctive black blotch covering the rear of the dorsal and anal fins. *C. unifasciatus* is relatively common on clear lagoon and seaward reefs at depths of 1 to 160 m, in both coral-rich and rubbly areas. It is a stalking predator that feeds primarily on fishes, to a lesser extent on crabs, brittle stars, sea urchins, and heart urchins. It often swims well above the substrate and will readily take a small trolled lure. In certain areas (e.g. Hawaii), it may be ciguatoxic.

West-central Pacific: Christmas Is., Indian Ocean, to the Hawaiian, Marquesan, and Tuamotu Is., n. to the Ryukyus, s. to Rowley Shoals, New Caledonia, and Rapa; throughout Micronesia; replaced by *C. rhodochrous* in the w. Indian Ocean.

Wetmorella albofasciata Schultz & Marshall, 1954
White-barred pigmy wrasse   Fig. 6a

SL: to 46 mm (1.8 in); D IX, (10)-11; A III, 8; P 11-(12); LP 13-15+5-7 (+3 past hypural); GR 11-16; depth 2.8-3.3.

The genus *Wetmorella* consists of two superficially similar species that also closely resemble small juveniles of *Cheilinus fasciatus* and *Epibulus insidiator*. Since they have identical or broadly overlapping meristics, color pattern is the only reliable distinguishing character. Both species are extremely secretive dwellers of caves or crevices of lagoon and seaward reefs and are rarely noticed without the application of an ichthyocide. *W. albofasciata* has been collected in the depth range of 8 to 42 m.

Indo-Pacific: E. Africa to the Hawaiian and Society Is., s. to the Great Barrier Reef; Pohnpei and Marshalls in Micronesia.

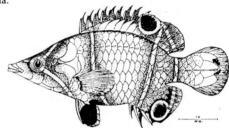

a. *W. albofasciata*

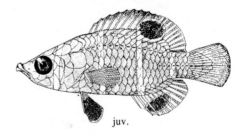

juv.

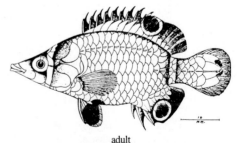

adult

b. *W. nigropinnata*

Fig. 7. Micronesian species of *Wetmorella* (a, after Schultz *in* Schultz et al., 1960).

Wetmorella nigropinnata (Seale, 1901)   Fig. 6b
Black-spot pigmy wrasse

(*W. ocellata*, *W. philippina bifasciata*, *W. triocellata* Schultz and Marshall, 1954)

SL: to 65 mm (2.6 in); D IX, (10)-11; A III, 8; P 11-(12);

LP 13-15+5-7 (+3 past hypural); GR 12-17; depth 2.55-3.15.
This species generally occurs shallower than *W. albofasciata*. It occurs on lagoon and seaward reefs at depths of 1 to 30 m.
Indo-Pacific: Red Sea to the Marquesan and Pitcairn Is., n. to the Ryukyus, s. to the s. Great Barrier Reef and New Caledonia; throughout Micronesia.

Epibulus insidiator (Pallas, 1770)   Pl. 92A,B,C,D
Slingjaw wrasse
SL: to 294 mm (11.6 in); D X-IX, 9-11(10); A III, (8)-9; P 12; LL 14-15+6-8; GR 5+12; depth 2.0-2.3.
The slingjaw wrasse is named for its remarkable mouth which unfolds into a tube easily half the length of the fish's body (Fig. 7). When not in use, the entire apparatus is conveniently folded under the head. Small juveniles are brown with thin white bars and closely resemble a species of *Wetmorella*. Subadults and females are brown or, not uncommonly, uniformly yellow. Terminal males are dark with a white head and a dark streak extending horizontally through the eye. The slingjaw wrasse is a fairly common inhabitant of coral-rich areas of lagoon and seaward reefs from the lower surge zone to a depth of at least 40 m. It uses its long tubular mouth to probe for coral-dwelling shrimps, crabs, and fishes. A second species of *Epibulus* with a slightly different color pattern has recently been discovered among the rock islands of Belau.
Indo-Pacific: Red Sea to the nw. Hawaiian and Tuamotu Is., n. to s. Japan, s. to New Caledonia; throughout Micronesia.

Fig. 7. Extended mouth of *Epibulus insidiator*.

Cymolutes praetextatus (Quoy & Gaimard, 1834)
Knife razorfish   Pl. 92E
SL: to 170 mm (6.7 in); D (IX)-X, 12-(13); A III, 11-(12); P 11-13(12); LL 48-68+15-22; GR 5-7+10-12; depth 3.6-3.7.
Species of *Cymolutes*, *Novaculichthys*, and *Xyrichtys* are highly compressed, moderately elongate fishes with a steep, keeled forehead. They typically occur over sand and feed on small benthic invertebrates. The unusual forehead seems to be an adaptation for diving into the sand which they readily do when frightened. *Cymolutes* is distinguished from the other two genera by having much smaller scales. This species often has a broad yellow lateral stripe. It occurs in sandy areas of reef flats and shallow lagoons with scattered algae, rubble, or seagrasses to a depth of at least 6 m. It is wary and not often noticed.

Indo-Pacific: E. Africa to the Society Is.; s. to Rowley Shoals; Marianas and Marshalls in Micronesia.

Cymolutes torquatus (Valenciennes, 1839)   Fig. 8
Finescale razorfish
(*C. lecluse* Masuda et al., 1984)
SL: to 97 mm (3.8 in); D IX, 12; A II-III, 12; P 12; LL 62-73+17-20; GR 18-20; depth 3.9-4.3.
This species differs from *C. praetextatus* by having 12 instead of 13 dorsal rays, dark brown markings on the head and body, and lacking the small black spot on the upper base of the caudal fin. It occurs over sandy areas of reef flats and shallow sandy lagoons to a depth of at least 6 m.
Indo-Pacific: E. Africa to New Britain and the Marquesas (?), n. to s. Japan, s. to Lord Howe Is.; Marianas and Marshalls in Micronesia.

Fig. 8. *Cymolutes praetextatus* (after Bleeker, 1862).

Novaculichthys macrolepidotus (Bloch, 1791)
Seagrass razorfish   Pl. 92F
(*Xyrichtys macrolepidotus*)
SL: to 121 mm (4.8 in); D IX, 12-14; A III, 12-14; P 12; LP 19-20+4-6(+1 past hypural); GR 19; depth 3.4-3.9.
This small razorfish inhabits seagrass beds and sandy algal flats of lagoons and mangrove channels at depths of 0.3 to over 4 m.
Indo-west Pacific: Red Sea to New Guinea, n. to the Ryukyus, s. to Lord Howe Is.; Marianas in Micronesia.

Novaculichthys taeniourus (Lacepède, 1801)
Dragon wrasse; Rockmover wrasse   Pl. 92G,H
(*Xyrichtys taeniourus*)
SL: to 272 mm (10.7 in); juvs. ≤60 mm; D IX, 12-13; A III, 12-13; P 13; LL 19-(20)+4-6; depth 2.65-3.1.
The dragon wrasse is a solitary inhabitant of semi-exposed reef flats and lagoon and seaward reefs to a depth of over 14 m. It is relatively common in areas of mixed sand and rubble that are subject to mild surge. It feeds on gastropods, bivalves, sea urchins, brittle stars, polychaetes, and crabs, and will turn over rocks in search of prey. Juveniles resemble a drifting piece of algae and mimic its movements. They make interesting aquarium fish and are easily approached, but may dive into the sand if pursued. Adults are quite wary.
Indo-pan-Pacific: Red Sea to Panama, n. to the Ryukyu and Hawaiian Is., s. to Lord Howe and the Tuamotu Is.; throughout Micronesia.

Xyrichtys aneitensis (Günther, 1862)   Pl. 93A,B
Yellowblotch razorfish

(*Hemipteronotus umbrilatus* (juv.); *H. niveilatus*)
SL: to 199 mm (7.8 in); D IX, 12; A III, 12; P 11-12; LL 20-22+4-5; GR 6-8+10-13=16-21.
This species inhabits expanses of fine sand on lagoon and seaward slopes below 12 m and has been observed from a submersible at depth of 92 m at Johnston Is.
Indo-Pacific: Chagos Is. to the Hawaiian Is., n. to the Ryukyus; Marianas and Marshalls in Micronesia.

Xyrichtys celebicus (Bleeker, 1856)   Fig. 9
Celebes razorfish
(*Hemipteronotus celebicus*)
SL: to 161 mm (6.3 in); D IX, 12; A III, 12; P 12-13; LL 20+6; GR 6+13.
This distinctive razorfish is known from Micronesia on the basis of a single individual from Bikini Lagoon.
West-central Pacific: Moluccas, Samoa, and Marshalls.

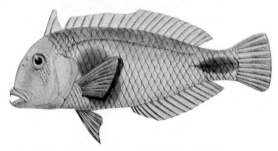

Fig. 9. *Xyrichtys celebecus* (after Bleeker, 1862).

Xyrichtys pavo Valenciennes, 1839   Pl. 93C,D
Indianfish (juv.); Blue razorfish (adult)
SL: to 337 mm (13.3 in); D II-VII, 12-13; A III, 12-13; P12; LL 20-22+4-6; GR 7-8+12-13=19-21.
This is the only Micronesian *Xyrichtys* in which the first two dorsal spines form a separate fin. In juveniles this fin is in the form of a long, bannerlike filament, but it shortens with age. Juveniles under about 60 mm are nearly uniformly greenish-tan to dark brown, larger juveniles are banded, and individuals over about 140 mm are primarily blue with various bright blue streaks on the head and edges of the fins. It has been suggested that the smallest uniformly colored individuals mimic a waterlogged leaf by swimming on their sides as if drifting with the current. This species occurs only over large expanses of fine to loose, coarse sand of lagoon and seaward reefs. Juveniles may occur in as little as 2 m, adults are rare in less than 20 m and may be fished from depths of over 100 m.
Indo-Pan-Pacific: Red Sea to Mexico, n. to s. Japan and the Hawaiian Is., s. to Lord Howe and the Society Is.; Marianas and Marshalls in Micronesia.

"Cirrhilabroid" genera: a group of six genera that are distinct from all other labrids in having the central portion of the scleral cornea obliquely to vertically divided into two subequal parts (Fig. 10). It has been suggested that this corneal modification serves as a close-up lens to facilitate feeding on small organisms. All have small mouths. *Cirrhilabrus* and *Paracheilinus* are planktivores that feed well into the water column, the remainder are carnivores of small benthic invertebrates. With the exception of a non-Micronesian species of *Pterogogus*, none get larger than 100 mm SL. In addition to the species included below, three species of *Cirrhilabrus* and one of *Paracheilinus* have recently been described from the Marshall Islands, and an undescribed species of *Pseudocheilinus* occurs throughout Micronesia.

Fig. 10. Eye of Cirrhilabroid
   genera.

Cirrhilabrus cyanopleura (Bleeker, 1851) Pl. 93E,F
SL: to 105 mm (4.1 in); D XI, 9; A III, 9; P 14-16; LL 15-18+6-11 (includes C base); GR 16-19.
All but four of the 25 species of *Cirrhilabrus* were undescribed prior to 1974. Several of these, including at least one in Micronesia, remain to be described. The genus *Paracheilinus* is very closely related to *Cirrhilabrus*, but differs by having IX, 11 instead of XI, 9 dorsal rays. Species of *Cirrhilabrus* and *Paracheilinus* typically occur in aggregations about 1 to 2 meters above coral or rocky bottoms and feed on zooplankton. Males are more colorful and sometimes quite differently colored than females, and may flash irridescent colors during courtship. Males are always larger than, and greatly outnumbered by females indicating that they are the result of sex inversion and are haremic. This species occurs along the edges of lagoon, channel, and outer reef slopes.

West Pacific: Christmas Is., Indian Ocean, to New Guinea, n. to the Izus, s. to Rowley Shoals; Belau in Micronesia.

Cirrhilabrus exquisitus Smith, 1857   Pl. 93G,H
Exquisite wrasse
SL: to 83 mm (3.3 in); D XI, 8-9; A III, 9; P 14-16(15); LL 16-18+5-7 (includes C base); GR 19-21; depth 3.2-3.5.
This species is uncommon in Micronesia where it occurs along current-swept seaward reefs at depths of 6 to 32 m.
Indo-Pacific: E. Africa to the Tuamotus, n. to the Izus; Belau and Kwajalein in Micronesia.

Cirrhilabrus n. sp.1   Pl. 94A,B
(*C. temmincki* Schultz 1960)
SL: to 85 mm (3.3 in); D XI-XII, 8-10; A III, 9-10; P 15-16; LL 16-18+5-6.
Juveniles and females are nearly uniformly orange-red. Males develop elongate pelvic fins and have brilliant blue bands on the dorsal and anal fins that can be "turned on" during courtship. This species occurs on clear lagoon patch reefs and outer reef slopes at depths of 10 to over 40 m. In the Marianas, it is common on seaward reefs below 15 m.
West-central Pacific: Philippines to the Line Is., n. to s. Japan, s. to the Great Barrier Reef (?); throughout Micronesia.

Cirrhilabrus luteovittatus Randall, 1988   Pl. 94C
Yellowband wrasse
SL: to 100 mm (3.9 in); D XI, 8-(9); A III, 9; P 14-(15); LL 15-18(16-17)+5-9(5-8)(includes C base); GR 16-18.
The initial phase of this species is orange-red becoming nearly white ventrally and resembles that of *Cirrhilabrus* n.

sp. 1. It typically occurs in small aggregations over lagoon patch reefs on rubble at depths of 7 to 25 m.
Micronesia: Pohnpei and Marshall Is.

Pseudocheilinops ataenia Schultz, 1960   Fig. 11
SL: to 41 mm (1.6 in); D IX, 1; A III, 9; P 13; LP 14-15+5-7; depth 2.2-2.5.
In life this small wrasse is wine red with yellow stripes. It is a secretive species, rarely noticed by divers.
Indo-Australian: Celebes, s. Philippines, and Belau.

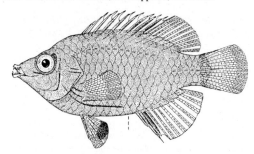

Fig. 11. *Pseudocheilinops ataenia*, 41 mm (after A. M. Awl *in* Schultz et al., 1960).

Pseudocheilinus evanidus Jordan&Evermann,1903
Striated wrasse   Pl. 94D
SL: to 64 mm (2.5 in); D IX, 11-13; A III, 9-11; P 14-15; LL 14-16+3-6(+1-2 on c); GR 11-15; depth 2.7- 3.3.
This small wrasse occurs among patches of rubble on seaward reef slopes at depths of 6 to over 40 m, but is rare in less than 20 m.
Indo-Pacific: Red Sea to the Hawaiian and Tuamotu Is., n. to the Izus; throughout Micronesia.

Pseudocheilinus hexataenia (Bleeker, 1857)
Sixline wrasse   Pl. 94E
SL: to 54 mm (2.1 in); D IX, 11-12; A III, 9; P 15-16; LL 16-18+5-8; GR 4+11=15.
The sixline wrasse inhabits seaward reefs at depths of 2 to 35 m. It occurs among the branches of live corals and feeds primarily on small crustaceans. Although it is perhaps the most common Micronesian *Pseudocheilinus*, it is quite secretive and seldom noticed.
Indo-Pacific: Red Sea to the Tuamotus, n. to the Ryukyus, s. to Lord Howe and the Austral Is.; throughout Micronesia.

Pseudocheilinus octotaenia Jenkins, 1900   Pl. 94F
Eightline wrasse
SL: to 95 mm (3.7 in); D IX, (11)-12; A III, 9-10; P 13-15 (14); LP 16-18+5-7(+1 on c); GR 12-14; depth 2.9-3.4.
This uncommon species lives among rubble or live coral of seaward reefs at depths of 2 to 50 m but is rare below 15 m. It feeds primarily on small benthic crustaceans and to a lesser extent on mollusks, echinoids, fish eggs, and crab larvae.
Indo-Pacific: E. Africa to the Hawaiian and Ducie Is., n. to the Yaeyamas; throughout Micronesia.

Pseudocheilinus tetrataenia Schultz, 1960   PL. 94G
Fourline wrasse
SL: to 60 mm (2.4 in); D IX, (11)-12; A III, 9; P (16)-17; LL 17-18+5-7; depth 2.7-3.2.
This secretive little species occurs among live coral or rubble of seaward reefs at depths of 6 to 44 m.
Pacific Plate: to the Hawaiian and Tuamotu Is., s. to the Australs; throughout Micronesia.

Pterogogus cryptus Randall, 1981   Pl. 95H ·
Cryptic wrasse
(*P. guttatus* Schultz, 1960)
SL: to 50 mm (2.0 in) in Micronesia; 74 mm (2.9 in) elsewhere; D X, 9-(10); A III, 9; P 12-(13); LP 23-(24)+2; GR 11-15 (modally 13; Micronesian specimens only).
This secretive little wrasse inhabits lagoon and seaward reefs at depths of 4 to 67 m. It prefers areas of rich soft or hard coral growth or scattered clumps of algae. As its name implies, it is secretive, and rarely exposes itself for more than a few seconds when moving among the bottom cover. Mature females as small as 36 mm and mature males as small as 45 mm have been collected. Further study may indicate that the western Pacific population is a distinct species, in which case it will require a new name.
Indo-Pacific: Red Sea; Indonesia to Samoa, n. to the Philippines, s. to the Great Barrier Reef; throughout Micronesia.

Pterogogus guttatus (Fowler & Bean, 1928)
SL: to 57 mm (2.2 in); GR 13-18 (modally 16).
This species differs from *P. cryptus* by having a concave rather than straight dorsal head profile, a higher modal gill raker count, and a series of five well-defined dark brown spots on the mid lateral line (these spots may be present on some *P. cryptus*, but are never well-defined).
Indo-Australian: Indonesia, Philippines, Solomons, New Guinea, and Belau.

Subfamily Corinae

This subfamily contains the bulk of the labrids. All species have a complete lateral line, usually bent sharply downward below the soft dorsal fin, and VIII to IX dorsal spines. Most are long and slender, have one or more pairs of prominent canines in the front of the jaws and well-developed pharyngeal teeth, and undergo dramatic changes in coloration related to age and sex. The vast majority are carnivores of benthic invertebrates or fishes. A few are planktivores and the Labrichthyiform genera are cleaners or corallivores.

Anampses caeruleopunctatus Rüppell, 1828
Blue-spotted wrasse   Pl. 95A,B; Fig. 12a
SL: 260 mm (10.2 in), ♀s 147-238 mm (5.8-9.4 in), ♂s 163-260 mm (6.4-10.2 in)(w. Pacific); 358 mm (14.1 in) (Easter Is.); D IX, 12; A III, 12; P 13; LP 27; GR 18-21; depth 2.3(>2.6)-3.0.
Species of *Anampses* are characterized by a single pair of broad projecting incisiform teeth in the front of the jaws (Fig. 13), a scaleless head, a smooth preopercular margin, a

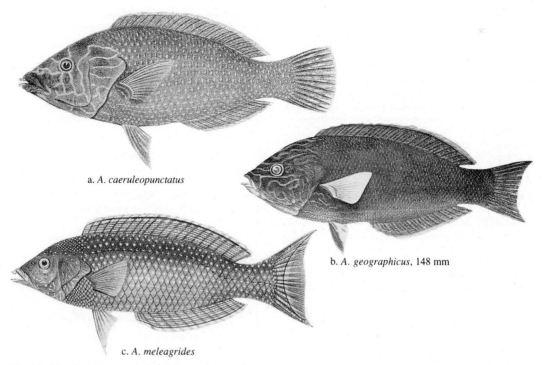

a. *A. caeruleopunctatus*

b. *A. geographicus*, 148 mm

c. *A. meleagrides*

Fig. 12. Terminal phases of some Micronesian species of *Anampses* (a, after Schultz, 1960; b, after Randall, 1972; c, after Bleeker, 1862).

complete lateral line, D IX, 12 dorsal rays, and A III, 12 anal rays. Most are sexually dichromatic and all have a primary phase consisting of juveniles and females and a terminal male phase consisting of sex-reversed females. The male of *A. caeruleopunctatus* is a deep blue-green with a light blue-green vertical line on each body scale and brownish horizontal streaks on the dorsal, anal, and caudal fins; a broad lighter band is often present on the sides behind the pectoral base. As far as is known, all species bury in the sand at night. *A. caeruleopunctatus* is common in the surge zone of seaward reefs, but occasionally ranges to a depth of 30 m. It feeds primarily on small crustaceans and polychaetes when small, switching to larger crustaceans and mollusks as well as polychaetes as an adult.

Indo-Pacific: Red Sea to the Line, Marquesan, and Easter Is., n. to s. Japan, s. to Lord Howe Is.; throughout Micronesia; replaced by *A. cuvier* in the Hawaiian Is.

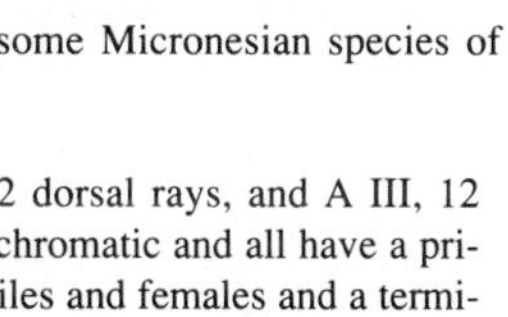

Fig. 13. Mouth of *Anampses caeruleopunctatus.*

Anampses geographicus Valenciennes, 1839
Geographic wrasse   Fig. 12b
SL: to 201 mm (7.9 in), ♀s to ≤152 mm (6.0 in); D IX, 12; A III, 12; LP 48-50; GR 17-20; depth 2.7-3.1.

This species has been recorded from Belau and Kosrae and appears to be relatively rare.

Indo-west Pacific: Mauritius to Fiji, n. to the Ryukyus, s. to Lord Howe Is.; Belau and Kosrae in Micronesia.

Anampses melanurus Bleeker, 1857   Pl. 95C
SL: to 94 mm (3.7 in); D IX, 12; A III, 12; LP 26; GR 14-17; depth 3.2-3.6.

The primary phase of this species closely resembles that of *A. meleagrides*, but never has a uniformly yellow tail, and the color pattern does not change much with growth or sex. *A. melanurus* inhabits seaward reefs at depths of 15 to 36 m, and is relatively rare.

West-central Pacific: Indonesia to the Marquesan and Society Is., n. to the Ryukyus, s. to Scott Reef; Belau in Micronesia; closely related to *A. lineatus* from the w. Indian Ocean.

Anampses meleagrides Valenciennes, 1839
Yellowtail wrasse   Pl. 95D; Fig. 12c
SL: to 162 mm (6.4 in), ♀s 92-137 mm (3.6-5.4 in), ♂s 129-162 mm (5.1-6.4 in); D IX, 12; A III, 12;P 13; LP 26; GR 18-20; depth 3.1- 3.4.

This lovely species inhabits areas of mixed coral, rubble, consolidated limestone, and sand of seaward reefs at depths of 4 to 60 m. It is relatively rare throughout Micronesia.

Indo-Pacific: Red Sea to the Tuamotus, n. to s. Japan; throughout Micronesia.

Anampses twisti Bleeker, 1856   Pl. 95E,F
Yellowbreasted wrasse

SL: to 146 mm (5.7 in); D IX, 12; A III, 12; LP 26; GR 16-19; depth 3.0-3.3.

This species' color does not change radically with growth or sex. It inhabits areas of mixed coral, rubble, consolidated limestone, and sand of clear lagoon and seaward reefs from the lower surge zone to a depth of 30 m. It is less common than *A. caeruleopunctatus* on exposed reefs, but more common on protected reefs.

Indo-Pacific: Red Sea to the Tuamotus, n. to the Ryukyus, s. to Rapa; throughout Micronesia.

Cheilio inermis (Forsskål, 1775)   Pl. 95G
Cigar wrasse

SL: to 450 mm (17.7 in); D IX, 12-14; A III, 11-12; P 12-13; LL 45-59; depth 5.5-8.0.

The cigar wrasse is named after its extremely elongate cylindrical body. Young individuals are usually a mottled brown or green, sometimes with a broad lateral stripe. Rare individuals may be uniformly yellow. Large males may develop a bright yellow, orange, black, white, or multicolored patch on their sides behind their pectoral fins. The cigar wrasse is common on algal-covered flats and in seagrass beds, but occasional individuals occur on lagoon and seaward reefs to a depth of at least 30 m. It feeds on benthic crustaceans, mollusks, and sea urchins.

Indo-Pacific: Red Sea to the Hawaiian and Easter Is., n. to s. Japan, s. to Lord Howe Is.; throughout Micronesia.

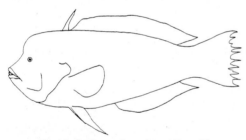

Fig. 14. *Coris aygula*, male ca. 46 cm SL.

Coris aygula Lacepède, 1801   Pl. 96A,B; Fig. 14
Clown coris

(*C. angulata*)

SL: to 100 cm (39.4 in); D IX, 12; A III, 12; P 14; LL 60-66; depth 3.0-3.3.

The distinguishing characters of *Coris* are: a moderately elongate compressed body with small scales (50->80 in LL), complete lateral line, naked head, except dorsally of eyes, IX, 12 dorsal rays, III, 12 anal rays, and a rounded caudal fin. Most species undergo dramatic changes in coloration with growth and sex. All species sleep under the sand at night and juveniles of some may also dive into the sand when frightened. Large male clown coris become nearly uniformly dark green and develop a gibbus forehead, elongate first dorsal spine, and broom-like tail. The clown coris occurs in the vicinity of sand or rubble patches of exposed outer reef flats and lagoon reefs as well as seaward reefs to a depth of 30 m. It feeds primarily on hard-shelled invertebrates such as mollusks, hermit crabs, crabs, and sea urchins. It uses its protruding canines to turn over rocks in search of prey as well as to pluck prey from the bottom. The prey are then crushed by the pharyngeal teeth. This species is not particularly common, and large males are quite wary.

Indo-Pacific: Red Sea to the Line and Ducie Is., n. to s. Japan, s. to Lord Howe and Rapa Is.; throughout Micronesia.

Coris gaimard (Quoy & Gaimard, 1824)
Yellowtail coris   Pl. 96C,D,E

SL: to 350 mm (13.8 in), juvs. ≤ 52 mm (2.0 in), interm. 60-82 mm (2.4-3.2 in), adults ≥ 78 mm (3.1 in); D IX, 12; A III, 12; P 13; LP 70-80 (+1-3 past hypural); GR 17-19; depth 3.3-3.7.

The yellowtail coris occurs in areas of mixed coral, sand, and rubble of exposed outer reef flats and lagoon reefs as well as seaward reefs to a depth of 50 m. It feeds primarily on hard-shelled invertebrates such as gastropods, bivalves, hermit crabs, crabs, and sea urchins, and occasionally on didemnid tunicates and foraminiferans. The yellowtail coris is generally more common than the clown coris, and juveniles of both are popular aquarium fishes.

Indo-Pacific: Red Sea to the Hawaiian, Marquesan, and Tuamotu Is., n. to s. Japan, s. to New Caledonia and the Austral Is.; throughout Micronesia; the subspecies *C. g. africana* from the w. Indian Ocean lacks the yellow tail.

Coris variegata (Rüppell, 1835)   Pl. 95H
Dapple coris

SL: to ca. 160 mm (6.3 in); D IX, 11; A III, 11; P 13-15 (14); LL 51-54.

Unlike the preceeding *Coris*, this relatively drab species does not undergo extreme changes in color with growth or sex. It occurs on lagoon as well as seaward reefs to a depth of 15 m or more. It feeds primarily on small crabs and gastropods and is relatively uncommon in Micronesia.

Indo-Pacific: Red Sea to the Marshalls; n. to s. Japan, s. to the s. Great Barrier Reef; Belau to the Marshalls in Micronesia.

Gomphosus varius Lacepède, 1801   Pl. 96F,G,H
Bird wrasse

(*G. tricolor* for ♂)

SL: to 180 mm (7.1 in); D VIII, 13; A III, 11; P 15-17(16); LL 26-27; depth 3.5-4.

The bird wrasse is named after its unusually long snout that vaguely resembles a bird's bill. Small juveniles lack the elongate snout. The bird wrasse is relatively common in coral-rich areas of lagoon and seaward reefs to a depth of at least 30 m. It is usually solitary but occasionally occurs in small groups. The distinctive snout is used to probe corals for prey. It feeds primarily on small benthic crustaceans and to a lesser extent on brittle stars, fishes, and mollusks. It is a fast swimmer that does well in the aquarium if given sufficient room.

Indo-Pacific: e. Indian Ocean to the Hawaiian, Marquesan, and Tuamotu Is., n. to s. Japan, s. to Rowley Shoals and Lord Howe and Rapa Is.; throughout Micronesia; replaced by *G. caeruleus* in the Indian Ocean.

Halichoeres biocellatus Schultz, 1960   Pl. 97A;
Two-spotted wrasse   Fig. 15
SL: to 84 mm (3.3 in); D IX, 12; A III, 11; P 13; LL 27; depth 2.9-3.2.
Halichoeres is the largest labrid genus. Its distinguishing characteristics are: IX dorsal spines, a continuous lateral line, large scales, naked head (except for the upper part of the opercle in some species), smooth preopercular margin, canine teeth in a single row in the jaws (except a few minute inner teeth) with one or two anteriormost pairs enlarged and a canine tooth at each corner of the upper jaw of adults, moderately thick lips with inner fleshy ridges, and a rounded caudal fin. Most species undergo dramatic changes in coloration with growth and sex. The primary phase typically consists of males as well as females, and the terminal male phase results from sex-inversion. As far as is known, all species sleep under the sand at night. *H. biocellatus* is named for the pair of ocelli on the dorsal fin of juveniles and subadults. Aside from the loss of the ocelli with growth, color changes related to size or sex are minor. In the Marianas, *H. biocellatus* is relatively common in mixed coral-reef rock areas of seaward reefs at depths of 7 to over 35 m. The closely related *H. ornatissimus* from s. Japan, and the Ryukyu, Hawaiian, and Society Is. may also be expected to turn up in Micronesia.
West Pacific: Philippines to Fiji, n. to s. Japan, s. to Rowley Shoals and the s. Great Barrier Reef; throughout Micronesia.

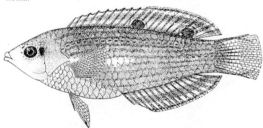

Fig. 15. *Halicheores biocellatus*, 63 mm (after A. M. Awl *in* Schultz et al., 1960).

Halichoeres chloropterus (Bloch, 1791)   Pl. 97B
SL: to 116 mm (4.6 in), ♀s to 116 mm (4.6 in), ♂s ≥ 108 mm (4.3 in); D IX, 10-(11); A III, 10-(11); P 13-15(14); LP 27+1; GR 17-20; depth (specs. ≥ 65 mm) 2.75-3.75.
The primary phase lacks the large dark patch behind the pectoral fins and very large terminal males become a darker green than the individual shown. At Belau, this relatively drab wrasse is common on protected lagoon reefs at depths of 0.5 to 10 m in areas of mixed sand, rubble, algae, and coral.
Indo-Australian: Sumatra to the Solomons, n. to the Philippines; Belau in Micronesia.

Halichoeres hartzfeldii (Bleeker, 1852)   Pl. 97C,D
Hartzfeld's wrasse
SL: to ca. 145 mm (5.7 in); D IX, 11; A III, 11; LL 27.
Juveniles are off-white with a broad yellow lateral band. Hartzfeld's wrasse inhabits open expanses of sand or mixed sand, rubble, and pavement usually below 11 m. It is localized in distribution and more commonly found on seaward than lagoon reefs. It typically occurs in loose groups of one male and numerous smaller females and juveniles.
Tropical w. Pacific: n. to s. Japan, ; may ultimately be regarded as a subspecies of *H. zeylonicus* of the Indian Ocean.

Halichoeres hortulanus (Lacepède, 1801) Pl. 97E,F
Checkerboard wrasse
(*H. centriquadrus*)
SL: to 212 mm (8.3 in); D IX, 11; A III, 11; P 13-(14); LP 26; GR 20-25; depth 2.95-3.25.
The checkerboard wrasse is a common inhabitant of sand patches of clear lagoon and seaward reefs at depths of 1 to at least 30 m. Juveniles are common among pockets of rubble or sand in the bottoms of surge channels or under ledges bordering sand-bottomed holes. Adults prefer large expanses of sand. It feeds primarily on small sand-dwelling gastropods and to a lesser extent on bivalves, hermit crabs, polychaetes, and fishes.
Indo-Pacific: Red Sea to the Line, Marquesan, and Tuamotu Is., n. to s. Japan, s. to the s. Great Barrier Reef; throughout Micronesia.

Halichoeres chrysus Randall, 1980   Pl. 97G
Canary wrasse
SL: to 79 mm (3.1 in); D IX, 12; A III, 11-(12); P 12-14 (13); LL complete, LP 27(+1 past hypural); GR 14-19; depth 3.4-3.8.
Aside from males losing the ocellus in the middle of the dorsal fin, this species exhibits no obvious color differences due to size or sex. This brilliant wrasse inhabits seaward reefs at depths of 7 to 60 m, but is usually below 20 m. It occurs around small isolated coral heads or rubble surrounded by sand, and in areas of dark sand stands out in sharp contrast to the bottom. It is relatively uncommon on Micronesian reefs.
West-central Pacific: Christmas Is., Indian Ocean, to the Solomon and Marshall Is., n. to s. Japan, s. to Rowley Shoals and New South Wales; Belau, Ulithi, and Marshall Is. in Micronesia; replaced by *H. leucoxanthus* in the Indian Ocean, but with overlapping distributions in Indonesia.

Halichoeres margaritaceus (Valenciennes, 1839)
Weedy surge wrasse   Pl. 97H
SL: to 102 mm (4.0 in), ♀s mature at 43-67 mm (1.7-2.6 in), ♂s ≥ 70 mm (2.8 in); D IX, 11; A III,11; P (13)-14; LP 27(+1 past hypural); GR 17-21.
This is among the most abundant wrasses of intertidal reef flats, reef margins, and rocky shores exposed to surge. Its complicated color pattern is similar at all sizes, becoming only slightly more colorful in terminal males, and blends in well with an algae-covered background. It feeds on small

benthic crustaceans, molluscs, polychaetes, foraminiferans, fishes, and fish eggs.

West-central Pacific: Cocos-Keeling Is., Indian Ocean, to the Line and Tuamotu Is., n. to s. Japan, s. to Rowley Shoals, New South Wales, and Lord Howe Is.; throughout Micronesia; replaced by *H. nebulosus* in the w. Indian Ocean.

Halichoeres marginatus Rüppell, 1835   Pl. 98A,B
Dusky wrasse

SL: to 140 mm (5.5 in), juvs. ≤ 40 mm (1.6 in); D IX, (13)-14; A III, (12)-13; P 13-(14); LP (27)-28; GR 17-20; depth 2.6-3.2.

Juveniles are black with numerous longitudinal white streaks. Most terminal males from the Pacific have a red patch behind the pectoral fin, but a courting male observed in Belau lacked this patch and instead had a conspicuous white spot in the middle of its side just beneath the lateral line. This species inhabits lagoon and seaward reefs at depths of .5 to 30 m. Juveniles are common on exposed outer reef flats and reef fronts; adults prefer coral-rich areas of high relief and usually occur along the upper edges of coral formations. Along the reef's edge, a large terminal male may patrol a large area and court and spawn with several less active females. The dusky wrasse feeds on a wide variety of small invertebrates including amphipods, isopods, copepods, small crabs, polychaetes, gastropods, chitons, and foraminiferans as well as fish eggs.

Indo-Pacific: Red Sea to the Hawaiian (1 spec.) and Tuamotu Is., n. to s. Japan, s. to the s. Great Barrier Reef and the Austral Is.; throughout Micronesia.

Halichoeres melanurus (Bleeker, 1851)   Pl. 98C,D
Pinstriped wrasse

(*H. hoeveni* Schultz, 1960 for ♀; *H. kallochroma* Schultz, 1960 for ♂)

SL: to 86 mm (3.4 in), os to 65 mm (2.6 in), os ≥ 51 mm (2.0 in); D IX, 12; A III, 12; P 14; LP 27+1; GR 17-20; depth 3.1-3.6.

This colorful wrasse inhabits lagoon patch reefs or rubble and sand patches near reefs at depths of 2 to 15 m. It feeds on small invertebrates such as polychaetes, copepods, isopods, and foraminiferans.

West-central Pacific: Indonesia to Samoa, n. to the Ryukyus, s. to the s. Great Barrier Reef; Belau to the e. Carolines and Marshalls in Micronesia.

Halichoeres melasmapomus Randall, 1980 Pl. 98E
Black-ear wrasse

SL: to 188 mm (4.6 in), ♀s ≤108 mm (4.3 in); D IX, 12; A III, 12; P 13; LL complete, LP 27(+1 past hypural); GR 14-18; depth 2.95-3.3.

Aside from juveniles losing the three ocelli on the dorsal fin and large males becoming somewhat more colorful, the color pattern of this species does not change much. The black-ear wrasse is an uncommon inhabitant steep outer reef slopes. It has been reported from depths of 10 to over 55 m, but is rare in less than 33 m. It typically occurs around patches of rubble or mixed rubble and coral along steep drop-offs.

West-central Pacific: Cocos-Keeling Is. and Rowley Shoals, Indian Ocean, to the Marquesan and Pitcairn Is., n. to the Philippines; throughout Micronesia.

Halichoeres prosopeion (Bleeker, 1853)   Pl. 98F

SL: to 101 mm (4.0 in); D IX, (12)-13; A III, 12; P 13-(14); LP (27)-28+1; GR 17-21; depth 2.85-3.5.

Small juveniles are light tan with four broad black longitudinal stripes and black stripes on the basal portions of the dorsal and anal fins. Adults loose the stripes but exhibit no obvious color differences between the sexes. At Belau, this small *Halichoeres* is moderately common in coral-rich areas of seaward reefs. It has been reported from the depth range of 5 to 40 m.

West Pacific: Indonesia to Samoa, n. to the Ryukyus, s. to Scott Reef and the s. Great Barrier Reef; Belau in Micronesia.

Halichoeres n. sp.?   Pl. 98G

This small wrasse was observed only in an area of sand and rubble near patch reefs among one of the rock islands of Belau. It may possibly be the unlinked primary phase of *H. richmondi*.

Halichoeres richmondi Fowler & Bean, 1928
Richmond's wrasse   Pl. 98H; Fig. 16

SL: to ca. 130 mm (5.1 in); D IX, 12; A III, 12; P 13-15 (14); LL 27; GR 23-26; depth 3.2-3.7.

The concave head profile of terminal males is distinctive. At Belau Richmond's wrasse inhabits shallow lagoon and channel reefs to a depth of at least 12 m.

Indo-Australian: Java, Philippines, Ryukyus, Moluccas, Belau, Truk, Pohnpei, and Kwajalein.

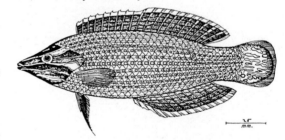

Fig. 16. *H. richmondi* male, 125 mm (after Fowler and Bean, 1928).

Halichoeres scapularis (Bennett, 1831) Pl. 99A,B
Zigzag wrasse

SL: to 156 mm (6.1 in); D IX, 11; A III, 11; P 14; LP 26-27; GR 17-21; depth 2.4-3.9, increasing with age.

The primary phase of this species is similar to *H. trimaculatus*, but always has a dark zigzaging longitudinal stripe along its back. At Belau, it is common in seagrass beds and shallow sandy areas of protected lagoon reefs.

Indo-west Pacific: Red Sea to New Guinea, n. to s. Japan, s. to the Great Barrier Reef; Belau in Micronesia.

Halichoeres trimaculatus (Quoy & Gaimard, 1824)
Three-spot wrasse   Pl. 99C,D
SL: to 219 mm (8.6 in); D IX, 11; A III, 10; P 14-15; LL
27-28; depth 3.2-3.3.
This is the most common wrasse of sandy areas of reef flats,
lagoons, and semi-protected seaward reefs to a depth of 18 m
or more. It feeds on a wide variety of sand and rubble-
dwelling invertebrates including crustaceans, mollusks, foraminiferans, and polychaetes as well as fish eggs and small
fishes. It has a predilection for closely following sand-
disturbing fishes such as goatfishes in order to intercept escaping prey. It will also closely follow a diver and search
through any areas of disturbed sand or rubble.
West-central Pacific: Christmas Is., Indian Ocean, to the
Line and Ducie Is., n. to s. Japan, s. to Rowley Shoals and
Lord Howe Is.; throughout Micronesia.

Hemigymnus fasciatus (Bloch, 1792)   Pl. 99E,F
Barred thicklip wrasse
SL: to ca. 430 mm (16.9 in), unconfirmed reports to 600
mm (23.6 in); D IX, 11; A III, 11; P 14; LL 26-30; GR
6+16-17=22-24; depth 2.4-2.6.
The two species of *Hemigymnus* have relatively deep bodies
with large scales, greatly enlarged lips, jaws with a pair of
protruding canine teeth anteriorly and small compressed teeth
on the sides, the upper jaw with some small nodular teeth
medially, and strong pharyngeal teeth. The basic color pattern of *H. fasciatus* changes little with growth, but the posteriormost white bands disappear on large individuals. It inhabits lagoon and seaward reefs at depths of 1 to at least 18
m. Juveniles occur around branching corals and feed chiefly
on demersal planktonic crustaceans. Adults are moderately
common in areas of mixed sand, rubble, and coral and feed
on benthic invertebrates, particularly sand-dwelling forms,
including crustaceans, polychaetes, brittle stars,sea urchins,
mollusks, and foraminiferans.
Indo-Pacific: Red Sea to the Line and Ducie Is., n. to s. Japan, s. to Lord Howe and Rapa Is.; throughout Micronesia.

Hemigymnus melapterus (Bloch, 1791)   Pl. 99G,H
Half-and-half wrasse (juv.);
Blackedge thicklip wrasse (adult)
SL: to ca. 710 mm (28.0 in); D IX, 11; A III, 11; P 14; LL
27-28; GR 8+21=26-29; depth 2.4-2.7.
Juveniles and subadults are almost white anteriorly and
abruptly dark green to black posteriorly; those under about 8
cm have a bright yellow tail which slowly fades with
growth. The colorful pink and blue facial markings around
the eyes of juveniles spreads with growth to cover nearly the
entire head in large adults. The thicklip wrasse inhabits subtidal reef flats and lagoon and seaward reefs to a depth of at
least 30 m. Like *H. fasciatus*, it is moderately common in
areas of mixed sand, rubble, and coral, with small juveniles
usually occuring among branching corals. Its diet is also
similar, changing from primarily demersal planktonic crustaceans to hard-shelled invertebrates with growth.
Indo-Pacific: Red Sea to the Society Is., n. to the Ryukyus,
s. to Lord Howe Is.; throughout Micronesia.

Hologymnosus annulatus (Lacepède, 1801)
Ring wrasse   Fig. 17
(*H. semidiscus*)
SL: to 327 mm (12.9 in), juvs. ≤ 120 mm (4.7 in), ♀s ≤
260 mm (10.2 in), ♂s ≥ 276 mm (10.9 in); D IX, 12; A III,
12; P 13; LP 100-118; GR 19-23; depth 3.3-5.1, deeper
with age.
The distinguishing characteristics of *Hologymnosus* are: an
elongate compressed body with very small scales, a continuous lateral line, naked head except for nape, jaws with two
pairs of canine teeth anteriorly and a row of small bluntly
conical teeth with an inner irregular series of small nodular
teeth on the sides, relatively poorly developed pharyngeal
teeth, and an emarginate to double emarginate caudal fin.
Juvenile *H. annulatus* very closely resemble juvenile *Malacanthus latovittatus* which also occur over sandy bottoms,
suggesting mimicry. This species has been recorded from
Micronesia on the basis of adult males collected at Guam
and observed at Pagan, and juveniles photographed in Kwajalein Lagoon. The poorly developed pharyngeal teeth are
reflected in the diet which consists primarily on fishes, to a
lesser extent on small crustaceans
Indo-Pacific: Red Sea to the Society and Pitcairn Is., n. to s.
Japan, s. to se. Australia and Rapa; Marianas and Kwajalein
in Micronesia.

Fig. 17. *Hologymnosus annulatus* juv.

Hologymnosus doliatus (Lacepède,1801)
Candy cane wrasse (juv.);   Pl. 100A,B,C
Longface wrasse (adult)
SL: to 308 mm (12.1 in), juvs. ≤ 100 mm (3.9 in), ♀s ≤
174 mm (6.9 in), ♂s ≥ 224 mm (8.8 in); D IX, 12; A III,
12; P 13; LL 97-112; GR 18-22; depth 3.75-5.35, deeper
with age.
In the Marianas, this species is an uncommon inhabitant of
clear lagoon and seaward reefs from the lower surge zone to a
depth of over 30 m. It typically occurs over pockets or
channels of sand and rubble. Small striped juveniles occur
in closely-knit groups that remain close to the substrate.
Adults are solitary or occur in loosely-knit groups and venture some distance from the substrate. This species feeds
primarily on fishes and crustaceans and to a lesser extent on
brittlestars and polychaetes.
Indo-Pacific: E. Africa to the Samoan and Line Is., n. to s.
Japan, s. to se. Australia; Ulithi and Guam in Micronesia.

Macropharyngodon meleagris (Valenciennes,1839)
Leopard wrasse   Pl. 100D,E
(*M. pardalis* for primary phase)
SL: to 120 mm (4.7 in), ♀s ≤ 96 mm (3.8 in), ♂s ≥ 62 mm
(2.4 in); D IX, 11; A III, 11; P 12; LL 27(+1 past hypural);
GR 15-19; depth 2.54-3.05.

Species of *Macropharyngodon* have moderately deep compressed bodies with moderately large scales, jaws with two pairs of enlarged canines anteriorly, the anteriormost projecting forward, the second recurved, and small conical teeth in a single row in the sides, the last tooth in the upper jaw a canine projecting diagonally forward and downward, and a lower pharyngeal plate with a single large molariform tooth flanked by 1 to 3 small conical teeth. *M. meleagris* inhabits subtidal reef flats and outer lagoon and seaward reefs at depths of 0.5 to at least 30 m. It is moderately common in areas of mixed coral, rubble, and sand of semi-protected seaward reefs. It is generally solitary and feeds on small hard-bodied benthic invertebrates and foraminiferans.

West-central Pacific: Cocos-Keeling Is., Indian Ocean, (but absent from Indonesia) to the Line, Marquesan, and Pitcairn Is., n. to s. Japan, s. to Scott Reef, New South Wales, and Lord Howe Is.; throughout Micronesia.

Macropharyngodon negrosensis Herre, 1932
Negros wrasse
Fig. 18

SL: to 102 mm (4.0 in); D IX, 11; A III, 11; P 12; LL 27 (+1 past hypural); GR 14-18; depth 2.67-2.94.

This rare species has recently been reported from Belau and the Marshalls. It is known from the depth range of 8 to 32 m, but usually occurs below 15 m.

West-central Pacific: Philippines to Samoa, n. to the Ryukyus, s. to nw Australia and the s. Great Barrier Reef; Belau and the Marshalls in Micronesia.

Fig. 18. *M. negrosensis*, anterior region of male.

Pseudocoris yamashiroi (Schmidt, 1930)
Yamashiro's wrasse
Pl. 100 F

SL: to ca. 140 mm (5.5 in); D IX, 12; A III, 12; P 13; LL 66-77; depth 3.3-4.6.

Members of this genus are similar to those of *Coris*, but the males develop filamentous outermost caudal rays. Males of this haremic species are dark green with a white belly. *P. yamashiroi* is an uncommon inhabitant of outer lagoon, channel, or seaward reefs. It occurs in zooplankton-feeding aggregations along the upper edges of coral slopes.

West-central Pacific: Ryukyus to the Marshalls, n. to s. Japan, s. to Rowley Shoals; Belau and Marshalls in Micronesia.

Pseudojuloides atavai Randall & Randall, 1981
Polynesian wrasse
Pl. 100G

SL: to 116 mm (4.6 in), ♀s 50-77 mm (2.0-3.0 in), ♂s ≥ 89 mm (3.5 in); D IX, 11; A III, 12; P 13; LL 27 (+1 past hy-

pural); GR 16-18; depth 4.05-4.45.

Pseudojuloides is characterized by a slender body with a continuous lateral line and moderately large scales, a single pair of canine teeth anteriorly in the jaws followed by incisiform teeth, well-developed pharyngeal teeth, and a small truncate or near-truncate caudal fin. The primary phase of *P. atavai* closely resembles juvenile *Thalassoma amblycephalum*; the terminal phase is orange-yellow anteriorly with dull violet squiggly lines on the head and reddish horizontal and vertical lines on the body, becoming abruptly bluish-black posteriorly. This species inhabits seaward reefs at depths of 12 to 31 m. It is known from Micronesia on the basis of a photograph taken off Guam by J. E. Randall.

Pacific Plate: Guam to the Society, Tuamotu, Austral and Ducie Is.

Pseudojuloides cerasinus (Snyder, 1904)
Smalltail wrasse
Pl. 101A,B

SL: to 103 mm (4.1 in), ♀s ≤ 90 mm (3.5 in), ♂s ≥ 58 mm (2.3 in); D IX, 11; A III, 12; P 13; LL 27 (+1 past hypural); GR 15-19; depth 3.8-4.4.

The primary phase of this species is salmon pink with yellowish fins. The smalltail wrasse inhabits clear lagoon and seaward reefs at depths of 2.5 to 61 m, but is rare in less than 21 m. It typically occurs over coral rubble with algal clumps and scattered live corals. It is quite rare in Micronesia where it has been observed or collected off Guam and in Enewetak Lagoon.

Indo-Pacific: E. Africa to the Hawaiian, Society, and Austral Is., n. to Izus, s. to Lord Howe Is.; Marianas and Marshalls in Micronesia.

Stethojulis bandanensis (Bleeker, 1851) Pl. 101C,D
Red-shoulder wrasse

(*S. axillaris* Schultz, 1960 for ♀; *S. linearis* for ♂)

SL: to 132 mm (5.2 in); D IX, 11-12; A III, 11 (1st spine minute or imbedded); P 13-15(14); LL 25-28; GR 9-10+19-20; depth 2.9-3.1.

Stethojulis is similar to *Anampses* and *Halichoeres* but lacks prominent canine teeth in the front of the jaws (Fig. 19). All species are sexually dichromatic with the primary phase consisting of both males and females. Terminal males typically have a series of partial to complete longitudinal thin blue lines on their sides. All species sleep under the sand at night. This species inhabits shallow reef flats and lagoon and seaward reefs to a depth of 30 m. It is common in clearwater areas of mixed sand, rubble, and coral. It occurs singly or in groups which usually consist of one terminal male and numerous females. Like other species of *Stethojulis*, it is an active swimmer that seldom stops. It feeds primarily on demersal planktonic crustaceans and small benthic invertebrates.

West-central Pacific: Christmas Is., Indian Ocean, to the Line, Marquesan, and Ducie Is., n. to s. Japan, s. to Rowley Shoals and Lord Howe and Rapa Is.; throughout Micronesia; replaced by *S. albovittata* in the w. Indian Ocean and *S. balteata* in the Hawaiian Is.

Fig. 19. Dentition
of *Stethojulis*.

Stethojulis strigiventer (Bennett, 1832)   Pl. 101E,F
Three-ribbon wrasse

(*S. renardi* for ♂)

SL: to 120 mm (4.7 in); D IX, 11; A III, 11 (1st spine minute or imbedded); P 14-16(15); LL 26; GR 8-11+16-20=22-28; depth 3.0-3.5.

Terminal males of *S. strigiventer* and *S. bandanensis* are similar, but in *S. strigiventer* the uppermost lateral blue streak rather than the lowermost one extends to the tail, and the colors are not as intense as they are in *S. bandanensis*. *S. strigiventer* tends to inhabit more protected turbid waters than does *S. bandanensis*. It is common in seagrass beds and areas of mixed sand, rubble, and algae of inner reef flats and shallow lagoons to a depth of about 6 m.

Indo-Pacific: E. Africa to Samoa, n. to s. Japan, s. to the s. Great Barrier Reef; throughout Micronesia.

Thalassoma amblycephalum (Bleeker, 1856)
Twotone wrasse   Pl. 101G,H

SL: to 120 mm (4.7 in); D VIII, 13; A III, 10-11; P 14-(15); LL 26 (+1 past hypural); GR 16-19; depth 3.9-4.1.

Species of *Thalassoma* have elongate, compressed bodies with 26 lateral line scales (+1 past the hypural), VIII, 12-14 dorsal rays, III, 10-12 (first spine rudimentary and often imbedded) anal rays, jaws with conical teeth in a single row becoming longer anteriorly, the anterior pair as slightly projecting canines, and emarginate to lunate caudal fins in adults. Most species have three color phases: a juvenile phase, a primary phase consisting of both males and females, and a brilliantly colored sex-reversed terminal male phase. The color differences between the phases are usually not as striking as in most other corine wrasses, and in some species are barely noticable. In the species thus far studied, sexuality is socially controlled with the presence of terminal males inhibiting females from changing sex. Primary males are apparently born males; they group spawn with similarly colored females, but are incapable of transforming to terminal males. Terminal males are territorial and pair spawn with individual females. Species of *Thalassoma* are typically rapid swimmers that sleep in rock or coral recesses rather than under the sand. Juveniles of *T. amblycephalum* resemble the primary phase. *T. amblycephalum* inhabits lagoon and seaward reefs at depths of 1 to about 15 m. It is fairly common around the tops of isolated coral pinnacles or the upper edges of steep slopes. It feeds primarily on crustacean zooplankton including shrimp and crab larvae, copepods, and mysids.

Indo-Pacific: Chagos Is. to the Line, Marquesan, and Tuamotu Is., n. to s. Japan, s. to Rowley Shoals, n. New Zealand, and Lord Howe and Rapa Is.; throughout Micronesia.

Thalassoma hardwickii (Bennett, 1828-30)
Sixbar wrasse   Pl. 102A,B

SL: to ca. 170 mm (6.7 in); D VIII, 12-14(13); A III, 11; P 15-17(16); LL 26 (+1 past hypural); GR 22-25; depth 2.9-3.2.

The color pattern of this species remains basically the same with terminal males becoming somewhat gaudier than primary males. Hardwick's wrasse inhabits shallow lagoon and seaward reefs to a depth of about 15 m. It is moderately common in clear water areas of mixed coral, rubble, and sand, particularly along the upper edges of protected reef slopes. It feeds on a wide variety of benthic and planktonic crustaceans, small fishes, and foraminiferans.

Indo-Pacific: E. Africa to the Line, and Tuamotu Is., n. to s. Japan, s. to Lord Howe and the Austral Is.; throughout Micronesia.

Thalassoma janseni (Bleeker, 1856)   Pl. 102C
Jansen's wrasse

SL: to ca. 170 mm (6.7 in); D VIII, 13; A III, 11; LL 26 (+1 past hypural); GR 21.

Jansen's wrasse also has a color pattern that remains similar throughout life. It inhabits exposed crests of seaward and lagoon reefs to a depth of 15 m. It is uncommon from Belau to the e. Carolines and extremely rare in the Marianas.

Indo-Pacific: Maldives to Fiji, n. to s. Japan, s. to Lord Howe Is.; throughout Micronesia.

Thalassoma lunare (Linnaeus, 1758)   Pl. 102D
Crescent wrasse

SL: to ca. 180 mm (7.1 in); D VIII, 13; A III, 11; P 15; LL 26 (+1 past hypural); GR 18-20; depth 3.1-3.7.

Although elements of the same basic color pattern of this species survive the transition from primary to terminal phase, the brilliance of the terminal phase is striking. The moon wrasse inhabits the upper portions of lagoon and coastal reefs, often in relatively turbid water, as well as clear protected seaward reefs to a depth of 20 m. It usually occurs in groups consisting of a territorial terminal male and several primary phase individuals. It feeds primarily on small benthic invertebrates, particularly crustaceans, fish eggs, and gastropod egg capsules. It is common from Belau to the e. Carolines, but absent from the Marianas and n. Marshalls.

Indo-Pacific: Red Sea to the Line Is., n. to s. Japan, s. to n. New Zealand and Lord Howe Is.; Belau to the e. Carolines and s. Marshalls (Jaliut) in Micronesia.

Thalassoma lutescens (Lay & Bennett, 1839)
Sunset wrasse   Pl. 102E,F

SL: to ca. 190 mm (7.5 in); D VIII, 13; A III, 11; P 15-17(16); LL 26 (+1 past hypural); GR 25.

The sunset wrasse inhabits clear outer lagoon and seaward reefs at depths of 1 to 30 m. It is quite common on shallow exposed seaward reefs. Individuals range widely over open sand and rubble as well as dense coral growth. It feeds primarily on a variety of shelled benthic invertebrates including crabs, shrimps, gastropods, bivalves, brittle stars, and sea urchins, as well as fish eggs.

Indo-pan-Pacific: Sri Lanka to Panama, n. to s. Japan and the Hawaiian Is., s. to Lord Howe, Kermadec, Rapa, and Ducie Is.; throughout Micronesia.

Thalassoma purpureum (Forrskål, 1775)
Surge wrasse   Pl. 102G,H

(*T. umbrostygma*)

SL: to 328 mm (12.9 in), os 70 - ≥ 220 mm (2.8-8.7 in), os ≥ 154 mm (6.1 in); D VIII, 12-14; A III, 10-12; P 15-17(16); LL 26 (+1 past hypural); GR 20-25 (modally 23); depth 2.8-3.6, increasing with age.

This species and *T. trilobatum* have nearly identical initial phases. They differ slightly in details of the head markings, and *T. purpureum* has a slightly longer head (HL in SL, 2.65-3.1 vs 3.05-3.3), shorter pectoral fins (pectoral length in head ≥ 1.5 vs ≤ 1.5), and attains a larger size (only initial phase *T. purpureum* get larger than 200 mm). The surge wrasse occurs almost exclusively in the surge zone of outer reef flats, reef margins, and rocky coastlines. It is constantly on the move and when pursued, seeks shelter by entering extremely shallow turbulent water. It feeds on a variety of animals including crabs, fishes, echinoids, mollusks, ophiuroids, and polychaetes.

Indo-Pacific: Red Sea to the Hawaiian, Marquesan, and Easter Is., n. to s. Japan, s. to Lord Howe, Kermadec, and Rapa Is.; throughout Micronesia.

Thalassoma quinquevittatum (Lay & Bennett,1839)
Five-stripe surge wrasse   Pl. 103A,B

SL: to 131 mm (5.2 in); D VIII, 12-14; A III, 10-12; P 15-17(16); LL 26 (+1 past hypural); GR 21-25 (modally 23); depth 3.2-3.6.

This species inhabits shallow lagoon reef margins and patch reef tops as well as seaward reefs, rarely to a depth of 18 m. It is abundant on shallow exposed seaward reefs. It feeds primarily on small benthic crustaceans·and to a lesser extent on fishes, gastropods, and echinoids.

Indo-Pacific: E. Africa to the Hawaiian (rare), Marquesan, and Tuamotu Is., n. to the Ryukyus, s. to Lord Howe Is.; throughout Micronesia; replaced by *T. cupido* in s. Japan and *T. heiseri* in the Pitcairn group.

Thalassoma trilobatum (Lacepède, 1801)
Christmas wrasse   Pl. 103C,D

(*T. fuscus*; *T. fuscum*, *T. umbrostygma* (in part))

SL: to 244 mm (9.6 in), os 61-< 200mm (2.4-7.9 in), os ≥ 90 mm (3.5 in); D VIII, 12-14; A III, 10-12; P 15-17(16); LL 26 (+1 past hypural); GR 17-24 (modally 20); depth 2.75-3.6.

The primary phase of this wrasse is almost indistinguishable from that of *T. purpureum* (the differences noted under that species). The Christmas wrasse also inhabits surge-swept reef flats, reef margins, and rocky coastlines, but ranges into somewhat deeper water, up to 10 m in certain areas. It is also an active swimmer that feeds primarily on crustaceans, mollusks, and ophiuroids.

Indo-Pacific: E. Africa to the Pitcairn Group, n. to the Ryukyus, s. to Tonga and Rapa; throughout Micronesia.

Labrichthyiform genera: a group of small (<14 cm SL) species with IX, 11 dorsal fin rays, II-III, 10-11 anal fin rays, a continuous lateral line, one or two prominent canines posteriorly on each side of the upper jaw, and a distinctive bilobed lower lip (*Labroides*) or pursed fleshy lips that form a short tube (*Diproctacanthus*, *Labrichthys*, and *Labropsis*) when the mouth is closed (Fig. 20).

a. *Labroides*   b. *Diproctacanthus*   c. *Labrichthys*
Fig. 20. Lip structures of Labrichthyiform genera.

Diproctacanthus xanthurus (Bleeker, 1856)
Wandering cleaner wrasse   Pl. 103E; Fig. 21

SL: to 62 mm (2.4 in); D IX, 9-(10); A II, (9)-10; P 12-14; LL 34-39 (+2 past hypural); GR 6-8; depth 3.1-3.7.

Juveniles are predominantly black with two white lateral stripes and a white streak down the belly. At Belau, this species inhabits shallow lagoons and sheltered seaward reefs in areas of rich coral growth. It feeds on both coral polyps and ectoparasites of other fishes. Unlike species of *Labroides* which occupy a well-defined cleaning station, *Diproctacanthus* roams over a relatively large home range and services mainly small territorial species such as pomacentrids.

Indo-Australian: Java, Moluccas, Philippines, New Guinea, and Belau.

Fig. 21. *Diproctacanthus xanthurus* juvenile, ca. 29 mm.

Labrichthys unilineatus (Guichenot, 1847)
Tubelip wrasse   Pl. 103F,G

(*L. cyanotaenia*)

SL: to 135 mm (5.3 in); D IX, (11)-12; A III, (10)-11; P (14)-15; LL 25-27(26)(+2 past hypural); GR 9-10; depth 2.6-3.2.

The single species of *Labrichthys* lacks teeth in the upper jaw between the two anterior pairs of canines and the large canine in each corner. Small juveniles are black with a conspicuous lateral white stripe and a smaller white stripe running from the lower jaw to the mid-base of the anal fin. The ventral stripe is lost at a small size, followed by the lateral stripe before the fish reaches 65 mm. *Labrichthys unilineatus* inhabits coral-rich areas of lagoon and semi-protected seaward reefs at depths of 0.5 to 20 m. It usually occurs in the vicinity of branching corals and feeds on coral polyps.

Indo-Pacific: E. Africa to Samoa, n. to the Ryukyus, s. to Lord Howe Is., throughout Micronesia.

Labroides bicolor Fowler & Bean, 1928
Bicolor cleaner wrasse   Pls. 5D, 103H, 133E

SL: to 98 mm (3.9 in); D IX, 10-(11); A III, 9-(10); LL 26-28 (+2 past hypural).

Species of *Labroides* are known as "cleaner wrasses" because they feed on external parasites or diseased or damaged tissue of other fishes. They are territorial around certain prominent coral formations known as "cleaning stations". They advertize their trade by "dancing" - swimming with a distinctive up-and-down motion. Their cleaning activities provide a valuable service, and they attract a wide variety of host fishes of all sizes. Many hosts will solicit cleaning by "posing" in unusual positions with their fins and gill-covers flared, or will literally wait in line for their turn. Cleaners are able to safely enter the mouths of large piscivorous fishes who recognize their value as a cleaner and resist the urge to take a one-time meal. Juvenile cleaners are solitary and often somewhat secretive, remaining near holes and providing their services to secretive species such as moray eels. Adults are often paired and may swim well above the reef. The bicolor cleaner wrasse inhabits lagoon and seaward reefs at depths of 2 to at least 40 m. Juveniles and subadults usually maintain a cleaning station along a large overhanging ledge or undercut coral slope. Adults are the nomads of cleaners and tend to travel over a large area within which they may actively "pursue" customers.

Indo-Pacific: E. Africa to the Line, Marquesan, and Society Is., n. to s. Japan, s. to Lord Howe Is.; throughout Micronesia.

Labroides dimidiatus (Valenciennes, 1839)
Bluestreak cleaner wrasse   Pls. 90F; 104A,B

SL: to 93 mm (3.7 in); D IX, 10-(11); A III, 10; P 13; LL 50-52 (+2 past hypural).

This is the most common and widespread of the cleaner wrasses. It inhabits virtually all coral reef habitats from inner lagoons and subtidal reef flats to seaward reefs at depths of over 40. Although haremic, it also occurs in pairs, and serves as a model for the remarkably similarly colored aggressive fin-nipping mimic *Aspidontus taeniatus* (p. 214; Fig. 22). At night, *L. dimidiatus* and presumably other *Labroides* retire to small holes in the reef, sometimes encasing themselves in a mucus cocoon. Although some cleaners do poorly in captivity, this species does well, learning to take a variety of standard aquarium foods.

Indo-Pacific: Red Sea to the Line, Marquesan, and Ducie Is., n. to s. Japan, s. to Lord Howe and Rapa Is.; throughout Micronesia.

a. *Labroides dimidiatus*   b. *Aspidontus taeniatuis*
Fig. 22. Cleaner wrasse mimicry by *Aspidontus*.

Labroides pectoralis Randall & Springer, 1975
Black-spot cleaner wrasse   Pl. 104C

SL: to 60 mm (2.4 in); D IX, 10-12; A III, 9-(10); P 13; LL 28 (+2 past hypural); GR 9-12, depth 3.29-3.95.

This is the smallest and least common of Micronesia's cleaner wrasses. It generally occurs in coral-rich areas of seaward and occasionally lagoon reefs at depths of 2 to 28 m. It maintains a well-defined station and usually occurs in pairs.

West-central Pacific: Christmas Is., Indian Ocean, to the Line, and Pitcairn Is., n. to the Bonins, s. to Rowley Shoals and the Great Barrier Reef; throughout Micronesia.

Labropsis alleni Randall, 1981   Pl. 104D
Allen's wrasse

SL: to 82 mm (3.2 in), ♀s ≤ 71 mm (2.8 in); D IX, 10-(11); A III, 9-10; P 13-15(14-15); LL 27 (+1 past hypural); depth 3.2-3.5.

Unlike other *Labropsis*, this species' coloration does not change greatly with age or sex. It inhabits lagoon and seaward reefs at depths of 4 to 52 m.

Indo-Australian: Indonesia, Philippines, New Guinea, Solomon Is., Belau, and the Marshall Is.

Labropsis micronesica Randall, 1981   Pl. 104E,F
Micronesian wrasse

SL: to 99 mm (3.9 in), ♀s 45-59 mm (1.8-2.3 in); D IX, 12; A III, 11; P 14; LL 35-40; GR 9-11; depth 3.1-3.3.

Juveniles under 40 mm are black with two broad white stripes. This species inhabits clear lagoon and seaward reefs at depths of 7 to over 33 m. Juveniles are usually associated with ramose *Acropora* corals and stay near the protection of the branches. Adults venture up to a meter or more above the reef. Both juveniles and adults engage in cleaning activity, usually servicing small fishes such as damselfishes.

Micronesia: Belau, Caroline, Mariana, and Marshall Is; closely related to *L. manabei* from Scott Reef and the Philippines to the Ryukyus and *L. australis* from the sw. Pacific.

Labropsis xanthonota Randall, 1981   Pl. 104G.H
Wedge-tailed wrasse

SL: to 101 mm (4.0 in), ♀s ≤ 72 mm (2.8 in); D IX, 11; A III, 10; P (14)-15; LL 46-49 (+2 past hypural); GR 7-9; depth 3.45-3.8.

Juveniles are black with several white pinstripes; females become lighter dorsally, and males develop golden centered scales, blue lines on the face, and a wedge-shaped white area in the center of the tail. This species is a relatively uncommon inhabitant of coral-rich areas of clear outer lagoon and seaward reefs at depths of 7 to 55 m. Juveniles are cleaners, adults feed on coral polyps.

Indo-Pacific: E. Africa to Samoa, n. to the Izus, s. to the Great Barrier Reef; Marianas and Marshalls in Micronesia.

SCARIDAE (PARROTFISHES)

Parrotfishes derive their common name from their beak-like dentition (Fig. 1) and often brilliant colors. They evolved from the wrasses and share many labrid characteristics, differing primarily in dentition, digestive tract morphology, and diet. All parrotfishes have a moderately elongate body, an unnotched dorsal fin with IX, 10 dorsal rays, III, 9 anal rays, large cycloid scales, a continuous lateral line with 22 to 25 scales, a terminal mouth with beak-like dentition formed by fused or closely-packed teeth, and a well-developed pharyngeal mill. The pharyngeal mill consists of a pair of interlocking upper bones and a lower bone, the opposing surface of each studded with rows of pavement-like molariform teeth. Most parrotfishes graze on the thin algal film or stubble that grows on bare coral rock, scraping off part of the relatively soft rock with each bite. The pharyngeal mill is used to grind the algal food against scrapings of coral rock, making it more digestible and giving parrotfishes a competetive edge over other herbivores. Their constant grazing makes parrotfishes the most important producers of sediment on most coral reefs. A few species feed partially or almost entirely on live coral while others feed on large leafy algae or seagrasses. At night parrotfishes sleep under ledges or wedged against coral or rock. Some species secrete a veil-like mucus coccoon around themselves as they settle in for the night. This may block their scent from certain nocturnal predators such as moray eels. Like the wrasses, parrotfishes (with one probable exception) are protogynous hermaphrodites that typically go through a series of color changes related to growth and sex. Small juveniles of many species are brown or gray with white stripes. The primary phase is usually a relatively drab gray to reddish-brown and the terminal phase is usually brilliantly colored in various combinations of green, blue, or pink. Most species are diandric, that is the primary phase consists of both males and females; the rest are monandric in which the primary phase consists entirely of females. Terminal males typically result from sex-reversal of females, but in exceptional cases may originate as primary phase males. Terminal males pair-spawn while primary phase males group spawn. Most species of parrotfishes occur in large, often mixed-species schools that may travel over a wide area of reef during the course of a day. Some are territorial and occur in smaller groups. A number of species aggregate at the extremities of underwater promontories to spawn. At Belau, this activity generally peaks from the sixth to the tenth day of the lunar month. Parrotfishes generally swim with their pectoral fins, using their tail only when rapid bursts of speed are required. At least 32 species of parrotfishes occur in Micronesia. In the species accounts below, preD refers to median predorsal scales. (Lit.: Bruce and Randall, 1985; Choat and Randall, 1986; Randall, 1963; Randall and Bruce, 1983; Randall and Choat, 1980; Randall and Nelson, 1979; Robertson et al., 1982; Schultz, 1969)

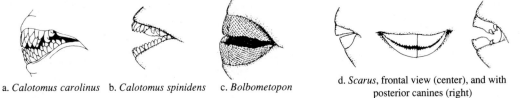

a. *Calotomus carolinus* b. *Calotomus spinidens* c. *Bolbometopon*

d. *Scarus*, frontal view (center), and with posterior canines (right)

Fig. 1. Examples of scarid dentiotion.

Subfamily Sparisomatinae

Sparisomatine parrotfishes have closely-packed conical teeth that are either discrete or are partially fused into rows of dental plates. The partially overlapping rows of teeth on the outer surface of the "beak" gives them a distinctive "bucktoothed" appearance (Fig. 1a). All Indo-Pacific species normally have 13 pectoral rays, a single row of 4 to 5 scales below the eye, 3 to 4 median predorsal scales, and 3 rows of teeth on each upper pharyngeal bone.

Calotomus carolinus (Valenciennes, 1839)
Bucktooth parrotfish; Stareye parrotfish (o)

(*C. sandvicensis* Gosline and Brock, 1960;   Pl. 105A,B
C. spinidens Schultz et al., 1960, in part)
SL: to 398 mm (15.7 in); LL 18-20(19)+6-(7); GR 10-14; depth 2.21-2.73; C of adults double emarginate to lunate; probably monandric.
The bucktooth parrotfish inhabits subtidal reef flats and la-

goon and seaward reefs to a depth of at least 27 m. It ranges widely over a variety of habitats including seagrass beds, coral-rich areas, sand patches, and algal-encrusted rubble or pavement. It occurs singly or in groups but does not seem to be particularly common anywhere. It feeds on seagrasses and a variety of benthic encrusting or leafy algae such as *Padina*. Spawning off the reef front during the falling tide has been observed at Aldabra Atoll (w. Indian Ocean).
Indo-pan-Pacific: E. Africa to the Galapagos Is., n. to the Ryukyu and Hawaiian Is., s. to the Great Barrier Reef and Pitcairn Is.; throughout Micronesia.

Calotomus spinidens (Quoy & Gaimard, 1824)
Spinytooth parrotfish   Fig. 2
SL: to 154 mm (6.1 in), i.p. ≤ 121 mm (4.8 in); LL (19)-20+6-(7); GR 8-11; depth 2.47-3.18; C rounded.
This small parrotfish occurs in shallow sheltered waters where it is restricted to seagrasss beds and patches of dense algae. It feeds on seagrasses, algae, and their associated epi-

phytes. At Aldabra (w. Indian Ocean), spawning occurs above grass flats during falling tides.

Indo-Pacific: E. Africa to the Marshalls, Fiji, and Tonga, n. to the Ryukyus, s. to the Great Barrier Reef; throughout Micronesia.

Fig. 2. *Calotomus spinidens*, 98 mm (after Gloerfelt-Tarp and Kailola, 1982).

Leptoscarus vaigiensis (Quoy & Gaimard, 1824)
Seagrass parrotfish   Pl. 105C

SL: to 268 mm (10.6 in); D X-(IX), 10; P 13; LL 18-20+6-8; GR 8-10; depth 2.84-3.82; 4 predorsal scales; C rounded. *Leptoscarus* differs from *Calotomus* by having teeth fused into rows of dental plates, the upper jaw enclosing the lower jaw, a more elongate body, and less angular head profile. Large males closely resemble females but have numerous blue spots. Examination of a large sample at Aldabra Atoll indicates that this species is unique among scarids by not undergoing sex-reversal. There it spawns in pairs or groups above seagrass flats during falling tides.

Indo-Pacific: Red Sea to Easter Is., n. to the Ryukyu Is., s. to Lord Howe Is. and n. New Zealand; Belau and s. Marianas in Micronesia.

Subfamily Scarinae

The upper and lower jaw teeth of all members of this subfamily are fused into two dental plates separated by a median suture (Fig. 1c-d). Large individuals of several species of *Scarus* may develop a number (usually 1 or two) of discrete canines that protrude from the corners of the upper jaw, and in some species, the lower jaw as well. The outer surface of the beaks of *Bolbometopon* and *Cetoscarus* is nodular and may superficially resemble sparisomatine dentinion. Many species of *Scarus* are so similar morphologically that they can be distinguished only on the basis of color. The color patterns of the small juvenile and primary phases of several species are nearly identical and practically impossible to differentiate in the field. This may be an adaptation against predation. The stripes, mottling or spots of juveniles may help conceal them as they school among coral rubble or algae; the similar drab coloration of the primary phase individuals may enable them to gain a measure of protection by forming large mixed-species schools in which no individual or species stands out. The terminal males are larger and less susceptible to predation, but must be colorful to facilitate species recognition for pair spawning. In the accounts below, the shape of the caudal fin applies to large terminal males only.

Bolbometopon muricatum (Valenciennes, 1839)
Humphead parrotfish   Pl. 105D

SL: to > 100 cm (3 ft 3 in); Wt.: to > 46 kg (100 lbs); possibly to 120 cm (3 ft 11 in) and 75 kg (165 lb); P 15-16; GR 16-18; depth 2.0-2.5; 3 scale rows on cheek; 3-5 predorsal scales; outer surface of beak nodular.

This is the giant of parrotfishes. It is sometimes confused with the humphead wrasse or other "humpheaded" parrotfishes. Unlike the wrasse, it has a vertical head profile, and unlike the other parrotfishes, it is uniformly colored except for the leading edge of the head which is often light green to pink, and has a nodular outer surface to its beak (Fig. 1b). The gibbus forehead begins showing at the small size of 20 cm. The primary phase is a dull gray with scattered white spots, gradually becoming uniformly dark green. The humphead parrotfish typically occurs in schools on clear outer lagoon and seaward reefs at depths of 1 to at least 30 m. In unfished areas it may enter outer reef flats at low tide. It is one of the few scarids that feeds substantially on live coral. It is reputed to use its forehead to ram the corals in order to break them into pieces more easily ingested. The crunching sound of this fish eating may be heard for quite a distance underwater. It is perhaps the wariest of parrotfishes. Yet it has the unfortunate habit of sleeping in large groups making itself highly vulnerable to slaughter at the hands of commercial spearfishermen. It has nearly disappeared from most of Guam's reefs and is rapidly declining in Belau. Although absent from the Marshall Is., it is common at the isolated outpost of Wake Is.

Indo-Pacific: Red Sea to the Line and Tuamotu Is., n. to the Yaeyama and Wake Is., s. to the Great Barrier Reef and New Caledonia; Belau to the e. Caroline, Mariana, and Wake Is. in Micronesia.

Cetoscarus bicolor (Rüppell, 1829)   Pl. 105E,F,G
Bicolor parrotfish

(*Chlorurus bicolor*; *C. pulchellus* for t.p.)

SL: to ca. 60 cm (23.6 in), juvs ≤ 30 cm, o to ca. 35 cm (13.8 in); Wt.: to > 1.5 kg (3.3 lb); P 13-15(14); GR 20-24; depth 2.5-2.8; 3 scale rows on cheek; 4-7 predorsal scales; outer surface of beak nodular; C lunate.

Both *Cetoscarus* and *Hipposcarus* have relatively elongate pointed heads, but are easily distinguished by color pattern as well as the texture of the beak (nodular in *Cetoscarus*; Fig. 1c)) and shape of the tail in adults. The color pattern of this species is unmistakable at all sizes. *Cetoscarus bicolor* inhabits clear lagoon and seaward reefs at depths of 1 to at least 30 m. The juveniles are unusual among scarids by being solitary rather than gregarious. Adult males are territorial and haremic, but may also range over a wide area. Adults seem to prefer the upper reaches of steep coral slopes. They are relatively common in those areas in Belau, but uncommon on the relatively heavily fished reefs of Guam. This is a wary species that is difficult to approach closely.

Indo-Pacific: Red Sea to the Tuamotus, n. to the Izus, s. to the s. Great Barrier Reef; throughout Micronesia.

Hipposcarus longiceps (Valenciennes, 1839)
Pacific longnose parrotfish   Pl. 106A,B,C

(*Scarus harid* Schultz et al., 1960)

SL: to 48 cm (18.9 in); P 14-16(15); depth ca. 2.5-2.9; 3 scale rows on cheek; 4 predorsal scales; C double emarginate.

Small juveniles are light brownish with a broad longitudinal orange band; the primary phase is a whitish brown to light gray with a yellowish tail; the terminal phase is light blue and green. *Hipposcarus longiceps* is common in relatively turbid lagoons, but large adults may occur off seaward reefs to depths of 40 m or more. Juveniles occur among coral rubble of lagoon patch reefs; subadults and adults usually occur over relatively sandy areas near lagoon reefs where their light color blends in well.

West-central Pacific: E. Indies to the Line and Tuamotu Is., n. to the Ryukyus, s. to Rowley Shoals, the Great Barrier Reef, and New Caledonia; throughout Micronesia; replaced by *H. harid* in the Indian Ocean.

Scarus altipinnis (Steindachner, 1879) Pl. 106D,E,F
Filament-finned parrotfish

(*S. brevifilis*; *S. chlorodon* Schultz et al., 1960)

SL: to 41 cm (16.1 in); P 14-16(15); 3 scale rows on cheek; 5-7 predorsal scales; C lunate.

This is the only *Scarus* in which one of the middle dorsal rays of terminal males is produced into a slightly elongate filament. Small juveniles have a distinctive yellow head and striped to mottled body. *S. altipinnis* inhabits outer reef flats and clear lagoon and seaward reefs to a depth of over 50 m. Juveniles and subadults often occur on shallow protected reefs; large adults prefer seaward reefs. This species is common along the seaward reef margin in relatively unexploited areas, but in heavily fished areas large numbers are usually seen only along deep dropoffs.

West-central Pacific: Ryukyu Is. to the Line and Ducie Is., n. to s. Japan, s. to Lord Howe and Rapa Is.; throughout Micronesia.

Scarus atropectoralis Schultz, 1958 Pl. 106G,H
Red parrotfish (i.p.); **Bluechin parrotfish** (t.p.)

SL: to 41.5 cm (16.3 in), i.p. ≤ 33 cm 13.0 in); P 14-(15); GR 38-52; depth 2.55-2.8; 3 scale rows on cheek; 6 predorsal scales; C lunate.

The red coloration and lunate caudal fin of large primary phase individuals are distinctive. Terminal males vaguely resemble those of *S. altipinnis* and *S. prasiognathos*, but the large irregular blue patch under the chin is intermediate in size and shape, and the dorsal fin lacks the filament of *S. brevifilis*. This species is a relatively rare solitary inhabitant of clear lagoon and seaward reefs. Few specimens exist in museum collections and little is known of its life history.

West-central Pacific: Ryukyu, Sulawesi, Belau, and Marshall Is; replaced by *S. caudofasciatus* in the w. Indian Ocean.

Scarus bleekeri (deBeaufort, 1940) Pl. 107A
Bleeker's parrotfish

(*S. troschelii* Schultz, 1969 in part)

SL: to ca. 39 cm (15.4 in); P 14-15; 2 scale rows on cheek;

4 predorsal scales; C truncate.

The initial phase is reddish-brown with a diffuse yellowish patch in the center of the caudal peduncle and markings on the lips similar to those of the terminal male. This species inhabits lagoon and channel reefs and is common at Belau and the high Caroline Islands of Truk and Pohnpei. Terminal males appear to be solitary.

West Pacific: Moluccas to Fiji, n. to the Marshalls, s. to Rowley Shoals (?), the Great Barrier Reef, and Vanuatu; Belau to the e. Carolines and Marshalls in Micronesia; closely related to *S. troschelii* from Java to w. Thailand.

Scarus bowersi (Snyder, 1909) Pl. 107B
Bower's parrotfish

SL: to ca. 25 cm (9.8 in); P 15; 2 rows of cheek scales; (4)-5 predorsal scales; GR 48; C truncate.

This small parrotfish has been recently collected at Belau.

West Pacific: Philippines, Java, Ryukyus, and Belau.

Scarus chameleon Choat & Randall, 1986
Chameleon parrotfish Pl. 107C

SL: to 24.8 cm (9.8 in), i.p. ≤17.6 mm (6.9 in), t.p. ≥15.0 cm (5.9 in); P 13-15(14); 3 scale rows on cheek; (4)-5 predorsal scales; C lunate.

This recently discovered parrotfish inhabits outer reef flats and exposed lagoon and seaward slopes to a depth of at least 30 m. At Belau, males were occasionally observed in coral-rich areas of outer lagoon and seaward reefs at depths of 3 to about 15 m. The initial phase was not distinguished from among the other numerous scarids nearby.

West Pacific: Philippines to Fiji, n. to the Ryukyus, s. to the Abrolhos Is., New South Wales (juvs. only), and Lord Howe Is., Belau in Micronesia.

Scarus dimidiatus Bleeker, 1859 Pl. 107D,E
Turquoise-capped parrotfish

SL: to 22.5 cm (8.9 in), i.p. ≤ 17.4 mm (6.9 in); P 14; depth 2.7-2.9; 3 scale rows on cheek; 5-(6) predorsal scales; C truncate.

This small species closely resembles *S. oviceps* and *S. scaber*. In *S. oviceps*, the initial phase has fewer, less vertical diagonal dark bars on the back and the terminal phase lacks the light-centered bar between the eye and the pectoral fin base, is darker and less brilliant blue on the upper head and back, and is usually larger. *S. dimidiatus* inhabits coral rich areas of protected reefs to a depth of over 12 m. It is relatively common on outer rock island and clear lagoon reefs of Belau.

West-central Pacific: Indonesia to Samoa, n. to the Ryukyus, s. to the Great Barrier Reef; Belau to the e. Carolines and s. Marshalls in Micronesia; replaced by *S. scaber* in the w. Indian Ocean.

Scarus festivus Valenciennes, 1840 Pl. 107F
Festive parrotfish

(*S. lunula*)

SL: to 34 cm (13.3 in), ♀ ≤ 29 cm (11.4 in); P 13-14; GR 38-46; depth 2.4-2.8; 3 scale rows on cheek; 4-5 predorsal scales; C lunate.

The coloration of this species changes slowly with growth. Only specimens under 20 cm are predominately brown. Males develop a distinctive lump on the forehead. *S. festivus* inhabits clear lagoon and seaward reefs at depths of 3 to at least 30 m. It is rare in the Marianas and not particularly common elsewhere in Micronesia.

Indo-Pacific: E. Africa to the Tuamotu Is., n. to the Ryukyus; throughout Micronesia.

Scarus flavipectoralis Schultz, 1958   Pl. 107G
Yellowfin parrotfish

SL: to 21 cm (8.1 in), i.p. ≤ 16 cm (6.3 in); P 14; 3 scale rows on cheek; 3-4 predorsal scales; C lunate.

Large initial phase individuals of this species are tan while terminal phase individuals have a distinctive transparent yellowish-tan pectoral fin. This small species has been observed as shallow as 2 m, it is rare in less than 20 m.

West-central Pacific: Philippines to the Solomon Is., n. to the Marshalls, s. to Scott Reef and the Great Barrier Reef; Carolines and Marshalls in Micronesia.

Scarus forsteni (Bleeker, 1861)   Pl. 108A,B
Forsten's parrotfish

(*S. lepidus* Schultz, 1969; *S. tricolor* Randall & Choat, 1980)

SL: to 40.2 cm (15.8 in), i.p. ≤ 26.5 cm (10.4 in); Wt.: to 2.5 kg (5.5 lb); P 13-15; depth 2.5-2.9; 3 scale rows on cheek; 5-7 predorsal scales; C lunate; diandric.

The initial phase of this species is distinctive, but terminal males closely resemble those of *S. tricolor*. During courtship, the upper head of terminal becomes a deep violet. This species inhabits clear outer lagoon and seaward reefs at depths of 3 to at least 30 m. It is generally solitary.

West-central Pacific: Philippines to Ducie Is., n. to the Ryukyu and Marcus Is., s. to the s. Great Barrier Reef and Rapa Is.; throughout Micronesia; close to *S. tricolor* (Pl. 108H) from the Indian Ocean, Indonesia, Belau, and Line Is.

Scarus frenatus Lacepède, 1802   Pl. 108C,D,E
Vermiculate parrotfish

(*S. sexvitttatus* for t.p.)

SL: to 36 cm (14.2 in), i.p. ≤ 27 cm (10.6 in); P 14-15; depth 2.2-3.0; 3 scale rows on cheek; 6-7 predorsal scales; C double emarginate.

This distinctive species usually occurs on exposed seaward reefs. Juveniles may occur among coral and rubble of clear lagoon reefs. This species is generally solitary and uncommon throughout Micronesia.

Indo-Pacific: Red Sea to the Line and Ducie Is., n. to s. Japan, s. to Shark Bay and Lord Howe and Rapa Is.; throughout Micronesia.

Scarus frontalis Valenciennes, 1839   Pl. 108F
Tan-faced parrotfish

(*S. jonesi*)

SL: to > 38 cm (15.0 in); P 15; 2 scale rows on cheek; 4 predorsal scales; C lunate.

The coloration of this species changes slowly with growth. The light green patch on the caudal peduncle is present on individuals as small as 15 cm and the distinctive tan facial markings are on most individuals above 20 cm. Large males develop a near-vertical forehead profile and long lobes and a well-developed lunate caudal fin. This species occurs in groups along exposed reef flats and seaward reefs to a depth of at least 40 m. In the Mariana and Marshall Islands, it is common along exposed reefs dissected by deep surge channels as well as on open hard-surfaced areas of outer reef slopes.

West-central Pacific: Ryukyus to the Line and Ducie Is., n. to the Ryukyus, s. to the Great Barrier Reef; Marianas and Marshalls in Micronesia.

Scarus ghobban Forsskål, 1775   Pl. 108G
Blue-barred parrotfish

SL: to 57 cm (22.4 in), i.p. ≤ 54 cm (21.3 in); Wt.: to 6.6 kg (14.5 lbs); P 14-16(15); GR 45-53; depth 2.3-3.0; 3 scale rows on cheek; 4-(6) predorsal scales; C lunate.

The yellow and blue-barred primary phase is distinctive, but the terminal phase resembles that of *S. forsteni*. This species inhabits shallow lagoon and seaward reefs to a depth of 30 m. It usually occurs on reefs adjacent to sandy areas of lagoons and bays, sometimes in relatively turbid water. Adults are generally solitary.

Indo-pan-Pacific: Red Sea to Panama, n. to s. Japan, s. to Perth, New South Wales, and Lord Howe and Rapa Is.; throughout Micronesia.

Scarus globiceps Valenciennes, 1840   Pl. 109A,B
Roundhead parrotfish

(*S. aeruginosus* Schultz et al., 1960)

SL: to 23.5 cm (9.3 in), i.p. to 16 cm (6.3 in), os mature at ≥ 10 cm (3.9 in); P (14)-15; GR 46-49; depth 2.6-3.0; 3 scale rows on cheek; ≥ 5 in ventral row; 5-7 predorsal scales; C emarginate; diandric.

The primary phases of *S. globiceps*, *S. psittacus*, and *S. rivulatus* are extremely difficult to distinguish from one another. The combination of number of scale rows on the cheek, number of scales in the ventral row, and number of pectoral rays are diagnostic: *S. globiceps* is the only one of the three with 3 scale rows and 5 or more scales in the ventral row. All three species form large mixed-species schools when feeding on hard open surfaces. *S. globiceps* inhabits clear outer reef flats and lagoons as well as outer reef slopes to a depth of at least 12 m. It has been observed to spawn in groups or in pairs, usually on an outgoing tide.

Indo-Pacific: E. Africa to the Line and Society Is., n. to the Ryukyus, s. to Shark Bay and the s. Great Barrier Reef and Rapa; throughout Micronesia.

Scarus hypselopterus (Bleeker, 1853)   Pl. 109F
Java parrotfish

(*Scarus javanicus*)

SL: to 26 cm (10.1 in); P 14; 3 scale rows on cheek; 4 predorsal scales; C lunate.

Males of this small parrotfish resemble males of *S. bowersi* and an undescribed species (p. 198) with the following differences: the tan area of *S. bowersi* does not extend as far back as the A fin and the undescribed species has a light submarginal band on the tail. Further study is needed to determine the differences between the juveniles and primary phases of these species. This species is rare in Belau.

Indo-Australian: Moluccas, Philippines, Ryukyus, and Belau.

Scarus microrhinos Bleeker, 1854   Pl. 109C,D,E
Steephead parrotfish
(*S. gibbus* of recent useage in the Pacific)

SL: to 49 cm (19.2 in), ♀ to 40 cm (15.8 in); Wt.: to 5.4 kg (11.9 lbs); P 14-17(15); GR 54-75; depth 2.4-2.6; 3 scale rows on cheek; 3-4 predorsal scales; C lunate.

Juveniles under about 8 cm are black with several horizontal white streaks. Larger ones up to about 20 cm are a dark, dull, greenish brown, slowly becoming bluer with age. The blue streak and patch extending behind the corner of the mouth of large males are often quite brilliant. Generally speaking, at a size above 20 cm, this species' coloration changes little with size or growth. Occasionally rare, uniformly yellowish-tan individuals may be seen. *S. microrhinos* inhabits lagoon and seaward reefs at depths of 2 to 35 m. It is among the more common of the large scarids throughout Micronesia. Juveniles are generally solitary, but large adults often school together.

West-central Pacific: e. Indonesia to the Line and Pitcairn Is., n. to the Ryukyus, s. to Shark Bay and Lord Howe and Rapa Is.; throughout Micronesia.

Scarus niger Forsskål, 1775   Pl. 110A
Black parrotfish
SL: to 31.5 cm (12.4 in), o to 25.5 cm (10.0 in); P 13-15 (14); GR 44-50; depth 2.2-2.5; 3 scale rows on cheek; 6-8 predorsal scales; C double emarginate; monandric.

The western Pacific population of this species is monochromatic, but the western Indian Ocean population has a distinctive reddish primary phase (formerly known as *S. madagascariensis*). This species inhabits coral-rich areas of clear lagoons, channels, and outer reef slopes at depths of 2 to over 15 m. It is generally solitary. Males maintain small harems and pair spawn.

Indo-Pacific: Red Sea to the Society Is., n. to the Ryukyus, s. to Shark Bay and the s. Great Barrier Reef; Belau to the e. Carolines and Marshalls in Micronesia.

Scarus oviceps Valenciennes, 1840   Pl. 109G,H
Dark-capped parrotfish
(*S. pectoralis* Schultz, 1958)

SL: to >23 cm (9.1 in); P 14; depth 2.65-3.0; 3 scale rows on cheek; 5-7(6) predorsal scales; C emarginate.

This species resembles *S. dimidiatus*; the differences are described in that species' account. *S. oviceps* inhabits clear outer lagoon reefs and exposed reef flats and seaward reefs to a depth of at least 10 m. It is relatively uncommon in Micronesia.

West-central Pacific: Philippines to the Line and Tuamotu Is., n. to the Ryukyus, s. to Shark Bay and the Great Barrier Reef; throughout Micronesia.

Scarus pyrrhurus (Jordan & Seale, 1906)   Fig. 3
(*S. japanensis* Randall and Choat, 1980; Masuda et al., 1984)

SL: to > 21.5 cm (8.5 in), IP to at least 11.7 cm (4.6 in); P 15; 2 scale rows on cheek; 4 predorsal scales.

The initial phase closely resembles that of *S. sordidus* and possibly *S. bleekeri*, but may be distinguished by its orange-red caudal fin. The dark brown anterior portion and oblique line separating it from the yellowish posterior portion will help distinguish the terminal phase from that of *S. sordidus*. This small parrotfish is known from Micronesia on the basis of observations of the terminal phase on upper reef slopes at Belau where it was relatively rare.

West Pacific: Ryukyus, Philippines, Solomons, Great Barrier Reef, Samoa, and Belau.

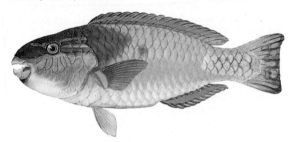

Fig. 3. *Scarus pyrrhurus*, t.p. (after Schultz, 1969).

Scarus prasiognathos Valenciennes, 1839   Pl. 110B
Greenthroat parrotfish
(*S. chlorodon*; *S. janthochir*)

SL: to ca. 51 cm (20.3 in); P 15; GR 56-61; depth 2.3-2.7; 3 scale rows on cheek; 6 predorsal scales.

The initial phase closely resembles that of *S. altipinnis*, but the terminal phase has the distinctive brilliant green throat and lacks the filamentous middle dorsal spine. At Belau, both phases of this species occur in large schools along the upper edges of steep outer reef dropoffs along the leeward barrier reef.

Indo-Australian: Maldives to New Ireland, n. to the Ryukyus, s. to Cocos-Keeling Is.; Belau in Micronesia; replaced by *S. falcipinnis* in the w. Indian Ocean.

Scarus psittacus Forsskål, 1775   Pl. 110C,D
Palenose parrotfish
(*S. forsteri*; *S. taeniurus*)

SL: to 27 cm (10.6 in), i.p. to 17.5 cm (6.9 in); P 13-15 (14); GR 40-50; depth 2.6-3.1; 2 scale rows on cheek; 3-5 (4) predorsal scales; diandric.

The initial phase closely resembles that of *S. globiceps* and *S. psittacus*; the differences are noted in the account of *S. globiceps*. This small species inhabits reef flats and lagoon and seaward reefs to a depth of at least 25 m. It is common over open hard substrates between corals where it often occurs in large mixed-species schools. It is among the most common of scarids at Guam where fishing has greatly reduced the stocks of most of its larger scarid competitors. At night, *S. psittacus* secretes a mucus cocoon.

Indo-Pacific: Red Sea to the Hawaiian, Marquesan, and Tuamotu Is., n. to s. Japan, s. to Shark Bay and Lord Howe Is.; throughout Micronesia.

Scarus quoyi Valenciennes, 1840   Pl. 110E
Quoy's parrotfish
(*S. blochii* Schultz, 1958, 1969)

SL: to 17 cm (6.5 in); P 14; depth ca. 2.4; 3 scale rows on cheek; 6 predorsal scales.

A few solitary terminal males have been observed in coral-rich areas of outer channels and seaward reefs at Belau.

Indo-west Pacific: India to Vanuatu, n. to the Ryukyus, s. to New Caledonia; Belau in Micronesia.

Scarus rivulatus Valenciennes, 1839   ' Pl. 110F
Rivulated parrotfish
(*S. fasciatus*)

SL: to 34 cm (13.4 in), i.p. ≤ 29 cm (11.4 in), t.p. ≥ 19 cm (7.5 in); P 13-15(14-15); 3 scale rows on cheek, (2)-4 in ventral row; 5-7(6) predorsal scales; C truncate with lobes slightly prolonged; diandric.

The initial phase closely resembles that of *S. globiceps* and *S. psittacus*; the differences are noted in the account of *S. globiceps*. At Belau, this species occured in schools in turbid lagoons as well as along the upper edges of clear seaward reefs. Both group and pair spawning have been observed. Reproductively active terminal males become bicolored.

West Pacific: Thailand to New Caledonia, n. to the Ryukyus, s. to Perth and New South Wales; Belau to Pohnpei in Micronesia.

Scarus rubroviolaceus (Bleeker, 1849)   Pl. 110G,H
Redlip parrotfish
SL: to 48 cm (18.8 in), i.p. ≤ 32 cm (12.4 in); Wt.: to 4.5 kg, i.p. to 1.3 kg; P 14-16; GR 52-58; 3 scale rows on cheek; 5-7 predorsal scales; C lunate; monandric.

Both phases of this large parrotfish are distinctively marked and usually have a bicolored appearance with the anterior half abruptly dark. Males develop a gibbus forehead. This species inhabits seaward reefs at depths of 1 to over 30 m. It prefers rocky substrates, particularly boulder-strewn slopes at the base of high-island cliffs where it may occur in large schools.

Indo-pan-Pacific: E. Africa to Panama, n. to the Ryukyu and Hawaiian Is., s. to Shark Bay and the s. Great Barrier Reef and Tuamotus; throughout Micronesia.

Scarus schlegeli (Bleeker, 1861)   Pl. 111A,B
Yellowband parrotfish
(*S. venosus*)

SL: to 31 cm (12.1 in), i.p. mature ≥ 11.6 mm (4.6 in), t.p. ≥ 16.5 cm (6.5 in); P 13-15(14); 2 scale rows on cheek; 4 predorsal scales; C double emarginate.

The initial phase is characterized by a series of irregular dark chevrons which may be difficult to see on dark individuals. The basic color can range from a pale gray to a deep mahogany. Large initial phase fish develop the dark greenish markings around the lip found in the terminal phase. The yellowbar parrotfish inhabits both lagoon and seaward reefs at depths of 1 to over 50 m. Juveniles school with other

species on exposed lagoon and reef flat areas. Adults are common on lagoon pinnacles and seaward reef areas of rich coral growth and high vertical relief. They feed in groups on rubble and mixed rubble-coral slopes rather than on flats. Males seem to be territorial with a limited home range. This species seems more abundant in the Mariana and Marshall Islands than the Caroline Islands.

West-central Pacific: Moluccas to the Tuamotu and Austral Is., n. to the Ryukyus, s. to Shark Bay and the s. Great Barrier Reef and Rapa; throughout Micronesia.

Scarus sordidus Forsskål, 1775   Pl. 111C,D,E
Bullethead parrotfish
SL: to 26 cm (10.2 in), ip. ≤ 21.5 cm (8.5 in); P 14-16 (15); GR 42-51; depth 2.3-3.0; 2 scale rows on cheek; 3-(4) predorsal scales; C truncate; diandric.

The initial phase is highly variable in coloration, both in shade and in pattern. Small individuals may be uniformly dark brown to light gray with or without the dark-centered light area on the caudal peduncle; large individuals may have a series of irregular rows of small light spots posteriorly or have the dark-centered light area on the caudal peduncle. The terminal phase is also somewhat variable with or without a large tan area on the side or the caudal peduncle. This small species occurs in both coral rich and open pavement areas of shallow reef flats and lagoon and seaward reefs to a depth of over 25 m. Small juveniles commonly occur among coral rubble of reef flats and shallow lagoons. This and other scarids may migrate over great distances of reef to get from their sleeping areas to daytime feeding grounds. All but the largest individuals secrete a mucus cocoon at night. At Aldabra Atoll, Indian Ocean, this species spawns throughout the year during high tide and the first two hours of the falling tide during daylight hours. Although common throughout Micronesia, this is perhaps the most abundant parrotfish in the southern Marianas. This may be the result of reduced competition from larger species whose stocks have been reduced by heavy fishing pressure. Small species with a high turnover rate seem better able to withstand exploitation and are more abundant in the southern Marianas than the relatively unexploited northern Marianas where they must compete with large numbers of larger species.

Indo-Pacific: Red Sea to the Hawaiian, Line, and Ducie Is., n. to the Ryukyus, s. to Perth, New South Wales, and Lord Howe and Rapa Is.; throughout Micronesia.

Scarus spinus Kner, 1868   Pl. 111F
Pygmy parrotfish
(*S. formosus* Schultz, 1960)

SL: to 22.5 cm (8.9 in); ip. mature at 11 cm (4.3 in), tp. at 13.1 cm (5.2 in); P 13-15(14); 3 scale rows on cheek; 3-5(4) predorsal scales; C emarginate; diandric.

The initial phase is dark brown with a reddish-brown head, belly, and fins and 4 to 5 indistinct broad pale bars that can be "turned" on or off at will. This small species inhabits coral-rich areas of outer lagoon and seaward reefs at depths of 2 to 15 m. It is uncommon and patchily distributed through much of its range. At Belau small numbers were observed in Ulong Channel and other coral rich areas of outer lagoon and seaward reefs.

West-central Pacific: Philippines to Samoa, n. to the Ryukyus, s. to the s. Great Barrier Reef; Belau to the e. Carolines and Marshalls in Micronesia.

Scarus n. sp.   Pl. 111G
Pale-margined parrotfish
SL: to ca. 25 cm (9.8 in).

This small parrotfish has been known from photographs taken off Guam for the past 10 years, but it took the widespread collecting efforts of J. E. Randall and colleagues as well as the process of elimination to finally determine that it has

never been described. The broad light green marginal band on the inner caudal rays will immediately distinguish this species from all other Micronesian scarids. The intensity of the stripes on the belly of the male can be changed at will. At Guam, this species is a relatively uncommon inhabitant of steep outer reef slopes and offshore banks at depths of 18 to over 40 m. Males appear to be territorial and haremic, dominating a small group of initial phase fish within a limited home range.

Indo-Australian: Philippines, Ryukyus, New Guinea, and Guam.

MUGILIDAE (MULLETS)

Mullets are silvery, somewhat cylindrical fishes with a short broadly rounded snout, small mouth with or without minute teeth, two widely separated dorsal fins, the first with IV spines, and pelvic fins located well behind the pectoral fins. They have moderately large, usually cycloid scales, and lack a well-developed lateral line. Some species have well-developed adipose eyelids. Lip development is variable with some genera characterized by normal lips, others by papillate, lobed, or folded lips. Mullets typically feed on fine algae and detritus from the surface of bottom sediments. The inorganic sediment is expelled through the gill chambers and the organic material is passed through a thick-walled, gizzard-like stomach and long intestine. Most species can tolerate a wide range of salinities. Some range into purely fresh water and are important in aquaculture. A few species are most at home on coral reefs. At least 8 species in 5 genera occur in Micronesia. Although listed in several technical reports, there are no verifiable literature records of the cosmopolitan *Mugil cephalus* in the region. LR= number of scales in the first continuous row above the pectoral fin base from directly above the rear margin of the head to the caudal fin base.

Key to Micronesian Mugilidae:

1a. Lips folded and lobed...*Oedalechilus labiosus*
1b. Lips not folded and lobed...2
2a. Lower jaw angle acute as seen from below..........................*Chaenomugil leuciscus*
2b. Lower jaw angle obtuse as seen from below..3
3a. A base short, ca. 11 in SL; upper lip wide, with prominent papilla.........................
....*Crenimugil crenilabis*
3b. A base broad, ca. 8 in SL; no papillae on upper lip...4
4a. Adipose eyelids well-developed, extend ≥ an eye diameter beyond eye (Micronesian records unverified)..(*Mugil cephalus*)
4b. Adipose eyelids not as well developed, extend < pupil diameter beyond eye, or absent.
....5
5a. Maxilla end mostly concealed when mouth shut; P axillary scale pointed and long; body scales with pliable membranous edges...6
5b. Maxilla end exposed when mouth shut; P axillary scale small or absent; no membranous edge to body scales..7
6a. Prominent black spot on upper P axil; C prominently forked...........*Valamugil seheli*
6b. No prominent black spot on upper P axil; C nearly truncate in juveniles, moderatley forked in adults...*Valamugil engeli*
7a. Second D origin above hind half of A fin base................................*Liza ceramensis*
7b. Second D origin above front half of A...8
8a. A III, 8, its base short, ca. 11 in SL; P black; C truncate and yellow to tan...............
....*Liza vaigiensis*
8b. A III, 9, its base broad, ca. 7 in SL; P pale to dusky; C lunate and dusky................
....*Liza melinoptera*

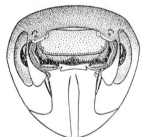

Oedalechilus labiosus,
frontal view*
1a

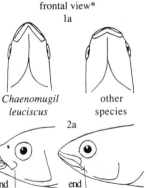

Chaenomugil   other
leuciscus   species
2a

end   end
exposed   hidden
a   b

*After A. M. Awl *in* Schultz et al., 1953.   5

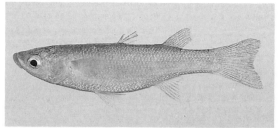

a. *Chaenomugil leuciscus*, 45 mm SL, Guam

d. *Liza vaigiensis*, 93 mm SL, Guam

b. *Crenimugil crenilabis*, 124 mm SL, Guam

e. *Valamugil engeli*, 118 mm SL, Guam

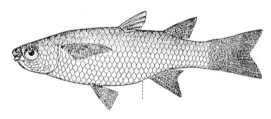

c. *Oedalechilus labiosus*, 150 mm SL, Bikini

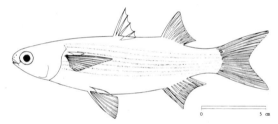

f. *Valamugil seheli*, ca. 161 mm SL

Fig. 1. Micronesian mullets (c, after A. M. Awl *in* Schultz et al., 1953; f, after FAO, 1974).

Chaenomugil leuciscus (Günther,1871)   Fig. 1a
Acute-jawed mullet
(*Neomyxus chaptalii*)
SL: to 46 cm (18.1 in); D IV+I, 10; A III, 10; P 15; LR 48.
In life, this species has a characteristic yellow spot on the upper base of the pectoral axil. This is the most common lagoon and seaward reef mullet in the Marshalls, but is rare in the Marianas.
Pacific Plate: Mariana and Bonin Is. to the Hawaiian, Line, and Ducie Is.; Ifaluk, Marianas, and Marshalls in Micronesia.

Crenimugil crenilabis (Forsskål, 1775)
Fringelip mullet   Pl. 112B; Fig. 1b
SL: to 50 cm (19.7 in); D IV+I, 8; A III, 9; P 16-17; LR 37-41.
This mullet occurs in sandy areas of lagoons and on reef flats. Helfrich and Allen (1975) observed spawning during the month of June at Enewetak Atoll. There, this species gathered in large aggregations (500 to 1500 individuals) over shallow open sandy areas of the lagoon slope for two to three days after new moon. The entire school spawned at

once, well after dark (1030 pm), then partially dispersed. Unlike many reef fishes, they spawned at the beginning of ebb tide so that the incoming tidal current washed the gametes into the lagoon rather than out to sea. The sex ratio was 1:1 and each female carried 195,000 to 897,000 eggs.
Indo-Pacific: Red Sea to the Line and Tuamotu Is., n. to s. Japan, s. to Lord Howe Is.; Ifaluk, Marianas, and Marshalls in Micronesia.

Liza ceramensis (Bleeker, 1852)
Ceram mullet
SL: to ca. 15 cm (5.9 in); D IV+I, 8-9; A III, 9; LR 30-31; C not deeply concave.
Helfrich and Randall (1973) list this coastal species from Belau (as *Mugil ceramensis*) without further comment.
Indo-west-Pacific: Sri Lanka to the Solomon Is.; Belau in Micronesia.

Liza melinoptera (Valenciennes, 1836)
Giantscale mullet
SL: to 24 cm (9.6 in); D IV+I, 8; A III, 9; P 15, no axillary scale; LR 26-28.
This species occurs in fresh-water rivers and lakes as well as

in marine waters. It has recently been listed from Belau.

Indo-west Pacific: E. Africa to Samoa, n. to the Philippines, s. to Tonga; Belau in Micronesia.

Liza vaigiensis (Quoy & Gaimard, 1824)   Fig. 1d
Yellowtail mullet; Squaretail mullet

SL: to 51.5 cm (20.3 in); D IV+I, 8; A III, 8; P 16, no axillary scale visible; LR 26-28; C truncate.

This unmistakable mullet occurs in lagoons and on reef flats where it is most common along protected sandy shorelines.

Indo-Pacific: E. Africa to the Tuamotus, n. to s. Japan, s. to the s. Great Barrier Reef and New Caledonia; throughout Micronesia.

Oedalechilus labiosus (Valenciennes, 1836) Fig. 1c
Foldlip mullet

SL: to > 40 cm (15.7 in); D IV+I, 7-9; A III, 9; P 17-18; LR 32-37.

This is the only Micronesian mullet that has peculiar folded and lobed lips (fig. 1 of key).   It occurs on reef flats and shallow lagoon reefs.

Indo-Pacific: Red Sea to the Marshalls, n. to s. Japan, s. to the s. Great Barrier Reef; Ifaluk and Marshalls in Micronesia.

Valamugil engeli (Bleeker, 1858)   Pl. 112A; Fig. 1e
Engel's mullet

SL: to 15 cm (5.9 in); D IV+I, 9-10; A III, 8-9; P 15-17; LR 31-35.

In the Marianas, this is perhaps the most common mullet of shallow protected sandy to muddy areas of reef flats and shallow lagoons. Juveniles have been found living in 40°C (104°F) water in tidepools.

Indo-Pacific: E. Africa to the Marquesan and Tuamotu Is., n. to the Yaeyamas; Ifaluk, Marshalls, and Marianas in Micronesia; introduced to the Hawaiian Is.

Valamugil seheli (Forsskål, 1775)   Fig. 1f
Bluespot mullet

SL: to 48 cm (18.9 in); Wt.: to 8 kg (17.6 lb); D IV+I, 9; A III, 9; P 18, axillary scale 3.2 in head; LR 38-42.

This mullet has recently been collected at Guam.   Small schools have been observed on the shallow lagoon slope of Luminao Reef.

Indo-west Pacific: Red Sea to Samoa, n. to s. Japan, s. to New Caledonia; Marianas in Micronesia.

POLYNEMIDAE (THREADFINS)

These odd looking relatives of the mullets have silvery bodies with an inferior mouth containing villiform teeth, 3-8 free, elongate simple rays connected to the lower base of the pectoral fins, two widely-spaced dorsal fins, a deeply forked caudal fin, and moderately large scales. The thread-like lower pectoral rays are used as feelers and become relatively shorter with growth. Threadfins typically occur over shallow sandy to muddy bottoms. Some species enter freshwater. One or more species occurs in Micronesia.

Polydactylus sexfilis (Valenciennes, 1831)
Sixfeeler threadfin; Moi   Pl. 111H

SL: to 25 cm (9.8 in); D VIII+I, 13; A III, 11; P 15+6 free rays; LP 66-67.

This species occurs along sandy shorelines and over sandy lagoon bottoms. The larger *P. plebeius* with 5 free pectoral rays and fewer pored lateral line scales (58-65) probably also occurs in the area.

Indo-Pacific: India to the Hawaiian, Marquesan, and Tuamotu Is., n. to the Yaeyama and Bonin Is.; throughout Micronesia.

SPHYRAENIDAE (BARRACUDAS)

Barracudas, like their close relatives, the mullets, are silvery and nearly cylindrical anteriorly, have two widely separated dorsal fins, pelvic fins located well behind the pectoral fins, and a forked caudal fin. They differ most obviously in their more elongate body, pointed head, and large mouth with projecting lower jaw and long knife-like teeth on the jaws and palatines. They have small cycloid scales and a well-developed lateral line. Barracudas are voracious predators of other fishes; a large one is capable of cutting a large parrotfish in two with a single bite. Some species are primarily diurnal, while others are nocturnal and occur in innactive schools during the day. The young of most species and adults of some are common in estuarine areas. Attacks on man have been documented but these are invariably the result of mistaken identity or outright provocation such as being speared! Attractants such as metalic jewelry flashing in the sun or speared fish, particularly in murky water, are frequently cited. The single genus is in need of revision and identification of some of the smaller species is difficult. At least 6 species occur in Micronesia; *S. chrysotaenia* and *S. putnamiae* may also be in the region. Lateral line counts are for all pored scales including those on the caudal base. (Lit.: DeSylva *in* Smith and Heemstra, 1986).

Key to Micronesian Sphyraenidae:

1a. GR absent...2

1b. GR present...5

2a. LL 75-85; sides of body with irregular black blotches below LL..............*S. barracuda*
2b. LL > 100; sides of body without irregular black blotches....................................3
3a. No crossbars or contrasted markings on body..*S. forsteri*
3b. Crossbars or contrasted markings on body...4
4a. Preopercle obliquely rounded; teeth us. slanted backwards; last rays of second D and A the longest..*(S. putnamiae)*
4b. Preopercle smoothly rounded; teeth erect; anterior rays of second D and A the longest..*S. genie*
5a. A single GR at angle of 1st gill arch; LL 120-155..6
5b. Two (rarely 3) GR on 1st gill arch; LL 80-96...7
6a. First D origin above or in front of V origin; LL 122-128, usually 124-127; body depth 6.5-8.5 in SL..*S. acutipinnis*
6b. First D origin distinctly behind V origin; LL 127-155, usually 127-140; body depth 9.5-10 in SL...*S. novaehollandiae*
7a. Tip of P reaches beyond first D origin; first D height ≥ postorbital head length and > than distance between first and second D......................................*(S. chrysotaenia)*
7b. Tip of P does not reach beyond first D origin; first D height < postorbital head length and < than distance between first and second D......................................*S. obtusata*

obliquely
rounded

last rays
long

4a

smoothly
rounded

last
rays short

4b

Sphyraena acutipinnis Day, 1876   Pl. 112C
Sharpfin barracuda
(S. helleri)
SL: to 69 cm (27.2 in); D V+I, 8; A II, 8; P 14; LP 122-128; GR 1; depth 6.5-8.5 in SL.
In life this small barracuda has two thin longitudial yellow stripes. It occurs in schools over lagoon and seaward reefs.
Indo-Pacific: E. Africa to the Hawaiian, Marquesan, and Tuamotu Is., n. to s. Japan; throughout Micronesia.

Sphyraena barracuda (Walbaum, 1792)   Pl. 112D
Great barracuda
SL: to 165 cm (5 ft 5 in); Wt.: to 38 kg (84 lbs); D V+I, 9; A I, 10; P 13-15; LP 77-85; GR 0; depth 6.4-8.3 in SL.
The great barracuda is most easily distinguished from its relatives by the double emarginate tail fin with pale tips on each lobe, and (usually) the presence of a few scattered black blotches on the lower sides. Juveniles occur among mangroves and in shallow sheltered inner reef areas. Adults occur in a wide range of habitats ranging from murky inner harbors to the open sea. This is a solitary, diurnal species that may be quite curious and approach a diver closely. It is also the species responsible for most attacks on man, but in clear water and unprovoked conditions, is not a danger. The greatest threat is from ciguatera. Fatal cases have been reported in the West Indies where it is banned from sale. Non-fatal cases have been reported from Guam where it is a commercially important troll-caught species. Large individuals should be treated with caution.
Indo-Pacific and Atlantic: Red Sea to the Hawaiian, Marquesan, and Tuamotu Is., n. to s. Japan, s. to Lord Howe Is.; throughout Micronesia.

Sphyraena forsteri Cuvier, 1829   Pl. 112E
Blackspot barracuda
SL: to 65 cm (25.6 in); D V+I, 9; A II, 9; P 14-15; LP 112-123; GR 0 (10-20 small spiny tubercles on lower limb); depth 6.9-7.7 in SL.
During the day this species occurs in large schools above lagoon patch reefs and along outer reef slopes to a reported

depth of 300 m.
Indo-Pacific: E. Africa to the Marquesan and Society Is., n. to the Ryukyus; s. to New Caledonia; throughout Micronesia.

Sphyraena genie Klunzinger, 1870   Pls. 6A;112F
Blackfin barracuda
SL: to 147 cm (4 ft 10 in); D V+I, 9; A II, 8; P 15; LP 120-130(127-130); GR 0; depth 6.0-7.9 in SL; ca. 18-22 crossbars.
During the day this "chevroned" barracuda often occurs in large, tightly-packed schools that have a tendency to occupy the same sites for months or even years at a time. An enormous school is usually present off a certain current-swept submarine terrace along the leeward dropoff of Belau known as "the Corner". At night they probably disperse to feed. Large adults may be solitary. This is the species of barracuda most often hooked by trolling between dusk and dawn.
Indo-pan-Pacific: Red Sea to Panama, s. to New Caledonia and the Tuamotu Is.; throughout Micronesia.

Sphyraena novaehollandiae Günther, 1860
Arrow barracuda   Pl. 112G
SL: to 50 cm (19.7 in); D V+I, 9; A II, 8; P 13-14; LP 127-155; GR 1; depth 9.5-10.0 in SL.
This small, extremely elongate species occurs in schools in channels and other semi-protected areas. Its distribution is uncertain due to past confusion with the deeper-bodied *S. acutipinnis*.
Indo-Pacific: E. Africa (?) to Papua New Guinea and n. Australia; Carolines and Marianas in Micronesia.

Sphyraena obtusata Cuvier, 1829   Pl. 112H
Pygmy barracuda
(S. chinensis; S. flavicauda?)
SL: to 33 cm (13.0 in); D V+I, 9; A II, 9; P 13; LP 80-90; GR 2; depth 6.8-8.3 in SL.
Considerable confusion surrounds the identities of several closely related small schooling barracudas (*chrysotaenia*, *flavicauda*, *pinguis*). Others may also be present in Micro-

nesia. This species occurs in schools above lagoon and seaward reefs.

Indo-west Pacific: E. Africa (?) to Samoa, n. to the Ryukyus, s. to Lord Howe Is.; Kapingamarangi and Marianas in Micronesia.

PINGUIPEDIDAE (SANDPERCHES)

Only one of the three pinguipedid genera, *Parapercis*, occurs in the Indo-Pacific. It is characterized by an elongate, nearly cylindrical body, a terminal protractile mouth, a long continuous dorsal fin with IV-VII spines and 20-24 rays, a long anal fin with 15-21 soft rays, a complete lateral line, small ctenoid scales, and a truncate to emarginate caudal fin. Species of *Parapercis* are benthic carnivores of small invertebrates and fishes. They typically occur on sandy bottoms, but some species range onto rubble, rock, or coral as well. Several species occur at depths of 100 to 360 m. Most species are sexually dichromatic; protogynous hermaphroditism is likely. Males are territorial and haremic. In the tropics, courtship and spawning occur just before sunset the year round. The eggs are pelagic and the larval period lasts from one to two months. Four shallow-water species occur in Micronesia. Most recent works use the invalid family name Mugiloididae. (Lit.: Cantwell, 1963; Rosa and Rosa, 1987)

Parapercis clathrata Ogilby, 1910   Pl. 113A,B
Latticed sandperch
SL: to 153 mm (6.0 in); D (IV)-V, 20-(21); A I, 17; P 17-18; LL 57-60; GR 3+11.

Males develop a conspicuous ocellus on each side of the nape. In the Marianas, this sandperch is common on both clear lagoon and seaward reefs at depths of 3 to 50 m. It occurs on open sand and rubble as well as on rocky surfaces between coral heads.

Indo-Pacific: Persian Gulf to the Phoenix and Samoan Is., n. to the Ryukyus, s. to the s. Great Barrier Reef; throughout Micronesia.

Parapercis cylindrica (Bloch, 1797)   Pl. 113C
Cylindrical sandperch
SL: to 126 mm (5.0 in), 170 mm (6.7 in) in s. Japan; D V, (21)-22; A I, 17; P 14-16; LL 48-52; GR 3+6.

This small sandperch occurs on sand and rubble lagoon bottoms depths of 1 to 20 m.

Indo-Pacific: Maldives to Fiji, n. to the Ryukyus, s. to Lord Howe Is.; Belau and the Marshalls in Micronesia.

Parapercis millipunctata (Günther, 1860)   Pl. 113D
Black-dotted sandperch
(*P. cephalopunctata*)

SL: to 153 mm (6.0 in), 170 mm (6.7 in) in s. Japan; D IV, 20-(21); A I, 16-17; LL 59-60.

This species and *P. clathrata* differ in details of coloration, which changes with growth. Unlike *P. clathrata*, *P. millipunctata* lacks spots on the anal fin and males do not develop a pair of conspicuous ocelli on the nape. *P. millipuncta-*

ta occurs primarily on seaward reefs at depths of 3 to 50 m. It is usually found on patches of rubble or pavement between corals.

Indo-Pacific: Mauritius to the Society Is., n. to the Ryukyus, s. to the s. Great Barrier Reef; throughout Micronesia.

Parapercis xanthozona (Bleeker, 1849)   Pl. 113E
Blotchlip sandperch
SL: to >130 mm (5.1 in); D V, 21; A I, 17-18; P 32-36; LP 58-62; LR ca. 55-64; GR 6-7+12.

This sandperch closely resembles *P. cylindrica*, differing by having a yellowish tail and an additional dark bar extending forward from the lower front of the eye. It inhabits sandy and weedy areas of reef flats.

Indo-west Pacific: E. Africa to Fiji, n. to s. Japan, s. to New South Wales; Belau in Micronesia.

TRICHONOTIDAE (SAND-DIVERS)

Sand-divers are extremely elongate, somewhat compressed fishes covered with moderately large cycloid scales. They have a large mouth with a projecting lower jaw and small sharp teeth, a long continuous dorsal fin, long anal fin, pelvic fin with I, 5 rays, and a continuous lateral line. During the day they occur in large groups that hover within 1 to 3 meters above open expanses of sand. Males are territorial and haremic. They have filamentous dorsal spines and large, fanlike pelvic fins which are extended during courtship. In a Red Sea species, spawning occurs at dawn, immediately after emergence from the sand.

Trichonotus sp.   Pl. 113F,G
Micronesian sand-diver
SL: to ca. 15 cm (5.9 in); D elements 44; A elements 41; P 14 (based on a single 34 mm specimen).

At Guam, this as yet unnamed species, is quite common on large sandy expanses of seaward reefs at depths of 9 to 18 m. It occurs in loose aggregations that hover within 2 meters above the sand. When pursued they either disappear, ghost-like into the distance, or dive beneath the sand. Large males often undertake a display in which they extend their long dorsal filaments and large fanlike pelvic fins. Either this or another undescribed species has recently been collected from shallow lagoon sand flats at Belau and Enewetak. It is closely related to *T. elegans* from the Ryukyus and the widespread Indo-Pacific *T. setigerus*.

CREEDIDAE (SAND BURROWERS)

These small trichonotid-like fishes are translucent in life (except for a series of narrow dark saddles in some species), lack spines on all fins but the pelvics, and have vertically-oriented eyes located on top of the head. Unlike the trichonotids, they remain on or just beneath the sand. They are virtually invisible to the diver, but commonly found in poison stations. (Lit.: Nelson and Randall, 1985)

Chalixodytes tauensis Schultz, 1943   Fig. 1
Saddled sandburrower

SL: to 40 mm (1.6 in); D 35-37; A 36-38; P 11-13; V I, 4;
LL 57-59; scaled on back in front of D, on LL, and on sides
far posteriorly.

This small fish lives in loose coral sand of shallow exposed
seaward reefs and sandy shorelines to a depth of at least 10
m.

West-central Pacific: Christmas Is. (Indian Ocean), Mariana,
Marshall, Samoan, Tuamotu, and Pitcairn Is.; possibly
conspecific with *C. chameleontoculis* of the w. Indian
Ocean.

Fig. 1. *Chalixodytes tauensis* (after A. M. Awl *in* Schultz,
1960).

Limnichthys donaldsoni Schultz, 1960   Fig. 2
Donaldson's sandburrower

SL: to 21 mm (0.8 in); D 19-22; A 23-26; P 11-12; V I, 5;
LL 36-38; completely scaled behind head.

This species inhabits surge-swept sand patches and shorelines.

West-central Pacific: Rowley Shoals, n. Great Barrier Reef,
and Marshall, Samoan, and Hawaiian Is.

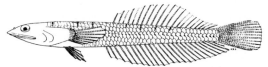

Fig. 2. *Limnichthys donalsoni* 17.5 mm SL (after D. B.
Schultz, *in* Schultz 1960).

URANOSCOPIDAE (STARGAZERS)

Stargazers are characterized by a thick body with a massive
dorsally-flattened armored head, a large vertically-oriented
mouth with fringed lips and small teeth, and a small first
dorsal fin of 3-5 spines (in genus *Uranoscopus*) followed by
a longer soft-rayed second dorsal fin. A large venemous
spine is present on each shoulder girdle above the pectoral
base and their is no lateral line. Stargazers typically lie buried in sand or mud with only their eyes and lips exposed.
Some have a worm-like tentacle in the lower jaw which is
used as a lure to attract small fishes which are immediately
engulfed. Most tropical species seem to occur in relatively
deep water.

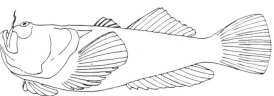

Fig. 1. Generalized uranoscopid.

Uranoscopus sp.

Two specimens, possibly of different species, have been col-
lected in the Marianas: one at a depth of 124-135 m on 45°
Bank nw of Rota, and the other from a depth of 57 m off
Guam by J. E. Randall.

TRIPTERYGIIDAE (TRIPLEFINS)

Triplefins are the only coral reef fishes that have three dorsal fins. All are quite small and moderately elongate with a continuous or divided lateral line, ctenoid scales, and I, 2 pelvic rays (spine short and imbeded). They are benthic carnivores of small
invertebrates that inhabit intertidal and shallow reef waters. At least 7 species in 3 genera occur in Micronesia. The two species figured in color (Pl. 113H,I) will likely remain unidentified until they are collected. (Lit.: Hadley-Hansen, 1986).

Key to Micronesian Trypterygiidae:

1a. First D with IV spines; A II; head mostly scaled behind eye...*Norfolkia brachylepis*
1b. First D with III spines; A I; head naked..2
2a. LL divided, the second series consisting of notched scales; body nearly completely scaled...genus *Enneapterygius*: 3
2b. LL continuous; body scaled anteriorly only on LL..genus *Helcogramma*: 5
3a. LP 16-19 pored scales+16-19 notched scales..*E. hemimelas*
3b. LP 11-14 pored scales+19-21 notched scales..4
4a. P, A, and body behind head pigmented; a small cirrus above eye..*E. minutus*
4b. P, A, and body behind head unpigmented; no cirrus above eye...*E. nanus*

5a. Second and third D with dark oblique bars...***H. hudsoni***
5b. Second and third D without dark oblique bars..6
6a. Upper jaw ending below anterior half of eye; dark facial pigment of males ≥ 20 mm covers chin.............***H. chica***
6b. Upper jaw ending below posterior half of eye; dark facial pigment of males ≥ 20 mm fades on chin.....***H. capidata***

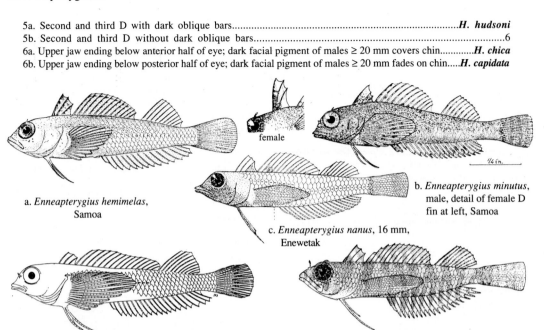

a. *Enneapterygius hemimelas*, Samoa

female

b. *Enneapterygius minutus*, male, detail of female D fin at left, Samoa

c. *Enneapterygius nanus*, 16 mm, Enewetak

d. *Helcogramma chica*, 21 mm, Phoenix Is.

e. *Norfolkia brachylepis*, 26 mm, Bikini

Fig. 1. Micronesian triplefins (a, b, after Jordan and Seale, 1905; c, g, after A. M. Awl *in* Schultz et al., 1960; d, e, after D. B. Schultz *in* Schultz et al., 1960).

Enneapterygius hemimelas
(Kner & Steindachner, 1866)   Fig. 1a
SL: to 27 mm (1.1 in); D III+XII-XIII+9-10; A I, 17-19(17-18); P ca. 15; LL 16-19(pored)+16-19 (notched).
This species inhabits surf-swept reef margins.
Pacific Plate: Ryukyu, Mariana, Marshall, Samoan, and Phoenix Is.

Enneapterygius minutus (Günther, 1877)   Fig. 1b
Minute triplefin
SL: to 21 mm (0.8 in); D III+X-XIII+8-9; A I, 15-17; P ca. 14; LL 11-14 (pored)+19-21(notched).
This species inhabits seaward reefs in areas of strong surge.
West-central Pacific: Vanuatu, and Ryukyu, Mariana, Marshall, Samoan, and Phoenix Is.

Enneapterygius nanus (Schultz, 1960)   Fig. 1c
Pygmy triplefin
SL: to 19 mm (0.7 in); D III+XI-XIII+9-10; A I, 16-19; P ca. 13; LL 11-14(pored)+19-21(notched).
This species inhabits high isolated tidal pools and waves-swept tops of lagoon reefs. Males are heavily pigmented under the head. Females as small as 14 mm (0.6 in) may contain about 12 ripe eggs.
Mariana and Marshall Is.

Helcogramma capidata Rosenblatt *in* Schultz, 1960
Hooded triplefin
SL: to 37 mm (1.5 in); D III+XIII-XV(XIV)+10-12; A I,

19-21; P 15-17; LP 20-27.
This species inhabits surge-swept reef margins. Males are dark-headed giving them a hooded appearance.
Pacific Plate: Belau to the Phoenix, Samoan, and Fiji Is.; throughout Micronesia.

Helcogramma chica Rosenblatt *in* Schultz, 1960
SL: to 25 mm (1.0 in); D III+XVI+9-12;   Fig. 1d
A I, 18-20; P 15-17; LP 18-23.
This species inhabits the surge zone of exposed reefs. Females may mature by a size of 15 mm (0.6 in).
Indo-Pacific: Sri Lanka to the Phoenix and Samoan Is., n. to the Izu Is.; throughout Micronesia.

Helcogramma hudsoni (Jordan & Seale, 1906)
Hudson's triplefin
SL: to 35 mm (1.4 in); D III+XII-XIV+9-11(10); A I, 17-20(19); P 15-17; LP 20-29.
Indo-Pacific: Laccadive Is. to Samoa, n. to the Izu Is., s. to the Coral Sea; Marshall Is. in Micronesia.

Norfolkia brachylepis (Schultz, 1960)   Fig. 1e
SL: to 25.5 mm (1.0 in); D IV+XIV+9; A II, 19; P 15; LP 14+22.
This heavily pigmented species lives on coral or rock, often under ledges, on clear lagoon and seaward reefs at depths of 2 to at least 12 m.
West-central Pacific: Christmas Is. (Indian Ocean), Mariana, Marshall, and Samoan Is.

BLENNIIDAE (BLENNIES)

Blennies are typically small, elongate, scaleless, blunt-headed fishes with a long continuous dorsal fin, anal fin with II spines (the first may be imbedded in in females), and V I, 2-4 pelvic rays. Blennies in general are bottom-dwelling territorial fishes that lay adhesive demersal eggs which are often guarded by the male. The family may be divided into two subfamilies, distinguished primarily by dentition and diet. The combtooth blennies (subfamily Salariinae) are feeble-toothed, wide-mouthed, blunt-headed herbivores; the sabretooth blennies (subfamily Blenniinae) are typically small-mouthed, large-fanged carnivores. Many of the combtooth blennies are well-camouflaged, and complexly yet similarly patterned, making identification in the field difficult. At least 59 species in 23 genera of blennies occur in Micronesia. (Lit.: Carlson, 1985; Smith-Vaniz, 1976, 1987; Smith-Vaniz and Springer, 1971; Springer, 1968, 1971, 1972, 1975, 1981, 1985, 1985, *in* Smith and Heemstra, 1986; Springer and Gomon, 1975; Williams, 1985, MS).

Subfamily Salariinae (Combtooth blennies)

The combtooth blennies have a wide downturned mouth with a single row of close-set incisiform teeth in each jaw that are used for scraping filamentous algae from the surfaces of rock or dead coral. Many species have tentacles or cirri over the eye, anterior nostril, or along the nape; some have a fleshy crest on top of the head (occipital or nuchal crest; Fig. 1). Most are well-camouflaged sedentary inhabitants of rocky shorelines, reef flats, or shallow seaward reefs.

Key to Micronesian genera of Salariinae:

1a. Elongate transverse series of cirri continuous across nape or interrupted briefly in center...................................2
1b. Nape cirri, if present, restricted to a single cirrus or a patch of cirri on each side of nape, widely separated......3
2a. A 14-16(rarely 14); both upper and lower jaw teeth freely movable, subequal in breadth......................***Cirripectes***
2b. A (14)-15; upper jaw teeth freely movable, lower jaw teeth barely movable and nearly twice as broad as upper jaw teeth...***Exallias***
3a. Nuchal and/or supraorbital cirri present; C rays unbranched or unbranched; lateralmost tooth on each dentary similar to adjacent teeth.....................................4
3b. Nuchal and supraorbital cirri absent; all C rays unbranched; lateralmost tooth on each dentary more robust than adjacent teeth.......................................***Ecsenius***
4a. D IX-XI; all C rays unbranched; P 15-18(16); color of head and body almost uniform...................***Atrosalarias***
4b. D XII-XVII (rarely XI); C rays branched or unbranched; P 13-16 (rarely 16); color not uniform......................5
5a. Total D elements 21-23, rays 9-12; A 10-13.....***Stanulus***
5b. Total D elements 26-38, rays 13-24; A 14-28.............6
6a. Teeth in upper jaw freely movable, usually >120 in adult... 7
6b. Teeth in upper jaw immovable or nearly so, 18-80.....11
7a. All C rays unbranched; A 23-28........................***Alticus***
7b. Some C rays branched near tips in adults; A 17-25......8
8a. The following combination of characters: occipital crest present, nuchal cirri absent, nasal cirri simple or with a short side branch, supraorbital cirri pinnately branched in adults...***Praealticus***
8b. The above combination of characters never present in combination...9
9a. V 2-3; nuchal crest present or absent.........................10
9b. V 4; nuchal crest absent or present only as a low fold.... ....***Entomacrodus***
10a. Terminal A ray completely free from C peduncle; D

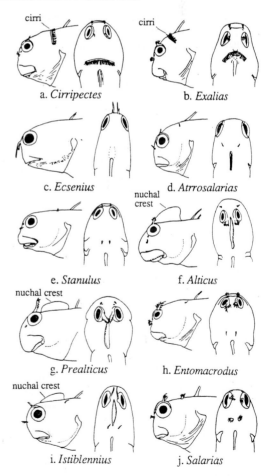

a. *Cirripectes*   b. *Exalias*

c. *Ecsenius*   d. *Atrrosalarias*

nuchal crest

e. *Stanulus*   f. *Alticus*

nuchal crest

g. *Prealticus*   h. *Entomacrodus*

nuchal crest

i. *Istiblennius*   j. *Salarias*

Fig. 1. Heads of Micronesian genera of Salariinae
(cont. on p. 206).

XIII-XIV, notched; V 3...........................***Istiblennius***

10a. Terminal A ray partially bound to C peduncle by membrane; D (XII)-XIII, not notched; V 2..............***Salarias***

11a. D 14-16; upper jaw teeth 74-80; lower jaw teeth 42-58...12

11b. D 17-21; upper jaw teeth 18-50; lower jaw teeth 16-38...13

12a. Fleshy crest on midline of nape (poorly developed in females); P 12-14; V 2; no vomerine teeth...***Glyptoparus***

12a. No fleshy crest on midline of nape; P 15; V 3; vomerine teeth present...............................***Nannosalarias***

13a. All C rays unbranched; minute nuchal cirri present.......
....***Litobranchus***

13b. Central C rays branched near tips; nuchal cirri absent...
....***Rhabdoblennius***

Alticus saliens (Lacepede, 1800)   Fig. 2a
Leaping blenny

SL: to 80 mm (3.1 in); D XIV, 21-23(22); A II, 25-(27); P 15; depth 6.0-6.4; o with nuchal crest.

This elongate species inhabits moist shaded pockets of pitted limestone in the spray zone above the water line. They have an amazing ability to leap from hole to hole when disturbed.
Indo-Pacific: Red Sea to the Society Is., n. to the Ryukyu and Bonin Is., s. to Queensland; Marianas in Micronesia.

Atrosalarias fuscus holomelas (Günther, 1866)
Highfin blenny   Fig. 2b

SL to ca. 70 mm; D X, 19-21; A II, 18-20; P 16-17; V I, 2.
This uniformly yellowish blenny lives among the branches of *Acropora* corals in lagoons and on the seaward reef crest.
Indo-Pacific: Sumatra to the Society Is., n. to the Ryukyus, s. to New Caledonia and Tonga; Belau to the e. Carolines and s. Marshalls in Micronesia; the subspecies *fuscus* (Rüppell, 1835) from the Red Sea to Pakistan.

Key to Micronesian species of ***Cirripectes***:

1a. Pelvic rays 3...2
1b. Pelvic rays 4...3
2a. Lateral line complete...................................***polyzona***
2b. Lateral line incomplete...............................***perustus***
3a. Nuchal cirri 47-66................................***fuscoguttatus***
3b. Nuchal cirri ≤ 47...4
4a. D rays normally 14 (rarely 13 or 15); A rays normally 16 (rarely 15)..5
4b. D rays normally 15 (rarely 14 or 16); A rays normally 15 (rarely 14 or 16)...6
5a. Nuchal cirri 23-36; body somewhat elongate, its depth 3.7-4.0 in SL...***quagga***
5b. Nuchal cirri 32-47; body deeper, its depth 3.1-3.3 in SL.
....***stigmaticus***
6a. Body relatively deep, its depth 2.8-3.2 in SL; nuchal cirri 29-46, with mid-dorsal hiatus; females with honeycomb pattern, males barred...........................***castaneus***
6b. Body more elongate, its depth 3.3-3.8 in SL; nuchal cirri 26-39, with a small mid-dorsal hiatus; color not honeycombed or barred, but dark and with red spots on head of males...***variolosus***

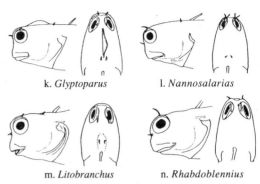

k. *Glyptoparus*   l. *Nannosalarias*

m. *Litobranchus*   n. *Rhabdoblennius*

Fig. 1. Heads of Micronesian genera of Salariinae (cont. from p. 205).

Cirripectes castaneus (Valenciennes, 1836)
Chestnut blenny

SL: to 99 mm (3.9 in); D XII, 13-15 (14); A II, 14-16(15); P (15)-16; V I, 4; depth > 2.8; 29-46 nuchal cirri.
Species of *Cirripectes* and *Exallias* are unique among Micronesian blennies by possessing a transverse fringe of cirri across the nape (termed nuchal fringe). They are also somewhat deeper-bodied than most blennies. They generally station themselves near holes into which they dart if approached. Adult females have a honeycombed pattern and adult males are barred (some preserved specimens may be uniformly brown). This species inhabits the wave-swept algal ridge (*Porolithon* ridge) of outer reef flats.
Indo-west Pacific: Red Sea to Tonga, n. to s. Japan; s. to Lord Howe Is.; Belau, Ifaluk, and Kapingamarangi in Micronesia.

Cirripectes fuscoguttatus Strasburg & Schultz, 1953
Spotted blenny   Fig. 2c

SL: to 125 mm (4.9 in); D XII, 14; A II, 15 (first spine rudim. in o); P 15; V I, 4; depth ca. 2.8; 47-66 nuchal cirri.
This species closely resembles females of *Exallias brevis* but has larger, more widely-spaced spots and lacks distinct papillae on its upper lip.
Pacific Plate: s. Taiwan to the Tuamotus, s. to Tonga; throughout Micronesia.

Cirripectes perustus Smith, 1959

SL: to 90 mm (3.5 in); D XII, 14; A II, 15; P 14-(15); V I, 3; depth ca. 3.25; 30-46 nuchal cirri.
Indo-Pacific: Kenya to Kiribati, n. to Taiwan; Belau, Yap, and Ifaluk in Micronesia.

Cirripectes polyzona (Bleeker, 1868)
Barred blenny   Pl. 114A,B; Fig. 2d

(*C. sebae* Schultz and Chapman, 1960)
SL: to 103 mm (4.1 in); D XII, 14; A II, 15; P 15; V I, 3; depth 3.1-3.5; 32-44(≤ 42) nuchal cirri.
Individuals under 50 mm have a broad lateral band; adults of both sexes are barred, but have more nuchal cirri than do similarly barred *C. quagga*. Both species inhabit the algal ridge and ridge crests between surge channels of exposed seaward reefs to a depth of about 3 m. They feed on filamen-

a. *Alticus saliens*, female, 50 mm (top); male, 51 mm, Saipan

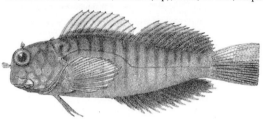

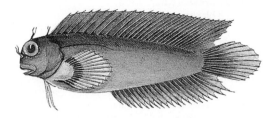

b. *Atrosalarias fuscus*

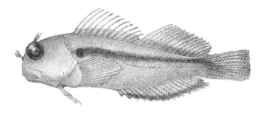

c. *Cirripectes fuscoguttatus*, Rongerik

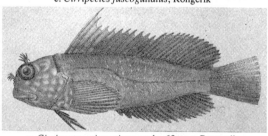

d. *Cirripectes polyzona*, female, 47 mm (top); male, 33 mm

e. *Cirripectes stigmaticus*, male, 63 mm, Rongerik

Fig. 2. Micronesian species of comtooth blennies (b, after Bleeker; c, after A. M. Awl *in* Schultz et al, 1960; d, e, after Strasburg and Schultz *in* Schultz et al, 1960).

tous algae and associated minute invertebrates such as foraminiferans, ostracods, and gastropods.

Indo-Pacific: S. Africa to Kiribati, n. to Taiwan; s. to Rowley Shoals and the s. Great Barrier Reef; throughout Micronesia.

Cirripectes quagga Fowler & Ball, 1924
Squiggly blenny

SL: to 75 mm (3.0 in); D XII, 14-(15); A II, 16; P 15; V I, 4; depth 3.7-4.0; 23-36 nuchal cirri.

This species is characterized by numerous squiggly bars on its sides. It inhabits the algal ridge and crests between surge channels of exposed seaward reefs.

Indo-Pacific: n. to s. Taiwan, e. to the Hawaiian, Marquesan, and Tuamotu Is.; throughout Micronesia.

Cirripectes stigmaticus Strasburg & Schultz, 1953
Red-streaked blenny   Fig. 2e

SL: to 100 mm (3.9 in); D XII, 14-16(15); A II, 15-(16); P 14-16(15); V I, 4; depth 3.1-3.3; 32-47(≥35) nuchal cirri,

the dorsalmost not all fused basally.

Large individuals of his species are dark green to black with red spots on the head and red spots to vertical streaks on the sides. It lives among *Acropora* and *Pocillopora* corals of the surf-swept algal ridge.

Indo-Pacific: w. Indian Ocean to Samoa, s. to the s. Great Barrier Reef and New Caledonia; Belau to the e. Carolines and Marshalls in Micronesia.

Cirripectes variolosus (Valenciennes, 1836)
Red-speckled blenny   Pl. 114C

SL: to 70 mm ; D XII, (14)-15; A II, (15)-16; P 15; V I, 4; depth 3.3-3.8; 26-39 nuchal cirri.

In the Marianas, this species is common on exposed seaward reefs at depths of .5 to 5 m. It typically shelters at bases or among the branches of *Pocillopora* corals.

Pacific Plate: Belau to Johnston Is., the Marquesas, and Pitcairn Is., n. to the Bonin Is., s. to Rapa; throughout Micronesia; closely related to *vanderbilti* from the Hawaiian and Johnston Is.

Exalias brevis (Kner, 1868)   Pl. 114D
Leopard blenny
SL: to 111 mm (4.4 in); D XII, 12-(13); A II, (14)-15; P 15; depth 2.6-2.7; 30-36 nuchal cirri; no canines posteriorly on lower jaw.

The numerous papillae on the upper lip, smaller and more closely spaced spots, and brighter red spotting in males distinguish this species from *Cirripectes fuscoguttatus*. *Exalias brevis* inhabits seaward reefs from the lower surge zone to a depth of over 20 m. It lives on corals of the genera *Acropora*, *Pocillopora*, *Seriatopora*, *Porites*, and *Millepora*, and feeds almost exclusively on coral polyps. Feeding is spread out over a large area of coral tissue and normally does little harm to the coral. Males are territorial as well as larger and more colorful than females. The reproductive biology of this blenny has been studied in the Hawaiian Islands. Males prepare a nesting site by overgrazing and killing a patch of coral, usually within the relative shelter of a crevice. Females may move freely between male territories and deposite their eggs in up to ten different male's nests. Nests may also contain more than one females eggs, and both males and females occasionally cannibalize eggs! Spawning occurs throughout the year with a peak from January to April.

Indo-Pacific: Red Sea to the Hawaiian, Marquesan, and Society Is, n. to the Ryukyu and Bonin Is., s. to New Caledonia and Rapa; throughout Micronesia.

Key to Micronesian species of *Ecsenius*:

1a. Segmented D rays 15-18 (rarely 15); segmented A rays 17-21 (rarely 17)...*bicolor*
1b. Segmented D rays 12-15; segmented A rays 14-17 (rarely 17)..2
2a. Large ocellate spots along bases of soft D and C...........
....*sellifer*
2b. No large ocellate spots along bases of soft D and C.....3
3a. P base with distinct Y-shaped dark mark; body with irregular light and dark spots or stripes........*yaeyamaensis*
3b. P base unmarked; body with 2 longitudinal rows of large light spots..*opsifrontalis*

E. sellifer   E. yaeyamaensis
2a   3a

Ecsenius bicolor (Day, 1888)   Pl. 114E,F
Bicolor blenny
SL: to 78 mm (3.1 in), o to 60 mm (2.4 in); D XI-(XII), 15-18(16-18); A II, 17-21(18-20); P 12-14(13); V I, 3.

Species of *Ecsenius* lack branched fin rays and have cirri only on the anterior nostrils. They are typically small colorful inhabitants of coral-rich areas. This species occurs in three color phases: one black anteriorly and yellow posteriorly (bicolor phase), the others black dorsally with a broad white lateral band and dusky belly with or without a yellow tail. It has been suggested that the bicolor phase mimics the poison-fang blenny, *Meiacanthus atrodorsalis*, but this seems doubtful since their behavior is quite different: *M. atrodorsalis* spends most of its time hovering while *E. bicolor* remains on the bottom. *E. bicolor* occurs on both lagoon and seaward reefs in areas of mixed corals and algae-covered rocks at depths of 2 to 25 m.

Indo-Pacific: Maldives to the Phoenix Is., n. to the Ryukyus, s. to the s. Great Barrier Reef; throughout Micronesia.

Ecsenius opsifrontalis Chapman & Schultz, 1960
Comical blenny   Pl. 114G
SL: to 39 mm (1.5 in), o to 35 mm (1.4 in); D XII, 12-14 (13); A II, 14-16(15); P 12-14(13); V I, 3.

This comical looking blenny is the most common species of *Ecsenius* throughout Micronesia. It inhabits coral-rich areas of lagoon and seaward reefs from below the surge zone to a depth of at least 30 m. It typically rests between corals or on the sides of crevices or shallow caves.

Micronesia, Gilbert Is., Rotuma, and Samoa: throughout Micronesia.

Ecsenius sellifer Springer, 1988   Fig. 3
Saddle blenny
SL: to 41 mm (1.6 in); D XII, 13-14; A II,(15)-16; P 13; V I, 3.

This species has been reported from depths of 6 m or less.

Belau, New Guinea, and Solomon Is.: many closely related forms in adjacent areas of the western Pacific.

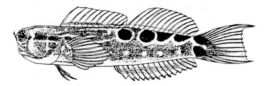

Fig. 3. *Ecsenius sellifer*.

Ecsenius yaeyamaensis (Aoyagi, 1954)   Pl. 114H
Yaeyama blenny
SL: to 52 mm (2.0 in), o to 43 mm (1.7 in); D XI-XIII (XII), 13-15; A II, 14-17(15-16); P 12-(13); V I, 3.

Indo-west Pacific: Sri Lanka to Vanuatu, n. to Taiwan and the Yaeyama Is., s. to Shark Bay and the s. Great Barrier Reef; Belau in Micronesia.

Key to Micronesian species of *Entomacrodus*:

1a. Orbital tentacle long, > diameter of eye, simple (rarely a single cirrus on inner edge); middle third of edge of upper lip crenulate; posterior canines minute; dark spot between first two D spines.................................*stellifer*
1b. Orbital tentacle short, < diameter of eye, 2-3 ciiri on inner edge; edge of upper lip not as above; posterior pair of canines in lower jaw well-developed; no dark spot between first two D spines..2
2a. Edge of upper lip entirely smooth; inner edge of orbital tentacle with 2-3 cirri; small black spot a little behind eye..*thalassinus*

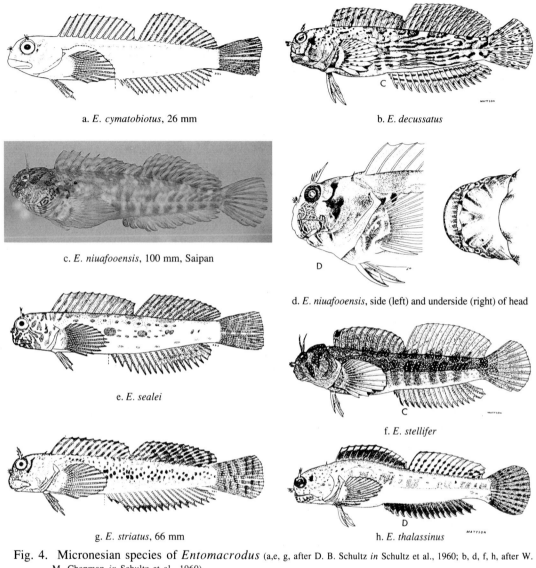

a. *E. cymatobiotus*, 26 mm

b. *E. decussatus*

c. *E. niuafooensis*, 100 mm, Saipan

d. *E. niuafooensis*, side (left) and underside (right) of head

e. *E. sealei*

f. *E. stellifer*

g. *E. striatus*, 66 mm

h. *E. thalassinus*

Fig. 4. Micronesian species of *Entomacrodus* (a,e, g, after D. B. Schultz *in* Schultz et al., 1960; b, d, f, h, after W. M. Chapman *in* Schultz et al., 1960).

2b. Part or all of edge of upper lip crenulate....................3
3a. Middle third of upper lip smooth, the remaining sides crenulate...4
3b. Edge of upper lip entirely crenulate............................5
4a. A black spot just above and behind P base.*caudofasciatus*
4b. No black spot just above and behind P base..........*sealei*
5a. Nuchal tentacle single, rather broad based, sometimes with 1-2 short cirri.....................................*decussatus*
5b. Nuchal tentacle single, simple without cirri on edges...6
6a. Orbital tentacle with 2 or more cirri that arise basally and not from edge of main cirrus; D 13-14; A 15..........
....*cymatobiotus*

6b. Orbital tentacle with a single base, 1-7 cirri on inner edge, with or without cirri on outer edge; D 15-17; A 15-19..7
7a. D 16-(17); A 18-19....................................*decussatus*
7b. D 15-16; A 15-17; no dark shoulder spot...................8
8a. Front of snout and upper lip with numerous dark streaks; sides plain dusky; head without white spots................
....*niuafooensis*
8b. Front of snout plain dusky except edge of upper lip with very narrow and faint dark streaks; sides with small dark spots grouped into 5-6 indistinct vertical bars; head with white spots..*striatus*

Entomacrodus caudofasciatus (Regan, 1909)
Tail-barred rockskipper

SL: to 62 mm (2.4 in); D XIII, 14-16(15-16); A II, 15-17 (16); P 14; V I, 4; GR 13-18.

Species of *Entomacrodus* inhabit rocky intertidal shorelines, benches, outer reef flats, and reef margins subject to some degree of wave action. Several species may occur in the splash zone above the high tide line. They are most often encountered by walking on the reef at low tide.

Indo-Pacific: Andamans to Ducie Is., n. to s. Japan, s. to Cocos-Keeling, Kermadec, and Rapa Is.; Belau and Marshalls in Micronesia.

Entomacrodus cymatobiotus
    Schultz & Chapman, 1960   Fig. 4a

SL: to 27 mm (1.1 in); D XIII, 13-14; A II, 15; P 14; V I, 4; depth 4.5-4.7.

This species inhabits surf-swept seaward reefs.

Pacific Plate: Caroline, Marshall, Kermadec, Line, and Tuamotu Is.

Entomacrodus decussatus (Bleeker, 1857) Fig. 4b
(*E. anietensis* Schultz and Chapman, 1960)

SL: to 67 mm (2.6 in); D XIII, 16-(17); A II, 17-19; P 14; V I, 4; depth 4.0-4.3.

This species inhabits surf-swept reef margins.

West-central Pacific: Thailand to the Society Is., n. to the Ryukyus, s. to New Caledonia and Tonga; Marianas, Kapingamarangi, and Marshalls in Micronesia.

Entomacrodus niuafooensis (Fowler, 1932)
Tatoo-chin rockskipper   Fig. 4c,d

SL: to ca. 100 mm (3.9 in); D XIII, 15-16; A II, 16-17; P 14; V I, 4; depth ca. 4.4.

The intricate pattern on the chin of this species is distinctive. It inhabits intertidal benches and exposed reef flats.

Indo-Pacific: Comore Is. to Easter Is., n. to the Ryukyu and Bonin Is., s. to the Kermadec and Rapa Is.; Marianas in Micronesia.

Entomacrodus sealei Bryan & Herre, 1903 Fig. 4e
Seale's rockskipper
(*E. incisolabiatus* Schultz and Chapman, 1960)

SL: to 61 mm (2.4 in); D XIII, 14-16; A II, 16-17; P 14; V I, 4; depth 4.2-5.1.

This species inhabits surf-swept seaward reefs.

Pacific Plate: Mariana and Caroline Is. to the Line and Pitcairn Is., s. to Rapa; throughout Micronesia.

Entomacrodus stellifer stellifer
    Jordan & Snyder, 1902   Fig. 4f
Stellar rockskipper

SL: to > 39 mm (1.5 in); D XIII, 16; A II, 18; P 14; V I, 4; depth ca. 4.3.

This species inhabits rocky shorelines.

West Pacific: Thailand, Taiwan, and the Ryukyu and Mariana Is.; the subspecies *lighti* from s. Japan.

Entomacrodus striatus (Quoy & Gaimard, 1836)
Pearly rockskipper   Pl. 114I; Fig. 4g
(*E. p. plurifilis* and *E. p. marshallensis* Schultz and Chapman, 1960)

SL: to 82 mm (3.2 in); D XII-XIV, 14-16; A II, 15-18; P 13-15; V I, 4; depth 4.8-5.2.

This species is common on intertidal reef flats. At low tide it inhabits small pockets of water left in pitted limestone.

Indo-Pacific: E. Africa to the Line and Ducie Is., n. to the Ryukyu, Bonin, and Marcus Is., s. to Lord Howe and Rapa Is.; throughout Micronesia.

Entomacrodus thalassinus thalassinus
    (Jordan & Seale, 1906)   Fig. 4h
Reef margin blenny

SL: to ca. 40 mm (1.6 in); D XIII, 13-15(14); A II, 15-17; P 14; V I, 4; depth 4.9-5.1.

This species inhabits surf-swept reef margins.

Indo-Pacific: Seychelles to the Line and Tuamotu Is., n. to s. Japan, s. to the s. Great Barrier Reef; throughout Micronesia; the subspecies *longicirrus* from Thailand to s. Taiwan.

Glyptoparus delicatulus Smith, 1959   Pl. 115C
Delicate blenny

SL: to ca. 40 mm (1.6 in); D XII, 16-17; A II, 18-19; P 13; V I, 3; depth ca. 5.5.

This species has a distinctive black bar across the chin and a dark spot on each side of the gill membrane just in front of the pectoral base. It occurs in protected areas of mixed coral and sand.

Indo-west Pacific: E. Africa to Rotuma, n. to the Ryukyus, s. to Rowley Shoals; Pohnpei and Guam in Micronesia.

Key to Micronesian species of *Istiblennius*:

1a. 22-25; A 23-25; edge of upper lip crenulate.......*lineatus*
1b. D <22; A usually <23 (rarely 23); edge of upper lip smooth or crenulate..2
2a. Edge of upper lip crenulate..................................3
2b. Edge of upper lip smooth......................................4
3a. Red spots on head large; no elongate bright silvery to bluish spots on sides.............................*chrysospilos*
3b. Red spots on head mostly tiny specks; 5-6 pairs of elongate bright silvery to bluish spots on sides.................
    ....*periophthalmus*
4a. Lower jaw with canine posteriorly on each side........
   5
4b. Lower jaw without canines posteriorly.......*edentulus*
5a. Black spot on membrane between first and second D spines..*gibbifrons*
5b. No black spot on membrane between first and second D spines..*cyanostigma*

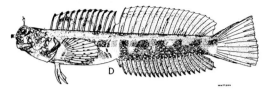

a. *I. chrysospilos*

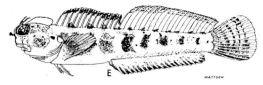

b. *I. cyanostigma*

d. *I. cyanostigma*, female, 57 mm, Guam

c. *I. edentulus*, male, 67 mm (top); female, 59 mm, Guam

e. *I. periophthalmus*, male, 63 mm, Guam

Fig. 5. Micronesian species of *Istiblennius* (a, b, after Chapman *in* Schultz et al., 1960).

Istiblennius chrysospilos (Bleeker, 1857)
Red-spotted blenny
Pl. 115A; Fig. 5a

(*I. coronatus*)

SL: to 107 mm (4.2 in); D XII, 20-21; A II, 21-22; P (14)-15; V I, ; depth 4.4-5.3.

Many species of *Istiblennius* have a fleshy occipital crest which tends to be better developed in males. Several species occur with species of *Entomacrodus* in rocky intertidal or supratidal areas but some range into slightly deeper water of outer lagoon and seaward reefs. This species is a common inhabitant of outer intertidal reef flats and surge-swept seaward reef to a depth of 6 m. It has the habit of wriggling into a small hole such as an abandoned worm tube, leaving only its colorful head protruding. It feeds on algae and associated detritus and minute invertebrates.

West-central Pacific: Indonesia to Samoa, n. to the Ryukyus, s. to Rowley Shoals and the s. Great Barrier Reef; throughout Micronesia.

Istiblennius cyanostigma (Bleeker, 1849) Fig. 5b,d
Blue-spotted blenny

SL: to 74 mm (2.9 in); D XIII, 19-20; A II, 20-22; P 14; depth 4.8-6.4.

Females have numerous longitudinal pinstripes on their sides and black specks on their fins while males have dark patches small blue spots on their sides. This species has been collected in rocky tidal pools.

West-central Pacific: Kapingamarangi, Kiribati, and the Moluccan, Mariana, Solomon, Society, and Tuamotu Is.

Istiblennius edentulus (Bloch & Schneider, 1801)
Rippled rockskipper
Pl. 115B; Fig. 5c

SL: to 137 mm (5.4 in); D XII-XIII, 19-21; A II, 21-23; P 14; depth 4.7-4.8.

This large blenny is common along the water line of rocky areas subject to slight to moderate wave action. It shelters in cracks or holes when not grazing on the adjacent rock surface.

Indo-Pacific: Red Sea to the Line, Marquesan, and Tuamotu Is., n. to s. Japan, s. to Lord Howe and Rapa Is.; throughout Micronesia.

Istiblennius gibbifrons rodenbaughi
Schultz & Chapman, 1960
Picture rockskipper

(*I. rodenbaughi* Schultz and Chapman, 1960)

SL: to 102 mm (4.0 in); D XII-XIII, 18-20; A II, 20-21; P 14; depth 5.0-5.8.

This species has a complex pattern of light spots that coalesce on the head and upper body to form a honeycomb-like network. It inhabits barren outer intertidal reef flats where the substrate consists of a thin carpet of algal turf and sand. Several geographically distinct subspecies have been named.

Micronesia: Marianas and Marshalls for the subspecies *rodenbaughi*. Other named subspecies include *insolitus* from the w. Indian Ocean; *afilinuchalis* from the Phoenix, Line, and Caroline (?) Is.; and *gibbifrons* from the Hawaiian and Johnston Is.; unspecified forms e. to Ducie and n. to Marcus Is.

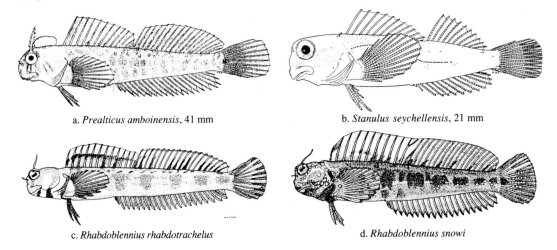

a. *Prealticus amboinensis*, 41 mm

b. *Stanulus seychellensis*, 21 mm

c. *Rhabdoblennius rhabdotrachelus*

d. *Rhabdoblennius snowi*

Fig. 6. Micronesian combtooth blennies (a,b, after D. B. Schultz; c,d, after Chapman, all *in* Schultz et al., 1960).

Istiblennius lineatus (Valenciennes, 1836) Pl. 115E
Lined rockskipper
SL: to 118 mm (4.6 in); D (XIII)-XIV, 22-25; A II, 23-25; P 14; depth 5.1-5.3.

Living specimens may exhibit a complex facial pattern similar to, but not quite as intricate as, that of *Entomacrodus niuafoouensis*, and barely discernable parallel pinstripes on their sides. It inhabits the intertidal zone of beach rock and outer reef flats.

Indo-Pacific: E. Africa to the Line and Society Is., n. to s. Japan, s. to s. Queensland; throughout Micronesia.

Istiblennius periophthalmus (Valenciennes, 1836)
Blue-dashed rockskipper   Pl. 115D; Fig. 5e
(*I. paulus* (Bryan & Herre, 1903) for w. Pacific color form)
SL: to 127 mm (5.0 in); D XII-XIII, (20)-21; A II, 20-(21); P, 14; depth 5.3-7.0 (based only on Micronesian specs.).

This species is common on exposed outer intertidal reef flats, particularly in areas with numerous cracks and holes. Like *I. coronatus*, it has the habit of disappearing in small holes with only its head protruding. It feeds on filamentous algae and associated minute invertebrates including foraminiferans, ostracods, copepods, and gastropods.

Indo-Pacific: Red Sea to the Marquesan and Tuamotu Is., n. to the Ryukyus; throughout Micronesia.

Litobranchus fowleri (Herre, 1936)
Fowler's rockskipper
SL: to 35 mm (1.4 in).

This small blenny inhabits tidepools and rocky shores to a depth of over 9 m.

Indo-Australian: Philippines, Moluccas, w. New Guinea, and Belau.

Nannosalarias nativitatus (Regan, 1909)
Pygmy blenny
SL: to ca. 40 mm (1.6 in); D XII, 15-16; A II, 16-18; P 14-15; V I, 3.

Males have a distinct black blotch ventrally on each side of the head. This species occurs on the seaward reef crest and outer reef slope.

West Pacific: Christmas Is., Indian Ocean, to Samoa, n. to the Ryukyus, s. to Rowley Shoals and the s. Great Barrier Reef and Tonga; Pohnpei in Micronesia.

Prealticus amboinensis (Bleeker, 1857)   Fig. 6a
Ambon rockskipper
SL: to ca. 120 mm (4.7 in); D XII-(XIII), 17-20; A II, 18-20; P 14-(15); V I, 4; depth 5.0-5.8.

This species occurs along semi-exposed rocky shorelines.

West Pacific: Moluccas to Samoa, n. to s. Japan; Guam in Micronesia.

Prealticus natalis (Regan, 1909)
Natal rockskipper
SL: to 53 mm (2.1 in); D XII-XIII, 17-18; A II, 18-20; P 14-(15); V I, 4; depth 4.8-5.0.

This species differs from *P. amboinensis* by possessing smooth-edged rather than crenulate lips, and dusky V-shaped bars on the snout and underside of the head. It occurs in the intertidal zone of rocky shorelines. An additional undescribed species has recently been photographed at Kwajalein.

West Pacific: Christmas Is., Indian Ocean, and the Marianas.

Rhabdoblennius rhabdotrachelus
(Fowler & Ball, 1924)   Fig. 6c
SL: to 41 mm (1.6 in); D XII, 18-19; A II, 20-21; P 14; V I, 3; depth 5.0-5.8.

Species of *Rhabdoblennius* lack the deep notch in the dorsal fin characteristic of *Alticus*, *Entomacrodus*, *Istiblennius*, and *Prealticus*, as well as an occipital crest and nuchal cirri. Both Micronesian species inhabit intertidal reef flats, benches, and rocky shorelines exposed to strong wave action.

Pacific Plate: central and e. Caroline, Mariana, Marshall, Wake, Marquesan, and Ducie Is.

Rhabdoblennius snowi (Fowler, 1928) Fig. 6d
Snow's rockskipper
SL: to 46 mm (1.8 in); D XII, 18-19; A II, 19-21; P 14; V I, 3; depth 5.1-5.5.
Tropical w. Pacific: Christmas Is., Indian Ocean, to Kiribati; throughout Micronesia.

Salarias fasciatus (Bloch, 1786) Pl. 115F
Jeweled blenny
SL: to 112 mm (4.4 in); D XII, 18-20; A II, 19-21; P 14; V I, 3; depth 3.7-4.3.
Throughout most of Micronesia, this large combtooth blenny is common in reef flat areas of mixed coral, sand, and rubble. It also occurs in shallow lagoons and seaward reefs to a depth of 8 m. It is usually seen perched on small rocks, coral, or clumps of algae and feeds by scraping algae from the surfaces of surrounding dead coral rock.
Indo-Pacific: Red Sea to Samoa, n. to the Ryukyus, s. to the Great Barrier Reef and New Caledonia; Marianas, Carolines, and s. Marshalls in Micronesia.

Salarias segmentatus Bath & Randall, 1990
Segmented blenny Pl. 115G
SL: to ≥32 mm (1.3 in).
At Belau, this distinctive species inhabits lagoon reefs.
West Pacific: distribution uncertain; Belau in Micronesia.

Salarias sp. 1 Pl. 115H
Spot-cheek blenny
The status of this species is uncertain. At Belau it is relatively common on algae-covered dead coral rocks in shallow lagoon areas.
West Pacific: Ryukyus, s. Japan; further distribution uncertain; Belau in Micronesia.

Stanulus seychellensis Smith, 1969 Fig. 6b
Seychelle's blenny
(*Fallacirripectes minutus* Schultz and Chapman, 1960)
SL: to 27 mm (1.1 in), o to 23 mm (1.0 in); D XII, 9-11 (10); A II, 10-12(11); V I, 4; GR 8-13.
This minute blenny matures at a length of under 24 mm (1.0 in). It occurs in surgy areas of exposed outer reef flats and seaward reefs. Another slightly larger species, *S. talboti*, has been collected in the Bonin Is. as well as the Great Barrier Reef and the Ryukyu, Lord Howe, and Marquesan Is.
Indo-Pacific: Seychelles to the Tuamotus, n. to s. Taiwan, s. to the s. Great Barrier Reef; throughout Micronesia.

Subfamily Blenniinae (Sabretooth blennies)

Sabretooth blennies have greatly reduced gill openings and relatively small mouths with stout teeth. They fall into two major groups (termed *tribes* by ichthyologists): tribe Omobranchini which consists of small sedentary forms that lack well-developed canine teeth in the lower jaw, and tribe Nemophini which consists of actively swimming species that possess greatly enlarged canine teeth in the lower jaw. Some

of the latter are specialized predators that attack the bodies and fins of larger fishes to feed on scales, skin, or mucus. Some are mimics of the cleaner wrasses or other sabretooth blennies. The lower jaw fangs of most, if not all species, are used for defense; those of the genus *Meiacanthus* are venemous.

Tribe Omobranchini

Key to Micronesian genera and species of the tribe Omobranchini:

1a. Mandibular pores 2..2
1b. Mandibular pores 3..3
2a. D XI-XII, 18-20....................*Parenchelyurus hepburni*
2b. D VII-VIII, 21-24........................*Enchelyurus kraussi*
3a. Total D elements > 30; A 20-23; 0-6 LL tubes present anteriorly..........................*Omobranchus rotundiceps*
3b. Total D elements ≤ 29; A 17-19; LL tubes absent.........
....*Omox biporos*

Enchelyurus kraussi (Klunzinger, 1871)
Krauss' blenny
SL: to 45 mm (1.8 in); D VII-VIII, 21-24; A II, 20-22 (united to C); P 14-16; V I, 2.
In life this small blenny is dark brown becoming yellowish posteriorly. It occurs among coral and rubble on reef flats and the upper portion of seaward reefs. It is quite secretive and usually only seen after application of an ichthyocide.
Indo-west Pacific: Red Sea to the Marianas, n. to the Ryukyus, s. to the s. Great Barrier Reef; Marianas in Micronesia.

Omobranchus rotundiceps obliquus(Garman,1903)
Mangrove blenny Fig. 7
SL: to 56 mm (2.2 in); D XI-XIII(XII), 18-21(18-20)=30-33(30-32); A II, 20-23 (spines visible on o); LP 0-6.
This small species lives among coral, rocks, and rubble of shallow brackish and marine coastal waters.
Indo-west Pacific: Nicobars to Samoa, n. to the Marianas, s. to New Caledonia Samoa; Belau to the Mariana and e. Caroline Is. in Micronesia; introduced to the Hawaiian and Line Is.; the subspecies *rotundiceps* (Macleay, 1881) in Australia.

Fig. 7. *Omobranchus rotundiceps obliquus*.

Omox biporos Springer, 1972
Omox blenny
SL: to 46 mm (1.8 in); D XII, 15-17=27-29; A II, 17-19; P 13; V I, 2.
In life this species is dark brown with black blotches on the sides and black bars on the head, and clear fins. It lives among mangroves.
West Pacific: Gulf of Thailand to Papua New Guinea, n. to the Ryukyus, s. to New Caledonia; Belau to Pohnpei in Micronesia.

Parenchelyurus hepburni (Snyder, 1908)   Fig. 8
Hepburn's blenny

SL: to 35 mm (1.4 in); D XI-XII, 18-20; A II, 20-23; P 13-14; V I, 2.

This small species is black with white specks. It is a secretive dweller of coral and rubble of reef flats.

Indo-Pacific: Madagascar to Samoa, n. to the Ryukyus, s. to the s. Great Barrier Reef; Marianas, Pohnpei, and Marshalls in Micronesia.

Fig. 8. *Parenchelyurus hepburni.*

Tribe Nemophini:

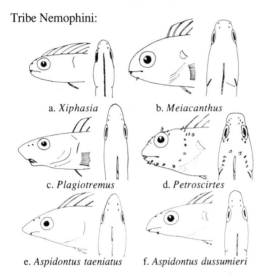

a. *Xiphasia*   b. *Meiacanthus*

c. *Plagiotremus*   d. *Petroscirtes*

e. *Aspidontus taeniatus*   f. *Aspidontus dussumieri*

Fig. 9. Heads of representative Micronesian genera and species of the tribe Nemophini.

Key to Micronesian genera of Nemophini:

1a. Body long and eel-like, depth > 40 in SL; D origin over eye in adults...*Xiphasia*
1b. Body not eel-like, depth < 10 in SL; D origin behind or over posterior rim of eye in adults.............................2
2a. Dentary canines with a deep groove along anterior surface and venom gland at base....................*Meiacanthus*
2b. Dentary canines without a deep groove and without a venom gland at base...3

Meiacanthus   Petroscirtes   Petroscirtes breviceps
1a   2a   2b

3a. P 11-13 (usually 12); LL absent...............*Plagiotremus*
3b. P 13-16; LL extending posteriorly beneath D to at least base of last spine..4
4a. Lower margin of gill opening entirely above P base; A and D 14-21..*Petroscirtes*
4b. Lower margin of gill opening distinctly below level of upper P base; A 25-30; D 26-34.................*Aspidontus*

Aspidontus dussumieri (Valenciennes, 1836)
Lance blenny   Fig. 9f

(*Petroscirtes fluctuans* Schultz, 1960)

SL: to 100 mm (3.9 in); D IX-XI, 28-34; A II, 25-30; P 13-15; V I, 3; depth 6.7-8.4.

The two species of *Aspidontus* have a pair of large canines in the lower jaw as well as a pair of smaller ones in the upper jaw. The lance blenny differs from the cleaner mimic by having a nearly terminal mouth and relatively dull color pattern with an elongate ocellus in the front of the dorsal fin. Unlike the cleaner mimic, it is not a mimic and does not prey on the fins or skin of other fishes, but rather feeds mainly on algae and detritus. Its large canines are used for defense.

Indo-Pacific: Red Sea to the Tuamotus, n. to s. Japan, s. to n. New South Wales; Belau to e. Carolines and Marshalls in Micronesia.

Aspidontus taeniatus taeniatus
    Quoy & Gaimard, 1834   Pl. 116A; Fig. 9e
Cleaner mimic

SL: to 100 mm (3.9 in); D X-XII, 26-28; A II, 25-28; P 13-15; V I, 3; depth 5.1-6.0.

This remarkable little blenny occurs in a wide variety of reef zones from lagoons and subtidal reef flats to a depth of over 20 m on outer reef slopes. It bears an amazing resemblance to the cleaner wrasse, *Labroides dimidiatus* (p. 191) in both appearance and behavior. Even subtle variations in coloration of local populations of the wrasse are copied by the local blennies. Since piscivorous fishes value the cleaner's services and won't eat it, this charade not only protects the mimic from predation, but enable it to approach unwary fishes and nip off pieces of fins, scales, and skin with its enlarged lower canines. Most adult fish learn to distinguish between cleaner and mimic; inexperienced juveniles are victimized most often. The two can be distinguished by the position of the mouth which is terminal in the wrasse but under the snout in the blenny. Unlike the wrasse, the blenny will take shelter in a small hole when threatened, leaving only its head protruding. The blenny's parasitism on other fishes is not universal since in many situations the bulk of its diet consists of tubeworms and demersal fish eggs. In some areas the blenny is an unwelcome intruder that is chased by the wrasse while in others it may even pose and be cleaned by the wrasse like the wrasses other customers. The blenny often lives in pairs in empty worm tubes or other narrow holes suitable for resting and nesting.

West-central Pacific: Vietnam to the Line, Marquesan, and Tuamotu Is., n. to s. Japan, s. to New South Wales; throughout Micronesia; the subspecies *tractus* from the Red Sea to Malaysia and Cocos Keeling.

Meiacanthus atrodorsalis (Günther, 1877) Pl. 116B
Poison-fang blenny

SL: to 68 mm (2.7 in); D IV, 25-28; A II, 15-18(17); P 13-(15); V I, 3; depth 3.6-4.9.

Species of *Meiacanthus* are unique among fishes by possessing a pair of large grooved fangs in the lower jaw with associated venom glands (see key). This apparatus produces a bite similar to that of a wasp sting and is used defensively. Consequently, species of *Meiacanthus* are avoided by most predators and have the habit of hovering up to a meter above the bottom where they casually feed on zooplankton. They also feed on the bottom on small benthic invertebrates. The unpalatability of this blenny as well as its innoffensive nature are the basis of a mimcry complex involving at least one other blenny, *Plagiotremus laudandus* (this page), and doubtfully *Ecsenius bicolor* (p. 208). The poison-fang blenny is common on both lagoon and seaward reefs below the surge zone at depths of 1 to at least 30 m. Males of the Red Sea species, *M. nigrolineatus* (and probably others) guard a nest of eggs laid by several females. At least 5 allopatric color morphs have been identified in *M. atrodorsalis*. Morph 3 (Pl. 116B) occurs at Belau, the Marianas, and Kapingamarangi; morph 4, which lacks the postorbital dark stripe, occurs in the Carolines from Sorol to the east except Kapingamarangi; and morph 5 which either lacks the postorbital stripe or has a faint partial stripe, occurs in the Marshalls. In addition to the species listed below, the estuarine and freshwater species, *M. anema*, may occur at Yap and Belau.

West-central Pacific: Philippines and Bali to Samoa, n. to the Ryukyus, s. to Rowley Shoals, the s. Great Barrier Reef, and New Caledonia; throughout Micronesia; replaced by the uniformly yellow subspecies *ovalauensis* in Fiji, and by *M. tongaensis* in Tonga.

Meiacanthus ditrema Smith-Vaniz, 1976 Fig. 10
One-striped poison-fang blenny

SL: to 40 mm (1.6 in), ♀ to 35 mm (1.4 in); D V-IV, 22-25; A II, 15-18; P 13-15; V I, 3.

This species inhabits shallow protected reefs to a depth of 15 m. It typically forms schools that hover well above the bottom to feed on zooplankton.

West Pacific: Philippines and Moluccas to Samoa, n. to the Ryukyus, s. to Rowley Shoals, the n. Great Barrier Reef, and Tonga; Belau in Micronesia.

Fig. 10. *Meiacanthus ditrema.*

Meiacanthus grammistes (Valenciennes, 1836)
Striped poison-fang blenny Pl. 116C

SL: to 87 mm (3.4 in), ♀ to 84 mm (3.3 in); D IV, 25-28; A II, 14-16; P 13-16; V I, 3.

This species is moderately common on the quiet inshore reefs of Palau's Rock Islands. It is mimicked by another sabretooth blenny, *Petroscirtes breviceps*.

West Pacific: Indochina to Papua New Guinea, n. to the Ryukyus, s. to nw. Australia and the Great Barrier Reef; Belau and Yap in Micronesia; replaced by *M. kamoharai* in s. Japan.

Plagiotremus laudandus laudandus (Whitley,1961)
Poison-fang blenny mimic Pl. 116F

SL: to 58 mm (2.3 in), ♀ to 52 mm (2. 0 in); D VII-X, 27-30; A II, 22-24; P 11-13; V I, 3.

Species of *Plagiotremus* attack other fishes for the purpose of feeding on pieces of skin, scales, and fins as well as mucus. They typically hover or swim well above the bottom with a characteristic wriggling motion. *P. laudandus* is an aggressive mimic of the poison-fang blenny, *Meiacanthus atrodorsalis*. Its mimicry serves the dual purpose of protecting it from predation while enabling it to closely approach its larger prey which are indifferent to the non-aggressive *Meiacanthus*. *P. laudandus* occurs in the same areas as *M. atrodorsalis*, lagoon and seaward reefs from below the surge zone to depths of 30 m or more, but is relatively rare. In Fiji, *P. laudandus* is represented by a uniformly yellow subspecies of identical coloration as the local subspecies of *M. atrodorsalis*.

West-central Pacific: Philippines and Ryukyus to the Gilberts, New Caledonia, and Samoa, n. to the Izus, s. to Rowley Shoals and Lord Howe Is.; throughout Micronesia; the uniformly yellow subspecies *flavus* from Fiji and Tonga.

Plagiotremus rhynorhynchus (Bleeker, 1852)
Bluestriped blenny Pl. 116G

SL: to 96 mm (3.8 in), ♀ to 70 mm (2.8 in); D X-XII, 31-37; A II, 29-33; P 11-13(12); V I, 3; depth 6.6-8.0.

Juveniles of this species are aggresive mimics of juveniles of the cleaner wrasse, *Labroides dimidiatus*, but adults are considerably different. The ground color of adults is variable, ranging from black (Pl. 116G) to yellow (lower right of Pl. 5A). The bluestriped blenny is a relatively uncommon inhabitant of clear, coral-rich areas of lagoon and seaward reefs at depths of 1 to at least 40 m. When alarmed it shelters in an abandoned worm tube or other small hole.

Indo-Pacific: Red Sea to the Line, Marquesan, and Society Is., n. to s. Japan, s. to Lord Howe Is.; throughout Micronesia; closely related to *P. ewaensis* from the Hawaiian Is.

Plagiotremus tapienosoma (Bleeker, 1857)
Piano blenny; Scale-eating blenny Pl. 116H

SL: to 121 mm (4.8 in), ♀ to 92 mm (3.6 in); D VII-IX (VIII), 34-39; A II, 28-33; P 11-13(12); V I, 3; depth 6.8-9.2.

This nasty little fish is common along seaward reefs, particularly the lower surge zone, to a depth of 20 m. It swims with a wriggling motion and may rise several feet above the bottom in its attempts to sneak up on an unsuspecting vistim - fish or diver! It apparently finds human skin just as palatable as the pieces of skin, fins, or scales and mucus of other fishes that it normally eats. When alarmed, it quickly retreats to the safety of an abandoned worm tube.

Indo-Pacific: Red Sea to the Line, Marquesan, and Tuamotu

Is., n. to s. Japan, s. to n. New Zealand and Rapa; throughout Micronesia; replaced by the closely related *P. goslinei* in the Hawaiian Is.

Key to Micronesian species of *Petroscirtes*:

1a. First D spine distinctly longer than 4th giving fin a notched appearance; outer V ray with dark spot near base (indistinct in juveniles)....................................*mitratus*

1b. First D spine subequal or shorter than 4th; outer V ray without dark basal spot..2

2a. Symphyseal mandibular cirrus multifid; preopercular pores with cirri, 3-6 pores per side....................*xestus*

2b. Symphyseal mandibular cirrus simple, if present; preopercular pores without cirri......................................3

3a. Body of adults with two or more dark stripes against pale background...*breviceps*

3b. Body of adults with one or no dark stripes against pale background...4

4a. Broad dark stripe along entire D base; usually 3 supratemporal pores..*breviceps*

4b. No dark stripe along entire D base; 3-5 supratemporal pores..5

5a. Snout elongate, bulbous; second D spine 6.6-8.6% SL... ....*thepasi*

5b. Snout not as above; second D spine 8.1-31.9% SL........ ....*variabilis*

Petroscirtes breviceps (Valenciennes, 1836)
Striped poison-fang blenny mimic

SL: to 110 mm (4.3 in), ♀ to 84 mm (3.3 in); D X-(XI), 17-21(18-20)=28-32(29-31); A II, 17-21; P 13-16; V I, 3.

Species of *Petroscirtes* are very similar to those of *Meiacanthus*, but lack a groove and venom apparatus on the lower jaw fangs. They feed on small crustaceans, diatoms, and perhaps other plant material associated with algal clumps or seagrasses. They use their fangs defensively and will not hesitate to bite if handled. Some species tend to be drab and cryptic while others mimic certain species of *Meiacanthus*. Mimicry in which two unpalatable species reinforce recognition by potential predators by resembling each other, is termed Müllerian mimicry after its describer, Fritz Müller. This species is a Müllerian mimic of *Meiacanthus grammistes*. By resembling each other, both *P. breviceps* and *M. grammistes* gain more protection than each would alone by increasing the odds of a predator having a bad experience with a fish of the common color pattern. *P. breviceps* inhabits sandy areas with clumps of *Sargassum* and other algae.

Indo-west Pacific: E. Africa to Papua New Guinea, n. to s. Japan, s. to New Caledonia; Belau and Yap in Micronesia.

Petroscirtes mitratus Rüppell, 1828   Pl. 116D
Floral blenny

SL: to 61 mm (2.4 in), ♀ to 54 mm (2.1 in); D X-(XI), 14-17(14-16)=25-28(25-27); A II, 14-16; P 13-16; V I, 3; depth 3.3-4.3.

This cryptically colored species has a distinctive dorsal fin in which the first three rays are elevated. It is relatively com-

mon in shallow protected lagoons and reef flats where their are clumps of algae or seagrasses. It swims with a tail-standing vertical orientation looking very much like a drifting piece of weed with its tail curled and only its clear pectoral fins moving. It nests in empty mollusk shells.

Indo-Pacific: Red Sea to the Phoenix and Samoan Is., n. to the Ryukyus, s. to Perth, the s. Great Barrier Reef, and New Caledonia; throughout Micronesia.

Petroscirtes thepasi
Thepas' sabretooth blenny

SL: to 59 mm (2.3 in), ♀ to 57 mm (2.2 in); D X-(XI), 16-18(16-17)=27-29(27-28); V I, 3; depth 5.9-8.3.

This species is very closely related to *P. variabilis*, but is usually more elongate and has a bulbous or elongate snout. It inhabits shallow seagrass beds and has swimming habits much like those of *P mitratus*. It hides by pressing itself against a blade of seagrass.

Indo-Australian: Moluccas, New Guinea, Solomon Is; Belau and Yap in Micronesia.

Petroscirtes variabilis Cantor, 1850
Variable sabretooth blenny

SL: to 125 mm (4.9 in), ♀ to 105 mm (4.1 in); D X-(XI), 16-19(17-18)=27-30(28-29); A II, 16-19; P 14; V I, 3; depth 4.5-7.1.

This species is sexually dimorphic: males are orange-brown while females are sea-green dorsally and lighter below. It inhabits seagrass beds of shallow lagoons. Although it feeds primarily on small crustaceans, it also takes an occasional scale from a fish that it ambushes.

Indo-west Pacific: Sri Lanka to Fiji; n. to s. Taiwan and the Yaeyamas, s. to the s. Great Barrier Reef; Belau in Micronesia.

Petroscirtes xestus Jordan & Seale, 1906   Pl. 116E
Xestus sabretooth blenny

SL: to 57 mm (2.2 in), ♀ to 34 mm (1.3 in); D X-(XI), 14-16(15)=25-27(26); V I, 3.

This species resembles *P. thepasi* and *P. variabilis* but usually has fewer total dorsal fin elements (26 vs. ≥ 27). It inhabits sandy areas of reef flats and shallow lagoons and uses empty mollusk shells as nesting sites.

Indo-Pacific: E. Africa to the Line and Society Is., n. to the Marianas, s. to the s. Great Barrier Reef; throughout Micronesia.

Xiphasia matsubarai Okada & Suzuki, 1952
Japanese snake blenny   Fig. 6a

SL: to 30 cm (11.8 in); D XI, 99-104; A II, 97-104; P 10-11; V I, 3.

This peculiar blenny more closely resembles an eel. It apparently occurs in relatively deep water and rises to the surface at night where it occasionally falls prey to pelagic fishes. Another larger species, *X. setifer* may also occur in Micronesia.

Indo-Pacific: Red Sea to Samoan and Ellice Is., n. to Japan, s. to Lord Howe Is.; Marianas in Micronesia.

CALLIONYMIDAE (DRAGONETS)

Dragonets are small, elongate, moderately depressed, broad-headed, scaleless fishes. They have separate dorsal fins, the first spinous, the second soft-rayed, an entirely soft-rayed anal fin, jugular pelvic fins with I, 5 rays, protrusible jaws typically with villiform teeth, preopercles with a stout spine, and gill openings restricted to a dorsal or sublateral hole. Dragonets are typically sexually dimorphic with the males attaining a larger size and having a large and often gaudy first dorsal fin that is displayed during courtship. Most species are intricately, but cryptically colored. A few spectacular species are popular in the aquarium trade. Dragonets typically live on sandy to muddy bottoms from estuarine areas to a depth of about 400 m and feed on small benthic invertebrates. At least 11 species in 4 genera occur in Micronesia. In the following accounts, the SL and depth measurements do not include the upper jaw, and the method of describing the preopercular spine follows the formula: a [b/c]d, where a=number of antrorse spines at the base, b=number of points or serrae on the dorsal margin, c=number of points or serrae on the ventral margin, and d=1 for the main tip (Fig. 1, modified from Fricke, 1981). (Lit.: Fricke, 1982, 1983, 1984)

Key to Micronesian genera and species of Callionymidae:

1a. Operculum with a free flap of skin; body without a ventrolateral fold of skin below LL...2
1b. Operculum without a free flap of skin; body with a ventrolateral fold of skin below LL...***Diplogrammus goramensis***
2a. Sides of body with small dermal cirri; a few relatively large teeth in jaws..................
....***Anaora tentaculata***
2b. Sides of body without small dermal cirri; small villiform teeth in bands in jaws.......3
3a. Soft D rays unbranched (except the last divided at base); gill opening dorsal in position; an antrorse spine at preopercular spine base; snout length usually > eye diameter..genus *Callionymus*: 4
3b. Soft D rays branched (if ≥ 25 mm); gill opening usually sublateral or lateral in position; usually no antrorse spine at preopercular spine base; snout length usually < eye diameter...genus *Synchiropus*: 6
4a. Dorsal margin of preopercular spine with 5-13 small antrorse serrae; main tip usually straight; P 18-20...(subgenus *Calliurichhys*) 5
4b. Dorsal margin of preopercular spine with 1-4 large curved points (occasionally an additional antrorse point); main tip usually recurved; P 16-18.....................................
....(subgenus *Callionymus*) ***enneactis***
5a. First D with one or two filamentous spines....................(*Calliurichhys*) ***delicatulus***
5b. First D without filamentous spines...........................(*Calliurichhys*) ***simplicicornis***
6a. Preopercular spine formula 0[1-2/0]1...7
6b. Preopercular spine formula 0[2-5/0]1...9
7a. Preopercular spine formula 0[1/0]1...8
7b. Preopercular spine formula 0[2/0]1...***morrisoni***
8a. Sides of body with large circular light spots; o without ocelli on first D; main tip of preopercular spine much larger than dorsal point.....................................***circularis***
8b. Sides of body without large circular light spots; o with ocelli on first D; main tip of preopercular spine shorter than dorsal point...***ocellatus***
9a. P 16-23; second D rays unbranched (except last divided at base); to ≤25 mm..........10
9b. P 28-35; second D rays branched; to 47 mm, immature <25 mm...............***splendidus***
10a. P 16-17; LL branched above P base...(*kiyoae*: see "sp.")
10b. P 19-23; LL not branched above P base...***laddi***

formula = a [b/c] d

Fig. 1. Method of counting
preopecular spines.

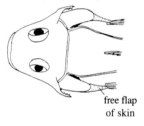

free flap
of skin

1a

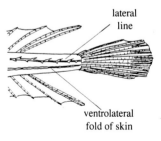

lateral
line

ventrolateral
fold of skin

1b

Anaora tentaculata Gray, 1835   Fig. 2a
Tentacled dragonet

SL: to 42 mm (1.7 in); D IV+8; A 7; P 21-27; depth 5.0-5.9; preopercular spine 0-1[1/0-1]1.

This cryptically colored species occurs on sand of shallow reefs from tidepools to a depth of 30 m.

West Pacific: Moluccas, Philippines, Ryukyus; Belau, Yap, and Guam in Micronesia.

Callionymus delicatulus Smith, 1963   Fig. 2b
Delicate dragonet

SL: to 51 mm (2.0 in); D IV+8; A 7; P 15-21; depth 6.4-9.7; preopercular spine 1[8-15/0]1.

This species has been collected from sand to mud bottoms of lagoon reefs at depths of about 1 to 20 m.

Indo-west Pacific: Red Sea to the Solomon Is.; Belau in Micronesia.

Callionymus enneactis Bleeker, 1879   Fig. 2c
Mangrove dragonet

SL: to 68 mm (2.7 in), ♀ to 49 mm (1.9 in), 40 mm (1.6 in) in Micronesia; D IV+8; A 7; P 18-20; depth 6.3-9.6; preopercular spine 1[1-4(rarely 4)/0]1.

This species inhabits sand and mud bottoms from brackish mangrove areas to a depth of 15 m in coral reef lagoons.

West Pacific: Gulf of Thailand to the Solomon Is., n. to s. Japan, s. to nw. Australia; Belau and Yap in Micronesia; also specimens from e. Indonesia, ne. Australia, and the Loyalty and Hawaiian Is. may also be this species.

Callionymus simplicicornis Valenciennes, 1837
Simple-spined dragonet   Pl. 117A; Fig. 2d

SL: to 40 mm (1.6 in); D IV+8; A 7-8; P 16-18; depth 6.5-10.5; preopercular spine 1[4-13(rarely 4-5)/0]1.

This species occurs on sand from subtidal reef flats to a depth of at least 40 m in deep lagoons and outer reef slopes. It is the most common dragonet of shallow, protected sandy flats in the Marianas.

West-central Pacific: Philippines to the Marquesan and Tuamotu Is., n. to the Marianas, s. to Samoa; throughout Micronesia.

Diplogrammus goramensis (Bleeker, 1858)
Goram dragonet   Fig. 2e

SL: to 68 mm (2.7 in), usually < 40 mm (1.6 in) in Micronesia; D IV+8; A 7; P 17-20; depth 6.8-10.4; preopercular spine 1[5-8/0]1.

This species inhabits sandy areas of lagoons and outer reef slopes at depths of 5 to 34 m.

West-central Pacific: Vietnam to Rarotonga, n. to se. China and the Ryukyu Is., s. to the s. Great Barrier Reef; throughout Micronesia.

Synchiropus circularis Fricke, 1984   Fig. 2f
Circled dragonet

SL: to 28 mm (1.1 in); D IV+8; A 7-8; P 21-23; depth 4.9-5.3; preopercular spine 0[1/0]1.

This species is known only from two rotenone collections on seaward reefs to a depth of 8 m, one at Guam, the other at Tinian. I have observed what may have been this species at a depth of 33 m off Orote cliffs, Guam.

Marianas

Synchiropus laddi Schultz, 1960   Fig. 2g
Ladd's dragonet

SL: to 24 mm (1.0 in); D IV+9; A 8; P 16-17; depth 4.6-5.0; preopercular spine 0[3-5(rarely 3)/0]1.

This small species inhabits sandy areas of lagoon and seaward reefs.

West-central Pacific: Philippines, Belau, Marshalls, and Tuamotus.

Synchiropus morrisoni Schultz, 1960
Morrison's dragonet   Pl. 117B; Fig. 2h

SL: to 62 mm (2.4 in), 48 mm (1.9 in) in Micronesia; D IV+8; A 7; p 18-23; depth 4.4-6.5; preopercular spine 0[2/0]1.

In life this species is a primarily greenish red. It occurs on algal covered rocks on seaward reefs at depths of 12 to over 33 m, but is rare in less than 25 m in most coral reef areas.

West-central Pacific: nw. Australia and the Ryukyu Is. to Samoa, n. to the Izu Is., s. to Fiji; throughout Micronesia.

Synchiropus ocellatus (Pallas, 1770)   Fig. 2i
Ocellated dragonet

SL: to 66 mm (2.6 in); D IV+8-10(8-9); A 7-9(8); P 18-23; depth 4.4-5.6; preopercular spine 0[1/0]1.

This relatively large dragonet inhabits sandy areas of lagoon and seaward reefs at depths of 1 to over 30 m (probably to 73 m).

West-central Pacific: Vietnam to the Marquesan and Pitcairn Is., n. to the Izu Is., s. to the s. Great Barrier Reef and Tonga; Belau to the e. Carolines and s. Marshalls in Micronesia.

Synchiropus splendidus (Herre, 1927)
Mandarinfish   Pl. 117C; Fig. 2j

SL: to 47 mm (1.9 in); D IV+8; A 6-8(7); P 28-35; depth 3.4-4.2; preopercular spine 0[2-5/0]1.

This spectacular little dragonet lives on shallow protected lagoon and inshore reefs to a depth of 18 m. At Belau, it may be found among corals and leaf litter on the slopes of the Rock Islands. It is a well-known aquarium fish exported from the Philippines. Rare individuals have a bright red ground color.

West Pacific: Philippines and Java to Pohnpei and New Caledonia (and possibly Tonga), n. to the Ryukyus, s. to Rowley Shoals and the s. Great Barrier Reef; Belau to the e. Carolines in Micronesia.

Synchiropus sp.   Pl. 117D

SL: probably < 25 mm (1.0 in).

This species is known only from photographs of a male and female taken at a depth of 7 m on an algal-covered rock inside Rota's west harbor. It appears to be very closely related to *S. kiyoae* from the Izu Is.

Rota

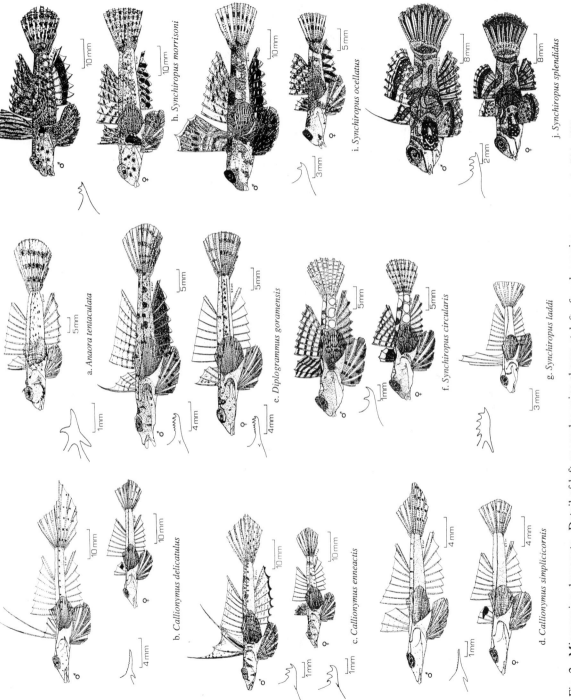

Fig. 2. Micronesian dragonets. Detail of left opercular spine shown at left of each species. (all drawings after Fricke, 1983)

h. *Synchiropus morrisoni*

i. *Synchiropus ocellatus*

j. *Synchiropus splendidus*

a. *Anaora tentaculata*

e. *Diplogrammus goramensis*

f. *Synchiropus circularis*

g. *Synchiropus laddi*

b. *Callionymus delicatulus*

c. *Callionymus enneactis*

d. *Callionymus simplicicornis*

Suborder GOBIOIDEI

This suborder consists of six families containing about 270 genera and 1,500 to 2,000 species, most of which belong to the most speciose marine fish family, the Gobiidae. Gobioids are typically small, elongate, moderately compressed fishes with two dorsal fins and somewhat upturned mouths. Many of the features that distinguish the families are internal and beyond the scope of this book. (Lit.: Hoese, 1984)

ELEOTRIDIDAE (SLEEPERS; GUDGEONS)

Eleotridids differ from gobiids by having six branchiostegals and widely separated pelvic fins. Most species are confined to freshwater and estuarine environments and form a major portion of the riverine fauna of high tropical islands. A few reach a size of over 30 cm (1 ft). One small species occurs on Micronesian coral reefs, at least four others inhabit rivers and estuaries. (Lit.: Hoese *in* Smith & Heemstra, 1986; Larson and Hoese, 1980)

Calumia godeffroyi (Günther, 1877)   Fig. 1
Tailface sleeper
(*Calumia biocellata* Smith, 1958)
SL: to 20 mm (0.8 in); D VI+I, 6-7; A I, 6-7; P 16-17; LS 21-23; lower GR 6, short and stubby; preD S 7-9.
This species is characterized by five dark bars and two dark spots at the base of the tail. It lives among coral and rubble at depths of 7 to 30 m.
Indo-Pacific: E. Africa to the Society Is.; Marianas and Pohnpei in Micronesia.

Fig. 1. *Calumia godeffroyi* (based on Smith, 1958).

XENISTHMIDAE (WRIGGLERS)

This family consists of a few genera and species of small, very elongate coral reef fishes with six branchiostegals, a depressed head with projecting lower jaw thicked anteriorly, and numerous small body scales or none at all. Some ichthyologists consider this to be a subfamily of the Gobiidae. At least three species occur in Micronesia. (Lit.: Springer, 1983)

Allomicrodesmis dorotheae Schultz, 1966   Fig. 1
Dorothea's wriggler
SL: 21 mm (0.8 in); D II, 32 (36 in 1); A 25-26 elements;

P 12; V I, 3; depth ca. 15; scales and LL pores absent.
Only two specimens are known, one of them an adult male.
Bikini and Great Barrier Reef

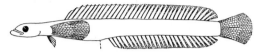

Fig. 1. *Allomicrodesmis dorotheae*, 21 mm, Bikini (after A. M. Awl in Schultz et al., 1966).

Xenisthmus polyzonatus (Klunzinger, 1871)
Barred wriggler   Fig. 2
SL: to ; D VI-I, 11; A I, 10; P 17; ; LS 58; preD S 20.
This species has numerous thin dark vertical bars. In addition to this species, unidentified species have been collected in the Marshall and e. Caroline Islands.
Indo-west Pacific: Red Sea to Samoa, n. to the Ryukyus; Marianas in Micronesia.

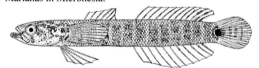

Fig. 2. *Xenisthmus polyzonatus*.

MICRODESMIDAE (DARTFISHES, HOVERGOBIES, and WORMFISHES)

Microdesmids typically have a moderately to greatly elongate body, five branchiostegals, and long-based dorsal and anal fins. There are two subfamilies: the Microdesminae which are extremely elongate forms with a continuous dorsal fin that typically live over open sand, and the Ptereleotrinae which have two dorsal fins and a nearly vertically oriented mouth, and are associated with hard reef substrates or small patches of sand or rubble. Members of both subfamilies hover above the bottom to feed on drifting zooplankton. Most known species occur in relatively shallow water, but one, *Ptereleotris lineopinnis*, and probably others that remain to be discovered, is only known from depths of over 90 m. (Lit.: Dawson, 1973; Randall & Allen, 1973; Randall & Hoese, 1985; Rennis & Hoese, 1985; Strasburg, 1967)

Subfamily Microdesminae (wormfishes):

Gunnellichthys monostigma Smith, 1958
Onespot wormfish   Pl. 117E; Fig. 1a
SL: to ≥92 mm (in); D XXI-XXII, 39-42 (total elements 60-63); A 38-43; P 14-16.
Wormfishes occur in colonies over open sandy bottoms. They characteristically hover a few centimeters above the bottom, undulating their bodies as they face the current. When approached they dive headfirst into a burrow. They feed primarily on small benthic and pelagic crustaceans. This species is common over sandy lagoon bottoms at depths of 6 to 20 m.

Indo-Pacific: E. Africa to the Marquesan and Society Is., n. to the Ryukyus, s. to the s. Great Barrier Reef; throughout Micronesia.

Gunnellichthys pleurotaenia Bleeker, 1858   Fig. 1a
Onestripe wormfish
SL: to ≥74 mm (2.9 in); D XIX, 39; A 36; P 13-14;V I, 4. This striped wormfish occurs in shallow, flat, sandy areas, often less than 3 m, but occasionally to 8 m or more.
West-central Pacific: Java and Philippines to w. Samoa, n. to the Ryukyus, s. to Rowley Shoals and the s. Great Barrier Reef; throughout Micronesia; closely related to *G. copleyi* from the w. Indian Ocean.

Gunnellichthys viridescens Dawson, 1968
SL: to > 34 mm.
This species has been collected as deep as 20 m but usually occurs in less than 5 m.
Indo-Pacific: Seychelles to the Marshalls, s. to the s. Great Barrier Reef; Carolines and Marshalls in Micronesia.

Paragunnellichthys seychellensis Dawson, 1967
Seychelle's wormfish   Fig. 1b
SL: to ≥ 34 mm (in); D XVI-XVIII (total elements 47-48). This wormfish is uniformly light in color.
Indo-west Pacific: Seychelles, Chagos Is., Belau, Kapingamarangi, and the Great Barrier Reef.

Subfamily Ptereleotrinae (dartfishes):

Ptereleotris evides (Jordan & Hubbs, 1925)
Blackfin dartfish   Pl. 117F,G
SL: to 112 mm (4.4 in); D VI+I, 23-26(24-26); A I, 23-26; P 21-24; GR 6-8+18-22=26-30; depth 5.2-6.9.
Species of *Ptereleotris* hover 1 to 2 m above the bottom to feed on zooplankton. This species typically inhabits exposed outer reef slopes at depths of 2 to 15 m, but occasionally occurs in lagoons and bays. Juveniles have an oval spot at the base of the tail. They occur in aggregations while adults are paired. It tends to move away when approached rather than dart immediately into its hole.
Indo-Pacific: Red Sea to the Society Is., n. to the Ryukyus, s. to New South Wales, Lord Howe and Rapa; Is. throughout Micronesia.

Ptereleotris hanae (Jordan & Snyder, 1901)
Filament dartfish   Pl. 117H
SL: to 100 mm (in); D VI+I, 24-26; A I, 22-25; P 21-24; GR 6-8+17-21=23-28; depth 6.45-8.0.
This is the only Micronesian dartfish that has filamentous extensions to the caudal rays. It occurs over rubble and sand near reefs, at depths of 3 to 43 m. It hides under rubble or in burrows of alpheid prawns that associate with gobies (*Amblyeleotris* spp.) but does not interact with the prawns.
West-central Pacific: Philippines to the Line Is., n. to s. Japan, s. to nw. Australia and New South Wales; Marshalls in Micronesia.

Ptereleotris heteroptera (Bleeker, 1855)   Pl. 118A
Spot-tail dartfish
SL: to 100 mm (3.9 in); D VI+I, 29-33; A I, 27-30; P 21-24(22-23); GR 5-6+17-20=22-26; depth 6.2-7.8.
This dartfish inhabits lagoon and seaward reefs at depths of 7 to 46 m. It occurs over hard substrates as well as patches of rubble or sand, usually at the base of the reef. It may feed as high as 3 m above the bottom. Juveniles occur in aggregations, adults are paired.
Indo-Pacific: Red Sea to the Hawaiian, Line, Marquesan, and Society Is., n. to the Ryukyus, s. to Lord Howe Is.; Marianas, Carolines, and Marshalls in Micronesia.

Ptereleotris microlepis Bleeker, 1856   Pl. 118C
Pearly dartfish
SL: to 99 mm (3.9 in); D VI+I, 25-29(25-28); A I, 24-27; P 21-24(22-23); GR 6-7+19-23=25-30; depth 5.5-7.0.
This species closely resembles *P. heropterus* but lacks the black mark on the tail. It occurs over rubble-sand or sand substrates of bays and lagoons, at depths of 1 to 22 m. Juveniles occur in small aggregations, adults are paired.
Indo-Pacific: Red Sea to the Line and Tuamotu Is., n. to the Ryukyus, s. to New South Wales; throughout Micronesia.

Ptereleotris zebra (Fowler, 1938)   Pl. 118E
Zebra dartfish
SL: to 95 mm (3.7 in); D VI+I, 27-29; A I, 25-28; P 23-26(24-25); GR 5-7+18-21=24-27; depth 4.8-6.0.
The spectacular zebra dartfish is common on exposed seaward reefs, usually at depths of 2 to 4 m, but occasionally as deep as 31 m. It typically forms large aggregations over hard, gently sloping bottoms, and is probably the wariest species in the genus. Usually small groups will occupy the same hole. It is marketed in the aquarium trade.
Indo-Pacific: Red Sea to the Line and Marquesan Is., n. to the Ryukyus, s. to the s. Great Barrier Reef; Marianas and Marshalls in Micronesia.

Nemateleotris decora Randall & Allen, 1973
Decorated dartfish   Pl. 118B
SL: to 67 mm (2.6 in); D VI+I, 27-32; A I, 28-31; P 20-21; V I, 5; LS ca. 135-160; GR 5-6+15-17=20-23; depth 4.8-5.7.
The three known species of *Nemateleotris* are perhaps the most spectacular of gobioids and as a result are popular aquarium fishes. Like species of *Ptereleotris*, they hover above the bottom to feed on zooplankton and dart into a hole when alarmed. This gorgeous dartfish is found over patches of sand, rubble, or hard open bottom at the bases of reefs at depths of 28 to 70 m. It frequently occurs in pairs.
Indo-west Pacific: Mauritius to Samoa, n. to the Ryukyus, s. to New Caledonia; Belau in Micronesia

Nemateleotris helfrichi Randall & Allen, 1973
Helfrichs' dartfish   Pl. 118D
SL: to 51 mm (2.0 in); D VI+I, 29-31; A I, 26-28; P 20-21; V I, 5; LS ca. 140-160; GR 5-7+16-18=22-24; depth 4.9-5.6.

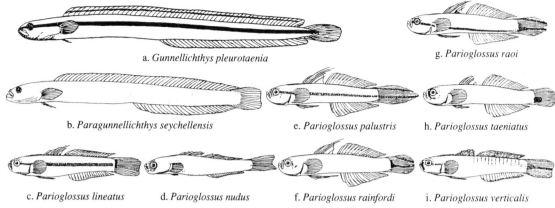

a. *Gunnellichthys pleurotaenia*

g. *Parioglossus raoi*

b. *Paragunnellichthys seychellensis*

e. *Parioglossus palustris*

h. *Parioglossus taeniatus*

c. *Parioglossus lineatus*   d. *Parioglossus nudus*

f. *Parioglossus rainfordi*

i. *Parioglossus verticalis*

Fig. 1. Micronesian wormfishes and hovergobies (a-c, after Dawson, 19; d-j after Rennis and Hoese, 1985).

This species, like *N. decora*, inhabits relatively deep water. It occurs over small patches of sand, rubble, or hard open bottoms of steep seaward reefs at depths of 25 to 69 m. It is relatively rare in less than 40 m and frequently occurs in pairs.

Pacific Plate: Belau to the Tuamotus, s. to Samoa and the Australs; Belau, Marianas, and Marshalls in Micronesia; photographed in the Ryukyus where it probably is a waif.

Nemateleotris magnifica Fowler, 1938   Pl. 118G
Fire dartfish; Fire goby
SL: to 54 mm (2.1 in); D VI+I, 28-32; A I, 27-30; P 19-20; V I, 5; LS ca. 110-130; GR 5-6+17-19=22-25; depth 4.4-4.8.

This magnificent dartfish inhabits seaward reefs at depths of 6 to 61 m. It is common on the upper portions of exposed outer reef slopes where it uses holes in hard substrate as well as patches of sand or fine rubble. It typically hovers within a half meter of the bottom, facing into the current to feed primarily on planktonic crustaceans, particularly copepods. Several fishes, particularly juveniles may utilize the same hole; adults are often paired. This dartfish has the habit of flicking its pennant-like first dorsal fin back and forth.

Indo-Pacific: E. Africa to the Hawaiian (as waifs only), Marquesan, and Pitcairn Is., n. to the Ryukyus, s. to New Caledonia and the Austral Is.; throughout Micronesia.

Parioglossus formosus (Smith, 1931)   Pl. 118F
Beautiful hover goby
SL: to 35 mm (1.4 in); D V-VI+I, 13-15(VI+I, 14); A I, 13-15(14); P 15-17(16-17); LS 66-78; GR 3-4+12-14.

Species of *Parioglossus* inhabit shallow coastal reefs and mangrove-lined inlets. Unlike other microdesmids, they typically occur in schools and do not dart into a hole when alarmed. This species hovers in schools among mangroves or near branching corals on protected coastal reefs to a depth of about 4 m. It is abundant among Palau's inner rock islands.

West Pacific: G. Thailand to Fiji, n. to the Yaeyamas., s. to nw. Australia and the s. Great Barrier Reef; Belau in Micronesia.

Parioglossus lineatus Rennis & Hoese, 1985
Lined hover goby   Fig. 1c
SL: to 33 mm (1.3 in); D VI+I, 15-16; A I, 15-16; P 18-20; LS 75-83; GR 3-4+15-16.

This species occurs among mangroves.

Belau and possibly the Solomon Is.

Parioglossus nudus Rennis & Hoese, 1985
Naked hover goby   Fig. 1d
SL: to 22 mm (0.9 in); D VI+I, 15-18(16-17); A I, (16)-17; P 16-18; body scaleless; GR 1-3+10-12=12-14.

This minute hover goby matures at a size of 17 mm (0.7 in) and never acquires scales. It is deeper dwelling than other *Parioglossus*, living on coastal reefs at depths of 5 to 37 m.

West Pacific: Philippines, New Guinea, Solomon Is., Fiji, and Belau.

Parioglossus palustris (Herre, 1945)   Fig. 1e
Palustris hover goby
SL: to 28 mm (1.1 in); D VI+I, 16-17; A I, 16-18(17); P 16-19(16-17); LS 78-89; GR 3+13-15.

This species is reddish-brown with red patches on the cheeks and a black spot at the base of the tail. It lives among mangroves.

West Pacific: Indonesia to Papua New Guinea, n. to the Yaeyama Is., s. to Queensland; Belau in Micronesia.

Parioglossus rainfordi McCulluch, 1921   Fig. 1f
Rainford's hover goby
SL: to 38 mm (1.5 in); D V-VI+I, 14-17(15-16); A I, 14-16(15); P 16-18(17-18); LS 90-109; GR 3-4+14-15.

This species lives in schools among mangroves and in coastal inlets, often with *P. formosus*.

West Pacific: Philippines to Papua New Guinea, n. to the Yaeyama Is., s. to Queensland; Belau and Pohnpei in Micronesia.

Parioglossus raoi (Herre, 1939)   Fig. 1g
Rao's hover goby
SL: to 25 mm (1.0 in); D VI+I, 14-16(15); A I, 14-16(15);

P 15-18(16-17); LS 70-85; GR 3-4+12-14=15-17.

This species is yellow to brown with a black longitudinal stripe and a bright blue spot between dorsal spines 5 and 6. It inhabits shallow coastal waters with mud, sand, or rock bottoms and among mangroves.

West Pacific: Andaman Is. to Fiji, n. to the Ryukyus., s. to Indonesia; Pohnpei in Micronesia.

Parioglossus taeniatus Regan, 1912   Fig. 1h
Taeniatus hover goby

SL: to 24 mm (0.9 in); D VI+I, 14-16(15); A I, 15-16; P 16-19(16-18); LS 76-86; GR 3-4+13-15=17-18.

This species inhabits areas of silt, sand, and rocks in coastal waters and among mangroves, sometimes with *P. formosus* and *P. taeniatus*.

Indo-west Pacific: Aldabra, Philippines, s. Great Barrier Reef, Fiji, and Belau.

Parioglossus verticalis Rennis & Hoese, 1985
Vertical hover goby   Fig. 1i

SL: to ≥21 mm (0.8 in); D VI+I, 17; A I, 17; P 18; LS 103; GR 4+15.

This species is known from a single male specimen collected in less than 1.5 m in coastal waters of Pohnpei. It is the only Micronesian species with vertical bars.

Pohnpei

GOBIIDAE (GOBIES)

The Gobiidae is the largest family of marine fishes, containing about 200 valid genera and 500 Indo-Pacific species as well as large numbers in other tropical and temperate seas. They are typically small, elongate, blunt-headed fishes with the following characteristics: a relatively large mouth with conical teeth; gill membranes broadly attached ventrally; 5 branchiostegals; pelvic fins usually connected to form a cup-shaped disc, or at least very close together; one or usually two dorsal fins, the first with II to VIII spines, the second and the anal fin each with I weak spine; and the absence of a lateral line, but numerous sensory head pores. Most species have small ctenoid or cylcoid body scales but a few lack scales. All but a few species that hover in the water column lack a gas bladder. Most gobies are relatively drab carnivorous bottom dwellers; a few are planktivores that swim above the bottom. Nearly all species whose reproductive habits are known are gonochorists (that is their sex is predetermined for life) that lay a small mass of demersal eggs guarded by the male. Most gobies inhabit shallow tropical waters, but many range into temperate waters or inhabit brackish or freshwater habitats. One group, the mudskippers (*Periophthalmus* and related genera), are amphibious dwellers of intertidal mudflats that spend most of their time out of the water. Gobies have invaded a wide variety of substrata ranging from mud to rock or coral or even on or within other marine organisms such as gorgonians or sponges. Many inhabit burrows, either of their own construction, or constructed by other animals. Several species are symbiotic with one or more species of prawn (snapping shrimp, family Alpheidae) and occupy their burrows. Several genera are in great need of revision and numerous species remain to be described. At least 159 species in 37 genera and 4 subfamilies occur in Micronesia. Only one subfamily, the Gobiinae occurs on coral reefs (approximately 148 species in 30 genera) but representatives of the others as well as many of the Gobiinae occur in adjacent coastal and estuarine waters. To aid the reader, a key is provided to the subfamilies and genera and the species are organized into functional groups. In the following key, brackets indicate genera that are primarily freshwater, parentheses indicate genera that are primarily estuarine or muddy coastal marine, and an asterisk indicates extralimital genera expected in Micronesia. Those genera are not treated further.

Key to Micronesian subfamilies and genera of Gobiidae:

1a. A and single D confluent with C; total A rays 30-51 (estuarine)...
....subfamily Amblyopinae: (*Taenioides*)

1b. C separate from 2nd D and A; total A rays 6-36...2

2a. Eyes elevated, with lower eyelids and deep sockets; first D spines 7-17; P base muscular and elongate; (mangroves)..Subfamily Oxudercinae: (*Periophthalmus*)

2b. Eyes not elevated; first D spines normally 6; P base normal...3

3a. Lower jaw teeth usually in one row; V frenum usually with fleshy processes (fresh-water).......
....Subfamily Sicydiinae: 4

3b. Lower jaw teeth usually in two or more rows; P frenum usually without fleshy process..........
....subfamily Gobiinae: 5

4a. LS ≥ 51 (freshwater)...[*Sicyopus*]

4b. LS ≤ 38 (freshwater)...[*Stiphodon*]

5a. Body naked or with a few scales on C peduncle...6

5b. Body completely or mostly scaled..9

6a. First gill slit closed by membrane; (V fused or seperate)................................***Hetereleotris***

6b. First gill slit open..7

7a. Eyes minute; V separate..***Austrolethops***

Periophthalmus
2a

Austrolethops
7a

7b. Eyes larger; V united..8

8a. Body slightly elongate, depth <4 in SL and quite compressed; teeth pointed.............*Gobiodon*

8b. Body elongate, depth >5 in SL; teeth tricuspid..*Kelloggella*

9a. Preopercle with a single large prominent spine..*Gladigobius*

9b. Preopercle with 0-9 small spines...10

10a. First spine of 1st and 2nd D stiff and thickened..11

10b. D spines all thin and flexible...13

11a. Preopercle with 1-3 flat spines...*Oplopomus*

11b. Preopercle without spines...12

12a. Opercle naked below level of upper P base...*Oplopomops*

12b. Opercle scaled to opposite at least upper 1/3 of P base...*Opua*

13a. Preopercle with 1-9 spines; cheek scaled...*Asterropteryx*

13b. No preopercle spines...14

14a. First gill slit closed by a membrane...*Hetereleotris*

14b. First gill slit open or at least partly open...15

15a. Anterior part of head with numerous short barbels...*Gobiopsis*

15b. Anterior part of head without barbels...16

16a. Thin dermal ridge on top of head in front of 1st D..17

16b. No dermal ridge in front of 1st D...18

17a. Dermal ridge low (<pupil diameter); body elongate, >4.7 in SL.................*Cryptocentroides*

17b. Dermal ridge high (>pupil diameter); body deeper, ≤4.2 in SL....................(*Cristatogobius*)

18a. Cheek with prominent vertical flaps...*Callogobius*

18b. Cheek without raised flaps...19

19a. Shoulder girdle (under opercle) with 1-3 finger-like flaps (freshwater)..............................20

19b. Shoulder girdle smooth or with minute bumps...21

20a. Head broader than deep; preD 23-32 (freshwater)...[*Awaous*]

20b. Head compressed, narrower than deep; preD 12-15; body with transverse bands (freshwater).....
....[*Stenogobius*]

21a.•Cheek scaled; teeth at sides of upper jaw directed medially (*Gnatholepis* only ?)................22

21b. Cheek naked; teeth at sides of jaws vertical or directed posteriorly..................................24

22a. D VI+I, 11; A I, 11; anterior interorbital pore paired; dark vertical bar extending below
eye...*Gnatholepis*

22b. D VI+I, 9-10; A I, 9; a single anterior interorbital pore; no dark vertical bar under eye.......23

23a. No large recurved canine at bend in dentary; depth <4.3 in SL; preD 8-12, cycloid on nape and
isthmus...*Exyrias*

23b. A large recurved canine at bend in dentary; depth >4.6 in SL; preD ≤7, all ctenoid................
....*Macrodontogobius*

24a. V thick, with fleshy lobes at tips of V spines..25

24b. V thin, without fleshy lobes at tips of spines..29

25a. Chin with tranverse or curved mental frenum...26

25b. Chin without a mental frenum...27

26a. Upper P rays free, silk-like..*Bathygobius*

26b. Upper P rays not free...*Cabillus*

27a. Head rounded, the ventral surface with numerous small bumps.......................*Paragobiodon*

27b. Head broad, without bumps...28

28a. Anterior half of body mostly naked; scales small, LS 29-60...........................*Bryaninops*

28b. Body completely scaled, scales large, LS 20-31..*Pleurosicya*

29a. Head pores absent; size not >50 mm..30

29b. Head pores present..32

30a. Interorbital broader than pupil; gill opening equal to P base; V frenum present (estuaries).......
....(*Mugilogobius*)

30b. Interorbital narrower than pupil; gill opening to below eye or preopercle; V frenum absent..31

31a. Gill opening ends below rear margin of preopercle; head broader than deep, with distinct vertical bars...*Priolepis*

31b. Gill opening extends to below eye or rarely to below rear margin of preopercle; head compressed, deeper than broad, uniform, spotted, or with irregular faint bands................*Trimma*

32a. V completely seperate..33

32b. V partly or completely connected...35

33a. V fringe-like; D VI+I, 7-11; LS 21-26; (size <30 mm)...*Eviota*

fins separate
7a; 32a

partially united

frenum

completely united
7b; 32b

large spine

Gladigobius
13a

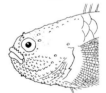

Paragobiodon
27a

Eviota
33a

33b. V normal; D VI+I,11-20; LS 58-146...34

34a. Snout ≤eye; upper jaw teeth in 3 or more rows; gill opening extends to below preopercle...........
....*Amblyeleotris*

34b. Snout much >eye; upper jaw teeth in 1 row; gill opening equal to P base...............*Valenciennea*

35a. Lower jaw curved upward at tip; C longer than head in adult; head pores Type B....................36

35b. Lower jaw normal; C longer or shorter than head; head pores Type A...........................39

head pore pattern B (no. of pores varia-ble, but all within area enclosed by dotted line)

35a

36a. Head compressed; D VI+I, 6-8; (size <50 mm)..37

36b. Head rounded; D VI+I, 10-13...38

37a. Mouth small and inferior or subinferior (estuaries)..*(Pseudogobius)*

37b. Mouth small and terminal in females, large and inferior or subinferior in males (estuaries)...........
....*(Redigobius)*

38a. Upper jaw teeth in 1 row; D VI+I, 12-13; LS 42-75 (estuaries)........................*(Oxyurichthys)*

38b. Upper jaw teeth in 2 or 3 rows; D VI+I, 10-11; LS 25-27................................*(Oligolepis)**

39a. Gill opening extending to below rear margin of preopercle (or farther forward)....................40

39b. Gill opening retricted to P base or slightly below...47

head pore pattern A

35b

40a. Scales small; LS 44-110; D VI+I, 9-14..41

40b. Scales large; LS 25-39; D VI+I, 10-19..45

41a. D VI+I, 9-12, usually <11..42

41b. D VI+I, 12-14..44

42a. Upper jaw teeth in 2 rows; A I, 10-12..*Ctenogobiops*

42b. Upper jaw teeth in 3-6 rows; A I, 9-10...43

43a. P without prominent black spots; first D without prominent black ocellus; color not as below.....
....*Cryptocentrus*

43b. P with 3-4 prominent black spots; first D with prominent black ocellus; body and head black with prominent dorsal white areas on head and nape, between the D fins, and on the C peduncle..*Lotilia*

44a. C pointed, longer than head; snout profile at an angle < 40° with body axis; papillae pattern longi-tudinal; A I, 13..*Vanderhorstia*

44b. C rounded, shorter than head; snout steep, forming an angle > 20° with body axis; papillae pattern transverse; A I, 10-12..*Amblyeleotris*

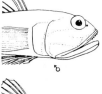

♂

45a. A I, 8; tongue tip bilobed; branchiostegal membranes forming free fold across isthmus; predorsal scaled at least to above opercle; (freshwater and estuaries)................................*(Glossogobius)*

45b. A I, 9; tongue tip truncate; branchiostegal membranes attached to side of isthmus; predorsal naked 46

46a. Head depressed; A I, 12-13..*Silhouettea*

46b. Head compressed; A I, 9...*Mahidolia*

♀

Redigobius

37b

47a. D VI+I, 13-15; upper gill arch with finger-like projections;10-15 short vertical papillae rows un-der eye; operculum with several scales dorsally...................................*Amblygobius*

47b. D VI+I, 7-15; upper gill arch without finger-like projections; 4-6 long vertical papillae rows only under eye; operculum naked or with 1 scale...48

48a. Mouth small, almost horizontal; snout broadly rounded, ending above front of upper lip; preD 6-9, reaching eyes; (body with several longitudinal light lines; midside with series of round spots)...*Istigobius*

48b. Mouth small to large, oblique; snout gently or steeply sloping, not broadly curved in lateral view, ending behind upper lip; preD 0-20, (except in *Fusigobius* which has pointed snout), often not reaching eyes...49

Drombus

51b

49a. V frenum low or absent preD 0-12; snout pointed in dorsal view; head triangular in cross-section (in *Palutrus*?)..50

49b. V frenum well developed; predorsal scales small, if reaching eyes, preD >15; snout rounded in dor-sal view; head rounded, depressed or compressed...51

50a. PreD 12; D VI+I, 8; LS ca. 30..*Palutrus*

50b. PreD 0-8, reaching to or near eye if present; D VI+I, 9-10; LS ≤24; (body translucent to white, with scattered blue and small black spots)..*Fusigobius*

51a. Head papillae pattern longitudinal..52

51b. Head papillae pattern transverse (mangroves)...*(Drombus)**

52a. Upper P rays free, silk-like; small bump under anterior nostril; cheek with a fold behind upper lip; a prominent truncate or curved mental frenum; predorsal at least partly scaled..........*Bathygobius*

52b. Upper P rays normal; no bump under anterior nostril; cheek without a fold; mental frenum indis-tinct (estuarine or coastal marine)..*(Acentrogobius)*

Bathygobius

52a

Fossorial species, prawn-associated: Species of *Amblyeleotris*, *Cryptocentroides*, *Cryptocentrus*, *Ctenogobiops*, *Vanderhorstia*, *Lotilia*, and *Mahidolia* (as well as several other genera which may also occur in Micronesia) share the interesting habit of living in a burrow constructed by an alpheid prawn. The prawn builds a burrow in sand or mud and is blind, or nearly so, and unable to see approaching danger. The goby uses the burrow as a refuge, and with its superior ability to detect danger, acts as a sentinel for the prawn. The gobies, usually singly or in pairs, spend most of their time at the entrance of the burrow and feed on small sand-dwelling invertebrates, many of which are exposed by the prawn's excavations. The prawn spends most of its time maintaining the burrow. When shoveling sand around the entrance it usually maintains contact with the goby by touching the goby's tail with one of its antennae. When alarmed the goby flicks its tail, signaling the prawn to retreat. If the danger persists, the goby dashes headfirst into the burrow. There seems to be less known of the prawns than the gobies. Approximately seven species of prawns associate with gobies in Micronesia. Some species host a single species of goby while others may host several. Some prawns construct burrows with multiple entrances and passages and most burrows reach depths of well over 50 cm (19 in). At least 25 species of prawn-associated gobies in 7 genera occur in Micronesia. (Lit.: Herre, 1953; Hoese & Allen, 1977; Hoese & Steene, 1978; Karplus et al., 1972; Koumans, 1953; Lubbock and Polunin, 1977; Polunin and Lubbock, 1977; Smith, 1959; Yoshino and Senou, 1983; Goren, 1978)

The following alpheid prawns construct burrows used by gobies in Micronesia:
Species 1 (*Alpheus rapax* ?): pale brown with white saddles.
Species 2 (*Alpheus bellulus* ?): marbled brown and white.
Species 3 (*Alpheus djiboutensis* ?): marbled bluish-green with a thin white saddle on anterior of abdomen.
Species 4 (*Alpheus rapicida* ?): olive-green with two transverse abdominal bands; abundant in seagrass beds.
Species 5 (*Alpheus ochrostriatus* ?): green with mottled dark blotches and two or more white abdominal saddles or spots (=sp. 2 or 3?).
Species 5: uniformly yellow, or yellow with numerous fine white longitudinal pinstripes.
Species 6: yellowish with blue spots.
Species 8: reddish-brown with thin white longitudinal pinstripes and spots on body (=sp. 5?).

Amblyeleotris fasciata (Herre, 1953)   Pl. 119A
Red-banded prawn-goby
SL: to 65 mm (2.6 in); D VI+I, 10-14; A I, 10-12; LS 70; depth 5.7-5.8.
This is among the more colorful of the prawn-associated gobies. It differs from *A. wheeleri* by having narrower red bands and lacking red markings on the second dorsal fin. It is moderately common in patches of coarse carbonate or volcanic sand of outer lagoon and seaward reefs at depths of 5 to over 20 m. It often occurs in pairs and utilizes the burrow of a uniformly yellow species of prawn (alpheid sp. 6).

West-central Pacific: Christmas Is., Indian Ocean, to Samoa, n. to the Marianas, s. to s. the Great Barrier Reef; Marianas and Marshalls in Mircronesia.

Amblyeleotris fontaseni (Bleeker, 1852)   Fig. 2a
Giant prawn-goby
SL: to ca. 152 mm (6.0 in); D VI+I, 15; A I, 16-17; P 20-21; LS 110; depth ca. 6.
This large prawn goby has been placed in the genus *Biat* by some ichthyologists. It is greenish red dorsally and pearly ventrally with 3 broad dusky bands, small pearly spots on the upper portion of the head and reddish yellow fins. It typically occurs on silty inshore bottoms.
Indo-Australian: Summatra to the Moluccas, n. to the Philippines; Belau in Micronesia.

Amblyeleotris guttata (Fowler, 1938)   Pl. 119B
Spotted prawn-goby
SL: to 71 mm (2.8 in); D VI+I, 12; A I, 12; P 19; LS 67.
This distinctive spotted species occurs in patches or expanses of coarse carbonate sand on outer lagoon and seaward reefs at depths of 10 to over 34 m. In the Marianas, it is a common prawn-associated goby of outer reef slopes.
West-central Pacific: Philippines to Samoa, n. to the Ryukyus, s. to Scott Reef and the s. Great Barrier Reef; throughout Micronesia.

Amblyeleotris periophthalma (Bleeker, 1853)
SL: to 75 mm (3.0 in); D VI+I, 12;
A I, 12; P 19; LS 70-80; depth ca. 5.5-6.5.
Specimens originally identified as this species have been collected on reef flats and lagoon reefs, but they should be re-examined.
Indo-west Pacific: Red Sea to Samoa; Ifaluk and Kapingamarangi in Micronesia.

Amblyeleotris randalli Hoese & Steene, 1978
Randall's prawn-goby   Pl. 119D
SL: to 73 mm (2.9 in); D VI+I, 12; A I, 12; P 18-19; LS 54-63; GR 2-3+10-12=12-15.
The ocellus on the rear base of the tall spinous dorsal fin is distinctive. This species lives on patches of carbonate sand at depths of 25 to 48 m. It lives with an olivaceus prawn with short white transverse marks (alpheid sp. 4?).
Indo-Australian: Moluccas to the Solomon Is., n. to the Ryukyus, s. to the n. Great Barrier Reef; Belau in Micronesia.

Amblyeleotris steinitzi (Klausewitz, 1974) Pl. 119E
Steinitz' prawn-goby
SL: to 60 mm (2.4 in); D VI+I, 12; A I, 12; P 18; LS 74-78; depth 4.7-5.4.
This species differs from *A. wheeleri* by having dull brown bars and more lateral scale rows. It occurs in sandy areas of outer lagoon and seaward reefs at depths of 6 to over 27 m. It seems to prefer slightly finer sand than does *A. wheeleri* and may be common in certain locations. It lives with a pale brown (alpheid sp. 1) and a marbled brown and white species of prawns (alpheid sp. 2, and rarely sp. 5).

Indo-Pacific: Red Sea to Samoa, n. to the Yaeyamas, s. to the s. Great Barrier Reef; throughout Micronesia.

Amblyeleotris wheeleri (Polunin & Lubbock,1977)
Gorgeous prawn-goby   Pl. 119C,F
SL: to 65 mm (2.6 in); D VI+I, 12; A I, 12; P 18-20; LS 62-68; GR 1-3+8-10; depth at V orig. 4.9-5.2.

This species differs from *A. fasciata* by having wider bands, red spots on the second dorsal fin, a broad red band along the basal part of the anal fin, and fused pelvic fins. It inhabits areas of coarse carbonate or volcanic sand of clear lagoon and seaward reefs at depths of 5 to 15 m.

Indo-Pacific: E. Africa to the Marshall Is., n. to the Ryukyus; s. to nw. Australia; Marshalls in Micronesia.

Cryptocentroides insignis (Seale, 1910)   Fig. 2b
Insignia prawn-goby
SL: to 69 mm (2.7 in); D VI+I, 11-13; A I, 12-13; P 16-17; LS 67-75; depth ca. 4.8-5.4.

This species has diagonal bars that run forward on the head and backwards on the body. Females are covered with numerous reddish spots, males are covered with blue spots. It is reported to inhabit brackish tidepools.

West Pacific: Java to the Solomon Is., n. to the Yaeyamas; Pohnpei in Micronesia.

Cryptocentrus cinctus (Herrre, 1936)   Pl. 119G,H
Banded prawn-goby; yellow prawn-goby
(*C. flavus* Yanisagawa, for yellow phase)
SL: to ≥58 mm (2.3 in); D VI+I, 10; A I, 9; P 16-18; LS 67-71.

Species of *Cryptocentrus* generally have fewer soft dorsal (10 vs 11-13) and anal (9-10 vs 12-14) rays than those of *Amblyeleotris* and tend to prefer more protected, often siltier areas. *Cryptocentrus cinctus* occurs in two color morphs, one with broad light and dark band, the other yellow. At Belau, this species is abundant on expanses of mixed fine and coarse carbonate sand in shallow lagoons, particularly off white sand beaches of the outer rock islands. It utilizes the burrows of alpheid species 4 and 8 (sp. 8 confirmed only for banded phase).

West Pacific: Singapore n. to the Yaeyamas, s. to the s. Great Barrier Reef; Belau and Truk in Micronesia.

Cryptocentrus koumansi (Whitley, 1935)   Pl. 120A
Kouman's prawn-goby
SL: to >44 mm (1.7 in); D VI+I, 10; A I, 9; P 17; LS 50.

In the Marianas this is the most common species of prawn-associated goby in turbid silty areas of shallow reef flats and lagoons. It utilizes the burrows of the same species of prawn (alpheid sp. 4) and occurs in the same basic habitats as do *C. octafasciatus* and *C. strigilliceps*.

West Pacific: e. to Fiji, n. to the Yaeyamas, s. to the n. Great Barrier Reef; Kosrae and Marianas in Micronesia.

Cryptocentrus octafasciatus Regan, 1908   Pl. 120B
Blue-speckled prawn goby
(*C. caeruleomaculatus*; *C. caeruleopunctatus*)
SL: to >44 mm (1.7 in); D VI+I, 10; A I, 9; P 17; LS 56-65; depth ca. 5.0.

This species resembles *C. koumansi*, but differs by having numerous small irridescent blue spots over a dark background with at least eight transverse bars and 3 to 4 dark round spots longitudinally along the sides. It inhabits fine sand or silt bottoms of shallow lagoons and coastal bays subject to terrestrial runoff at depths of 0.3 to 4 m. It is relativley common off southern Guam, and appears to utilize the burrows of the same species of prawn as do *C. koumansi*. and *C. strigilliceps* (alpheid sp. 4).

Indo-Pacific: E. Africa to the Marianas, n. to s. Japan; Belau, Ifaluk, and Guam in Micronesia.

Cryptocentrus strigilliceps (Jordan & Seale, 1906)
Target goby   Pl. 120C
(*Cryptocentrus koumansi* Smith, 1959(non-Whitley, 1935))
SL: to 44 mm (1.7 in); D VI+I, 9-10; A I, 9-10; P 16-17; LS 47-53; GR 3-4+10-12.

This species has a large ocellus below the first dorsal fin, followed by three smaller ones posteriorly. It inhabits silty bottoms at the bases of reefs or coral heads at depths of 1 to over 6 m. It is common near areas of terrestrial runoff and utilizes the burrow of a green prawn with a white transverse band (alpheid sp. 4).

Indo-Pacific: E. Africa to Samoa, n. to the Yaeyamas, s. to the n. Great Barrier Reef; Guam, e. Carolines, and Marshalls in Micronesia.

Cryptocentrus singapurensis (Herre, 1936)   Fig. 1
Singapore prawn-goby
SL: to 82 mm (3.2 in); DVI+I, 10; A I, 10; P 18; LS 75.

This species has numerous blue and blue-rimmed red spots on the head and upper body as well as numerous broad brown bands. It inhabits silty bottoms of coastal reefs.

West Pacific: Singapore, Yaeyamas, and Belau.

Fig. 1. *Cryptocentrus singapurensis*, 1 m, New Caledonia.

Cryptocentrus sp. A   Pl. 120D
This species was observed at the entrance of a burrow next to those of *C. cinctus* off the white sand beaches of Belau's Seventy Islands. It may be the same as *Cryptocentrus* sp. 2 (pl. 243-M) of Masuda, et al. 1984 from the Yaeyama Is. (D VI+I, 10; A I, 9; P 17; LR 65)

Ctenogobiops aurocingulus (Herre, 1935)
Gold-streaked prawn-goby   Fig. 2c

SL: to 45 (1.8 in); D VI+I, 11; A I, 11; P 18-20(19); LS 48-56; depth 4.7-5.5.

All Micronesian species of *Ctenogobiops* closely resemble one another except *C. tangaroai* which has an elongate first dorsal filament. *C. aurocingulus*, *C. feroculus*, and *C. pomastictus* can be distinguished in the field by differences in the spotting on the head and body. *C. aurocingulus* is the only one that has elongate gold-centered dark markings both on the head and vertically on the lower sides of the body.

West-central Pacific: Philippines, Ryukyus, Fiji, Samoa, Carolines, and Marshalls.

Ctenogobiops feroculus Lubbock & Polunin, 1977
Sandy prawn-goby   Pl. 120E

SL: to 45 mm (1.8 in); D VI+I, 10-12(11); A I, 10-(11); P (19)-20; LS 50-67; lower GR 9; depth 5.0-5.7.

This species lacks elongate gold-centered spots on the head and the orientation and shape of the dark head and body markings differ from those of its congeners. In the Marianas, it is common in areas of fine sand of shallow lagoons and subtidal reef flats to a depth of over 4 m, often with *C. pomastictus*. It frequently occurs in pairs and utilizes the burrow of alpheid species 1, 2 and 4.

Indo-west Pacific: Red Sea to New Caledonia, n. to the Ryukyus; Truk and Guam in Micronesia.

Ctenogobiops pomastictus
    Lubbock & Pulonin, 1977   Pl. 120F
Gold-specked prawn-goby

SL: to 47 mm (1.9 in); D VI+I, (11)-12; A I, (11)-12; P 18-20(19-20); LS 52-64; lower GR 9-10; depth 4.6-5.0.

This species occurs singly or in pairs on fine sand and silt bottoms of subtidal reef flats and lagoons to a depth of over 20 m. It is abundant in certain areas of the Marianas. It utilizes the burrows of alpheid species 3, 4, and 5. Some burrows have two or three entrances.

Indo-Australian: s. Great Barrier Reef n. to the Ryukyus, s. to Rowley Shoals; Marianas in Micronesia.

Ctenogobiops tangaroai Lubbock &Pulonin,1977
Tangaroa prawn-goby   Pl. 120G

SL: to 51 mm (2.0 in); D VI+I, 10-(11); A I, 10-11; P (18)-20; LS 46-54; lower GR 10; depth 4.4-5.2.

This species inhabits patches of fine sand on seaward reefs at depths of 4-40 m. In Micronesia it has only been reported from Guam where it is rare and occurs below 12 m. It utilizes the burrow of alpheid sp. 6.

West Pacific: Ryukyus, Guam, and Samoa.

Lotilia graciliosa Klausewitz, 1960   Pl. 120H
Graceful prawn-goby

SL: to ≥31 mm (1.2 in); D VI+I, 9-10; A I, 9; P 16; LS 44-50; depth ca. 3.75.

This atypical prawn-associated goby has large, spotted, fan-like pectoral fins that it constantly waves in a very ungoby-like manner as it hovers close above the entrance to its burrow. It has been observed on patches of fine carbonate sand

on subtidal reef flats and seaward reefs to a depth of over 20 m, but seems to be rare everywhere. It utilizes the burrow of alpheid sp. 7.

Indo-Pacific: Red Sea, to the Marshalls, n. to the Ryukyus; s. to Rowley Shoals; Belau, Guam, and Marshalls.

Mahidolia mystacina (Valenciennes, 1837) Pl. 121A
Flagfin prawn-goby

SL: to ca. 65 mm (2.6 in); D VI+I, 10; A I, 9; P 15-17; LS 33-39.

This distinctive goby is known from Micronesia on the basis of photographs taken at a depth of 16 m on a mud bottom at the base of the reef at Toguan Bay, Guam. It utilized the burrow of a mottled brown alpheid with two or more short white saddles or spots (alpheid sp. 7)

Indo-Pacific: E. Africa to the Society Is., n. to s. Japan (?), s. to n. Australia and Samoa; Guam and Pohnpei (?) in Micronesia.

Vanderhorstia ambanoro (Fourmanoir, 1957)
Ambanoro prawn-goby   Pl. 121C

SL: to 107 mm (4.2 in); D VI+I, 13; A I, 13; P 19; LS 73-85; GR 5+10; depth ca. 6; tongue bilobed.

Adults of this species hover close above the entrance of the burrow rather than rest on the substratum. It is rare in the Marianas where it inhabits expanses of fine sand in protected bays or lagoons at depths of 4 to 12 m.

Indo-west Pacific: E. Africa to Samoa; n. to the Yaeyamas; Marianas and Marshalls in Micronesia.

Vanderhorstia ornatissima Smith, 1959   Fig. 2d
Ornate prawn-goby   Pl. 121B

SL: to >41 mm (1.6 in); D VI+I, 13-14; A I, 13; P 17-20; LS 52-60; lower GR 8-10; depth at P base 6.3-7.1.

This intricately patterned goby inhabits shallow (usually <3 m) sandy areas among seagrasses. It utilizes the burrows of alpheid sp. 4.

Indo-Pacific: E. Africa to Samoa, n. to the Ryukyus, s. to the s. Great Barrier Reef and Rapa; throughout Micronesia.

Fossorial species, non-prawn associated: Most of the following 13 species will shelter in a burrow constructed by themselves or another animal but do not share an intimate relationship with other burrowing animals. (Lit.: Koumans, 1953; Smith, 1959)

Amblygobius decussatus (Bleeker, 1855) Pl. 121D
Crosshatch goby

SL: to ≥53 mm (2.1 in); D VI+I, 14; A I, 14; P 17; LS 57; preD scales 23.

Species of *Amblygobius* are relatively large, active gobies that hover a short distance above the bottom and feed by sifting mouthfuls of sand through their gill rakers to capture small invertebrates and organic matter. Most species retreat to a burrow when alarmed. This species inhabits muddy bottoms of inshore bays, and lagoons at depths of about 3 to at least 20 m. It uses a vertical, tube-like burrow of an unidentified invertebrate.

West-central Pacific: Philippines to New Caledonia, n. to

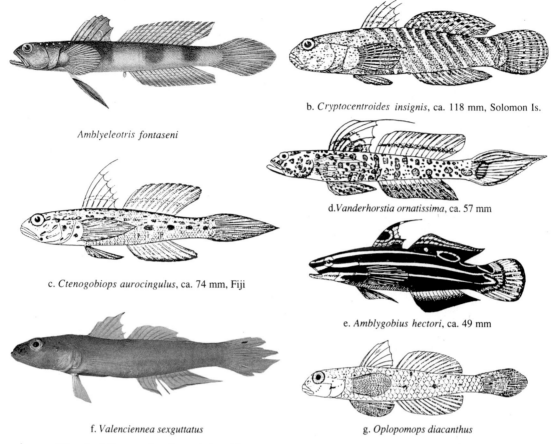

b. *Cryptocentroides insignis*, ca. 118 mm, Solomon Is.

Amblyeleotris fontaseni

d.*Vanderhorstia ornatissima*, ca. 57 mm

c. *Ctenogobiops aurocingulus*, ca. 74 mm, Fiji

e. *Amblygobius hectori*, ca. 49 mm

f. *Valenciennea sexguttatus*

g. *Oplopomops diacanthus*

Fig. 2. Micronesian fossorial gobies (a, after Bleeker; b, c, after Herre, 1936; g, after Schultz, 1943).

the Yaeyamas, s. to the Great Barrier Reef; throughout Micronesia.

Amblygobius hectori (Smith, 1956) Fig. 2e
Hector's goby
SL: to 45 mm (1.8 in); D VI+I, 15-(16); A I, 15-(16); P 15-(16); LS 53-55; preD S 23-25, not reaching eye; lower GR 4-5; depth 4.3-4.9.

This species has a pattern similar to that of *A. rainfordi*, but is bluish-black rather than green, with yellow longitudinal stripes and a chain of ocelli from the base of the second dorsal fin to the upper caudal rays. It occurs over sand at the base of reefs.

Indo-west Pacific: Red Sea, Aldabra, Seychelles, Ryukyus, Yaeyamas, Belau, Truk, and Pohnpei.

Amblygobius nocturnus (Herre, 1945) Pl. 121E
Nocturn goby
SL: to >40 mm (1.6 in); D VI+I, 14; A I, 14; P 17; LS 66.
This species differs from *A. decussatus* by having two somewhat broader longitudinal red bands (sometimes dark edged) as well as red bands basally on the soft dorsal and anal fins,

and lacking scattered red spots on the body. This species inhabits fine sand to mud bottoms at the bases of inner lagoon and coastal reefs at depths of 3 to at least 30 m.

West-central Pacific: Philippines to the Tuamotus, n. to the Yaeyamas, s. to Rowley Shoals, the s. Great Barrier Reef and Rapa; Guam, and Kapingamarangi in Micronesia.

Amblygobius phalaena (Valenciennes, 1837)
Brown-barred goby Pl. 121F
SL: to 120 mm (4.7 in); D VI+I, 14; A I, 14; P 19; LS 57; preD scales 28.
This large goby is a common inhabitant of sandy or rubbly areas of subtidal reef flats and lagoons to a depth of 20 m. It occurs singly or in pairs and constructs a burrow under a rock or rubble. It feeds by taking a mouthful of sand and expelling it through the gills, capturing small invertebrates and organic matter as well as on large quantities of algae.

Indo-Pacific: Philippines to the Society Is., n. to the Ryukyus, s. to sw. Australia, New South Wales, and Lord Howe and Rapa Is.; throughout Micronesia; replaced by the closely related *A. albimaculatus* in the w. Indian Ocean.

Amblygobius rainfordi (Whitley, 1940) Pl. 121G
Old glory; Rainford's goby
SL: to ≥ 47 mm (1.9 in); D VI+I, 11; A I, 11; P 17; LS ca. 58; depth ca. 4.5.
This spectacular goby inhabits the sandy or muddy bases of turbid coastal reefs. Unlike its closest relatives, it does not seem to use a burrow and will venture over coral growth.
West-central Pacific: Philippines to the Marshalls, s. to Rowley Shoals and the s. Great Barrier Reef; Belau to the e. Carolines and Marshalls in Micronesia.

Oplopomops diacanthus (Schultz, 1943) Fig. 2g
Hole goby
SL: to 45 mm (1.8 in); D VI+I, 10; A I, 9-11; P 17-18; LS 27-28; pred S 7-8.
Oplopomops differs from *Oplopomus* by lacking spines on the preopercle. With its speckled body, *O. diacanthus* resembles species of *Istigobius*. It is uncertain whether or not it associates with invertebrate burrows.
West-central Pacific: Kapingamarangi (?), Marshalls, and Phoenix Is.

Oplopomus oplopomus (Valenciennes, 1837)
Blue-spotted hole goby Pl. 121H
SL: to ca. 64 mm (2.5 in); D VI+I, 10; A I, 10; P 18-19; LS 24-26; preD S 13.
Species of *Oplopomus* more closely resemble a number of non-burrow rather than burrow-associated gobies. They occur on bottoms of fine sand or mud of lagoons and coastal bays at depths of 1 to over 20 m. When frightened they dart into a hole made by an invertebrate. Males have more intense blue spots on the head as well as more colorful markings on the fins than do females. Subadults lack the blue and yellow spotting but have more black spots. At Guam, this species is abundant on fine sand to silt bottoms of shallow lagoons and coastal bays to a depth of at least 12 m.
Indo-Pacific: Red Sea to the Society Is., n. to the Yaeyamas; Carolines and Marianas in Micronesia.

Signigobius biocellatus Hoese & Allen, 1977
Signal goby; Crab-eye goby Pl. 122A
SL: to 56 mm (2.2 in); D VI+I, 10-(11); A I, 10-(11); P 20-22(20-21); LS 48-55; GR 4-6; depth 4.3-5.6.
This unmistakable goby is named after its conspicuous ocellated dorsal fins and habit of raising them to flash the "eyespots" at an approaching predator. Presumably this deters the predator by convincing it that the "eyes" belong to a much larger fish! *Signigobius* inhabits sandy to silty bottoms of lagoons and coastal bays near coral, rubble or leaf litter shelter at depths of 2 to 30 m. It feeds on small interstitial invertebrates in the same manner as species of *Valenciennea*, by sifting mouthfuls of sand through its gill rakers. It is common among the Rock Islands of Belau.
Indo-Australian: Philippines to the Solomon Is. and Vanuatu, s. to the s. Great Barrier Reef; Belau in Micronesia.

Silhouettea sp.
Meristics for genus: D VI+I, 10-11; A I, 11-13; P 13-16; LS 23-28.

An unidentified species has been collected in the Marshall Islands.

Valenciennea muralis (Valenciennes, 1837) Pl. 122B
Mural goby
SL: to ca. 125 mm (4.9 in); D VI+I, 12; A I, 12; P 19-20; LS 85-95; depth ca. 4.5.
Species of *Valenciennea* and *Amblygobius* are similar in both morphology and behavior. Differences include a more elongate body, smaller scales, and fully developed gill rakers on the entire arch rather than posteriorly in *Valenciennea*. Species of *Valenciennea* feed on small invertebrates such as copepods, amphipods, ostracods, nematodes, and foraminiferans by sifting mouthfuls of sand through their gill rakers. This species has 2 to 3 blue-bordered red longitudinal stripes on the head that extend faintly on the body, as well as red basal stripes on the dorsal and anal fins, a dark tip to the first dorsal fin, and red ocelli on the caudal fin. It inhabits areas of fine sand of shallow lagoon reefs.
Indo-Pacific: India to Fiji, n. to the Ryukyus, s. to nw. Australia and the s. Great Barrier Reef; Belau in Micronesia.

Valenciennea puellaris (Tomiyama, 1956) Pl. 122D
Maiden goby
SL: to 14 cm (5.5 in); D VI+I, 11-(12); A I, 11-(12); P 19-21; LS 85-92; depth 4.5-5.6.
This species inhabits large patches of coarse carbonate sand of seaward reefs at depths of about 15 to over 20 m. It frequently occurs in pairs or small groups and shelters in burrows in the sand under rocks or rubble.
Indo-Pacific: Red Sea to Samoa, n. to s. Japan, s. to the s. Great Barrier Reef and New Caledonia; Marshalls and Marianas in Micronesia.

Valenciennea sexguttata (Valenciennes, 1837)
Ladder goby; six-spot goby Pl. 122C; Fig. 2f
SL: to ca. 90 mm (3.5 in); D VI+I, 12; A I, 11-13(12); P 19-21; LS 68-80; depth 5.0-5.7.
This species occurs on fine sand to silt bottoms of lagoons and bays. It usually occurs in pairs and builds a burrow under rocks.
Indo-Pacific: Red Sea to Samoa, n. to the Yaeyamas; e. Carolines and Marshalls in Micronesia.

Valenciennea strigata (Brousonet, 1782)
Blue-sreak goby Pl. 122E,F
SL: to ca. 140 mm (5.5 in); D VI+I, 17-19; A I, 16-19; P 21-23; LS 103-120; GR 1-2+6-8.
This large, colorful goby is a common inhabitant of clear outer lagoon and seaward reefs at depths of 1 to 20 m. It occurs over hard bottoms between corals as well as over sand and rubble and will use a hole in hard as well as soft bottoms. It usually occurs in pairs and feeds on a wide variety of small benthic invertebrates, fishes, and fish eggs. It is well-suited for the aquarium. An additional, possibly undescribed species has recently been reported from Enewetak.
Indo-Pacific: E. Africa to the Line, Marquesan, and Society Is., n. to the Ryukyus, s. to Lord Howe Is.; throughout Micronesia.

Non-fossorial species: Most of the remaining gobiids are small, drably colored bottom-dwellers that do not construct or utilize a burrow. Most live on sand or mud bottoms and shelter under ledges or rocks or among debris. Many species (e.g.*Eviota*) live on algae coated rocks, rubble, or corals while others live exclusively on or within other organisms. Some species live among the branches of corals (*Gobiodon* and *Paragobiodon*), or on whip corals, gorgonians, or sponges (e.g. *Bryaninops*), or hover in the water column near or in caves and crevices (e.g. *Trimma*).(Lit.: Goren 1978, 1979; Hoese, 1975; Hoese *in* Smith and Heemstra, 1986; Jewett and Lachner, 1983; Karnella and Lachner, 1981; Lachner and Karnella, 1978, 1980; Lachner & McKinney, 1978; Larson, 1976, 1983, 1985; Larson and Hoese, 1980; Lobel, 1979; McKinnney and Lachner, 1984; Murdy, 1985; Murdy and Hoese, 1985; Winterbottom, 1983).

Acentrogobius sp.
Mangrove goby
Species of *Acentrogobius* typically inhabit coastal marine and brackish waters of continental islands. An unidentified species is common in Jellyfish Lake in Belau's Rock Islands. Other species in the genus likely occur in estuarine waters from Belau to the e. Caroline Is.

Asterropteryx ensiferus (Bleeker, 1874)
SL: to ca. 25 mm; D VI-I, 10: A I, 9; P 17; LR 23-24; PreD 8; preopercle with single spine.
This species differs from the more common *A. semipunctatus* by having a single spine on the preopercular margin.
Indo-Pacific: Red Sea to the Society Is., n. to the Yaeyamas, s. to New Guinea; Marshalls in Micronesia.

Asterropteryx semipunctatus Rüppell, 1830
Bluespotted goby   Pl. 122G
SL: to ca. 52 mm (2.1in), us. <40 mm (1.6 in); D VI+I, 9-11(10); A I, 8-9; P 16-18; LS 23-25; preD 6-8; preopercle with 3-9 short spines; depth 3.0-3.4.
This small blue-dotted species is common on algal coated reef rock and rubble of inner reef flats and turbid lagoons.
Indo-Pacific: Red Sea to the Hawaiian, Line, and Tuamotu Is., n. to s. Japan, s. to Lord Howe and Rapa Is.; Marianas, Kapingamarangi, and Marshalls in Micronesia.

Austrolethops wardi Whitley, 1935   Fig. 3
Small-eyed goby
SL: to ca. 50 mm (2.0 in); D VI+14-15; A 13-14; P 16-17; eye minute; head compressed.
This rare unusually small-eyed goby occurs among coral rubble.
Indo-Pacific: E. Africa, s. Great Barrier Reef, and Guam.

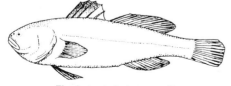

Fig. 3. *Austrolethops wardi.*

Key to Micronesian species of *Bathygobius*:

1a. Head distinctly depressed; anterior nostrils usually with a small flap; lateral canal behind eye continuous to above end of operculum; cheek with a distinct fold behind upper jaw covering part of papillae; upper 5-7 P rays free ....*cotticeps*

1b. Head slightly depressed or rounded; no flap on nostrils; lateral canal with a detached tube over operculum; cheek without a fold or (rarely) with a low fold; upper 3-4 P rays free...2

2a. Predorsal scales extending forward to above rear preopercular margin; mental frenum distinctly covered with long free lateral lobes; body with elongate midlateral blotches and no large ventral blotches...........*cocosensis*

2b. Predorsal scales extending almost to eyes; mental frenum with straight margin, and no or short lateral lobes; body with large irregular-shaped blotches, extending ventrally on body..*fuscus*

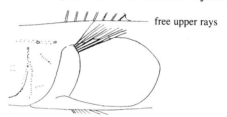

pectoral fin of *Bathygobius*

Bathygobius cocosensis (Bleeker, 1854)   Fig. 4a
Cocos frill-goby
SL: to ca. 66 mm (2.6 in); D VI+I, 9; A I, 8; P 18-20, upper 3-4 rays partly free; LS 33-35; preD 8-12.
Species of *Bathygobius* have somewhat "pudgy" looking cheeks. They are relatively drab bottom-dwellers that live among rubble, in sand pockets, or on reef rock. This species has about 6-8 elongate black spots on its midsides which are mottled in females and have numerous longitudinal lines in males. It is abundant on silty intertidal reef flats.
Indo-Pacific: E. Africa to Johnston, Marquesan, and Tuamotu Is., n. to s. Japan, s. to the s. Great Barrier Reef and Rapa; Marianas and Marshalls in Micronesia.

Bathygobius cotticeps (Steindachner, 1879)
Cheekscaled frill-goby   Fig. 4b
SL: to ca. 91 mm (3.6 in); D VI+I, 9; A I, 8; P 23-24, upper 5-7 rays partly free; LS 35-38; preD 21-32.
This species has a distinctly depressed head. The young have broad dark saddles beneath the dorsal fins and mottled to banded dorsal, pectoral and caudal fins that become dusky to black in adults.
Indo-Pacific: E. Africa to the Hawaiian, Marquesan, and Tuamotu Is., n. to s. Japan; Guam in Micronesia.

Bathygobius fuscus fuscus (Rüppell, 1828)
Dusky frill-goby   Pl. 122H
SL: to ca. 66 mm (2.6 in); D VI+I, 9; A I, 8; P 17-19, up-

per 3 rays free; LS 29-36; preD 13-18.

This species inhabits inner reef flats and shallow lagoons where it lives among rubble and sand or on algal covered reef rock.

Indo-Pacific: Red Sea to the Hawaiian, Line, and Tuamotu Is., n. to s. Korea and s. Japan; s. to the s. Great Barrier Reef; throughout Micronesia.

Key to Micronesian species of *Bryaninops*: *

1a. A curved canine tooth at middle of side of lower jaw, jaw rounded in ventral view, rows of different-sized sharp curved teeth present...2
1b. No curved canine at midside of lower jaw, jaw somewhat triangular in ventral view, rows of upright even pointed teeth present, mostly toward side of jaw (commensal on the corals, *Porites* and *Millepora* spp.).................*ridens*
2a. P unbranched at all sizes; gill opening extends to below posterior edge of eye; ventral half of body dark to dusky (deep violet when alive), internal bars rarely visible...... ....*erythrops*
2b. Some P rays always branched if >11 mm; gill opening variable; usually faint or dark internal bars visible or with head and body compressed and eyes lateral...........3
3a. Posterior interorbital pore or pair of pores absent; scales on sides of body usually extend only as far forward as 2nd D origin; TRB only 1-2 scale rows; head and body compressed..*natans*
3b. Posterior interorbital pore or pair of pores usually pre-sent; scales on sides usually extend forward to behind P; TRB 9-14; head somewhat depressed.........................4
4a. Body bars golden-brown to brown when alive (generally distinct when preserved); head depth ≥50% od HL; scal-loped grooves present along lower edge of preoperculum (commensal on the sea whip *Cirrhipathes anguina*)........ ....*youngei*
4b. Body bars brownish-orange to red when alive (usually indistinct when preserved); head depth usually <50% of HL; no scalloped grooves but occasionally slight inden-tations along lower edge of preoperculum...........*amplus*

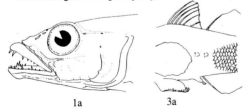

1a   3a

Bryaninops amplus Larson, 1985   Pl. 122 I
Gorgonian goby

SL: to 46 mm (1.8 in); D VI+I, 6-9(8); A I, 6-9(8); P 14-17(15-17); LS 37-69(≥41, x=53); GR 1-3+5-8=6-10; depth at anus, 6.6-9.6.

Species of *Bryaninops* live exclusively on, or in close asso-ciation with gorgonians, antipatharian whip corals, and cer-

tain species of tabular or branching *Acropora* corals. This species occurs primarily on the gorgonian seawhips *Junce-ella fragilis* and *J. juncea*, but may also occur on other spe-cies (e.g. *Ellisella maculata*), or even man-made objects such as mooring lines. The seawhips usually occur in groups in areas exposed to currents at depths of 5 to over 16 m. The goby nests on the living tissue of the sea whip by laying an encircling band of eggs about 10 to 15 cm from the tip. Settlement occurs at a size of about 10 mm and growth to a large adult size (35 mm) may occur within 6 months. An-other species, *B. tigris*, may be expected to occur on the black coral, *Antipathes dichotoma*, throughout Micronesia.

Indo-Pacific: Madagascar to the Hawaiian Is., n. to s. Japan, s. to the s. Great Barrier Reef; Belau and Guam in Microne-sia.

Bryaninops erythrops (Jordan & Seale, 1906)
Translucent coral goby   Fig. 4c

SL: to 17 mm (6.7 in); D VI+I, 7-9(8); A I, 7-9(8); P 13-16(14-15); LS 26-49(≥37, x=40); GR 1-2+7-10=7-11; depth at anus, 5.8-9.6.

This tiny goby lives in groups on certain branching forms of fire corals (*Millepora* spp.) and other branching or mas-sive corals (*Porites cylindrica*, *P. lutea*) in shallow lagoons at depths of 1 to 10 m.

Indo-Pacific: Chagos Is., Philippines, Great Barrier Reef, Fiji, and Samoa; Marianas, e. Carolines and Marshalls in Micronesia.

Bryaninops natans Larson, 1985   Pl. 122 J
Hovering goby

(*Trimma* sp.- Myers and Shepard, 1980)

SL: to 20 mm (0.8 in); D IV-VIII(VI)+I, 7-9(8); A I, 8-9; P 14-17(15-16); LS 19-40(≤35, x=31); GR 1-4+6-9=8-13; depth at anus, 4.1-6.2.

This tiny goby occurs in groups that hover a short distance above, or among, the branches of certain tabular or branch-ing *Acropora* corals. It typically occurs in shallow lagoons and has been reported from depths of less than 7 to 27 m. At Guam, it is common in Apra Harbor above appropriate *Ac-ropora* corals at depths of 12 to over 20 m.

Indo-Pacific: Red Sea to the Cook Is., n. to the Ryukyus, s. to the n. Great Barrier Reef; Guam and Kapingamarangi in Micronesia.

Bryaninops ridens Smith, 1959   Fig. 4d

SL: to 16 mm (0.6 in); D (VI)-VII+I, (7)-8; A I, 8; P 13-15(13-14); LS 25-37; depth at anus, 6.0-7.7.

This tiny goby has been collected on lagoon and seaward reefs. It has been found on a large *Porites* knoll and a branching *Millepora* (*M. tenella*?).

Indo-Pacific: Red Sea, E. Africa, Chagos Is., Yaeyamas, Great Barrier Reef, Ulithi, Pohnpei, and Enewetak.

Bryaninops youngei (Davis & Cohen, 1969)
Whip coral goby   Pl. 122K

SL: to 28 mm (1.1 in); D VI+I, 7-9(8-9); A I, 7-10(8-9); P 13-17(15-16); LS 25-58(≥31, x=40); GR 2-3+8-9=10-11; depth at anus, 5.4-8.1.

---

* Adapted from Larson, 1985; TRB=transverse scale count backwards, from A origin to 2nd D base.

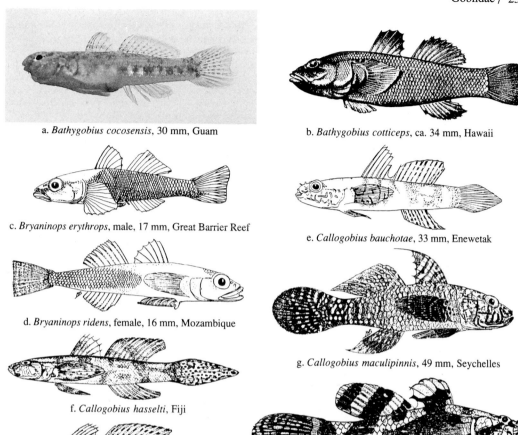

a. *Bathygobius cocosensis*, 30 mm, Guam

b. *Bathygobius cotticeps*, ca. 34 mm, Hawaii

c. *Bryaninops erythrops*, male, 17 mm, Great Barrier Reef

e. *Callogobius bauchotae*, 33 mm, Enewetak

d. *Bryaninops ridens*, female, 16 mm, Mozambique

g. *Callogobius maculipinnis*, 49 mm, Seychelles

f. *Callogobius hasselti*, Fiji

h. *Callogobius okinawae*, 47 mm,

i. *Callogobius plumatus*, 50 mm, Tanzania

Fig. 4. Micronesian gobies (b, after Jordan and Evermann, 1903; c, after Larson, 1985; d, g, i, after Smith, 1959; e, after Goren, 1979; f, h, after Fowler, 1936).

This goby lives exclusively on the sea whip, *Cirripathes anguina* which occurs along current-swept dropoffs or backreefs at depths of 3 to 45 m. The goby occurs in pairs, occasionally with juveniles or a smaller female. Sex-reversal from female to male probably occurs. The gobies nest by clearing the tissue from a 2 to 3 cm band about 15 to 25 cm from the tip.

Indo-Pacific: Red Sea to the Hawaiian and Rapa Is., n. to the Ryukyus, s. to the n. Great Barrier Reef; Belau in Micronesia.

Cabillus tongarevae (Fowler, 1927)
Tongareva goby

SL: to ca. 23 mm (0.9 in); D VI+I, 9; A I, 8; P 18; LS 28; preD 0.

This small goby has been collected from sandy bottoms of lagoon and seaward reefs to a depth of over 9 m.

West-central Pacific: Yaeyamas, s. Great Barrier Reef, Hawaiian Is., Tongareva (n. Cook Is.); Marshalls in Micronesia.

Key to Micronesian species of *Callogobius*:

1a. LR ca. 40; cycloid scales only......................*okinawae*
1b. LR ≤32; no cycloid scales on C peduncle..................2
2a. V united, frenum present...4
2b. V separate, frenum absent......................................3
3a. LR 25; preD 6..*bauchotae*
3b. LR 27-28; preD 12-13....................................*sclateri*
4a. LR ca. 32; preD ca. 22; TR ≥16....................*hasseltii*
4b. LR ≤28; preD ≤15; TR ≤12....................................5
5a. Soft D rays 7; LR >25....................*centrolepis*
5b. Soft D rays 8-10; LR 22-25....................................6
6a. LR 23-25 (7-9 cycloid+16-17 ctenoid); irregular vertical

crossbars on body............................*plumatus*
6b. LR 22-23 (3-4 cycloid+20-22 ctenoid); horizontal lines or spots on body............................*maculipinnis*

Callogobius bauchotae Goren, 1979   Fig. 4e
Bauchot's goby
SL: to 33 mm (1.3 in); D VI+I, 9; A I, 7; P 17; LS 25; preD 6.
Species of *Callogobius* have large vertical flaps on the head. **Marshall Is.**

Callogobius centrolepis Weber, 1909
SL: to 40 mm (1.5 in); D VI+I, 7; A I, 7; P 16?; LS 28; preD 10-12.
West Pacific: n. Java, Moluccas, Marshalls, Samoa.

Callogobius hasselti (Bleeker, 1851)   Fig. 4f
Hasselt's goby
SL: to ca. 58 mm (2.3 in); D VI+I, 10; A I, 8; P 18; LS 32; preD 22; scales on c.ped. ctenoid.
This species inhabits tidepools and lagoons.
West-central Pacific: India to Fiji; n. to s. Japan, s. to New South Wales (?); Belau to the e. Carolines and Marshalls in Micronesia.

Callogobius maculipinnis (Fowler, 1918)   Fig. 4g
Ostrich goby
(*Drombus irrasus* Smith, 1959)
SL: to ca. 53 mm (2.1 in); D VI+I, 9; A I, 7; P 17-19; LS 22-25, 1st 2-3 cycloid; preD 6-7; GR 2-3+9.
This species has been collected among corals.
Indo-Pacific: Red Sea to Samoa, n. to the Philippines; Guam and the Marshalls in Micronesia.

Callogobius okinawae (Snyder, 1908)   Fig. 4h
Okinawa flap-headed goby
SL: to ca. 49 mm (1.9 in); D VI+I, 10; A I, 8; P 16; LS 40; preD 2; all scales cycloid.
This species has been collected from tidepools in estuaries.
West-central Pacific: Philippines to Vanuatu, n. to the Ryukyus; Marshalls in Micronesia.

Callogobius plumatus (Smith, 1959)   Fig. 4i
Feather goby
SL: to ca. 39 mm (1.5 in); D VI+I, 9; A I, 6-7; P 18-19; LS 23-25, anterior 7-9 cycloid, posterior 16-17 ctenoid; preD 9-10; GR 0+8.
Indo-Pacific: E. Africa to Guam.

Callogobius sclateri (Steindachner, 1880)
Pacific flap-headed goby
SL: to ca. 23 mm (0.9 in); D VI+I, 9; A I, 7; P 17;LS 27-28,anterior 3-4 cycloid, posterior 23-25 ctenoid; preD 12-13.
Indo-Pacific: E. Africa to the Society Is., n. to s. Japan, s. to Queensland; Marianas, Kapingamarangi (?), and Marshalls in Micronesia.

Genus *Eviota*: A large genus of very small gobies with at least 24 named species and a few undescribed species in Micronesia. Identification is difficult and often requires a dissecting microscope. Meristics are of limited use in distinguishing species of *Eviota*, leaving details of coloration and sensory pore pattern as the most important factors. Useful field characteristics have not yet been worked out for most species. Cephalic pore patterns, and morphology of the pelvic fins and genital papillae are important in identification (Figs. 5-7). All the named species are included in the key, but illustrations could be obtained for only a few of them.*

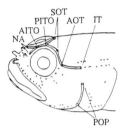

NA: paired nasals
AITO: anterior interorbital
PITO: posterior interorbital
SOT: paired supraotic
AOT: paired anterior otics
IT: paired intertemporals
POP: paired upper and lower preoperculars

Fig. 5. Cephalic pore locations of species of *Eviota*.

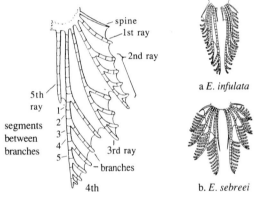

a *E. infulata*

b. *E. sebreei*

c. left side showing number of rays and segments between branches of the 4th ray

Fig. 6. Features of ventral fin and method of counting.

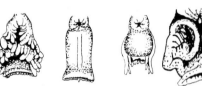

E. prasina   *E. guttata*   *E. prasina*   *E. saipanensis*
(male)   (male)   (female)   (male)
a. fimbriate b. nonfimbriate c. bulbous   d. cup-shaped

Fig. 7. Types of genital papillae.

* Illustrations and key adapted from Lachner and Karnella, 1980; Karnella and Lachner, 1981; Jewett and Lachner, 1983; and Larson, 1976.

Key to Micronesian species of *Eviota*:*

1a. Cephalic sensory pore system complete (Fig. 5)..........2

1b. Cephalic sensory pore system incomplete.................8

2a. Soft D rays usually 9:..3

2b. Soft D rays usually 8..6

3a. A dark, prominent occipital spot.............................4

3b. No dark occipital spot...5

4a. Dorsal midline of trunk with a series of small dark spots; segments between branches of 4th V ray modally 4 (Fig. 6a); a broad, diffuse dark band at base of spinous D..*smaragdus*

4b. Dorsal midline of trunk without dark spots; segments between branches of 4th V ray modally 2; no dark band at base of spinous D...................................*melasma*

5a. Head dorsally and nape with well-defined dark transverse bars; a dark spot on mid-C peduncle, about 3 scale rows anterior to C base; 5 dark spots on ventral midline from A origin to vertical passing through mid-C peduncle spot; spinous D not elongate; P membrane reduced........ ....*fasciola*

5b. Head and nape without transverse bars; no dark spot on mid-C peduncle, about 3 scale rows anterior to C base; 6 dark spots on ventral midline from A origin to vertical passing through normal position of mid-C peduncle spot; spinous D may be elongate in males; P membrane well developed..*albolineata*

6a. V membrane reduced, 5th ray rudimentary or absent; either a large, dark rectangular C peduncle spot located above midline; P base pale..........................*nebulosa*

6b. V membrane moderate to well-developed, 5th ray 10-20% length of 4th ray; C peduncle spot variously developed; P base with 2 dark spots or without spots..........7

7a. Prominent dark spots on head and 2 dark spots on P base in males; body more slender, depth at spinous D origin 21.0-25.0% of SL.......................................*distigma*

7b. Prominent dark spots lacking on head P base in both sexes; body stouter, depth at spinous D origin 24.8-28.5% of SL..*herrei*

8a. Cephalic sensory pore system lacking only the IT pore; P rays simple or branched; male genital papilla variously shaped (Fig. 7)..9

8b. Cephalic sensory pore system lacking the IT pore and either the NA, PTIO, or POP pores, or both the NA and PTIO pores; P rays always simple; male genital papilla nonfimbriate (Fig. 7b)...20

9a. P rays always simple; V membrane almost always well-developed; branches of 4th V ray fewer, modally 5-7, the segments between branches modally 2-4; male genital papilla nonfimbriate..10

9b. Some P rays always branched; V membrane almost reduced; branches of 4th V ray numerous, modally 7-12, (≥7) the segments between branches modally 1-2; male genital papilla fimbriate, nonfimbriate,or cup-shaped (Fig. 7 a, b, or d)..14

10a. 5th V ray absent................................*sigillata*

10b. 5th V ray present...11

11a. 5th V ray short, modally 10% length of 4th ray.......12

11b. 5th V ray long, modally 40% length of 4th ray.......13

12a. A dark postocular spot present; series of well-developed dark spots on middorsal and midventral areas; chromatophores in scale pockets form crescent-shaped marks..*storthynx*

12b. A dark postocular spot absent; lacks well developed body pigmentation except basicaudal spot and a dark horizontal streak on lower C; 5th V ray short...*cometa*

13a. A large, dark spot at base C base, below midline; P base with a dark to dusky spot on uppermost portion; a dark spot at D origin followed by a series of ca. 11 less intense spots along dorsal midline.................*prasites*

13b. Head and body pale, lacking any outstanding color marks...*pellucida*

14a. Extensive branching of the 4th V ray, modally ≥12 (ave.=13.2); scale pockets dark and bodly marked; small distinct dark spots on D and C...........*punctulata*

14b. Less extensive branching of the 4th V ray, modally 7-12; color not as above.......................................15

15a. 2nd D almost always I, 8; A mostly darker than other fins; dark basicaudal spot deeper than wide; spinous D not elongate...*latifasciata*

15b. 2nd D almost always I, 9-10; A may be dark, but not darker than other fins; when present, dark basicaudal spot centrally located, circular or chevron-shaped; 1 or more spines of spinous D may be elongate.............16

16a. C peduncle with a large, dark spot, moderately well-developed; genital papilla in male fimbriate or cup-shaped; 5th V ray absent or rudimentary; 4-5 dark spots posteriorly on ventral midline from D origin...........17

16b. C peduncle lacking a large, dark spot or with weak subcutaneous spot; genital papilla in male simple, nonfimbriate, or cup-shaped; 5th V ray present but short, ca. 10% length of 4th; 5-7 dark spots posteriorly on ventral midline from D origin..............................¦9

17a. Subcutaneous dark bars posteriorly from A origin, 4; dark postocular spots or clusters of chromatophores absent; cheek with scattered chromatophores or chromatophores clustered into 2 bars below eye; P base pale; a moderately intense, circular dark spot at midbase of C; spinous D uniformly dusky....................*saipanensis*

17b. Subcutaneous dark bars posteriorly from A origin, 5; 2 weak to well-developed postocular spots or clusters of large chromatophores present; cheek with >2 barlike clusters of chromatophores below eye; P base pale; a moderately intense, no spot at midbase of C, but dark spot centrally located on or above midline of C peduncle; spinous D not uniformly dusky....................18

18a. A large, dark rectangular subcutaneous spot on middle and upper portion of C peduncle, circular to chevron-shaped at surface of mid-peduncle, overlying posteriormost subcutaneous bar; spinous D darkest at band through middle; postocular spots mainly weak clusters of chromatophores; D almost always 9............*zonura*

18b. A well-developed, dark circular to chevron-shaped spot at mid-C peduncle at surface overlying posteriormost subcutaneous bar; spinous D with 3 light spots at base; 2 postocular spots made of weak to moderately developed clusters of chromatophores; D almost always 9-10...*prasina*

19a. P base with 2 dark prominent spots; 2 dark postocular spots and dark spots on nape, cheek, and opercle, some as intensely developed as spots on P base; scale pockets often with prominent dark pigmentation, the margins broad and deep; a series of 12-15 dark spots along dorsal midline from origin of spinous D to procurrent C rays...*queenslandica*

19b. P base variable but never with 2 prominent spots (with 2 pale areas, with 2 very weak spots, or with faint scattered chromatophores); 2 dark postocular spots absent, nape mostly pale, cheek with faint clusters of chromatophores; scale pockets weakly pigmented at most; dorsal midline spots not noticably developed......
....*afelei*

20a. Cephalic sensory pore system lacking either the NA or PTIO pores or both...21

20b. Cephalic sensory pore system lacking the PTIO pores..*sparsa*

21a. Cephalic sensory pore system lacking the NA and IT pores; a large, irregular to W-shaped mark on upper anterior trunk above and just posterior to P base; length of 5th V ray <1/2 length of 4th; 7 dark ventral midline spots and subcutaeneous bars on lower trunk posteriorly from A origin (Fig. 6b)........................*infulata*

21b. Cephalic sensory pore system lacking either the combination of the NA, PTIO, and IT pores or the PTIO and IT pores; no dark mark above P base; length of 5th V ray ≥1/2 length of 4th; ventral midline spots and subcutaeneous bars trunk absent or obscure.................22

22a. Cephalic sensory pore system lacking the NA, PTIO, and IT pores; a large dark spot present at mid-C base, the lower portion extending to end of C; 4th V ray with 11-17 (modally 14) branches, almost always without segments between its branches; no elongation of spinous D (Fig. 6c)................................*sebreei*

22b. Cephalic sensory pore system lacking the PTIO, and IT pores, the AITO pore enlarged or paired; large dark spots at mid-C base absent, or without lower portion extending posteriorly; 4th V ray with <6 branches, with 3-10 segments between its branches; spinous D elongate in both sexes.......................................23

23a. D almost always 8; A 6-7; a large black spot at mid-C base, the posterior margin developed into a black crescent that extends forward, above and below, to bases of anterior procurrent caudal rays, and the central dark spot bordered above and below by smaller whitish spots; P base with deep, dark spot.........................*lachdeberei*

23b. D almost always 9; A 8-10; no large black spot at mid-C base; P base without or with faint dark spot............
....*bifasciata*

Eviota afelei Jordan & Seale, 1906
Afele's fringefin goby

SL: to 18 mm (0.7 in), ♀s≥10 mm (0.4 in) gravid; D VI+I, 8-(9); A I, 6-(8); P 14-17(≥15); LS 23-25.
This species inhabits the algal mat of shallow exposed reefs. One or two species from the Marianas and Marshalls remain unidentified.
West-central Pacific: Ashmore Reef (Timor Sea) to the Tu-

amotus, n. to Wake Is., s. to the s. Great Barrier Reef; Marianas amd Marshalls in Micronesia.

Eviota albolineata Jewett & Lachner, 1983
Spotted fringefin goby

SL: to 25 mm (1.0 in), ♀s≥11 mm (0.4 in) gravid; VI+I, 8-(9); A I, 8; P 16-20.
This species has been collected from shallow lagoon and channel reefs, usually in less than 3 m.
Indo-Pacific: E Africa to the Tuamotus, n. to Taiwan, s. to Lord Howe and the Tubuai Is.; throughout Micronesia.

Eviota bifasciata Lachner & Karnella, 1980
Twostripe pygmy goby

SL: to 23 mm (1.0 in), ♀s≥13 mm (0.5 in) gravid; D VI+I, 8-10(9); A I, 8-10(8-9); P 14-16; LS 22.
This species has been collected at Belau's Rock Islands.
Indo-Australian: Java to Papua New Guinea, n. to the Philippines, Belau in Micronesia.

Eviota cometa Jewett & Lachner, 1983
Comet pygmy goby

SL: to 18.5 mm (0.7 in), gravid ♀s 11.6-14.8 mm (0.5-0.6 in); D VI+I, 7-10(8-9); A I, 6-8(7-8); P 13-17(≥15); LS 21-23(≥22), breast scaleless; spinous D may be filamentous in males, rarely in females.
This species has been collected from depths of less than 1 to over 30 m.
West-central Pacific: Pohnpei, Great Barrier Reef, Gilbert, Fiji, Phoenix, and Line Is.

Eviota distigma Jordan & Seale, 1906
Twospot pygmy goby

SL: to 20 mm (0.8 in), ♀s≥12 mm (0.5 in) gravid; D VI+I, 7-9(8); A I, 7-(8); P 14-17(15-16); LS 22-25(23-24).
Indo-Pacific: Red Sea to the Line and Pitcairn Is., s. to the s. Great Barrier reef; throughout Micronesia.

Eviota fasciola Karnella & Lachner, 1981
Barred pygmy goby

SL: to 19 mm (0.8 in); D VI+I, 8-9; A I, (8)-9; P 16-17; LS 23-25.
This species inhabits the wave-swept reef margin.
West-central Pacific: Ryukyus, Kiribati, Great Barrier Reef, and throughout Micronesia.

Eviota herrei Jordan & Seale, 1906
Herre's pygmy goby

SL: to 14mm (0.6 in); D VI+I, 8; A I, 8; P 14-16(≤15); LS 6-7.
West-central Pacific: Java to Samoa, Tonga, and Rapa, sw. to Scott Reef; Belau in Micronesia.

Eviota infulata (Smith, 1956)
Infulata pygmy goby

Fig. 8a

SL: to 20 mm (0.8 in), ♀s≥9 mm (0.4 in) gravid; D V-(VI)+I, 7-(8); A I, 6-(7); P 13-15; LS 21-23(21-22).
This species has been collected at Belau's Rock Islands.
Indo-Pacific: Seychelles to the Line and Pitcairn, s. to and

the s. Great Barrier Reef and Rapa; Belau, Kapingamarangi, and Marshalls in Micronesia.

Eviota lachdeberei Giltay, 1933   Pl. 123A
Lachdebrere's pygmy goby
SL: to 21 mm (0.8 in), ♀s≥12 mm (0.5 in) gravid; D VI+I, 7-9(8); A I, 6-(7); P 14-16; LS 21-23(22).
This species has been collected at Belau's Rock Islands.
Indo-Australian: Moluccas, Rowley Shoals, Papua New Guinea, Belau, Guam, Truk, and Pohnpei.

Eviota latifasciata Jewett & Lachner, 1983
Broad-banded pygmy goby
SL: to 14.7 mm (0.6 in), gravid ♀s 10.7-13.2 mm (0.4-0.5 in); D VI+I, 7-9(8), spinous part not elongate; A I, (8)-9; P 15-18(≥16); LS 23-25.
This species has been collected from depths of less than 5 to between 8 and 24 m.
West Pacific: Christmas Is. (Indian Ocean),Gilberts; Kapingamarangi and Pohnpei in Micronesia.

Eviota melasma Lachner & Karnella, 1980
Melasma pygmy goby
SL: to 27 mm (1.1 in); ♀s≥14 m (0.6 in) gravid; D IV-(VI)+I, 8-10(9); A I, (8)-9; P 14-18(≥16); LS 23-25(≤24).
West-central Pacific: Cocos-Keeling Is. to Samoa, n. to the Yaeyamas, s. to Scott Reef (?) and the s. Great Barrier reef; Belau, Truk, and Enewetak in Micronesia.

Eviota nebulosa Smith, 1958
Nebulous pygmy goby
SL: to 19 mm (0.7 in), ♀s≥10 mm (0.4 in) gravid; D VI+I, 8; A I, (8)-9; P 14-17(≥15); LS 23-24.
West-central Pacific: E. Africa to Rotuma, s. to the s. Great Barrier Reef; Belau, Guam, and Enewetak in Micronesia.

Eviota pellucida Larson, 1976
Pellucida pygmy goby
SL: to 21 mm (0.8 in), ♀s≥ 10 mm (0.4 in) gravid; D VI+I, 7-9(7-8); A I, 7; P 15-16; LS 21-22; GR 1+6-7; depth 3.6 to 4.0.
This species has been collected from depths of 3 to over 12 m.
West-central Pacific: Rowley Shoals, Kiribati, Pohnpei, and Guam.

Eviota prasina (Klunzinger, 1871)   Fig. 8b
Green bubble goby
SL: to 31 mm (1.2 in), ♀s≥11 mm (0.4 in) gravid; D VI+I, 8-11(9-10); A I, 7-9(8); P 14-19(15-18); LS 23-25(23-24).
Indo-west Pacific: Red Sea to Rotuma, n. to s. Japan, s. to Lord Howe Is.; Belau in Micronesia.

Eviota prasites Jordan & Seale, 1906   Pl. 123B
Prasites pygmy goby
SL: to 21 mm (0.8 in), ♀s≥13 mm (0.5 in) gravid; D VI+I, (8)-9; A I, 6-(7); P 14-16(≥15); LS 21-23.
West Pacific: Moluccas to Samoa, s. to Scott Reef and New Caledonia; Yap in Micronesia.

Eviota punctulata Jewett & Lachner, 1983
Pepperfin pygmy goby
SL: to 15.7 mm (0.6 in), gravid ♀s ≥11.8 mm (0.5 in); D VI+I, 8-10(9); A I, 7-(8); P 15-18(≤17); LS 23-26(≤25); male genital papillae nonfimbriate, extensive branching of 4th V ray; little or no elong of D.
This species has been collected from depths of 0 to between 14 and 18 m.
West Pacific: Philippines and Java Sea to Fiji, s. to the Great Barrier Reef; Belau, Kapingamarangi, and Pohnpei in Micronesia.

Eviota queenslandica Whitley, 1932
Queensland pygmy goby
SL: to 24 mm (1.0 in), ♀s≥13 mm (0.5 in) gravid; DVI+I, 8-10(9); A I, 7-9(8); P 15-17; LS 23-25(23-24).
This species has been collected at Belau's rock islands.
Indo-Australian: sw. Thailand to Vanuatu, n. to s. Taiwan, s. to the s. Great Barrier Reef; Belau and Yap in Micronesia.

Eviota saipanensis Fowler, 1945   Fig. 8c
Saipan pygmy goby
SL: to 26 mm (1.0 in), ♀s≥12 mm (0.5 in) gravid; D VI+I, 9-10; A I, 7-(8); P 15-17(≥16); LS 22-25(≥23).
West-central Pacific: s. Taiwan to Rapa; Belau, Fais Atoll, Guam, and Saipan in Micronesia.

Eviota sebreei Jordan & Seale, 1906
Sebree's pygmy goby
SL: to 20 mm (0.8 in), ♀s≥12 mm (0.5 in) gravid; D V-(VI)+I, 8-10(9); A I, 8-(9); P 15-17; LS 23-24.
Indo-Pacific: Red Sea to Samoa, s. to the n. Great Barrier Reef; e. Caroline and Marshall Is. in Micronesia.

Eviota sigillata Jewett & Lachner, 1983
Seven-figure pygmy goby
SL: to 21.0 in (0.8 in), gravid ♀s ≥12.5-15.0 mm (0.5-0.6 in); D VI+I, 8-10(8-9); A I, 7-(8); P 14-19(16-18); LS 21-24(≤23); D spinous in both sexes, male genital papillae nonfimbriate.
This species differs from *storthynx* by lacking a postocular spot, and from *zebrina* by having dark spots on the upper and lower portions of caudal base instead of a central dark spot. It has been collected from depths of less than 4 to between 17 and 21 m.
Indo-west Pacific: Seychelles to the Great Barrier Reef and Pohnpei; Yap, Kapingamarangi, and Pohnpei in Micronesia.

Eviota smaragdus Jordan & Seale, 1906
Smaragdus pygmy goby
SL: to 23 mm (0.9 in), ♀s≥11 mm (0.4 in) gravid; D VI+I, 8-(9); A I, 7-(8); P 15-17; LS 23-25.
West-central Pacific: Ryukyus to Samoa, s. to Scott Reef and Norfolk Is.; Guam, and Marshalls in Micronesia.

Eviota sparsa Jewett & Lachner, 1983
Speckled pygmy goby
SL: to 21.3 mm (0.8 in), gravid o at 15.9 mm (0.6 in); D VI+I, 8-10(9); A I, 7-(8); P 14-18(≥16); LS 23-25.

This species has a uniform, unaccentuated color pattern consisting of scattered melanophores over body. It has been collected from depths of 0-14 to 15-31m.

West Pacific: Philippines and Indonesia to Samoa, s. to the Great Barrier Reef; Belau in Micronesia.

Eviota storthynx (Rofen, 1959)
Storthynx pygmy goby

SL: to 21 mm (0.8 in), ♀s≥11 mm (0.4 in) gravid; D VI+(I)-II, (8)-9; A I, 7; P 14-16(≥15); LS 22-23.

This species has been collected at Belau's Rock Islands.

Indo-Australian: Seribu Is. (Java), Philippines, Belau, and Yap.

Eviota zonura Jordan & Seale, 1906
Zoned pygmy goby

SL: to 21 mm (0.8 in), ♀s≥11 mm (0.4 in) gravid; D VI+I, 8-10(9); A I, 7-(8); P 15-17(≥16); LS 23-24.

This species has been collected at Belau's Rock Islands.

West-central Pacific: Ashmore Reef (Timore Sea) and Waigeo to Samoa, s. to Dampier Arch.(?) and Fiji; throughout Micronesia; nearly absent from continental shelves.

Exyrias belissimus (Smith, 1959)   Pl. 123G
Mud reef-goby

SL: to 115 mm (4.5 in); D VI+I, 11-12; A I, 10; P 17-19; LS 30-34; preD 8-9; depth 3.5-4.3.

This large drably colored goby inhabits lagoons at depths of 0 to over 20 m. It typically occurs on silty bottoms near or under overhanging corals. It feeds by sifting sediment through its gill rakers. At Guam it is common in parts of Apra Harbor and in the Piti "bomb holes".

Indo-west Pacific: E. Africa to Samoa, n. to the Yaeyamas, s. to Fiji; Belau, Kosrae, and Guam in Micronesia.

Exyrias puntang (Bleeker, 1851)
Puntang goby

SL: to 122 mm (4.8 in); D VI+I, 11; A I, 9-(10); P 15-18; LS 30-33(but 28 on 2 Guam specs.); preD 10-12; depth 3.6-4.2.

This species differs from *E. belissimus* by having fewer predorsal scales and slightly different details of coloration. It occurs on mud bottoms of shallow, turbid marine to brackish coastal inlets and estuaries to a depth of 3 m.

Indo-west Pacific: Sri Lanka to Vanuatu, n. to the Ryukyus, s. to New Caledonia; Guam in Micronesia.

Fusigobius longispinus Goren, 1978   Pl. 123H
Longspine goby

SL: to ca. 62 mm (2.5 in); D VI+I, 9; A I, 7-8; P 18-20; LS 24-26; preD 6-8; GR 0-1+6-7, lower 1/4 of arch fused to cover; depth ca. 5.0.

Species of *Fusigobius* have somewhat transparent bodies and triangular heads. This species is covered with evenly-spaced round orange spots and develops an elongate first dorsal spine as it grows. It lives on the sandy floors of caves of seaward reefs at depths of about 9 to over 18 m. Two unidentified *Fusigobius* from the Marshalls are probably this species and *Fusigobius* sp. A..

Indo-west Pacific: Red Sea to the Great Barrier Reef; Guam and the Marshalls (?) in Micronesia.

Fusigobius neophytus (Günther, 1877)   Pl. 123I
Common fusegoby

SL: to ca. 60 mm (2.4 in); D VI+I, 9; A I, 8; P 18; LS 22-24; preD 5-6(at side of nape); GR 1+6-7, lower 1/4 of arch fused to cover.

This species is relatively common on subtidal reef flats and in shallow lagoons. It lives on patches of carbonate sand between corals or among rubble.

Indo-Pacific: E. Africa to the Tuamotus, n. to the Ryukyus, s. to Lord Howe Is.; throughout Micronesia.

Fusigobius signipinnis Hoese & Obika, 1988
Signal-fin goby   Pl. 123J

SL: to ca. 24 mm (0.9 in); D VI+I, 9; A I, 8; P 17-18; LS 23-24; preD 0.

This undescribed goby is abundant in Apra Harbor, Guam where it lives on patches of silty carbonate sand near the shelter of coral, rock, or rubble at depths of 3 to at least 20 m. Males have a taller, more heavily pigmented first dorsal fin that they frequently raise and lower when courting.

Ryukyus, Guam, and Marshalls (?)

Gladiogobius ensifer Herre, 1933
Gladiator goby

SL: to ca. 38 mm (1.5 in); VI+I, 10; A I, 10; P 16; LS 26; preD 0; large spine at lower posterior edge of preoperculum.

This is the only species of goby that possesses a huge preopercular spine. It inhabits tidepools of sandy intertidal areas of lagoons, bays, and river mouths.

Indo-Pacific: Red Sea to w. New Guinea, n. to the Yaeyamas; Belau in Micronesia.

Gnatholepis cauerensis (Bleeker, 1853)   Pl. 124A
Eyebar goby

(*G. anjerensis; G. deltoides*)

SL: to ca. 61 mm (2.4 in), us. <50 mm(2.0 in); D VI+I, 10-(11); A I, 10-(11); P 15-17; LS 28-29; preD 8-9.

Gnatholepis is badly in need of revision. The original description of *G. deltoides* from Guam is sketchy. The species figured in Yoshino *in* Masuda et al. (1984) as *G. deltoides* does not seem to occur in the Marianas, hence is not *deltoides* and is probably undescribed. The eyebar goby inhabits reef flats, and lagoon and sheltered seaward reefs at depths of 1 to 46 m. It lives on silty carbonate sand and is abundant on inner subtidal reef flats in the Marianas.

Indo-Pacific: Red Sea to the Hawaiian, Marquesan, and Society Is., s. to Rapa; throughout Micronesia; a similar species from the w. Indian Ocean.

Gnatholepis scapulostigma Herre, 1953   Pl. 124B
Shoulder-spot goby

(*Gnatholepis* sp.2 Hoese *in* Smith and Heemstra, 1986?)

SL: to 35 mm (1.4 in); D VI+I, 11; A I, 10-11; LS 29-30; (+2 on C); preD 8-9; depth ca. 4.7.

This goby occurs on fine sand bottoms of sheltered reefs near the shelter of rubble, rocks, or coral.

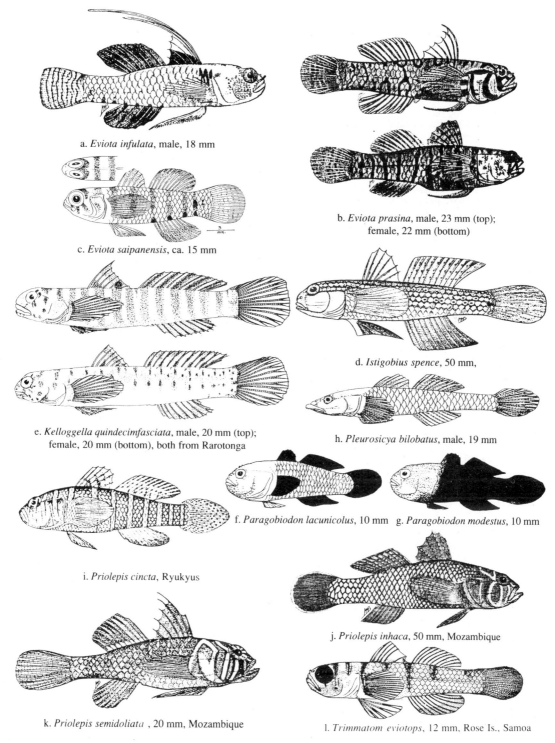

a. *Eviota infulata*, male, 18 mm

b. *Eviota prasina*, male, 23 mm (top);
female, 22 mm (bottom)

c. *Eviota saipanensis*, ca. 15 mm

d. *Istigobius spence*, 50 mm,

e. *Kelloggella quindecimfasciata*, male, 20 mm (top);
female, 20 mm (bottom), both from Rarotonga

h. *Pleurosicya bilobatus*, male, 19 mm

f. *Paragobiodon lacunicolus*, 10 mm   g. *Paragobiodon modestus*, 10 mm

i. *Priolepis cincta*, Ryukyus

j. *Priolepis inhaca*, 50 mm, Mozambique

k. *Priolepis semidoliata* , 20 mm, Mozambique

l. *Trimmatom eviotops*, 12 mm, Rose Is., Samoa

Fig. 8. Micronesian gobies (a, b, e, j, k, after Smith, 1959; c, after Fowler, 1945; i, after Snyder, 1912; h, after Larson and Hoese, 1980; l, after Schultz, 1943).

Indo-Pacific: E. Africa(?) to the Ryukyu, Bonin, Mariana, and Marshall Is.; a similar species from the w. Indian Ocean.

Gnatholepis sp. A   Pl. 124C

This species occurs on patches of carbonate sand of seaward reefs to a depth of over 20 m.

Guam

Gobiodon albofasciatus Sawada & Arai, 1972
Whitelined coral goby   Pl. 124D

SL: to ca. 28 mm (1.1 in); DVI+I, 9-10; A I, 9; P 17.

Species of *Gobiodon* are highly compressed, scaleless (except on the caudal peduncle of some species), have a pair or more of enlarged teeth on the inner row of the lower jaw, and produce large amounts of a bitter, toxic mucus. They live among the branches of living corals. They typically wedge themselves tightly between the branches and will remain in the coral even after it has been removed from the water. Although widespread, most species are relatively uncommon. Adults of this species are uniformly black. It lives among the branches of certain species of *Pocillopora* and *Stylophora*.

West Pacific: Ryukyus, Rowley Shoals, and Belau.

Gobiodon citrinus (Rüppell, 1838)   Pl. 124E
Lemon coral goby

(*G. erythrospilus*)

SL: to ca. 51 mm (2.0 in); D VI+I, 9-11(10); A I, 9; P 18-20; depth 2.2-2.7, width 2.5-3.0.

This large and distinctive coral goby lives within heads of branching *Acropora* corals.

Indo-Pacific: Red Sea to Samoa, n. to s. Japan, s. to the s. Great Barrier reef; throughout Micronesia.

Gobiodon okinawae Sawada, Arai, & Abe, 1972
Yellow coral goby   Pl. 124F

SL: to ca. 28 mm (1.1in); D VI+I, 10; A I, 9; P 17.

This coral goby is uniformly lemon yellow except for a pale area on the cheek. It occurs among staghorn *Acropora* corals in lagoons and will hover among or slightly above the branches as well as rest on them.

West Pacific: n. to s. Japan, s. to Rowley Shoals and the s. Great Barrier Reef; Belau and Marshalls in Micronesia.

Gobiodon quinquestrigatus (Valenciennes, 1837)
Five-lined coral goby

SL: to ca. 28 mm (1.1 in); D VI+I, 10-11; A I, 8-9; P 19-20; (*G. ceramensis*=?).

This species may be uniformly brown, reddish-brown, or gray or black with a reddish head. It inhabits tabletop *Acropora* corals.

West-central Pacific: Philippines to the Society Is., n. to s. Japan, s. to Rowley Shoals and the s. Great Barrier Reef and Tonga; Marianas and Carolines in Micronesia.

Gobiodon rivulatus (Rüppell, 1830)
Rippled coral goby

SL: to ca. 39 mm (1.5 in); D VI+I, 10-11; A I, 8-9; P 19-21; ca. 40 small scales from C to mid-body.

This coral goby is uniformly dark brown to light brown or bright green with a longitudinal thin red stripe, a red stripe at base of dorsal fins, and red face with vertical blue lines. It inhabits tabletop *Acropora* corals.

Indo-west Pacific: Red Sea to the Tuamotus, n. to the Ryukyus; Marianas and Marshalls in Micronesia.

Gobiopsis bravoi (Herre, 1940)
Bravo's bearded goby

SL: to 34 mm (1.3 in); D VI+I, 9-11(10); A I, 8-10(9); P 18-20(18-19); LS 35 (+1-2 on C base); preD 6-10; depth 5.3-6.7.

Species of *Gobiopsis* have numerous short barbels on the front part of the head. This species has been collected from among live and dead corals on sand in tidepools and on shallow reefs to a depth of 5 m.

West Pacific: Philippines, Ryukyus, Irian Jaya, and Belau (specimens from Okinawa and Belau tentatively identified as *G. bravoi*).

Heteroeleotris sp.

Mersistics for genus: D VI+I, 8-13; A I, 7-12; P 15-19; LS 0-52. This genus is easily confused with *Corygalops* or *Monisha*, but lacks an open first gill slit. The species inhabit coral and rocky reefs. An unidentified species has been collected in the Carolines and Marshalls.

Key to the Micronesian species of *Istigobius*:*

1a. Upper P rays entire; recurved canines present at angle of lower jaw...2
1b. Upper 3-4 p rays free; no recurved canines at angle of lower jaw..***ornatus***
2a. Total segmented and nonbranching C rays 3 (rarely 2); branching C rays 14 (rarely 15); spotting pattern on sides normally prominent in preservative, spots black or dark brown in life...3
2b. Total segmented and nonbranching C rays 4 (rarely 3); branching C rays 13 (rarely 14); spotting pattern on sides faint in preservative, spots orange in life....***rigilius***
3a. Isthmus scaled forward to, or almost to, a vertical beneath eye; no dusky spot on membrane between D spines I-III; maximum size <50 mm SL.............***spence***
3b. Isthmus scaled forward to a vertical at posterior portion of preoperculum; a dusky spot typically on membrane between D spines I-III; maximum size >75 mm SL.......
....***decoratus***

Istigobius decoratus (Herre, 1927)   Pl. 124G
Decorated goby

SL: to 81 mm (3.2 in); D VI+I, 11; A I, 11; P 17-19(18-

---

*Adapted from Murdy and Hoese, 1985.

19); LS 30-33; depth 4.9-6.1.

This relatively drab speckled goby is very common on coral-line sand in areas of clear water at depths of less than 1 to over 18 m.

Indo-west Pacific: Red Sea to Samoa, n. to Taiwan, s. to Lord Howe Is.; Guam and Marshalls in Micronesia.

Istigobius ornatus (Rüppell, 1830)　　　　Pl. 124H
Ornate goby

SL: to 80 mm (3.1 in); D VI+I, (11)-12; A I, 9-11(10); P 16-20(18-19); LS 29-32; depth 4.6-5.3.

This is the only species of *Istigobius* having 3-4 free upper pectoral rays. It occurs among mangroves and on silty inner reefs to a depth of 1 or 2 m. At Guam, it is quite common on the inner reef flats of bays with river mouths.

Indo-Pacific: Red Sea to Fiji, n. to s. Taiwan, s. to New Caledonia; throughout Micronesia.

Istigobius rigilius (Herre, 1953)
Rigilius goby

SL: to 79 mm (3.1 in); D VI+I, 10-(11); A I, 9-10; P 15-19(18); LS 29-32; depth 4.7-6.1.

This species differs in details of coloration of the other Micronesian *Istigobius*, particularly on the head. It inhabits sandy areas between corals or coral rubble in areas of clear water at depths of 0 to 30 m.

West-central Pacific: Philippines and Moluccas to Kiribati and Fiji, s. to Rowley Shoals; Marshalls in Micronesia.

Istigobius spence (Smith, 1947)　　　　Fig. 8d
Pearl goby

SL: to 79 mm (3.1 in); D VI+I, 10-(11); A I, 10; P 17-20 (18-19); LS 30-32; depth 4.9-6.1.

This species has a facial pattern similar to that of *I. ornatus*, but lacks free upper pectoral rays. It inhabits turbid coastal areas near river mouths at depths of under 1 to at least 12 m.

Indo-west Pacific: E. Africa to Papua New Guinea and the Great Barrier Reef; Pohnpei in Micronesia.

Kelloggella cardinalis Jordan & Seale, 1906
Cardinal goby

SL: to 25 mm (1.0 in); D 6+12-13; A 8-9; P 13-15(14).

This minute scaleless goby has a green body with red dorsal, anal, and caudal fins. It inhabits raised algal ridges and benches and feeds on algae and minute crustaceans. It is able to tolerate a wide range of temperature and salinity.

West Pacific: Taiwan, Philippines, Ryukyus, Guam, Vanuatu, Samoa, and Tonga.

Kelloggella quindecimfasciata (Fowler, 1946)
Central goby　　　　　　　　　　　　　Fig. 8e

(*K. centralis*, Hoese, 1975)

SL: to 20 mm (0.8 in); D (6)-7+10-12(11); A (8)-9; P 12-13.

This species is still only known from a few scattered specimens.

Indo-Pacific: Chagos, Ryukyus, Enewetak, Rarotonga, and Pitcairn group.

Macrodontogobius wilburi Herre, 1936
Largetooth goby

SL: to 52 mm (2.0 in); D VI+I, 9-11; A I, 9-10; P 15-17; LS 27-31; preD 6-7; depth 6.3-8.5.

This drab species inhabits sandy bottoms of bays at depths of 0 to 7 m.

Indo-Pacific: Seychelles to the Line Is., n. to the Ryukyus, s. to the s. Great Barrier Reef and New Caledonia; Belau, Pohnpei, and Marshalls in Micronesia.

Opua nephodes E. K. Jordan, 1925
Cloudy goby

SL: to ca. 40 mm (1.6 in); D VI+I, 8; A I, 9? (based on an illustration in Tinker, 1977).

This small goby inhabits shallow protected waters.

Marshall and Hawaiian Is.

Paragobiodon echinocephalus (Rüppell, 1830)
Redhead coral goby

SL: to 27 mm (1.1 in); D VI+I, 8-9; A I, 9-10; P 19-21; LS 22-23; midline of belly scaled.

Species of *Paragobiodon* have the same general body form and ecology as species of *Gobiodon*, but are scaled and have numerous small bumps or papillae on the head. They occur exclusively among the branches of small bush-like corals of the genera *Pocillopora*, and *Seriatopora*, and *Stylophora*. This species has a reddish-orange head and black body and fins. It occurs among the branches of *Stylophora mordax*.

Indo-Pacific: Red Sea to the Marquesan and Tuamotu Is., n. to the Ryukyus, s. to Lord Howe Is.; Marianas and Marshalls in Micronesia.

Paragobiodon lacunicolus
　　　(Kendall & Goldsborough, 1911)　　Fig. 8f
Blackfin coral goby

(*Paragobiodon kerri*)

SL: to 24 mm (0.9 in); D VI+I, 9-10; A I, 8-9; P 21; LS 21-23; midline of belly naked.

This species has a tan body, sometimes with an orange head, and blackish vertical fins. It occurs exclusively among the branches of the coral *Pocillopora damicornis*, occasionally as deep as 20 m.

Indo-Pacific: Chagos Is. to the Line and Tuamotu Is., n. to the Ryukyu and Bonin Is., s. to Lord Howe Is.; throughout Micronesia.

Paragobiodon modestus (Regan, 1908)　　Fig. 8g
Warthead goby

SL: to 27 mm (1.1 in); D VI+I, 8-9; A I, 9-10; P 19-23; LS 22-24; midline of belly naked.

This species has the same color pattern as *P. echinocephalus* but has shorter papillae on the head. It is associated with *Pocillopora* corals, and occurs primarily in lagoons to a depth of at least 7 m.

Indo-Pacific: E. Africa to the Marshalls, n. to the Ryukyus, s. to the Cord Pove Is. ba Marshalls in Micronesia.

Paragobiodon melanosomus (Bleeker, 1852)
Black coral goby

SL: to 31 mm (1.2 in); D VI+I, 8-9; P 20-21; LS 23-24.
This coral goby is uniformly black. It occurs in pairs in colonies of *Seriatopora* spp.
Indo-west Pacific: Madagascar to New Guinea, n. to the Ryukyus, s. to the s. Great Barrier Reef; throughout Micronesia.

Paragobiodon xanthosomus (Bleeker, 1852)
Emerald coral goby

SL: to 31 mm (1.2 in); D VI+I, 8-9; A I, 8-9; P 20-22; LS 22-24; midline of belly scaled; top of head with elongate flaps in adult.
This species is green to greenish yellow, often with a dark caudal margin. It occurs in pairs in the coral *Seriatopora hystrix*, primarily on reef flats
Indo-Pacific: Chagos Is. to Samoa, n. to the Ryukyus, s. to Lord Howe Is.; Marshalls in Micronesia.

Periophthalmus kalolo Lesson, 1830
Common mudskipper

(*P. koelreuteri* Eggert, 1935)

SL: to 95 mm (3.7 in); D VII-XV+I, 10-12; A I, 9-11; P 12-13; LS 70-95; preD ca. 35; depth 5.7-7.3 in TL.
Mudskippers are essentially amphibious and spend most of their time out of the water. As long as they remain wet, they are able to meet their oxygen requirements. They are typically found resting on mud, rocks, or mangrove roots with their tails dipped in the water. When disturbed they rapidly jump away by flipping themselves with strong strokes of the tail. They feed on worms, crustaceans, and insects.
Indo-west Pacific: Red Sea to Samoa, s. to n. Australia; Belau, Guam, Pohnpei, Kosrae in Micronesia, but expected on all high islands as well as certain atolls).

Periophthalmus argentilineatus Valenciennes, 1837
Barred mudskipper

SL: ≥ 71 mm (2.8 in); D XII-XVI+I, 9-10; A I, 8-11; P 11-13; LL 70-90; preD 30-35.
This species differs from *P. kalolo* by having each half of the ventral fin separated at the base (connected by a low membrane in *P. kalolo*).
Indo-Australian: Malaysia, Indonesia, New Guinea, n. Australia, and Belau.

Pleurosicya bilobatus (Koumans, 1941)   Fig. 8h
Bilobed ghost goby

SL: to 20 mm (0.8 in); D VI+I, 8; A I, 8; P 16-17; LS 25; preD 0.
Species of *Pleurosicya* closely resemble species of *Bryaninops* but have a completely scaled body with larger scales. They normally occur on various invertebrate hosts such as sponges and soft or hard corals. This species occurs on the blades of seagrasses and is common on *Enhalus*.
Indo-Pacific: India to the Moluccas, n. to the Ryukyus; throughout Micronesia.

Pleurosicya muscarum (Jordan & Seale, 1906)
Ghost goby

SL: to 17 mm (0.7 in); D VI+I, 7-8; A I, 7-9; P 17-19; LS

22-25; preD naked; GR 2+3-6, very rudimentary, lower portion of gill arch bound to cover.
This minute goby lives on soft corals.
Indo-Pacific: E. Africa to Samoa; Guam and Marshalls in Micronesia.

Priolepis cincta (Regan, 1908)   Fig. 8i
Pacific convict goby

(*P. naraharae* Snyder, 1908)

SL: to ca. 46 mm (1.8 in); D (VI)-VII+I, 11; A I, 9; P 17-19; LS 29-33; preD 15-20; GR 3+11-13.
Species of *Priolepis* are similar in form to species of *Trimma*, but have a more restricted gill opening and a color pattern of numerous vertically-oriented light lines on at least the anterior part of the body of most species. Unlike most species of *Trimma*, they rest on the bottom. The entire body of the convict goby, except the fins, is barred. It occurs among corals or rock at depths of 1 to at least 70 m.
Indo-west Pacific: E. Africa to the s. Great Barrier Reef, n. to s. Japan; Maug and Kapingamarangi (?; as *Quisquilius eugenius*) in Micronesia; a similar undescribed species from the Pacific Plate.

Priolepis farcimen (Jordan & Evermann, 1903)
Farcimen goby

SL: to ca. 24 mm (0.8 in); D VI+I, 10; A I, 8; LS 27-29(?).
This reddish-brown species has a few relatively narrow (<pupil dia.) light bars restricted to the head. No differences between it and *P. inhaca* could be gleaned from the literature available to me.
Pacific Plate: Marshall, Marcus, Johnston, Hawaiian, Tongan, Marquesan, Society, Tuamotu, Pitcairn, and Austral Is.

Priolepis inhaca (Smith, 1949)   Fig. 8j
Brick goby

SL: to ca. 31 mm (1.2 in); D VI+I, 9-10; A I, 8; P 15-17; LS 25-28; preD 13-18; GR 2+9-10.
This reddish-brown species has a few relatively narrow (<pupil diameter) light bars restricted to the head. It has been collected from lagoons and dropoffs at depths of 12 to 26 m.
Indo-Pacific: E. Africa to the s. Great Barrier Reef, n. to the Ryukyus; Guam in Micronesia.

Priolepis semidoliata (Valenciennes, 1837) Fig. 8k

SL: to 24 mm (0.9 in); D VI+I, 8; A I, 7; P 17; LS 27; preD 0, scales mostly restricted to abdomen.
This species has relatively wide (≥pupil diameter) light bars from the snout to the pectoral base, and few if any scales anterior of the operculum. It is very similar to *P. farcimen*.
Indo-Pacific: India to Ducie, n. to s. Japan, s. to Norfolk Is.; throughout Micronesia.

Trimma caesiura Jordan & Seale, 1906   Pl. 124I
Caesiura goby

SL: to ≥20 mm (0.8 in); D VI+I, 8-9; A I, 8; P 15-17; LS 23-25; preD ca. 8.
As presently defined, the genus *Trimma* consists of over 60 Indo-Pacific species, most of which are undescribed. It is

quite likely that the genus will be split into two or more genera. The species included here fall in two groups: those that hover in the water and those that sit on the bottom. *T. caesiura* is bottom-dwelling species of seaward reefs that closely resembles two other bottom dwellers, *T. naudei* and *T. okinawae*.

West-central Pacific: Samoa, Guam, and Marshalls.

Trimmatom eviotops (Schultz, 1943)   Fig. 81
Red-barred rubble goby

SL: to 16 mm (0.6 in); D VI+I, 9-10; A I, 8-9; P 17-(18); LS 26-27; preD 0; GR 2+10-11.

This species is characterized by thin red bars on the head and body. It has been collected in lagoons and on the "reef top".
Indo-Pacific: Chagos, Great Barrier Reef, Fiji, Samoa, Society, Tuamotu, Rapa, and Ducie Is.; Ulithi, Maug, Pohnpei, and Enewetak in Micronesia.

Trimma naudei Smith, 1956
Naude's rubble goby

SL: to 26 mm (1.0 in); D VI+I, 7-(8); A I, 8; P 16-18; LS 24-25; preD 6-8; GR 3+14-15.

This species inhabits lagoons and seaward reefs at depths of about 3 to 30 m. It is a bottom-dweller, living on rubble and reef rock and feeds on copepods, ostracods, and radiolarians. It has the same general appearance and behavior as *T. caesiura* and *T. okinawae*.
Indo-Pacific: Seychelles, Aldabra, Chagos, Ryukyu, and Loyalty Is.; Marianas and Marshalls in Micronesia.

Trimma okinawae (Aoyagi, 1949)
Okinawa rubble goby

SL: to ca. 23 mm (0.9 in); D VI+I, 9-10; A I, 8-9; P 16-18; LS 26-27.

This species has the same general appearance and behavior as *T. caesiura* and *T. naudei*.
West-central Pacific: Ryukyus s. to Rowley Shoals, e. to Rotuma; the Marshalls in Micronesia.

Trimma taylori Lobel, 1979
Yellow cave goby

SL: to 20 mm (0.8 in); D VI+I, (10)-11; A I, 9-(10); P 13-15; LS 23-(24); preD 6-8; GR 2-4+13-15=16-19.

Males have longer dorsal spines and yellow spotting on the fins. The identification of individuals photographed at Guam remains tentative since specimens have not yet been collected. This goby inhabits caves of dropoffs at depths of about 25 to at least 50 m. It occurs in loose schools near the roofs or sides of caves and disappears into holes or crevices when approached. It often occurs with other species of *Trimma* and feeds on harpacticoid copepods.
Indo-Pacific: Chagos and Hawaiian Is.; Guam(?) in Micronesia.

Trimma tevegae Cohen & Davis, 1969   Pl. 124 J
Tevega cave goby; Blue-striped cave goby

(*T. caudomaculata*)
SL: to 35 mm (1.3 in); D VI+I, 8-9; A I, 8-9; P 13-15(13-14); LS 24-28; preD 9-12(10-11); 1 -3 rows of cheek scales

below eye; depth 3.8-4.8.

This species occurs in loose aggregations associated with shallow pockets and caves of steep dropoffs at depths of 9 to over 36 m. It typically hovers in a head-up orientation and feeds on copepods.
Tropical w. Pacific: Ryukyu and Izu Is. to New Britain, s. to Rowley Shoals; Belau and Guam in Micronesia.

Trimmatom sp.   Pl. 124K

This undescribed species closely resembles *T. eviotops*, but differs in the position of the red bars. It is known from Micronesia on the basis of photographs taken at Belau. At least 6 additional species of *Trimma* or *Trimmatom* remain to be identified or described from Micronesian collections.

KRAEMERIIDAE (SAND DARTS)

Sand darts are small, elongate, scaleless fishes with long continuous dorsal and anal fins, V I, 5 pelvic rays, minute eyes, and a forward projecting chin. They live buried in sand of shallow coral reefs, along shorelines, or near river mouths.

Kraemeria bryani Schultz, 1941
Bryan's sand dart

SL: to 19 mm (0.7 in); D V, 14; A I, 12-13; P 3-5.
Pacific Plate: Marshall, Hawaiian, and Society Is.

Kraemeria samoensis Steindachner, 1906   Fig. 1
Sand dart

SL: to ca. 29 mm (1.1 in); D V, 14; A I, 13; P 7-9; GR 0+9; 6-7 flaps on lower edge of preopercle, 5-6 flaps on lower edge of operculum; tongue bilobed.

This species lives in loose coral sand subject to strong wave action. The w. Indian Ocean population may represent a distinct species, *K. nudum*, characterized by fewer opercular flaps.
Indo-Pacific: E. Africa to the Society Is.; Guam and Marshalls in Micronesia.

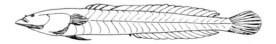

Fig. 1. *Kraemeria samoensis*.

Kraemeria cunicularia Rofen

SL: to ca. 37 mm (1.5 in); D V, 14; A I, 13; P 8-9; ca. 5 flaps on lower edge of preopercle, ca. 10 flaps on lower edge of operculum.

This sand dart inhabits sandy shorelines and estuaries penetrating fresh water.
Ryukyus and Belau

ACANTHURIDAE (SURGEONFISHES and UNICORNFISHES)

The acanthurids are characterized by an ovate to elongate compressed body, a small terminal mouth with a single row of small, close-set lanceolate or incisiform teeth (which may be spatulate with denticulate edges), continuous unnotched dorsal and anal fins, pelvic fins with 1 spine and 5 rays (except *Paracanthurus hepatus* with 3 rays), gill rakers in a double row on each arch, a continuous lateral line, a tough skin with minute ctenoid scales, and one or more pairs of sharp spines on the caudal peduncle. They typically have a long larval lifespan and settle out at a large size resulting in widespread distribution for most species. Acanthurids are among the most conspicuous and abundant inhabitants of shallow coral reefs. They are diurnal herbivores or planktivores that shelter on the reef at night. Two of the three subfamilies occur in Micronesia: the Acanthurinae, with a single scalpel-like peduncular spine which folds into a groove, and the generally more elongate Nasinae with 1 or 2 sharp fixed keel-like bony peduncular plates. The spines are used offensively or defensively, against one another in struggles for dominance or against predators, and are capable of inflicting a deep and painful wound. Reproduction typically takes place on a lunar cycle with peak activity during the winter or early spring, but with some activity throughout the year. Spawning typically occurs at dusk and involves groups, pairs, or both. Acanthurids are important foodfishes on most tropical islands. A number of the more colorful species are important aquarium fishes.

Subfamily Acanthurinae (Surgeonfishes)

Surgeonfishes have a tough skin with minute ctenoid scales, a single scalpel-like peduncular spine which folds into a groove (Fig. 1), spatulate to slender teeth, and 3 anal spines. They have a distinctive late-larval stage known as the *acronurus* stage. Species of *Ctenochaetus* feed primarily on detritus, *Paracanthurus* and a few *Acanthurus* feed on zooplankton, and the remaining *Acanthurus* graze on benthic algae. \Some species of *Acanthurus* have a thick-walled gizzard-like stomach and ingest sand as they feed. Many species are brilliantly and distinctively colored, but a few have a similar brown to black coloration and are difficult to distinguish in the field. All but 5 of the 50 species in 4 genera occur in the tropical Indo-Pacific. At least 30 species occur in Micronesia. In the following accounts, either the upper and lower gill raker counts are combined, or the anterior series is identified with an "a" and the posterior series with a "p". (Lit.: Randall 1955a&b, 1956, 1960.)

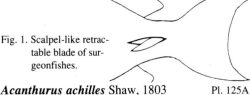

Fig. 1. Scalpel-like retractable blade of surgeonfishes.

Acanthurus achilles Shaw, 1803   Pl. 125A
Achilles tang

SL: to 197 mm (7.8 in); D IX, 29-33; A III, 26-29; P 16; C lunate; depth 1.75-1.9.

Juveniles lack the large orange spot. This beautiful surgeonfish inhabits clear seaward reefs, primarily in the surge zone to a depth of 4 m. It is territorial and browses on filamentous and small fleshy algae. It is quite rare in Micronesia, but abundant throughout most of Polynesia where it often occurs in small groups. Hybrids between this species and its close relative *A. nigricans* occasionally occur where one or the other is rare and unable to spawn with its own kind. These were once known as *A. rackliffei*.

Pacific Plate: w. Caroline Is. and Torres Str. to the Hawai-

ian, Marquesan, and Ducie Is., s. to New Caledonia; Carolines, Marianas, and Marshalls in Micronesia; a waif reported from Cabo San Lucas, Mexico.

Acanthurus bariene (Lesson, 1830) Pl. 125B; Fig. 2
Bariene surgeonfish

SL: to 29 cm (11.4 in); D IX, 26-28; A III, 25-26; P 17; GR 19-23(a), 22-24(p); depth 1.9-2.1.

Large males of this species as well as *A. leucocheilus*, *A. maculiceps*, and *A. nigricauda* develop highly convex foreheads that extend beyond the mouth (Fig. 2). The combination of white lips, tan bar above and beneath the pectoral fin, and dark caudal spine distinguish *A. bariene* from those species as well as all other large brown surgeonfishes. *A. bariene* inhabits clear seaward reefs to a depth of at least 30m.

Indo-Australian: E. Africa to the Solomons, n. to the Ryukyus, s. to the Great Barrier Reef; Belau in Micronesia.

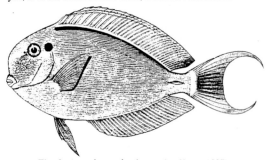

Fig. 2. *Acanthurus bariene* (after Herre, 1927).

Acanthurus blochii Valenciennes, 1835   Pl. 125C
Ringtail surgeonfish

(*A. mata* non-Cuvier)

SL: to 317 mm (12.5 in); D IX, 25-27; A III, 23-25; P 17; C emarginate (juv) to lunate (ad); GR 20-25; depth 1.9-2.1.

This species closely resembles the larger species *A. dussumieri*, *A. mata*, and *A. xanthopterus* which have similar facial patterns. It differs from *A. dussumieri* by having black vertical stripes instead of spots on the blue central area of the caudal fin, from *A. mata* by having a lunate caudal fin, and from *A. xanthopterus* by having plain brown to blueish-grey pectoral fins. The white ring around the base of the tail varies in intensity and may occasionally be absent. It inhabits outer lagoon and seaward reefs to a depth of over 12 m and feeds primarily on the algal film covering compacted sand. At Belau, large spawning aggregations have been observed on the reef flat around the time of the new and full moons of May.

Indo-Pacific: E. Africa to the Hawaiian and Society Is., n. to the Ryukyus, s. to Lord Howe Is.; Marianas and Marshalls in Micronesia.

Acanthurus chronixis Randall, 1960   Fig. 3
Chronixis surgeonfish
SL: to ≥211 mm (8.3 in); D VIII, 26; A III, 24; P 17; C lunate.

Acanthurus chronixis, *A. pyroferus*, and *A. sohal* are the only species in the genus that have eight dorsal spines. This species is known for certain only from the holotype collected at a depth of less than 20 m over a sand and coral bottomed channel at Kapingamaringi. Its life colors are unknown; the preserved specimen is dark brown with two small oval spots, one above and the other slightly behind the upper end of the the gill opening, and a dark brown band at the base of the dorsal fin. Specimens or photographs of juveniles reported from Ifaluk, New Guinea, and the Maldive and Ryukyu Islands as mimics of *Centropyge vrolicki* are actually *A. pyroferus*.

Kapingamarangi

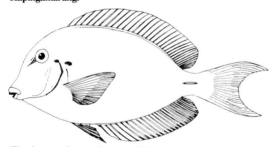

Fig. 3. *Acanthurus chronixis*, 211 mm (after Randall, 1960).

Acanthurus dussumieri Valenciennes, 1835
Eye-stripe surgeonfish   Pl. 125D
SL: to 38 cm (15.0 in); D IX, 25-27; A III, 24-26; P 16-(17); C lunate in adults; GR 22-26(Atlantic), 23-27(Indo-Pacific); depth 1.9-2.1.

The combination of black spots on the blue central area of the tail and absence of yellow on the outer portion of the pectoral fins will distinguish this species from *A. blochii*, *A. mata*, and *A. xanthopterus*. This species inhabits seaward reefs, usually at depths greater than 9 m, and has been observed at a depth of 131 m at Johnston Is. In Micronesia, it has only been recorded from Guam where it is rare. It occurs singly or in small groups and usually grazes on the surface film of fine green and bluegreen algae, diatoms, and detritus covering sand, but may also occasionally browse on

hard surfaces. It is a pair-spawner.

Indo-Pacific: E. Africa to the Hawaiian and Line Is., n. to s. Japan, s. to Rowley Shoals, s. Great Barrier Reef and Lord Hawe Is, Guam in Micronesia; absent from most of the central Pacific.

Acanthurus guttatus (Bloch & Schneider, 1801)
Whitespotted surgeonfish   Pl. 125E
SL: to 215 mm (8.4 in); D IX, 27-30; A III, 23-26; P 15-17; C emarginate; GR 21-24(a), 19-23(p); depth 1.5-1.6.

This deep-bodied surgeonfish lives primarily in the surge zone, sometimes in large schools. The white spots on the posterior half of the body may help conceal it in turbulent water that is often filled with small bubbles. It browses on filamentous and certain articulate calcareous algae.

Tropical w. Pacific: Christmas Is., Indian Ocean, to the Hawaiian, Marquesan, and Tuamotu Is., n. to the Ryukyus, s. to New Caledonia and Rapa; throughout Micronesia.

Acanthurus leucocheilus Herre, 1927   Pl. 125F
Palelipped surgeonfish
SL: to >20 cm (7.8 in); D IX, 24-25; A III, 23;depth 2-2.4.

This species was observed at a depth of 16 m along the edge of a precipitous dropoff off leeward Belau. It differs from all other Micronesian surgeonfishes by the combination of pale lips, a pale bar on the chin, and a white peduncular spine. A color painting in the original description has the lips, chin bar, and ring around the base of the tail white and three submarginal pinstripes on the soft dorsal fin instead of one. The photograph used here is believed to be the first taken of this species as well as the first record outside of the Philippines; the only known specimens were destroyed during World War II. Randall has recently observed this species at Fanning Atoll, Line Islands.

West-central Pacific: Philippines, Belau, and Line Is.

Acanthurus leucopareius (Jenkins, 1903)   Pl. 126A
Whitebar surgeonfish
SL: to 20 cm (7.9 in); D IX, 25-27; A III, 23-25; P (16)-17; C emarginate; depth 1.7-1.85.

This species occurs primarily in boulder-strewn areas of the surge zone. It is common among large basalt boulders in the northern Marianas where it usually occurs in schools, but rare along limestone clifflines of Guam and Saipan. In the Hawaiian Islands, it has been observed to a depth of 85 m from a submersible. It browses on filamentous algae.

Pacific Plate: primarily antiequatorial; known only from the Marianas, s. Japan, Marcus Is., and Hawaiian Is., in the north and New Caledonia, Rapa, the Tuamotu and Austral Is., Pitcairn group, and Easter Is. in the south.

Acanthurus lineatus (Linnaeus, 1758)   Pl. 126B
Bluebanded surgeonfish
SL: to 238 mm (9.4 in); D IX, 27-29; A III, 25-28; P 16; C lunate; GR 14-16(a), 13-15(p); depth ca.2.2.

This spectacular surgeonfish is a common inhabitant of the surge zone of exposed seaward reefs, usually in less than 3 m. It is territorial and aggressive with large males controlling well-defined feeding territories and harems of females. At

Belau, a small group was observed to spiral and spawn a few meters above the edge of a steep dropoff shortly after sunrise during the April new moon. The caudal spine is venomous. Small individuals are popular in the aquarium trade. Like most surgeonfishes they require a large tank with well-areated water.

Indo-Pacific: E. Africa to the Hawaiian (as a rare waif), Marquesan, and Tuamotu Is., n. to s. Japan; s. to the s. Great Barrier Reef and New Caledonia; throughout Micronesia; replaced by the closely related A. sohal in the Red Sea.

Acanthurus maculiceps (Ahl, 1923) Pl. 126C
White-freckled surgeonfish
SL: to 19 cm (7.5 in); D IX, 24-26(25); A III, 22-24(23); P 16-17; C lunate; GR 19-23(a), 21-24(p); depth 2.0-2.1.

Large adults develop a distincly convex head profile. This species inhabits clear outer reef flats and seaward reefs to a depth of 15 m.

Tropical w. Pacific: Philippines and Christmas Is., Indian Ocean, to the Line Is., n. to the Ryuykyus, s. to Samoa; Belau to the Carolines and s. Marshalls in Micronesia.

Acanthurus mata Cuvier, 1829 Pl. 126D
Elongate surgeonfish
(*A. bleekeri*)

SL: to 375 mm (14.8 in); D IX, 24-26; A III, 23-24; P 16-17; C of adults lunate; depth 2.1-2.5.

This species differs from *A. blochii*, *A. dussumieri*, and *A. xanthopterus* by having an emarginate rather than deeply lunate caudal fin, slightly more elongate body. The yellow area around its eye is in the form of two parallel bands anteriorly. This surgeonfish occurs in groups along steep reef slopes often in turbid water and feeds primarily, if not entirely, on zooplankton,.

Indo-Pacific: Red Sea to the Marquesan and Tuamotu Is., n. to s. Japan; s. to the s. Great Barrier Reef and New Caledonia; Marshalls in Micronesia.

Acanthurus nigricans (Linnaeus, 1758) Pl. 126E
Whitecheek surgeonfish
(*A. aliala*; *A. glaucopareus*)

SL: to 159 mm (6.3 in); D IX, 28-31; A III, 26-28; P 16; C emarginate; GR 17-19(a), 18-20(p); depth 1.7-1.85.

This surgeonfish inhabits hard substrate areas of clear lagoon and seaward reefs from the lower surge zone to at least 67 m. It is a territorial species and feeds on filamentous algae. It is common throughout Micronesia and hybridizes with the rare *A. achilles*.

Tropical-pan-Pacific: Christmas Is., Indian Ocean, to Panama, n. to the Ryukyu and Hawaiian Is., s. to the s. Great Barrier Reef, New Caledonia, and Tuamotus; throughout Micronesia.

Acanthurus nigricauda Dunker & Mohr, 1929
Epaulette surgeonfish Pl. 126F
(*A. nigricans* Schultz and Woods, 1953; *A. gahhm* Randall, 1956)

SL: to 229 mm (9.0 in); D IX, 25-28; A III, 23-26; P 17; C of adults stongly lunate; depth 1.9-2.2 (juv. deeper bodied).

This species inhabits clear lagoon and seaward reefs to a depth of at least 30 m, particularly around isolated coral heads or rocks on barren pavement or sand. Over open areas of the submarine terrace, adults may occur in large mixed-species schools with *A. olivaceus* as well as other acanthurids and scarids.

Indo-Pacific: E. Africa to the Tuamotus, n. to the Ryukyus, s. to the s. Great Barrier Reef; closely related to *A. gahhm* from the Red Sea.

Acanthurus nigrofuscus (Forsskål, 1775) Pl. 127A
Brown surgeonfish
(*A. elongatus* Schultz and Woods, 1953 (in part))

SL: to 149 mm (5.9 in); D IX, 24-27; A III, 22-24; P 16-17; C lunate; GR 20-24(a), 18-23(p); teeth spatulate, ≤14 upper, ≤16 lower; depth 1.9-2.3.

This small surgeonfish inhabits hard substrates of shallow lagoon and seaward reefs from the lower surge zone to a depth of over 15 m. It generally occurs in large schools, sometimes with *A. triostegus*, and feeds on filamentous algae. It is at the bottom of the "pecking order" among surgeonfishes, and as a result employs the strategy of feeding in large schools that overwhelm the territorial defenses of other herbivores.

Indo-Pacific: Red Sea to the Hawaiian and Tuamotu Is., n. to s. Japan, s. to the s. Great Barrier Reef (also Lord Howe Is.?), New Caledonia, and Rapa; throughout Micronesia.

Acanthurus nigroris Valenciennes, 1835 Pl. 127B
Bluelined surgeonfish
(*A. elongatus* Schultz and Woods, 1953 (in part))

SL: to 179 mm (7.0 in); D IX, 24-27; A III, 23-25; P 15-16; C emarginate; depth 1.8-2.0.

This drab surgeonfish inhabits clear lagoon and seaward reefs at depths of 1 to 90 m. It occurs singly or in small groups over mixed coral, pavement, rubble, and sand substrates. It feeds on filamentous algae as well as the diatom and fine algal film of compacted sand. It is relatively uncommon throughout Micronesia.

Indo-Pacific: Aldabra and Seychelles to the Hawaiian, Marquesan, and Tuamotu Is., s. to the s. Great Barrier Reef; throughout Micronesia.

Acanthurus olivaceus Bloch & Schneider, 1801
Orangeband surgeonfish Pl. 127C,F
SL: to 25 cm (9.8 in); D IX, 23-25; A III, 22-24; P 16-(17); C of adults lunate; depth 2.0-2.4.

This species undergoes a dramatic change in coloration with growth: juveniles under about 6 cm are uniformly yellow (the larger ones bear an orangeish precursor to the shoulder bar); subadults become a dirty yellow to brown, and finally adopt the adult color pattern at a size of about 12 cm. This surgeonfish generally inhabits areas of bare rock or mixed rubble and sand of seaward reefs at depths of 9 to at least 46 m. Juveniles may occur singly or in small groups in as little as 3 m in protected bays and lagoons. Adults occur singly or in schools and feed on the surface film of detritus, diatoms, and fine filamentous algae covering sand as well as bare rock.

Tropical w. Pacific: Christmas Is., Indian Ocean, to the Hawaiian, Marquesan, and Tuamotu Is., n. to s. Japan, s. to Lord Howe Is.; throughout Micronesia; closely related to *A. tennenti* from the Indian Ocean.

Acanthurus pyroferus Kittlitz, 1834   Pl. 127D,G
Chocolate surgeonfish
(*A. leucosternon* Schultz and Woods, 1953)
SL: to 19 cm (7.5 in); D VIII, 27-30; A III, 24-28(25-27); P 16; GR 23-26(a), 25-27(p); depth 1.6-2.0.
This species also undergoes dramatic changes in coloration with growth. Juveniles mimic certain locally common angelfishes of the genus *Centropyge*, then slowly change into the adult coloration when they exceed the largest size attained by the angelfishes. Presumably there is an advantage to mimicking an angelfish which has a sharp preopercular spine when the surgeonfish and its peduncular spine are small. At Guam, juveniles only mimic *C. flavissimus* but at Belau where *C. flavissimus* is absent, they mimic *C. vrolicki*. The chocolate surgeonfish inhabits lagoon and seaward reefs at depths of 4 to 60 m. It is typically solitary and prefers areas of mixed coral, rock, or sand at the base of reefs or ledges.
Indo-Pacific: Seychelles to the Marquesan and Tuamotu Is., n. to s. Japan, s. to the s. Great Barrier Reef and New Caledonia; throughout Micronesia.

Acanthurus thompsoni (Fowler, 1923)   Pl. 128A
Thompson's surgeonfish
(*A. philippinus*)
SL: to 189 mm (7.5 in); D IX, 23-26; A III, 23-26; P 16-19(16-17); C lunate; depth ca. 2.3.
This surgeonfish inhabits steep outer reef slopes and dropoffs at depths of 4 to over 75 m. It occurs in loose aggregations in the water column and feeds on zooplankton, particularly large gelatinous forms, as well as on fish eggs and crustaceans. It is common in as little as 4 m off the vertical walls of Belau but rare in less than 18 m in the Marianas.
Indo-Pacific: E. Africa to the Hawaiian, Marquesan, and Ducie Is., n. to s. Japan, s. to Rapa; throughout Micronesia; the Indian Ocean population lacks the white caudal fin.

Acanthurus triostegus triostegus (Linnaeus, 1758)
Convict tang   Pl. 128B
SL: to 206 mm (8.1 in), us. ≤14 cm (5.5 in) in Micronesia; D IX, 22-26(23-24); A III, 19-22(21); P 14-16; C truncate to slightly emarginate; GR 18-22 (a), 19-24 (p); depth 1.8-2.0; Hawaiian population with diagonal bar rather than one or more spots or short dash under P fin.
The convict tang is among the most common and ubiquitous as well as most widespread of coral reef fishes. It inhabits hard substrate areas of lagoon and seaward reefs to a depth of at least 90 m. It occurs singly, in small groups, or in vast schools of 1,000 or more individuals and feeds on a wide variety of filamentous algae. It has a very small caudal spine and is near the bottom of the acanthurid "pecking order". Consequently, it often feeds in large roving aggregations that collectively overwhelm the defenses of territorial herbivores, including large and aggressive species like *A.*

lineatus. Spawning occurs at dusk among small groups that break off from a large milling aggregation at a channel entrance or along the reef edge. At Belau, spawning has been reported from the 4th to 10th lunar days of May to August. The larval life span lasts 2 1/2 months. Post-larvae settle in intertidal areas of reef flats and benches.
Indo-pan-Pacific and e. Atlantic: E. Africa to Panama, n. to s. Japan, s. to Lord Howe, Rapa, and Ducie Is.; throughout Micronesia; subspecies *sandvicensis* in the Hawaiian Islands.

Acanthurus xanthopterus Valenciennes, 1835
Yellowfin surgeonfish   Pl. 128C
SL: to 425 mm (16.7 in); wt.: to ≥2.7 kg (6.0 lb); D IX, 25-27; A III, 23-25; P 16-(17); C lunate; GR 16-24(a),17-22(p); depth 1.95-2.25.
This is the largest species of *Acanthurus*. The yellow outer third or more of the pectoral fins distinguish it from *A. blochii*, *A. dussumieri*, and *A. mata*, and absence of a shoulder bar distinguishes it from *A. nigricaudus*. It may or may not have a white or tan bar at the base of the tail. The yellowfin surgeonfish inhabits lagoon and seaward reefs to a depth of 91 m. Juveniles occur in shallow, protected, turbid inshore waters; adults prefer deeper areas of protected bays and lagoons and range over sand flats far from shelter. They feed on the diatom and detritus film on sand as well as filamentous algae or even animal material such as hydroids or pieces of fish. At Belau, it is reported to spawn around the new and full moons from January to May.
Indo-pan-Pacific: E. Africa to Mexico, n. to s. Japan and the Hawaiian Is., s. to the s. Great Barrier Reef, New Caledonia, and Tuamotus; throughout Micronesia.

Ctenochaetus binotatus Randall, 1955
Twospot bristletooth   Pls. 128D, 129C
SL: to 141 mm (5.6 in); D VIII, 24-27; A III, 22-25; P 15-16; GR 23-29(a),22-27(p); depth 1.9-2.15; teeth of adults ≤42(u), ≤45(l).
Species of *Ctenochaetus* differ from those of *Acanthurus* by having fewer dorsal spines (8 vs 9, the 1st very small) and a differently shaped mouth and teeth. Their teeth are more numerous, flexible, and elongate with incurved tips that are denticulate on one side. They feed by scooping the film of detritus and unicellular algae from the surfaces of dead coral, rock, seagrasses, or other algae and sucking it into the mouth but are incapable of feeding on attached filamentous algae itself. This surface film may contain high concentrations of the unicellular bluegreen algae (e.g. the dinoflagellate *Gambierdiscus toxicus*) that produce the ciguatera toxin and make species of *Ctenochaetus* a key link in the ciguatera food chain. In certain areas *Ctenochaetus* as well as their predators may concentrate enough ciguatoxin to cause illness in humans. *Ctenochaetus binotatus* is characterized by a prominent black spot at the rear base of the dorsal and anal fins. Adults have a blueish ring around the eye. It inhabits coral and rubble areas of deep lagoon and seaward reefs at depths of 12 to 53 m.
Indo-Pacific: E. Africa to the Tuamotus, n. to the Ryukyus, s. to the s. Great Barrier Reef and Tonga; throughout Micronesia.

Fig. 4. Mouth and teeth of
Ctenochaetus striatus.

Ctenochaetus hawaiiensis Randall, 1955 Pl. 129A,D
Chevron tang (juv.); **Black surgeonfish** (adult)
SL: to 209 mm (8.2 in); D VIII, 27-29; A III, 25-26; P 16;
C slightly emarg.; GR 21-25(a),25(p); depth 1.75-2.05; lips
finely crenulate.

The spectacular juveniles of this species differ greatly from
adults. They have a deeper body and are bright orange-red
with numerous dark chevrons. Adults appear uniformly
black from a distance but actually have numerous dark green
horizontal pinstripes. This species is rare throughout most
of Micronesia except Pagan where it was observed in small
groups in a shallow, semi-sheltered area among large basalt
boulders. Juveniles occur in relatively deep coral-rich areas
of seaward reefs. The individual photographed at Belau represents a westernmost range extension for this species.
Pacific Plate: Belau, Marcus, Mariana, Marshall, Hawaiian,
Samoan, Marquesan, Society, Tuamotu, Austral, Pitcairn,
and Ducie Is.

Ctenochaetus marginatus (Valenciennes, 1835)
Blue-spotted bristletooth Pl. 128E
(*C. cyanoguttatus*; *C. magnus*)
SL: to 225 mm (8.9 in); D VIII, 26-28; A III, 24-25; P 16-
17; C emarg.; GR 26-29(a),34-37(p);
depth 1.85-2.15; lower lip papillate posteriorly.

This species has small brilliant blue spots covering the
head, body, and pectoral fins and blue longitudinal pinstripes
on the dorsal, anal, and caudal fins. Juveniles have blue
lines extending onto the posterior portion of the body. At
Kosrae, it was observed in small groups along the upper
edge of the outer Okate Channel and adjacent outer reef slope
at depths of 2 to 6 m.
Pan-Pacific: Lukunor Atoll (Mortlock group), Kosrae, Kapingamaringi (?), s. Marshall, Gilbert, Phoenix, Line, Marquesan, Society, and Cocos Is. (e. Pacific).

Ctenochaetus striatus (Quoy & Gaimard, 1825)
Striped bristletooth Pl. 129B,E
SL: to 195 mm (7.7 in); D VIII, 27-31; A III, 24-28; P 16-
17; C lunate; GR 28-36(a),29-42(p); depth 1.9-2.3; teeth
≤45 (u), ≤53 (l).

This is by far the most abundant and ubiquitous member of
its genus throughout Micronesia. It occurs over coral, rock,
pavement, or rubble substrates of reef flats and lagoon and
seaward reefs to a depth of over 30 m. It occurs singly or in
small to very large, often mixed-species aggregations. By
feeding directly on the surface film of bluegreen algae and diatoms, it is a key link in the ciguatera food chain and is one
of the few herbivorous fishes which is occasionally toxic.
Small juveniles are incredibly colorful, but the brilliant colors disappear within a span of a few weeks once the fish

reaches a length of about 5 cm. Group-spawning takes place
near the mouths of channels or other areas of off-reef currents on an outgoing tide. Occasionally partially or entirely
xanthic, albinistic, or melanistic individuals occur.
Indo-Pacific: Red Sea to the Tuamotus, n. to s. Japan, s. to
the s. Great Barrier Reef and Rapa; throughout Micronesia;
absent from Malden and Jarvis Is.

Ctenochaetus strigosus (Bennett, 1828) Pls. 127E,
Goldring surgeonfish 128F
SL: to 139 mm (5.5 in); D VIII, 25-28; A III, 21-25; P 15-
(16); C moderately emarginate; GR 27-31(a),27-34(p); depth
1.7-2.0; teeth ≤47 (u), ≤60 (l), lips smooth.

This species differs from *C. striatus* by having a more truncate tail and a pale yellowish ring around the eye (this ring
is prominent in the Hawaiian and French Polynesian populations; the latter also has a white caudal fin). It is rare in Micronesia as in other areas where both species co-exist. At
Guam, solitary individuals have been observed in coral-rich
areas of deep lagoon and seaward reefs. Pair-spawning has
been reported.
Indo-Pacific: E. Africa to the Hawaiian, Marquesan, and Ducie Is., s. to the s. Great Barrier Reef and New Caledonia;
throughout Micronesia; absent from Malden and Jarvis Is.;
Indian Ocean population lacks pinstripes on the body.

Ctenochaetus tominiensis Randall, 1955 Pl. 129F
Tomini surgeonfish
SL: to 100 mm (3.9 in); D VIII, 24-25; A III, 22-23; P 15-
16; C forked (juv.) to lunate (ad.); GR 20-21(a),20(p); depth
1.8-2.04; margins of lips papillate.

In addition to having a distinctive coloration, this is the
only species of *Ctenochaetus* with angular dorsal and anal
fins. It typically occurs singly or in small groups along
steep coral-rich dropoffs of sheltered coasts to a depth of at
least 21 m. It is known from Micronesia on the basis of a
subadult observed in the "blue hole" at Turtle Cove, Belau.
Indo-Australian: Bali, Sulawesi, Solomon Is., and Belau.

Paracanthurus hepatus (Linnaeus, 1758) Pl. 129G
Palette surgeon; Hepatus tang
SL: to 205 mm (8.1 in); D IX, 19-20; A III, 18-19; P 16; V
I, 3 (I, 5 in all other spp.); depth ca. 2.3.

This is among the most spectacular of coral reef fishes. The
intensity of its blue is rivaled only by the damselfish *Chrysiptera cyanea*. It inhabits clear, current-swept terraces of
seaward reefs at depths of 2 to 40 m. It occurs in loose aggregations 1 or 2 meters above the bottom and feeds on zooplankton. Juveniles and subadults typically occur in groups
near isolated *Pocillopora eydouxi* coral heads and when
alarmed, wedge themselves tightly among the branches. The
hepatus tang is relatively uncommon and highly localized in
occurrence throughout most of Micronesia. It is a popular
and relatively hardy aquarium fish. Unfortunately, its habit
of occurring in groups and wedging itself among coral
branches make it easy for collectors to remove an entire population from a reef.
Indo-Pacific: E. Africa to the Line Is., n. to s. Japan, s. to
the s. Great Barrier Reef, New Caledonia, and Samoa;

throughout Micronesia.

Zebrasoma flavescens (Bennett, 1828)   Pl. 130A
Yellow tang

SL: to 164 mm (6.5 in); D V, 23-26(24-26); A III, 19-22 (20-21); P 14-16(15-16); depth 1.4-1.75.

Members of this genus are characterized by an unusually deep body with tall dorsal and anal fins and an elongate tubular snout. The yellow tang inhabits coral-rich areas of lagoon and seaward reefs from below the surge zone to at least 46 m. It occurs singly or in loose groups and browses on filamentous algae from hard surfaces. It is moderately common but somewhat localized in occurrence in the Marianas. It is a popular aquarium fish and the top marine fish export from Hawaii. Group-spawning as well as pair-spawning by territorial males that court passing females has been observed.

Pacific Plate: Ryukyu, Mariana, Marshall, Marcus, Wake, and Hawaiian Is.

Zebrasoma scopas (Cuvier, 1829)   Pl. 130B
Brown tang

(*Z. flavescens* Scultz and Woods, 1953 (in part))

SL: to 153 mm (6.0 in); D IV-V, 23-25(24); A III, 19-21 (19-20); P 14-16(15); depth 1.5-1.7.

Small juveniles have thin yellowish bars and more prominent yellow specks than adults. The brown tang inhabits coral-rich areas of lagoon and seaward reefs at depths of 1 to 60 m. It occurs singly or in small groups and throughout most of Micronesia is more common than *Z. flavescens*. Dirty-yellow hybrids between the two species occasionally turn up. Group-spawning and pair-spawning have been observed.

Indo-Pacific: E. Africa to the Tuamotus, n. to s. Japan, s. to Lord Howe and Rapa Is.; throughout Micronesia.

Zebrasoma veliferum (Bloch, 1797)   Pl. 130C
Sailfin tang

SL: to 298 mm (11.7 in); D V, 29-33; A III, 23-26; P 15-17(16); depth 1.8-2.0.

Small juveniles have alternating yellow and black bars. This large and gaudy *Zebrasoma* inhabits lagoon and seaward reefs from the lower surge zone to a depth of at least 30 m. Solitary juveniles occur among rocks or coral of shallow protected, sometimes turbid reefs. Pair-spawning has been reported.

Indo-Pacific: Red Sea to the Hawaiian and Tuamotu Is., n. to s. Japan, s. to the s. Great Barrier Reef, New Caledonia, and Rapa; throughout Micronesia; Indian Ocean population ("*A. desjardinii.*") differs slightly in coloration and has modally fewer D and A soft rays.

Subfamily Nasinae (Unicornfishes)

Unicornfishes belong to a single tropical Indo-Pacific genus, *Naso* (3 by some authors) with 1 or 2 sharp fixed keel-like bony peduncular plates (Fig. 5), 2 anal spines (excluding a rudimentary nubbin), thick leathery skin with tiny non-overlapping scales, and small lanceolate teeth with finely serrate edges (except incisiform in *N. lituratus*). They have a distinctive late-larval stage similar to the *acronurus*, termed the *keris* stage. Most species develop a distinctive rostral horn, convex foreheads, or a humped back and many develop filamentous caudal lobes. Juveniles of many species are difficult to identify. Adults of most species occupy the water column to feed on large zooplankton during the day and shelter within the reef during the night. Some feed on fleshy brown algae. Males of many species are able to display spectacular iridescent blue and white markings during courtship. At least 9 species occur in Micronesia.

Fig. 5. Peduncular plates of species of *Naso*.

Naso annulatus (Quoy & Gaimard, 1825)
Whitemargin unicornfish   Pl. 130D,E

(*N. herrei*)

FL: to ≥100cm (39.4 in); D V, 28-29; A II, 27-28; P 17-19; GR 4+9-10; depth 2.8-3.3 in FL.

Juveniles of this plantivorous unicornfish may occur in as little as 1 m on clear lagoon reefs, but large adults are rarely seen in less than 25 m, primarily off outer reef dropoffs. At Belau, this species is reported to spawn along the inner barrier reef edge and slope around the new and full moons of May and probably other months.

Indo-Pacific: E. Africa to the Hawaiian, Marquesan, and Tuamotu Is., n. to s. Japan, s. to Lord Howe Is.; throughout Micronesia.

Naso brachycentron (Valenciennes, 1835)   Fig. 6
Humpback unicornfish

FL: to 90 cm (35.4 in); D IV-V, 28-30; A II, 27-28; P 17; GR 4+8; depth 2.6-2.9 in FL.

The grotesquely humped back of this species is distinctive. The hump develops at a length of about 20 cm and the horn only develops in adult males. This species appears to be rare in Micronesia where it probably occurs along steep outer reef slopes.

Indo-Pacific: E. Africa to the Marquesan and Society Is., n. to the Ryukyus, s. to Vanuatu; Belau and Guam in Micronesia.

Fig. 6. *Naso brachycentron*.

Naso brevirostris (Valenciennes, 1835)   Pl. 130F
Spotted unicornfish
FL: to 60 cm (23.6 in), SL: to 45 cm (17.7 in); D VI, 27-29; A II, 27-30; P 15-17(16); GR 3-5+9-10; depth 2.5-3.0 in FL, 2.4-2.7 in SL; teeth ca. 50 (ea. jaw).

Juveniles lack the prominent horn of adults. This species typically occurs in mid-water groups along steep outer lagoon and seaward reef dropoffs at depths of 4 to over 46 m. Juveniles and subadults feed on benthic algae; adults feed mainly on zooplankton. Pair-spawning has been reported.

Indo-Pacific: Red Sea to the Hawaiian, Marquesan, and Ducie Is., n. to s. Japan, s. to Lord Howe Is.; throughout Micronesia.

Naso lopezi Herre, 1927   Fig. 7
Lopez' unicornfish
FL: to 54 cm (21.3 in), SL: to 45 cm(17.7 in); D V, 28-31 (28-29); A II, 27-29(28-29); P 17; depth 3.4-4.6 in FL, 2.8-3.8 in SL.

This elongate unicornfish lacks a horn, has numerous black close-set spots on the upper half of its body and tail, and is white ventrally. It is a deeper water species occasionally observed in as little as 6 m along the vertical walls of leeward Belau.

Indo-Australian: w. Indonesia, Philippines, Ryukyus, and Belau.

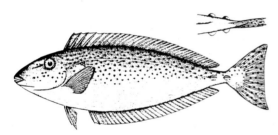

Fig. 7. *Naso lopezi* (after Herre, 1927).

Naso hexacanthus (Bleeker, 1855)   Pl. 131A
Blacktongue unicornfish; Sleek unicornfish
FL: to 75 cm (29.5 in), SL: to 60 cm (23.6 in); D VI, 27-29; A II, 28-30; P (17)-18; GR 4+10; depth 2.7-3.2 in FL, 2.6-3.0 in SL; teeth of lg. adults ≥100 (u),≥85 (l).

This hornless unicornfish usually occurs in aggregations off seaward reef dropoffs at depths of 6 to 137 m, but usually below 18 m. It feeds primarily on larger animals in the zooplankton, including crab larvae, arrow worms, and pelagic tunicates, but has also been reported to occasionally take filamentous red algae. Courting males develop a large pale blue area on the upper head and nape as well as pale blue vertical lines and spots on the sides.

Indo-Pacific: Red Sea to the Hawaiian, Marquesan, and Ducie Is., n. to s. Japan, s. to Lord Howe Is.; throughout Micronesia.

Naso lituratus (Bloch & Schneider, 1801)   Pl. 131B
Orangespine unicornfish

FL: to ca. 31 cm (12.1 in), SL: to ca. 27 cm (10.5 in); D VI, 27-30; A II, 28-30; P 16-17; C lobes filamentous in lg. os; GR 4+8-9; depth 2.2-2.7 in FL,1.9-2.4 in SL; teeth ca. 30-35 (ea. jaw).

This spectacular hornless unicornfish inhabits areas of coral, rock, or rubble of lagoon and seaward reefs from the lower surge zone to a depth of 90 m. It feeds primarily on leafy brown algae such as *Sargassum* and *Dictyota*.. Juveniles are an important aquarium fish export from Hawaii. Pair-spawning has been reported.

Indo-Pacific: Red Sea to the Hawaiian, Marquesan, and Tuamotu Is.; n. to s. Japan, s. to the s. Great Barrier Reef, New Caledonia, and Rapa; throughout Micronesia; Indian Ocean population differs slightly in color pattern.

Naso tuberosus Lacepède, 1801   Pl. 131C
Humpnose unicornfish
FL: to 60 cm (23.6 in); D V, 27-29; A II, 26-27; P 16-18; GR 4-6+7-8; depth of adults 2.6-2.7 in FL, 2.3-2.7 in SL.

This unicornfish develops an unusual protruberance on the snout as well as a slight hump on the back. It occurs in groups around channel mouths and seaward reefs at depths of 3 to at least 20 m and probably feeds primarily on fleshy benthic algae.

Indo-Pacific: E. Africa to the Gilbert and Samoan Is., n. to the Ryukyus, s. to the s. Great Barrier Reef and New Caledonia; throughout Micronesia.

Naso unicornis (Forsskål, 1775)   Pl. 131D
Bluespine unicornfish
FL: to 70 cm (27.6 in); D VI, 27-30; A II, 27-30; P 17-18; GR 4+9-10; depth of adults<3.0 in FL,1.8-2.6 in SL; teeth ca. 50-60 (ea. jaw).

This unicornfish is a common inhabitant of channels, moats, and seaward reefs, particularly areas of strong surge, to as deep as 80 m. It typically occurs in small groups, often in very shallow surgy water and feeds mainly on coarse leafy brown algae such as *Sargassum*. At Belau it migrates in schools around the outer reef edge and spawns around both new and full moons. Adult males tend to have better a developed horn, peduncular spines, and caudal filaments than females of the same size. Pair-spawning at the periphery of a foraging group has been observed.

Indo-Pacific: Red Sea to the Hawaiian, Marquesan, and Tuamotu Is., n. to s. Japan, s. to Lord Howe and Rapa Is.; throughout Micronesia.

Naso vlamingii (Valenciennes, 1835)   Pl. 131E
Bignose unicornfish
FL: to ca. 50 cm (19.7 in); D VI, 26-27; A III, 27-29; P 17-19; GR 3+9; depth 2.6-2.9 in FL.

Adults of this species develop a convexly rounded prominent snout and unusually tall dorsal and anal fins. They normally have a good deal of bright blue markings, but courting males are able to instantaneously turn the blue into spectacular display of irridescence. This unicornfish inhabits deep lagoon and seaward reefs at depths of 4 to over 50 m. During the day, it occurs in mid-water aggregations off steep slopes where it feeds on zooplankton.

Indo-Pacific: E. Africa to the Line, Marquesan, and Tuamotu Is., n. to s. Japan, s. to the s. Great Barrier Reef and New Caledonia; throughout Micronesia.

ZANCLIDAE (MOORISH IDOL)

This family consists of a single distinctively shaped species that shares many characteristics with the surgeonfishes, differing mainly in lacking a peduncular spine. The moorish idol has a strongly compressed discoid body, tubular snout with a small mouth containing numerous elongate bristle-like teeth, and dorsal spines elongated into a whip-like filament. It has a long larval stage and settles at a large size (>6 cm SL), resulting in a widespread distribution.

Zanclus cornutus (Linnaeus, 1758)   Pl. 131F
Moorish idol
(*Z. canescens*)
SL: to 14 cm (5.5 in); D VI-VII, 39-43; A III, 31-37; P 18-19; GR 1+10, short; depth 1.0-1.4.
The moorish idol is ubiquitous in areas of hard substrates from turbid inner harbors and reef flats to clear seaward reefs as deep as 182 m. It usually occurs in small groups, but occasionally may occur in large schools of well over 100. It feeds primarily on sponges, but will also take other animal and plant material. Despite its popularity as an aquarium fish, it is a finicky eater that is dificult to maintain.
Indo-pan-Pacific: E. Africa to Mexico, n. to s. Japan and the Hawaiian Is., s. to Lord Howe, Rapa, and Ducie Is.; throughout Micronesia.

SIGANIDAE (RABBITFISHES, SPINEFOOTS)

Rabbitfishes are highly compressed, somewhat deep-bodied fishes with venemous fin spines, a small terminal mouth with a row of small close-set bicuspid or tricuspid incisiform teeth in the jaws, a complete lateral line, minute cycloid scales, and 5 branchiostegals. All species have XIII, 10 dorsal rays preceded by an imbedded forward projecting spine (Fig. 1), VII, 9 anal rays, and pelvic fins with an outer and inner spine and 3 soft rays. The venemous dorsal, anal, and pelvic spines can inflict an extremely painful wound that fortunately is not normally as dangerous as that of a stonefish. Rabbitfishes are diurnal herbivores of algae and seagrasses named for their voracious appetites. Some species may also occasionally feed on tunicates or sponges. They generally spawn on a lunar cycle with peak activity during the spring and early summer. Spawning occurs in pairs or groups on outgoing tides either at night or in the early morning. Juveniles of some species are estuarine. Rabbitfishes are highly esteemed foodfishes that may make up over half the standing crop of marketable reef flat fishes in some areas. Some species are used in aquaculture. The more colorful species are popular aquarium fishes. When alive most species are easily distinguished by color pattern, but when stressed or dead, may be extremely difficult to distinguish due to obliterating color patterns and nearly identical meristics. Approximately 16 species in the single genus *Siganus* occur in Micronesia. (Lit.: Herre, 1927; Tsuda and Bryan, 1975; Woodland, 1983, 1986; Woodland and Allen, 1977; Woodland and Randall, 1979)

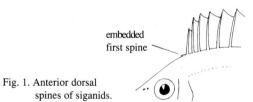

embedded
first spine

Fig. 1. Anterior dorsal spines of siganids.

Tropical w. Pacific: s. China Sea and Indonesia to the Gilberts, n. to the Ryukyu and Ogasawara Is., s. to the s. Great Barrier Reef and New Caledonia; Belau to the e. Carolines and Marshalls in Micronesia; replaced by *S. magnificus, S. uspi*, and an undescribed species in the Andaman Sea, Fiji, and Tonga, respectively.

Siganus argenteus (Quoy & Gaimard, 1825)
Forktail rabbitfish   Pl. 132B,C
(*S. rostratus*)
SL: to 29 cm (11.3 in); P 17-19(18); GR 17-20; cheek scaleless; depth 2.3-3.0.
The forktail rabbitfish superficially resembles two others, *S. canaliculatus* and *S. fuscescens*, particularly when young, but differs by having a much more deeply forked tail. It has the longest larval stage of all siganids, resulting in the widest distribution and the largest size at settlement (6-8 cmFL). In the Marianas, silvery post-larvae recruit to reef flats in large "balls", primarily at the last quarter moons of April and May. Within about three days they become completely pigmented and adopt a herbivorous diet. Adults inhabit primarily areas of mixed coral and rubble or bare rock

Siganus (Lo) vulpinus (Schlegel and Müller, 1844)
Foxface rabbitfish   Pl. 132A
(*S. unimaculatus*)
SL: to 18 cm (7.1 in); P 15-17(16-17); depth ca. 2.1-2.3.
This long-snouted rabbitfish inhabits coral-rich areas of lagoon and seaward reefs to a depth of 30 m. It usually occurs singly or in pairs, but juveniles and subadults occasionally occur in large schools among staghorn *Acropora* corals where they feed on algae growing on the dead bases of the coral branches. Juveniles and subadults from the Philippines, Ryukyus, Ogasawara Is., and Rowley Shoals have a large black blotch on the sides beneath the soft dorsal rays. This form has often been regarded as a separate species, *S. unimaculatus*.

of lagoon and seaward reefs to a depth of at least 30 m where they occur in large roving schools.

Indo-Pacific: Red Sea to the Marquesan and Tuamotu Is., n. to s. Japan, s. to the Great Barrier Reef, New Caledonia, and Rapa; throughout Micronesia.

Siganus canaliculatus (Park, 1797) Pl. 132D
Seagrass rabbitfish

SL: to 23 cm (in); P 16-17; C emarg.(juv) to forked (ad); depth 2.4-2.8.

This species is similar to *S. argenteus* and *S. fuscescens* in color pattern. It differs from the very similar *S. fuscescens* by having a slightly more pointed snout and longer pectoral fins (contained 1.1-1.3 in HL vs. 1.4-1.5 in *S. fuscescens*). *Siganus canaliculatus* is a schooling species generally found in seagrass beds of turbid inshore water (to a depth of 50 m) whereas *S. argenteus* and *S. fuscescens* prefer clearer water. In the Ryukyus, large runs of juveniles settle on reef flats during flood tides of May and June.

Indo-Australian: India to the Moluccas, n. to the Ryukyus; Belau and Yap in Micronesia.

Siganus corallinus Valenciennes, 1835 Pl. 132E
Coral rabbitfish

SL: to 23 cm (9.1 in); P (16)-17; C deeply forked; lower GR 18-22; depth 1.8-2.3.

This species inhabits coral-rich areas of lagoon reefs. Juveniles often occur among staghorn *Acropora* corals and may form schools while adults usually occur in pairs.

Indo-west-Pacific: Seychelles to Papua New Guinea, n. to the Ryukyus, s. to the s. Great Barrier Reef and New Caledonia; Belau in Micronesia. closely related to *S. trispilos* from nw. Australia.

Siganus doliatus Cuvier, 1830 Pl. 132F
Pencil-streaked rabbitfish

SL: to ca. 20 cm (7.8 in); C truncate to emarginate; GR 5+17; depth ca. 2.0-2.1.

At Belau, this species was observed along coral-rich lagoon and channel slopes. It was uncommon and usually occurred in pairs. At Yap, it has been reported (as *S. virgatus*) from reef flats as well as lagoon and seaward reefs. Records of *S. virgatus* from Micronesia are probably based on misidentifications of *S. doliatus*.

Tropical w. Pacific: Dampier Arch. and Philippines to Tonga, s. to the s. Great Barrier Reef and New Caledonia; Belau, Yap, and Ponape in Micronesia.

Siganus fuscescens (Houttuyn, 1782) Fig. 2
Fuscescens rabbitfish

SL: to 25 cm (9.8 in); P 16-17; C emarginate becoming forked in large fish; depth 2.3-2.9.

The differences between this species, *S. argenteus*, and *S. canaliculatus* are noted under those species' accounts. This species is sandy-brown to green above becoming silvery below, with a golden sheen and numerous (500-600) pearly spots in horizontal rows on the sides and fins marbled in brown. It occurs in schools on reef flats and in lagoons.

Tropical w. Pacific: Philippines to Samoa, n. to s. Japan, s. to the s. Great Barrier Reef; Belau in Micronesia.

Siganus guttatus (Bloch, 1787) Pl. 133A
Golden rabittfish

SL: to 33 cm (13.0 in); P 15-17(16); C naearly truncate; depth 1.8-2.3.

This rabbitfish occurs in large schools on turbid inshore reefs or among mangroves, often entering brackish waters.

Indo-Australian: Malaysia to Papua New Guinea, n. to the Ryukyus, s. to the Great Barrier Reef; Belau and Yap in Micronesia.

Siganus lineatus (Valenciennes, 1835) Pl. 133B
Lined rabbitfish

SL: to ca. 34 cm (13.5 in); depth ca. 2.

At Belau, this species was observed in schools in shallow, sheltered, murky inshore waters. Gravid individuals form large schools among the mangroves, then migrate seaward to the mouths of channels where they aggregate to spawn on about the 9th to 10th lunar day. Spawning occurs throughout the year with peaks from March to June and in November.

Indo-Australian: Philippines to Vanuatu, s. to the s. Great Barrier Reef and New Caledonia; Belau and Yap in Micronesia.

Siganus oramin (Schneider, 1801) Fig. 2b
White-spotted rabbitfish

SL: to 22 cm (8.5 in); P 16-19; C emarg.; Gr 5-6+16-17; depth ca. 2.6.

This species superficially resembles *S. canaliculatus* and *S. fuscescens*, but has a deeper body with larger elongate white spots. It lives in schools in weedy areas of lagoon and coastal reefs.

Indo-west-Pacific: India to New Caledonia, n. to Taiwan; Belau in Micronesia; closely related to *S. sutor* of the w. Indian Ocean.

Siganus puellus (Schlegel, 1852) Pl. 133C
Masked rabbitfish

SL: to 23 cm (9.1 in); P 15-17(16); GR 4-5+16-20; depth 2.3-2.6.

This colorful rabbitfish inhabits shallow, coral-rich areas of clear lagoon and seaward reefs to a depth of 30 m. Adults are usually seen in pairs.

Tropical w. Pacific: Cocos-Keeling and s. China Sea to the Gilbert Is., n. to the Ryukyus, s. to the s. Great Barrier Reef and New Caledonia; Belau to the e. Carolines and s. Marshalls in Micronesia; closely related to *S. puelloides* from the Andaman Sea and Maldives.

Siganus punctatissimus Fowler & Bean, 1929
Peppered rabbitfish Pl. 133D

SL: to 28 cm (11.0 in); P 16; GR 6+16; depth 2.0-2.1.

A single pair of this rabbitfish was observed at a depth of 12 m along a lagoon channel slope among Belau's Rock Islands.

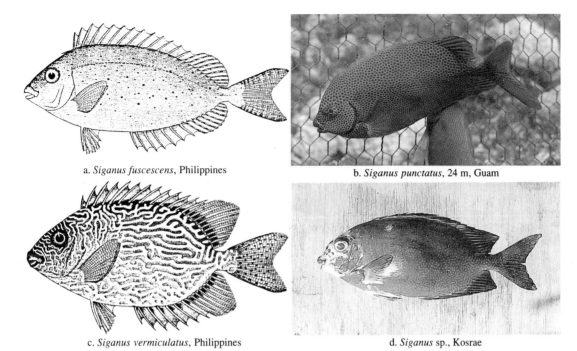

a. *Siganus fuscescens*, Philippines

b. *Siganus punctatus*, 24 m, Guam

c. *Siganus vermiculatus*, Philippines

d. *Siganus* sp., Kosrae

Fig. 2. Micronesian rabbitfishes (a, c, after Herre and Montalban, 1927).

Indo-Australian: Philippines and Sulawesi, n. to the Yaeyamas, s. to Scott Reef; Belau in Micronesia.

Siganus punctatus (Schneider, 1801) Pl. 133E
Gold-spotted rabbitfish

(*S. chrysospilos*)

SL: 35 cm (13.8 in); P 16-17; C emarginate in juveniles to deeply forked in adults; lower GR 16; depth 1.8-2.2.

The spots on this deep-bodied rabbitfish appear dark brown from a distance, but are actually a bright orange on a blue background. This species inhabits clear lagoon and seaward reefs at depths of 1 to 40 m. It is relatively uncommon throughout Micronesia. Adults are usually paired. Spawning occurs around either new or full moons, or both. At Belau, it spawns at low tide on the outer reef flat just inshore of the breaking waves.

Tropical w. Pacific: Philippines and Moluccas to Samoa, n. to the Ryukyu and Ogasawara Is., s. to nw. Australia, the s. Great Barrier Reef, and New Caledonia; throughout Micronesia.

Siganus spinus (Linnaeus, 1758) Pl. 133F
Scribbled rabbitfish

SL: to 23 cm (9.1 in); P 16-18(16-17); C emarginate becoming truncate in large fish; lower GR 13-17; depth 2.4-2.8.

In the Marianas, this is the most common rabbitfish of reef flats and shallow lagoons. It occurs in large roving schools in seagrass beds and areas of mixed coral, rubble, or sand. Large masses of post-larvae settle on the reefs around the last quarter moons of April and May. In some years the run is so great that their filamentous algal food is wiped out and large numbers of juveniles die of starvation! Newly recruited post-larvae as well as juveniles and adults are an important traditional food.

Indo-Pacific: Persian Gulf to the Society Is., n. to s. Japan, s. to the s. Great Barrier Reef; Yap, Kosrae, and Guam in Micronesia.

Siganus vermiculatus (Valenciennes, 1835) Fig. 2c
Vermiculated rabbitfish

SL: to 35 cm (13.8 in); P 16-(17); depth ca. 1.9.

This is the largest species of *Siganus*. Juveniles live among mangroves, then move out to lagoon and coastal reefs as they mature. Both juveniles and adults occur in schools.

Indo-Australian: Sri Lanka to Fiji, n. to the Ryukyus, s. to the n. Great Barrier Reef; Guam in Micronesia.

Siganus sp. Fig. 2d

This species is covered with numerous light spots that grade into fine vermiculations. The specimen shown was speared on the outer reef terrace near the north side of Okate Channel, Kosrae. Unfortunately, it was eaten. Two large rabbitfishes speared in Agat Bay, Guam had a similar color pattern. Unfortunately, they were also eaten before they could be photographed or examined in detail. Subsequent attempts to secure additional specimens have failed.

Kosrae

SUBORDER SCOMBROIDEI

SCOMBRIDAE (TUNAS and MACKERELS)

Scombrids are elongate, fusiform to moderately compressed silvery fishes with a large pointed terminal mouth, a beak-like premaxillary, usually separate dorsal fins (the first depressable into a groove), several detached finlets behind the dorsal and anal fins, a deeply forked tail, two or more peduncular keels, and a simple lateral line (Fig. 1). The forward portion of body of most tunas is covered with a smooth hard sheath called the corselet (consisting of a layer of thick elongate and closely overlapping scales) and the remainder covered with tiny scales or naked. Scombrids are typically swift predators of the near-surface waters of the open sea, but a few species are closely associated with coral reefs. They spend their lives continuously swimming, eat large quantities of food, and grow rapidly. Many species maintain core body temperatures several degrees higher than the surrounding water. The open sea species feed primarily on epipelagic fishes, squids, and crustaceans. When near reefs, they also prey heavily on the larval and early juvenile stages of coral reef-dwelling fishes and crustaceans, particularly species that grow to a large size before settlement such as mullids, acanthurids, and tetraodontiforms. If they swim past steep outer reef dropoffs or enter deep atoll lagoons they may also prey upon adult reef fishes. Reef-associated species prey either on large zooplankton or fishes that occupy the water above the reef. All species are utilized as food. The tunas are the basis of the world's largest commercial fishery and are among the most important gamefishes. At least 10 species occur in Micronesia, but only the 4 reef-associated species are included below. (Lit.: Collette,1983; *in* Smith and Heemsta,1986)

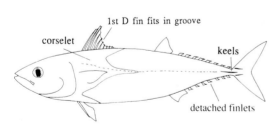

1st D fin fits in groove

corselet

keels

detached finlets

Fig. 1. External features of a scombrid.

Grammatorcynos bilineatus (Rüppell, 1836)
Double-lined mackerel Pl. 134A

FL: to 60 cm (23.6 in); Wt.: to 3 kg (6.6 lb); D XII+10-14+6-7; A 10-14+6; P 22-25; two lateral lines; GR 3-5+1+13-18=19-24; depth ca. 5.0 in FL.

The double-lined mackerel inhabits near-surface inshore and offshore waters. It is not uncommon to encounter solitary individuals swimming within 2 to 3 meters of lagoon pinnacles or seaward reefs.

Indo-Pacific: Red Sea to Samoa, n. to the Ryukyus, s. to Scott Reef, Queensland, and Tonga; throughout Micronesia.

Gymnosarda unicolor (Rüppell, 1836) Pl. 134B
Dogtooth tuna
(*G. nuda*)

FL: to 206 cm (6 ft, 9 in); Wt.: to 131 kg (289 lb; s. Korea), rarely over 180 cm (5 ft 11 in) and 60 kg (132 lb) in Micronesia; D XIII-XV+12-14+6-7 finlets; A 12-13+6 finlets; P 25-28; GR 11-14; depth 3.9-4.0 in FL.

The dogtooth tuna is named for its numerous large conical teeth (in a single row in each jaw). It is one of the few tunas that is primarily a reef dweller. It occurs in mid-water along steeply sloping lagoon pinnacles, channel walls, and seaward reefs from the surface to a depth of at least 100 m. It is a voracious predator of fishes, particularly planktivores. Prey items identified from dogtooth stomachs include fusiliers, the unicornfishes *Naso brevirostris* and *N. vlamingi*, round scads, and a small wrasse, *Cirrhilabrus* sp. Large individuals may be ciguatoxic in certain areas.

Indo-Pacififc: Red Sea to the Marquesan and Tuamotu Is., n. to s. Korea and s. Japan, s. to New Caledonia and Rapa; throughout Micronesia.

Rastrelliger kanagurta (Cuvier, 1829) Fig. 1
Striped mackerel

FL: to 35 cm (13.8 in); D IX-XI+12+5 finlets; A I+12+5 finlets; P 19-20; GR 15-22+31-41=48-59; depth 3.4-4.0 in FL.

This small tuna inhabits coastal bays, harbors, and deep lagoons, particularly in somewhat turbid plankton-rich waters. It occurs in large tightly-packed schools and oftem swims with its mouth open to strain the water with its gill rakers. Another, deeper-bodied species, *R. brachysoma* may also occur at Belau or the FSM.

Indo-west-Pacific: Red Sea to Samoa, n. to the Ryukyus; Belau in Micronesia; introduced to the e. Mediterranean.

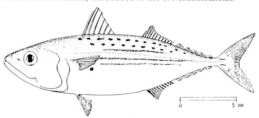

Fig. 1. *Rastrelliger kanagurta* (after FAO, 1972).

Scomberomorus commerson (Lacepède, 1800)
Narrow-barred king mackerel Pl. 134C

FL: to 220 cm (7 ft 2 in); Wt.: to 46.4 kg (102 lb); D XV-XVIII+16-18+9-10 finlets; A 17-19+9-10 finlets; P 21-23; GR 0-1+3-5=3-6; depth 5.0-6.3 in FL.

This large predator is frequently encountered patrolling dropoffs where it may sometimes be observed chasing schools of fusiliers. It occasionally patrols shallow, gently sloping reef or lagoon waters. Divers often mistake it for the wahoo, a more fusiform, narrow-bodied scombrid that is less inclined to closely approach the reef.

Indo-west-Pacific: Red Sea to Fiji, n. to Korea and sw. Japan, s. to New South Wales and Lord Howe Is.; Belau in Micronesia; introduced to the e. Mediterranean.

ORDER PLEURONECTIFORMES (FLATFISHES)

BOTHIDAE (LEFTEYE FLOUNDERS)

Flatfishes are unique for having both eyes on one side of the head and greatly compressed bodies modified for living with one side flat against the bottom. The larvae have an eye on each side of the head, but as they begin transformation to benthic juveniles, one of the eyes migrates over the top of the head to the other side. The blind side settles on the bottom and remains unpigmented. Flatfishes have a long continuous dorsal and anal fins and all but the most primitive of the 7 families lack fin spines. They are carnivores of small fishes and crustaceans that live on silt, sand or gravel bottoms. Most species can change their color pattern to closely match the bottom on which they rest and can partially bury themselves as well. Flatfishes are among the worlds most important foodfishes. The Bothidae have both eyes on the left side and a shortened right pelvic fin. In all Micronesian species the eyed side has ctenoid scales and the blind side has cycloid scales. Most of the world's more than 200 species inhabit continental shelves of tropical and temperate seas. At least 3 species occur on shallow Micronesian coral reefs. In addition, an unidentified species of *Engyprosopon* has been taken from the mouth of a grouper caught at a depth of 180 m off Guam. (Lit.: Henesley, 1986)

Asterorhombus intermedius (Bleeker, 1866) Fig. 1
Intermediate flounder

(*Arnoglossus intermedius* Woods *in* Schultz et al., 1966)
SL: to ca. 115 mm (4.5 in); D 77-84; A 55-62; P 9-11; LL 43-54; GR 0+8-9; depth 2.0-2.4.
Asterorhombus is distinguished from all other Micronesian genera by having a nearly continuous bony ridge extending from the anterior margin of the lower eye to the posterior margin of the upper eye, and a narrow interorbital space, always less than the greatest eye diameter. This species inhabits sandy areas of coral reefs to a depth of 45 m. It is known from Micronesia on the basis of a post-larval specimen taken in less than 12 m in Bikini lagoon, and possibly a 44 mm specimen regurgitated from a fish taken off Guam.
Tropical w. Pacific: Java Sea to the Marshalls, s. to nw. Australia and the s. Great Barrier Reef; possibly also the Marianas.

Fig. 1. *Asterorhombus intermedius*, 100 mm (after Gloerfelt-Tarp and Kailola, 1984).

Bothus mancus (Brousonet, 1782) Pl. 134D
Peacock flounder

SL: to 39 cm (15.4 in); D 96-104; A 74-81; P 10-13 (both sides); GR 0+9-11; LL 76-90; depth 1.7-2.0.
This flatfish is covered by beautiful blue flower-like patterns, yet it somehow blends into its sandy environment perfectly. Males of the genus *Bothus* develop greatly elongate upper pectoral rays (which may nearly reach the tail) and a wider interorbital space than do females. The peacock flounder is common on sandy bottoms from the inner reef flat to as deep as 84 m on seaward reefs. Occasionally, it rests on bare rock.
Indo-pan-Pacific: to Mexico, n. to the Ryukyu and Hawaiian Is., s. to Lord Howe, Rapa, and Ducie Is.; throughout Micronesia.

Bothus pantherinus (Rüppell, 1830) Pl. 134F
Leopard flounder

SL: to 35 cm (9.8 in); D 84-97; A 61-73; P 9-12 (eyed), 9-11 (blind); V 6; GR 0-7(all rudim.)+6-8; LL 74-87 (67-92 in lit.); depth 1.6-1.9.
This species differs from *B. mancus* in the placement of the eyes (in *B. mancus* the lower eye is completely in front of the upper eye so that an imaginary vertical line will fit between them, while it will not in *B. pantherinus*) and by generally lacking blue-borders on the numerous flower-like patterns of its dorsal surface. *B. pantherinus* is about as common as *B. mancus* and occurs in the same habitats to a depth of 110 m, but does not get as large.
Indo-Pacific: Red Sea to the Hawaiian, Marquesan, and Society Is., n. to s. Japan, s. to Lord Howe Is.; throughout Micronesia.

PLEURONECTIDAE (RIGHTEYE FLOUNDERS)

Members of this family normally have eyes on the right side of the head and have a free preopercular edge. Most of the worlds 100 or so species occur on continental shelves of all seas. A few inhabit coral reefs, one of which occurs in Micronesia. (Lit.: Smith and Heemstra, 1986)

Samariscus triocellatus Woods, 1966 Fig. 1
Threespot flounder

SL: to 65 mm (2.6 in); D 62-70; A 47-56; P 4 (excl. basal nubbin); LL 71-76(82-87 by Winterbottom, 1978); GR rudim.; depth 2.4-3.1.
This boldy marked flounder inhabits coral heads of lagoon and seaward reefs at depths of 5 to 20 m. It usually occurs in shallow caves or under ledges and can lie flat against vertical rock surfaces.
Indo-Pacific: E. Africa to the Hawaiian, Marquesan, and Society Is.; Kapingamarangi and Marshalls in Micronesia.

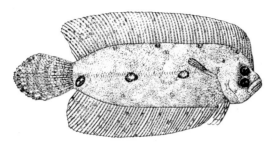

Fig. 1 (Pleuronectidae). *Samariscus triocellatus*, 53 mm, Bikini (after A. M. Awl *in* Schultz et al., 1966).

SOLEIDAE (SOLES)

Soles have their eyes on the right side of the head. They have a non-projecting lower jaw and rounded caudal fin, lack a free preopercular margin and ribs, have a tubular anterior nostril on the eyed side, and either ctenoid or cycloid scales. Some species lack pectoral fins. At least 5 species have been reported from Micronesian coral reefs. (Lit.: Clark and George, 1979; Wongratrana, 1975)

Aseraggodes melanostictus (Peters, 1876) Pl. 134E
Black spotted sole

(*A. dubius* Rofen, 1961?)
SL: to >39 mm (1.5 in); D 74; A 57; P absent; V 5; LL 67; scales ctenoid; GR 2 (rudim.); depth 2.29.
This small sole is a common inhabitant of protected sandy bottoms of lagoon and seaward reefs at depths of 1 to 73 m. It seems likely that a 39 mm specimen collected from a reef flat at Kapingamarangi is this species.
Tropical w. Pacific: Christmas Is., Indian Ocean, to the Society Is.; Marianas, Kapingamarangi (?), and Marshalls in Micronesia.

Aseraggodes smithi Woods, 1966 Fig. 1a
Smith's sole

SL: to >19 mm (0.7 in); D 67; A 44; P absent; P 5 (eyed), 4 (blind); LL 65; GR rudim.; depth 2.57 (data for holotype). This species is known from Micronesia on the basis of a single juvenile specimen taken from the "ocean reef" of Rongerik Atoll.
Tropical w. Pacific: Christmas Is. (?), Indian Ocean and Marshall and Society Is.

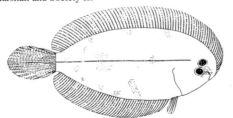

Fig. 1a. *Aseraggodes smithi*, 19 mm, Rongerik (after A. M. Awl *in* Schultz et al., 1966).

Aseraggodes whitakeri Woods, 1966 Fig. 1b
Whitaker's sole

SL: to ≥38 mm (1.5 in); D 72; A 51; P absent; V 6 (eyed), 5 (blind); LL 72; GR rudim.; depth 2.45 (data for holotype). This species differs from *A. smithi* by having the eyes closer together and more pelvic rays. The single known Micronesian specimen was collected from a lagoon coral head at a depth of 6 m at Rongerik Atoll.
Pacific Plate: Marshall and Society Is.

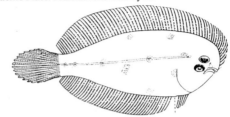

Fig. 1b. *Aseraggodes whittakeri*, 38 mm, Rongelap (after A. M. Awl *in* Schultz et al., 1966).

Pardachirus pavoninus (Lacepède, 1802) Fig. 1c
Peacock sole

SL: to ca. 22 cm (8.7 in); D 62-73; A 48-55; P absent; V 5; LP 83-102; scales cycloid; LP 76-95; depth 2.3-2.5.
Members of this genus secrete a highly toxic milky fluid from glands at the base of all but the first and last dorsal and anal rays and have an extremely bitter skin. The peacock sole inhabits sandy bottoms of lagoon and seaward reefs at depths of 3 to 40 m. It usually remains completely buried in sand except for its eyes and the tubular anterior nostril.
Indo-Pacific: Sri Lanka to Samoa, n. to s. Japan, s. to New South Wales and Tonga; Belau in Micronesia; closely related to *P. marmoratus* from the Indian Ocean.

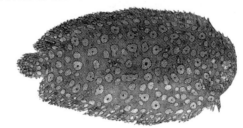

Fig. 1c. *Pardachirus pavoninus*, 119 mm (after Gloerfelt-Tarp and Kailola, 1982).

Soleichthys heterohinos (Bleeker, 1856) Pl. 134G
Banded sole

(*Aesopia heterohinos*)
SL: to 140 mm (5.5 in); D 87-98; A 72-87; P 8-9; V 4; LL 105-122 (both sides); depth 2.7-3.5.
The banded sole inhabits shallow protected sandy areas of lagoon and seaward reefs. It remains buried beneath the sand with only its eyes and tubular nostril exposed. It seems to be more active at night. When disturbed it moves extremely rapidly and is difficult to detect when it resettles.
Indo-Pacific: India to Samoa, n. to s. Japan, s. to New South Wales; Marianas and Marshalls in Micronesia.

ORDER TETRAODONTIFORMES

Triggerfishes, filefishes, trunkfishes, puffers, and porcupinefishes are among the eight families comprising the order Tetraodontiformes. They all have greatly restricted gill openings, stout incisiform teeth which may be fused into a beak, highly modified scales or none at all, and lack anal fin spines. They probably evolved from acanthurid-like ancestors, but have numerous specializations that set them apart and often give them a bizarre appearance. Tetraodontiformes generally have an extended larval stage and some species have become entirely pelagic.

BALISTIDAE (TRIGGERFISHES)

Triggerfishes have relatively deep, compressed bodies with eyes set high on the head, a small terminal mouth, non-protrusible jaws, each with eight long protruding close-set incisiform teeth buttressed by an inner row of six smaller teeth, a first dorsal fin consisting of three spines which fold into a groove, second dorsal and anal fins consisting entirely of soft rays, pelvic fins reduced to a spinous knob at the end of a long depressable pelvic bone, and a tough skin covered with moderately large armor-like non-overlapping scales (often with a patch of enlarged scales behind the gill opening). The large, greatly thickened first dorsal spine may be locked upright and depressed only by lowering the second smaller "trigger" spine which fits into a groove in the first spine (Fig. 1). Triggerfishes normally swim by undulating their second dorsal and anal fins, but will use their tail for rapid bursts. When alarmed, or at night, they wedge themselves in a small hole by erecting the first dorsal spine and pelvic girdle. They can easily be removed from their hole if one is able to reach inside and unlock the first dorsal spine. Most triggerfishes are solitary diurnal carnivores of a wide variety of benthic animals including crustaceans, mollusks, sea urchins, other echinoderms, coral, tunicates, and fishes. Some feed largely on zooplankton or benthic algae. Their powerful jaws and teeth are easily able to crush hard-shelled prey, snip off pieces of coral, or if given the opportunity, inflict a nasty wound on a careless diver! Triggerfishes lay demersal eggs in a nest which is aggressivley guarded by the male. In some instances they will attack and bite an intruding diver. Although many species are eaten in Micronesia, a few may be ciguatoxic in certain areas. Several of the more colorful species are popular aquarium fishes, but most are extremely aggressive towards any tankmates. At least 20 species occur in Micronesia. Pectoral counts include the rudimentary upper ray and depth is measured at the origin of the anal fin. (Lit.: Lobel and Johannes, 1979; Matsuura, 1980; Nellis, 1980; Randall et al., 1978; Randall and Klausewitz, 1973; Randall and Steene, 1983)

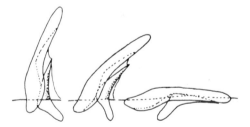

Fig. 1. First dorsal fin showing locking mechanism.

Abalistes stellatus (Lacepède, 1798)   Fig. 2a
Starry triggerfish

SL: to ca. 48 cm (18.9 in); D III+ 25-27; A 24-26; P13-16; LS 33-41.

This is the only triggerfish with a depressed caudal peduncle (wider than it is deep). It inhabits muddy to sandy bottoms to a depth of 120 m.

E. Atlantic & Indo-Pacific: Red Sea to Fiji, n. to s. Japan, s. to the s. Great Barrier Reef and New Caledonia; Belau in Micronesia.

Balistapus undulatus (Mungo Park, 1797)
Orangestriped triggerfish   Pl. 135A,B

SL: to 23 cm (9.1 in); D III+24-27(25-26); A 20-24(22-23); P 13-16(14); LS 36-45.

This spectacular triggerfish inhabits coral-rich areas of deep lagoon and seaward reefs from the lower surge zone to at least 50 m. It feeds on a wide variety of marine organisms including the tips of corals (particularly *Acropora*), benthic algae, sea urchins, heart urchins, crustaceans, fishes, mollusks, brittle stars, tunicates, polychaete worms, sponges, and hydrozoans. It occurs singly or in small groups and is relatively common throughout Micronesia. It is one of the few sexually dimorphic triggerfishes with adult males lacking stripes on most of the snout. Spawning behavior may involve loose aggregations and nesting occurs in channels. The eggs are laid in a single spongy cluster in a shallow excavation on rubble or sand. Hatching takes place at night. Despite its territorial nature and nasty disposition, the orangestriped triggerfish makes a colorful and interesting aquarium pet.

Indo-Pacific: Red Sea to the Line, Marquesan, and Tuamotu Is., n. to s. Japan, s. to the s. Great Barrier Reef and New Caledonia; throughout Micronesia.

Balistoides conspicillum (Bloch &Schneider,1801)
Clown triggerfish   Pl. 135C,D
(*B. niger* Woods, 1966)

SL: to >254 mm (10.0 in); D III+25-27; A 21-22; P 14-15; LS 39-50.

The stunning fish inhabits clear seaward reefs at depths of 3 to 75 m. It seems to prefer coral-rich areas of outer reef terraces adjacent to steep dropoffs. Juveniles usually occur in

a. *Abalistes stellatus*, 275 mm   b. *Canthidermis maculatus*, 25 cm, at sea near Guam

Fig. 2. Micronesian triggerfishes (a, after Gloerfelt-Tarp and Kailola, 1984).

or near ledges and caves of steep dropoffs below 20 m. Although uncommon to rare throughout most of its range, at certain locations up to three or four individuals may be seen on a dive. The clown triggerfish is among the most highly prized of aquarium fishes. Unfortunately, it is also among the nastiest and usually requires a tank of its own.

Indo-Pacific: E. Africa to Samoa, n. to s. Hokkaido, s. to Lord Howe Is.; throughout Micronesia.

Balistoides viridescens (Bloch & Schneider, 1801)
Mustache triggerfish; Titan triggerfish   Pl. 135F

SL: to ca. 63 cm (24.7 in); D III+25-26; A 23-24; P 15; LS 29-32.

This giant triggerfish is also among the ugliest. It inhabits lagoon and seaward reefs to a depth of at least 40 m. Juveniles are most often associated with isolated patches of branching coral or rubble of shallow sandy protected areas. Adults generally occur singly or in pairs on the slopes of deep lagoon pinnacles or seaward reefs. Its diet includes sea urchins (*Diadema* and *Echinometra*), heart urchins, corals (*Acropora* and *Pocillopora*),crabs, bivalves, gastropods, chitons, tube worms, algae, and detritus. One 7 kg (16 lb) specimen had its stomach crammed full of 3/4 inch long tips of *Pocillopora* branches. This species is normally among the wariest of fishes, but when guarding a nest it has been known to attack and bite divers. In certain areas it may be ciguatoxic.

Indo-Pacific: Red Sea to the Line and Tuamotu Is., n. to s. Japan, s. to New Caledonia; throughout Micronesia.

Canthidermis maculatus (Bloch, 1786)   Fig. 2b
Spotted oceanic triggerfish

(*C. senticosus*; *C. viola*)

SL: to ca. 41 cm (16.1 in); D III+23-25; A 20-22; P 14-16 (15); LS 37-46.

The two species of *Canthidermis* are epipelagic throughout nearly all of their lives. Adults as well as juveniles are most often associated with drifting objects. Occasionally they may occur off current-swept points. Juveniles of this species occasionally occur off piers. The Atlantic species, *C. sufflamen* is known to nest demersally off outer reef slopes. It also guards the eggs and even the newly hatched fry.

Circumglobal: tropical and temperate seas n. to Hokkaido, s.

to French Polynesia; throughout Micronesia.

Melichthys niger (Bloch, 1786)   Pl. 136A
Black triggerfish

(*Melichthys radula*; *M. buniva* for pelagic early juvenile stage)

SL: to 281 mm (11.1 in); D III+30-35; A 28-31; P 15-17; LS 57-66.

This cosmopolitan triggerfish occurs primarily on clear seaward reefs, from the reef front to a depth of 75 m. It is relatively common on most Micronesian reefs, but at certain isolated outposts such as Johnston Atoll, it may be super abundant. It feeds primarily on calcareous algae (70% in one study), often as detached drifting fragments, and zooplankton. Transformation from the pelagic early juvenile to the demersal stage occurs at the large size of 90 to 144 mm.

Circumtropical: n. to the Ryukyu and Ogasawara Is., s. to the Tuamotus; throughout Micronesia.

Melichthys vidua (Solander, 1844)   Pl. 136B
Pinktail triggerfish

(*Melichthys nycteris* for pelagic early juvenile stage)

SL: to 280 mm (11.0 in) 40 cmtl; D III+31-35; A 28-31; P 14-16(15-16); LS 62-74.

The pinktail triggerfish inhabits seaward reefs at depths of 4 to at least 60 m. It is relatively common along clear shallow areas of moderate to high coral cover exposed to currents. It feeds primarily on algae (often detached drifting pieces) and detritus but also will eat crustaceans, octopuses, sponges, and fishes. Transformation may occur at a size as large as 133 mm (5.2 in).

Indo-Pacific: E. Africa to the Hawaiian, Marquesan, and Tuamotu Is; n. to s. Japan, s. to the s. Great Barrier Reef and New Caledonia; throughout Micronesia.

Odonus niger (Rüppell, 1837)   Pl. 136C
Redtooth triggerfish

SL: to 285 mm (11.2 in); D III+33-36; A 28-31; P (15)-16; LS 29-34.

This triggerfish inhabits current-swept seaward reefs at depths of 3 to over 35 m. It is particularly abundant above the outer portions of terraces where it occurs in large plankton-feeding aggreggations up to several meters above the bottom. It also feeds on sponges. Juveniles are generally solitary and associated with isolated patches of rubble or crevices with proper-sized shelter holes. They are a popular aquarium fish that are less aggressive than most other triggerfishes.

Indo-Pacific: Red Sea to the Marquesan and Society Is., n. to s. Japan, s. to the s. Great Barrier Reef and New Caledonia; throughout Micronesia.

Pseudobalistes flavimarginatus (Rüppell, 1829)
Yellowmargin triggerfish   Pls. 135E; 136D
SL: to 535 mm (21.1 in); D III+24-27(25-26); A 22-25(24); P 15-(16); LS 28-33.

This is the other giant triggerfish, but is not quite as ugly as *B. viridescens*. It usually inhabits the relatively sheltered waters of lagoons, deep channels, and bays at depths of 2 to 50 m. It is generally solitary or paired. Its diet includes the tips of coral branches, gastropods, crustaceans, foraminiferans, and tunicates. It is ciguatoxic in certain areas. At Belau, nesting occurs in sand-bottomed channels and shallow cuts through the barrier reef. The nests consist of depressions up to 2 m wide and 0.7 m deep. As many as 430,000 or more eggs are deposited in a spongy fist-sized cluster that is weighted down with pieces of rubble. Eggs are laid within a few days before both new and full moons during the months of Nov., Dec., Mar., April, and May, if not throughout the year. At a depth of 12 m on the sand floor of Ulong channel, up to 10 or more nests may be lined up, each within 4 m of one other.

Indo-Pacific: Red Sea to Tuamotus, n. to s. Japan, s. to Samoa; throughout Micronesia.

Pseudobalistes fuscus (Bloch & Schneider, 1801)
Blue triggerfish; Rippled triggerfish   Pl. 136E,F
SL: to ca. 413 mm (16.2 in); D III+24-27; A 19-24; P 15-16; LS 35-46.

This moderately large triggerfish inhabits clear shallow lagoons as well as seaward reefs to a depth of 50 m. It prefers sandy areas near patch reefs or the reef edge, but is rare throughout Micronesia. Juveniles are tan with numerous bright blue wavy lines on the body and fins. The wavy lines tend to break up into shorter lines and spots with growth.

Indo-Pacific: Red Sea to the Society Is., n. to's. Japan, s. to the s. Great Barrier Reef and New Caledonia; throughout Micronesia.

Rhinecanthus aculeatus (Linnaeus, 1758) Pl. 137A
Picassofish; Humuhumu
SL: to 205 (8.1 in); D III+23-26; A 21-23; P 13-15; LS 32-39.

The picassofish is the most common triggerfish of subtidal reef flats and shallow protected lagoons to a depth of about 4 m. It is abundant over sandy areas with scattered rubble or patches of rock bottom with suitable shelter holes. It is territorial and feeds on a wide variety of marine life including algae, detritus, mollusks, crustaceans, worms, sea urchins, heart urchins, fishes, corals, tunicates, foraminiferans, and eggs. It has a reputation for biting the legs of reef walkers or even snorkelers, but probably does so only when guarding

a nest, and is generally quite wary. Its complete Hawaiian name "humuhumu-nukunuku-a-pua'a" means "grunts like a pig" and is derived from its habit of grunting loudly when disturbed. Species of *Rhinecanthus* are popular aquarium fishes. They do best if provided with a diverse diet that includes plant material, and are suitable for the community aquarium if they are somewhat smaller than more docile tankmates.

Indo-Pacific: E. Africa to the Hawaiian, Marquesan, and Tuamotu Is., n. to s. Japan, s. to Lord Howe Is.; throughout Micronesia.

Rhinecanthus rectangulus
(Bloch & Schneider, 1801)   Pl. 137B
Wedge picassofish; Humuhumu
(*R. echarpe*)
SL: to 177 (7.0 in); D III+22-25; A 20-22(21); P 13-15(14); LS 33-39.

This picassofish inhabits outer reef flats and shallow seaward reefs in areas subject to surge. It is common over barren rock or the spur-and-groove zone where there is a mixture of bare rock, rubble and coral. Its diet includes algae, detritus, mollusks, crustaceans, worms, brittle stars, sea urchins, heart urchins, fishes, sponges, foraminiferans, and eggs. It is territorial and generally quite wary.

Indo-Pacific: Red Sea to the Hawaiian, Marquesan, and Ducie Is., n. to the Ryukyus, s. to Lord Howe and the Kermadec Is.; throughout Micronesia.

Rhinecanthus verrucosa (Linnaeus, 1758) Pl. 137C
Blackbelly picassofish
SL: to 187 mm (7.4 in); D III+23-26; A 21-23; P 14-15; LS 34-37.

This picassofish inhabits subtidal reef flats and protected lagoon and coastal reefs to a depth of 20 m. It is considerably less common than *R. aculeatus* or *R. rectangulus*, and is more likely to occur in areas with seagrasses than in coral-rich areas.

Indo-Pacific: Chagos Is. and Sri Lanka to the Solomons, n. to s. Japan, s. to Vanuatu; Belau, Yap, and Kapingamarangi in Micronesia; closely related to *R. lunula* from the s. tropical Pacific (Great Barrier Reef to Pitcairn), *R. assasi* from the Red Sea, and *R. cinereus* from the sw. tropical Indian Ocean.

Sufflamen bursa (Bloch & Schneider, 1801)
Scythe triggerfish; Boomerang triggerfish Pl. 137D
SL: to 200 mm (7.9 in); D III+27-30; A 25-27; P 13-15; LS 43-50.

This small triggerfish inhabits seaward reefs below the surge zone at depths of 3 to 90 m. In Micronesia, it seems to prefer steeply sloping areas of rich coral growth with caves and crevices. Its diet includes crabs, bivalves, gastropods, algae and detritus, echinoids, also worms, eggs, and tunicate. The characterisitc scyth mark crossing the pectoral base is yellowish-tan to green in juveniles and subadults.

Indo-Pacific: E. Africa to the Hawaiian, Marquesan, and Ducie Is., n. to s. Japan, s. to the s. Great Barrier Reef, New Caledonia, and Rapa; throughout Micronesia.

 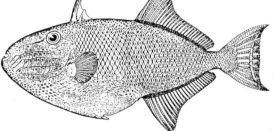

a. *Xanthichthys caeruleolineatus*, ca. 219 mm, Guam   b. *Xanthichthys mento*, o, ca. 156 mm, Hawaii

Fig. 3. Micronesian species of *Xanthichthys* (b, after Jordan and Evermann, 1903).

Sufflamen chrysoptera (Bloch & Schneider, 1801)
Halfmoon triggerfish Pl. 137E,F

SL: to ca. 245 mm (9.7 in); D III+26-28; A 23-26; P 12-15(14); LS 41-47.

The halfmoon triggerfish inhabits shallow lagoon and seaward reefs at depths of 1 to at least 30 m. It is relatively common over open sandy to hard bottomed areas with low scattered corals, particularly the submarine terrace. It is generally solitary and territorial and feeds on a wide variety of benthic invertebrates. Juveniles are bicolored: dark brown dorsally and white ventrally. Adult coloration is quite variable; the bar running through the pectoral base can be either yellow or black, and some individuals may be largely yellowish posteriorly.

Indo-Pacific: E. Africa to Samoa, n. to s. Japan, s. to Lord Howe Is.; throughout Micronesia; replaced by the closely related *S. albicaudatus* in the Red Sea.

Sufflamen freanatus (Latreille, 1804) Pl. 138A,B
Bridle triggerfish

(*S. capistratus*)

SL: to ca. 329 mm (13.0 in); D III+27-31; A 24-28; P 14-16(15); LS 43-54.

This triggerfish inhabits seaward reefs at depths of 12 to 186 m. It prefers relatively barren areas with patches of sand and rubble below 18 m. It is the triggerfish most commonly caught by bottomfishing between 30 and 150 m. Juveniles are sand-colored with numerous thin black pinstripes and may occasionally occur in as little as 8 m. Its diet includes echinoids, fishes (including moray eels), bivalves, gastropods, tunicates, brittle stars, crustaceans, algae, polychaete worms, foraminiferans, and detritus.

Indo-Pacific: E. Africa to the Hawaiian, Marquesan, and Tuamotu Is., n. to s. Japan, s. to Lord Howe Is.; throughout Micronesia.

Xanthichthys auromarginatus (Bennett, 1831)
Bluechin triggerfish (♂); **Guilded triggerfish**

SL: to 156 mm (6.1 in); D III+27-30; A   Pl. 138C,D
25-27; P 13-15; LS 42-47; depth 2.45-2.68.

Most species of *Xanthichthys* are sexually dimorphic. In this species, females lack the blue chin of males. The bluechin triggerfish inhabits the upper margins of current-swept

seaward dropoffs and ledges at depths of 8 to 147 m, but is rarely seen in less than 24 m. Like other members of its genus, it occurs in loose aggregations a few meters above the bottom where it feeds on zooplankton, particularly copepods.

Indo-Pacific: Mascarene Is. to the Hawaiian Is., n. to the Ryukyus, s. to Cocos Keeling Atoll and New Caledonia; throughout Micronesia.

Xanthichthys careuleolineatus
Randall, Matsuura, & Zama, 1978   Fig. 3a
Bluelined triggerfish

SL: to 327 mm (12.9 in); D III+26-28; A 23-25; P 14; LS 40-48; depth 2.70-3.20.

This species of *Xanthichthys* is not sexually dimorphic. It inhabits deep seaward reefs, usually at depths of 75 to 200 m or more, but one collection outside Micronesia was made at 15 m. It is occasionally caught by bottomfishing.

Indo-Pacific: St. Brandon's Shoals (w. Indian Ocean), Sumatra, Ryukyu, Izu, Mariana, Marshall, Marcus, Ocean, Samoan, Baker, Marquesan, Society, and Tuamotu Is.; Mariana and Marshall Is. in Micronesia.

Xanthichthys mento (Jordan & Gilbert, 1882)
Crosshatch triggerfish Fig. 3b

SL: to 240 mm (9.4 in); D III+29-32; A 26-29; P 13-15 (14); LS 41-50; depth 2.84-3.43.

Males of this spectacular triggerfish are straw-yellow with each scale outlined in black, creating a crosshatched appearance, and have a red tail with a neon submarginal blue band. Females are also croosshatched, but with a slate gray to blue ground color and tail. The crosshatch triggerfish is known from Micronesia only from the upper leeward dropoff of Wake Island, but may be expected to occur off some of the northernmost Marianas and associated banks. Elsewhere, it typically is common around small isolated subtropical oceanic islands rather than coastlines of larger islands or continents.

Pan-Pacific: primarily antitropical; s. Japan and the Ryukyu, Izu, Marcus, Wake, Hawaiian, Revillagigedo, and Clipperton Is., and s. California in the north; Pitcairn and Easter Is. in the south.

MONACANTHIDAE (FILEFISHES; LEATHERJACKETS)

Filefishes are closely related to the triggerfishes. They differ by having more compressed bodies, a longer and thinner first dorsal spine (sometimes adorned with spikes), much smaller or no second and no third dorsal spine (Fig. 1), somewhat smaller and fewer teeth (six on the outer row and four on the inner row), and much smaller non-overlapping scales, each with setae that give the skin a coarse file-like texture. Most species have a brushlike patch of elongate setae in front of the caudal peduncle which are usually better developed or even hooked in males (Fig. 2). Unlike the triggerfishes most species are able to change their color to closely match their surroundings and are relatively secretive. The species whose reproductive behavior is known lay demersal eggs that may be guarded by at least one of the parents. At least 17 species occur in Micronesia. Pectoral counts include the very short upper rudimentary ray. (Lit.: Hutchins, 1986; Hutchins and Randall, 1982; Hutchins and Swainston, 1985)

Fig. 1. First dorsal fin of a filefish.

Acreichthys tomentosus (Linnaeus, 1758) Fig. 3a
Seagrass filefish
SL: to 8 cm (3.1 in); D 27-30; A 26-29; P 10-13.
This small nondescript filefish inhabits sand and seagrass bottoms of protected lagoon reefs. It is known only from Belau in Micronesia.
Indo-west-Pacific: E. Africa to Fiji, n. to the Ryukyus, s. to New South Wales; Belau in Micronesia.

Aluterus monoceros (Linnaeus, 1758) Fig. 3b
Unicorn filefish
SL: to 500 mm (19.7 in); D II+45-52; A 47-53; P 15; snout convex in adults.
This species is known from Micronesia on the basis of a specimen collected off the northern Marianas. Although circumtropical in distribution, it does not seem to be particularly common on coral reefs.
Circumtropical: n. to s. Japan, s. to n. New Zealand; n. Marianas in Micronesia.

Aluterus scriptus (Osbeck, 1765) Pl. 138E
Scribbled filefish
SL: to ca. 71 cm (28 in); Wt.: to ≥2.5 kg (5.5 lb); D II+43-50; A 46-52; P 14-16; snout prominently concave.
This large and bizarre filefish inhabits lagoon and seaward reefs at depths of 2 to at least 80 m. Juveniles and occasionally adults may occur in the open sea around drifting objects. It is generally solitary and rare throughout Micronesia. It feeds on a wide variety of sessile marine organisms including algae, seagrasses, hydrozoans, gorgonians, colonial anemones, and tunicates.
Circumtropical: n. to s. Japan, s. to the s. Great Barrier Reef, New Caledonia, and Tuamotus; throughout Micronesia.

Amanses scopas (Cuvier, 1829) Pl. 138F; Fig. 2
Broom filefish
SL: to 20cmtl; D II+26-29; A 22-25; P 14; os with a group of 5-6 long spines posteriorly, os with a toothbrush-like mass of setae.
Males of this filefish have numerous long spines in front of the caudal peduncle and females have a toothbrush-like mass of setae. The broom filefish inhabits areas of mixed sand, rubble, and coral heads on semi-protected seaward reefs at depths of 3 to over 18 m. It is relatively uncommon throughout Micronesia. At Guam, it can generally be encountered in the deeper holes on the landward side of Double Reef.
Indo-Pacific: Red Sea to the Society and Tuamotu Is., s. to the s. Great Barrier Reef; throughout Micronesia.

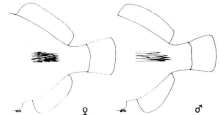

Fig. 2. Caudal peduncle of *Amanses scopas.*

Brachaluteres taylori Woods, 1966 Fig. 3c
Taylor's inflator filefish
SL: to 48 mm (1.9 in); D II+27-29(27-28); A 23-27(≤25); P 11-13(≤12); depth 1.1-1.3.
Members of this genus are unique among filefishes for their ability to greatly inflate their abdomens in the same manner as puffers. This small species is known from Micronesia on the basis of a 14 mm post-larval specimen collected from Rongelap Lagoon. In life, adults of this species are yellowish green with numerous thin dark brown lines and spots on the head and body. Three other species, also with restricted distributions, are known from the Red Sea, southern Australia, and Japan, respectively.
Tropical w. Pacific: Queensland, Lord Howe Is., Papua New Guinea, and the Marshall Is.

Cantherhines dumerilii (Hollard, 1854) Pl. 139A
Barred filefish

(*Amanses carolae*)

SL: to ca. 314 mm (12.4 in); D II+34-39; A 28-35; P 15-(16); 2 pairs spines on C ped.

This large, stocky filefish inhabits clear lagoon and seaward reefs at depths of 1 to 35 m. It is not particularly common, but is conspicuous. It often occurs as pairs that swim well above the bottom, sometimes in a curious tilted posture. It is most common on shallow clear reefs supporting an abundance of branching corals. It feeds primarily on the tips of branching corals (including *Acropora*, *Pocillopora*, *Porites*, and *Heliopora*) as well as on smaller quantities of a wide variety of organisms including sea urchins, mollusks, bryozoans, sponges, and algae. It is sexually dimorphic with males having longer and deeper orange peduncular spines and a deeper orange tail. Juveniles and subadults have diffuse white spots scattered on the head and body. Adults generally have several dusky bars in the middle of their sides posteriorly.

Indo-pan-Pacific: E. Africa to the Sea of Cortez, n. to s. Japan, s. to Lord Howe, Rapa, and Ducie Is.; throughout Micronesia.

Cantherhines fronticinctus
(Playfair & Günther, 1867)   Fig. 3d
Specktacled filefish

SL: to 187 mm (7.4 in); D II+33-36; A 31-32; P 13-15(13-14); C long (2.2-2.4 times least peduncle depth), peduncle without spines.

This brown filefish sometimes resembles the mottled color phase of *C. pardalis*. It most often has a pattern of about four broad dusky bands converging posteriorly and has a longer tail. It inhabits seaward reefs from the intertidal to a depth of 43 m. It is generally uncommon throughout its range, and rare in Micronesia. At Guam, it has been observed at a depth of 24 m inside the Blue Hole off Orote Peninsula.

Indo-west-Pacific: E. Africa to Papua New Guinea, n. s. Japan, s. to nw. Australia; Guam and Kwajalein in Micronesia; closely related to *longicaudus* from the Society and s. Cook Is., *verecundus* from the Hawaiian Is., and *rapanui* from Easter Is.

Cantherhines pardalis (Rüppell, 1837)   Pl. 139B
Wire-net filefish

SL: to 206 mm (8.1 in); D II+32-36; A 29-32; P 13-15(14); C short (1.6-2.0 times least peduncle depth), peduncle without spines.

(*Amanses sandwichiensis*Woods, 1966)

This species can adopt three basic color patterns: mottled grey and brown, dark brown, or grey with a network of close-set polygonal spots (as shown); all three have a small white spot at the rear base of the second dorsal and sometimes the anal fin. It inhabits clear seaward reefs at depths of 2 to at least 20 m. It occurs in areas of rich coral growth as well as barren surge-swept rocks. It is solitary and moderately common, but seldom noticed due to its wary and somewhat secretive nature.

Indo-Pacific: Red Sea to the Marquesan and Ducie Is., n. to s. Japan, s. to Lord Howe and Rapa Is.; Marianas and Mar-

shalls in Micronesia; replaced by *C. sandwichiensis* in the Hawaiian Is.

Oxymonacanthus longirostris
(Bloch & Schneider, 1801)   Pl. 139C
Longnose filefish

SL: to 102 mm (4.0 in); D II+31-35; A 29-32; P 11-13; V rudiment absent; bristlles on C ped of o longer than others on body.

This spectacular little filefish inhabits clear lagoon and seaward reefs at depths of 0.5 to at least 30 m. It feeds exclusively on the polyps of *Acropora* corals and is common wherever these corals abound and the surge is not too great. It uses its pointed snout to snip the polyps from their cuplike skeletal calices. It often occurs in pairs or small groups and nests near the dead bases of corals, often on a small clump of algae.

Indo-Pacific: E. Africa to Samoa, n. to the Ryukyus, s. to the s. Great Barrier Reef, New Caledonia, and Tonga; throughout Micronesia; replaced by the closely related *O. halli* in the Red Sea.

Paraluteres prionurus (Bleeker, 1851)   Pl. 139D
Blacksaddle mimic

SL: to ca. 8 cm (3.1 in); D II+25-28, membrane of 1st nearly reaching 2nd; A 22-25; P 11-12; V rudiment and ventral flap absent; C ped. of o with 2 pairs of recurved spines on ea. side.

This colorful filefish inhabits clear lagoon and seaward reefs at depths of 2 to at least 25 m. It is a remarkable mimic of the poisonous puffer, *Canthigaster valentini* (p. 269) which it greatly resembles. This is a classic example of Batesian mimicry in which a relatively uncommon harmless species mimics a generally more common toxic or noxious species. Potential predators can't distinguish one from another and avoid both. Close examination reveals that the filefish has broad based second dorsal and anal fins while the puffer has short based ones and lacks the first dorsal fin entirely.

Indo-Pacific: E. Africa to the Marshalls, n. to s. Japan, s. to the s. Great Barrier Reef and New Caledonia; throughout Micronesia; replaced by the closely related *P arquat* in the Red Sea.

Paramonacanthus cryptodon (Bleeker, 1855)

SL: to ca. 7 cm (2.8 in);D I+26; A 26; P 10-11; depth 1.5-2.3.

This species is known from Micronesia on the basis of two immature specimens (39.5 and 26 mm) dredged from depths of 36 and 51 m in Rongelap and Bikini lagoons, respectively. In Micronesia, adults of *Paramonacanthus* most likely inhabit depths of over 50 m.

Tropical w. Pacific: Thailand to Sulawesi, n. to the Philippines; Marshalls in Micronesia.

Paramonacanthus japonicus (Tilesius, 1801)
(*P. oblongus*)   Fig. 3e

SL: to 11 cm (4.3 in); D II+24-30; A 24-30; P 11-14; depth 1.9-2.4 (female), 2.5-3.5 (male).

This species is known from Micronesia on the basis of two

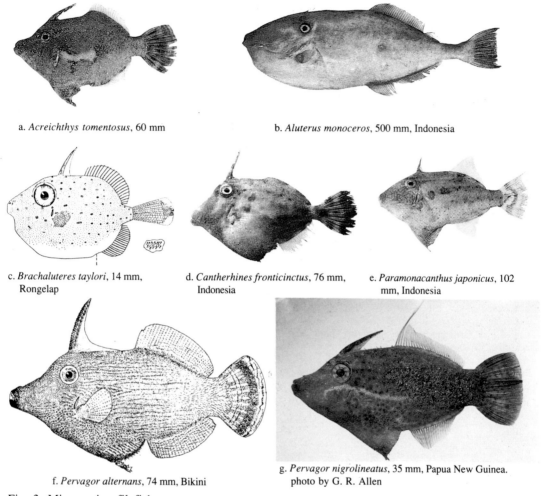

a. *Acreichthys tomentosus*, 60 mm

b. *Aluterus monoceros*, 500 mm, Indonesia

c. *Brachaluteres taylori*, 14 mm, Rongelap

d. *Cantherhines fronticinctus*, 76 mm, Indonesia

e. *Paramonacanthus japonicus*, 102 mm, Indonesia

f. *Pervagor alternans*, 74 mm, Bikini

g. *Pervagor nigrolineatus*, 35 mm, Papua New Guinea. photo by G. R. Allen

Fig. 3. Micronesian filefishes (a, b, d, e, after Gloerfelt-Tarp and Kailola, 1984; c, f, after Woods *in* Schultz et al., 1966).

immature specimens (27.5 and 36 mm) dredged from a depth of 36 m from Rongelap lagoon.

Indo-Pacific: Red Sea to Papua New Guinea, n. to s. Japan, s. to nw. Australia and the s. Great Barrier Reef; Marshalls in Micronesia.

Pervagor alternans (Ogilby, 1899) Fig. 1f
Yelloweye filefish
(*P. melanocephalus marshallensis*)

SL: to 147 mm (5.8 in; s. hemisphere), 82 mm (3.2 in; Marshall Is.); D II+31-34; A 27-31(28-30); P 13-14.

This species is distinguished by a bright yellow ring around the eye; it is otherwise pale pinkish-brown to dark brown with black tubercles on the scales and a mostly orange tail. It inhabits coral and rocky reefs to a depth of about 15 m.

Tropical w. Pacific: antiequatorial; s. Great Barrier Reef,

New South Wales, Lord Howe Is., New Caledonia, and Marshall Is.

Pervagor aspricaudus (Hollard, 1854) Pl. 139E
Orangetail filefish
(*P. melanocephalus johnstonensis* Woods, 1966)

SL: to 99 mm (3.9 in); DII+31-35(31-33); A 28-32(28-30); P 13-14.

This species tends to be more common on insular reefs whereas *P. janthinosoma* tends to be more common on continental reefs.

Indo-Pacific: antiequatorial; Mauritius, Christmas Is., Indian Ocean, s. Taiwan, s. Japan, Marcus Is., n. Great Barrier Reef, New Caledonia, Johnston Is., Hawaiian Is., and Marshall Is.; replaced by *P. marginalis* in the Line and Marquesan Is.

Pervagor janthinosoma (Bleeker, 1854)   Pl. 139F
Blackbar filefish
SL: to 113 mm (4.4 in); D II+29-34(29-32); A 26-30; P 11-14(13).
This species has most often been misidentified as *P. melanocephalus* by most recent authors. It inhabits shallow lagoon and seaward reefs to a depth of about 15 m. It is relatively common in areas of abundant coral cover, but is secretive and often unnoticed.
Indo-Pacific: E. Africa to Samoa, n. to s. Japan, s. to New South Wales and Tonga; Belau, Carolines, and Marianas in Micronesia.

Pervagor melanocephalus (Bleeker, 1853)
Blackheaded filefish
SL: to 88 mm (3.5 in); D II+30-33; A 27-30; P 13-14.
This species is deep orange over just about the entire poste-

rior portion of its body becoming dark brown anteriorly. It is reported to occur in slightly deeper water (to 40 m) than *P. janthosoma*.
Tropical w. Pacific: Sumatra to Fiji and Tonga, n. to the Ryukyus, s. to the s. Great Barrier Reef; Belau and Marshalls in Micronesia.

Pervagor nigrolineatus (Herre, 1927)   Fig. 3g
Blacklined filefish
SL: to 78 mm (3.1 in); D II+29-33(29-32); A 25-30(26-29); P 11-13(12-13).
This *Pervagor* is distinguished by the several rows of distinct black pinstripes on the body (ca. 10-15 vs ≥20 in other species, if present). It has been taken from shallow lagoon coral heads reefs as well as by trawls.
Indo-west-Pacific: Sumatra to the Solomon Is., n. to the Philippines, s. to Rowley Shoals; Belau in Micronesia.

OSTRACIIDAE (TRUNKFISHES)

Trunkfishes are named for the armor-like carapace of bony polygonal plates encasing the head and body (Fig. 1). This shell has small gaps for the mouth, eyes, gill openings, anus, and caudal peduncle. The surface of the plates is often rough and numerous species have angular ridges which may be armed with prominent spines. The mouth is small and low with thick lips and a single row of conical to incisiform teeth with rounded tips. Trunkfishes are slow-moving diurnal predators of a wide variety of small sessile invertebrates and algae. Those species studied to date are haremic with males defending a large territory containing non-territorial females and subordinate males. Spawning in pairs occurs at dusk, usually above a conspicuous outcrop. When under stress trunkfishes secrete a highly toxic substance (ostracitoxin) which may be lethal to other fishes or even themselves in the confines of an aquarium. When properly maintained they make safe and interesting aquarium pets. Six species in the subfamily Ostraciinae are known from Micronesia. Pectoral counts include the rudimentary upper ray. (Lit.: Randall, 1972)

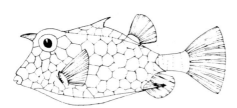

Fig. 1. A trunkfish, *Lactoria fornasini*, showing distribution of bony plates.

Fig. 2. *Lactoria diaphana* (after Jordan and Evermann, 1903).

Lactoria cornuta (Linnaeus, 1758)   Pl. 140A
Longhorn cowfish
SL: to 30 cm (11.8 in); D 8-9; A 8-9; P 10-11; C 9-10.
This large, solitary cowfish occurs over sand and rubble bottoms of subtidal reef flats, lagoons, and bays to a depth of 50 m. It feeds on polychaetes and other benthic invertebrates that it exposes by blowing away the sand. Occasionally, faster fishes such as wrasses or emperors will station themselves nearby and dash in to rob the cowfish of its meal.
Indo-Pacific: s. Red Sea to the Marquesan and Tuamotu Is., n. to s. Korea and s. Japan, s. to Lord Howe Is.; Marianas in Micronesia.

Lactoria diaphana (Bloch & Schneider, 1801)
Spiny cowfish   Fig. 2
SL: to 19 cm (7.5 in), ≤3.5 cm (1.4 in) in Micronesia; D 9; A 9; P 10-11; C 10.
This species is known from Micronesia on the basis of specimens from the stomachs of pelagic gamefishes taken from the vicinity of Guam. Some of these are ripe females as small as 20 mm, and the largest is 35 mm. Clearly this species can live its entire life pelagically. Yet off southern Japan it settles to the bottom as an adult and spawns in much the same manner as *L. fornasini*. There, as elsewhere, it reaches a much larger size.

Indo-pan-Pacific: E. Africa to Panama, n. to s. Japan, the Hawaiian Is., and s. Calif., s. to New Caledonia, Easter Is., and Peru; Marianas in Micronesia.

Lactoria fornasini (Bianconi, 1846)   Pl. 140B
Thornback cowfish

SL: ca. 19 cm (7.4 in), ≤10 cm (3.9 in) in w. Pacific; D 9; A 9; P 11-12; C 10; strong spine on middle of dorsal ridge.
This cowfish is characterized by a prominent spine in the middle of its back. It inhabits sandy areas with rubble, algae, or corals of clear outer lagoon and seaward reefs. It is quite rare in the Marianas, where the only specimens are juveniles taken from the stomachs of pelagic gamefishes and an adult has been photographed underwater. Courting males flash brilliant streaks of blue. At Miyake Island, off southern Japan, spawning occurs at dusk, at the apex of a paired ascent synchronized by a high-pitched "humming" sound emitted by the male.
Indo-Pacific: E. Africa to the Hawaiian and Rapa Is., n. to s. Japan, s. to Lord Howe Is.; Marianas and Marshalls in Micronesia; unknown throughout most of Oceania.

Ostracion cubicus Linnaeus, 1758   Pl. 140C,D
Cube trunkfish

(*O. lentiginosum*)
SL: to 312 mm (12.3 in); D 8-9; A 9; P 10-11; C 10-12.
The small juvenile stage is bright yellow with black spots. The spots become proportionately smaller and the yellow becomes a dirty mustard color with growth. Large adults become blueish with yellowish seams between the plates. The cube trunkfish is a solitary inhabitant of lagoon and semi-sheltered seaward reefs at depths of 1 to 35 m. Juveniles generally occur among the shelter of corals or rocks; adults range further out in the open, but seem to prefer areas near the shelter of ledges and crevices near sand. This species feeds on a wide variety of benthic organisms including algae, sand-dwelling polychaetes, mollusks, crustaceans, foraminiferans, and fishes.
Indo-Pacific: Red Sea to the Hawaiian (as a rare stray) and Tuamotu Is., n. to the Ryukyus, s. to Lord Howe Is.; throughout Micronesia; Red Sea population differs slightly in coloration and has been known as *O. argus*; closely related to *O. immaculatus* from s. Japan.

Ostracion meleagris meleagris Shaw, 1796
Spotted trunkfish   Pl. 140E,F

(*O. sebae* for initial phase; *O. lentiginosus* for males)
SL: to 151 mm (5.9 in); D 9; A 9; P 10-11; C 10.
This species is strongly sexually dimorphic; the colorful males are undoubtedly sex-reversed females. It is a generally solitary inhabitant of clear lagoon and seaward reefs from the lower surge zone to a depth of at least 30 m. Specimens examined from the Hawaiian Islands had fed primarily on didemnid tunicates as well as smaller quantities of polychaetes, algae, sponges, mollusks, and copepods.
Indo-pan-Pacific: E. Africa to Mexico, n. to s. Japan and the Hawaiian Is., s. to New Caledonia and the Tuamotus; throughout Micronesia; the subspecies *m. camurum* in the Hawaiian Is., and *m. clippertoneuse* in the e. Pacific; replaced by *O. cyanurus* in Red Sea and Gulf of Aden.

Ostracion solorensis Bleeker, 1856   Pl. 141A,B
Reticulate boxfish

SL: to ca. 100 mm (4.0 in); D 9; A 9; P 9.
This small trunkfish is also sexually dimorphic. At Belau, it is a relatively uncommon inhabitant of coral-rich areas of seaward reefs. It has been reported from depths of 1 to 20 m.
Indo-Australian: Christmas Is., Philippines, Moluccas, Papua New Guinea, and Belau.

Rhynchostracion nasus (Bloch, 1785)   Fig. 3a
Smallnose boxfish

SL: to >278 mm (10.9 in); D 9; A 9; P 10.
This trunkfish has a small protuberance above the mouth and a distinctly concave snout profile. It has been reported from depths of 2 to 80 m around rocky and sandy substrates. It is known from Belau and Truk on the basis of some old literature records which should be verified.
Indo-Australian: Sumatra to Fiji, n. to the Philippines; Belau and Truk in Micronesia.

Rhynchostracion rhynorhynchus (Bleeker, 1852)
Largenose boxfish   Fig. 3b

SL: to ca. 23 cm (9 in);
This trunkfish has a large protuberance on the snout, giving it a highly convex profile. A single individual has been observed by the author along the edge of a steep dropoff in the Ngemelis area of Belau.
Indo-west-Pacific: E. Africa to the Moluccas and n. Australia, n. to the Philippines.

a. *R. nasus*   b. *R. rhynorhynchus*

Fig. 3. Species of *Rhynchostracion* (after Gloerfelt-Tarp and Kailola, 1984).

TETRAODONTIDAE (PUFFERS)

The puffers are named for their ability to greatly inflate themselves by drawing water into a specialized chamber near the stomach. The resulting prickly spherical ball deters many predators. They have a tough, highly flexible scaleless and often prickly skin, beak like dental plates with a median suture, a single posterior dorsal fin, and lack fin spines, pelvic fins, or ribs. The lateral line is inconspicuous or absent. Puffers are well-known for harboring one of nature's most powerful toxins, tetrodontoxin. The viscera, gonads, and skin are usually the most toxic portions. The flesh is often safe, and in some areas is considered a delicacy, but occasionally it may be toxic and has been responsible for the death of many a gourmet! Toxicity varies greatly with species, area, and season. This toxicity does not always seem to affect predatory fishes, though. Species of *Canthigaster* have a repellent skin secretion that deters predation. All species known to date lay demersal eggs. At least one species of *Canthigaster* is haremic. Puffers inhabit all tropical and temperate seas; a few have invaded estuarine and fresh waters. At least 17 species in 2 subfamilies and 4 genera occur in Micronesia. Additional genera and species may be expected to occur at depths exceeding 50 m. Not included below is the pelagic *Lagocephalus lagocephalus*. (Lit.: Allen & Randall, 1977; Lubbock & Allen, 1979; Matsuura & Toda, 1981; Randall, 1985)

Fig. 1. Tetraodontid
    dentition.

Subfamily Tetraodontinae (puffers): characterized by a relativley short snout (1.8-3.1 in head), two pairs of nostrils on either side of the snout, and a large size (to ≥23 cm).

Amblyrhinchotus honckenii (Bloch, 1785)   Fig. 1
Evileye puffer
SL: to ca. 244 mm (9.6 in); D 9-10; A 8; P 14-16; nasal organs covered by a sack with 2 nostrils.
This puffer differs from species of *Arothron* by having a more elongate body, a somewhat upturned mouth situated closer to the top than the bottom of the head, and both nostrils encased in a sack-like cover. In Micronesia, it has been reported only from Arno Atoll. Elsewhere it has been collected from the intertidal zone to a depth of 400 m. It is reputed to be extremely toxic.
Indo-west-Pacific: E. Africa to China; Arno in Micronesia.

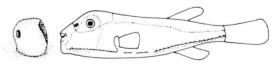

Fig. 1. *Amblyrhinchotes honckenii*, showing nostril at left.

Arothron hispidus (Linnaeus, 1758)   Pl. 141D
Whitespotted puffer
SL: to 45 cm (17.7 in); D 10-11; A 10-11; P 17-19.
Species of *Arothron* are solitary and slow moving. They are often encountered resting on the bottom during the day as well as at night. This species occurs in a wide range of habitats from estuaries and inner reef flats and lagoons to a depth of at least 50 m on outer reef slopes. It tends to be more common in sandy to rubbly areas than in coral-rich areas. It feeds during both the day and night on a wide range of marine organisms including fleshy, calcareous, or coralline algae, and detritus, mollusks, tunicates, sponges, corals,

zoanthid anemones, crabs, hermit crabs, tube worms, sea urchins, brittle stars, starfishes (including the crown-of-thorns, *Acanthaster*), and hydroids.
Indo-pan-Pacific: Red Sea to Panama, n. to s. Japan and the Hawaiian Is., s. to Lord Howe and Rapa Is.; throughout Micronesia; the Red Sea population is characterized by smaller and more numerous white spots.

Arothron manilensis (Procé, 1822)   Pl. 141C
Narrow-lined puffer
SL: to 228 mm (9.0 in); D 9-11(10); A 9-(10); P 16-19; GR 6-8.
This puffer inhabits estuaries, sheltered reef flats, and lagoons to a depth of at least 17 m. It is relatively common in seagrass beds and sandy areas, and penetrates brackish waters. Juveniles occur among mangroves.
Tropical w. Pacific: Borneo, Philippines, and nw. Australia to Samoa (possibly in the Society Is. or represented by a different species there), n. to the Ryukyus, s. to New South Wales and Tonga; throughout Micronesia; closely related to the non-striped *A. immaculatus* from the Philippines and Ryukyus to the Red Sea.

Arothron mappa (Lesson, 1826)   Pl. 142A
Map puffer
SL: to 540 mm (21.3 in); D 11-12; A 11; P 18-19.
This intricately patterned puffer is an uncommon inhabitant of shallow lagoons. Two specimens from Arno Atoll had their stomachs crammed with chunks of sponge and smaller amounts of fragmented tunicates, gastropods, crabs, coralline algae, the calcareous algae *Halimeda*, and bubble algae *Valonia*.
Indo-Pacific: E. Africa to Samoa, n. to the Ryukyus and w. sea of Japan, s. to Queensland and New Caledonia; Belau, Guam, and s. Marshalls in Micronesia.

Arothron meleagris (Lacepède, 1798)   Pl. 141E,F
Guineafowl puffer
SL: to 40 cm (15.7 in); D 10-12; A 11-13; P 16-19.
This conspicuously spotted puffer has as a bright yellow phase in which the spots may be partially to completely ob-

scured. It inhabits coral-rich areas of clear lagoon and seaward reefs to a depth of over 14 m. It feeds primarily on the tips of branching corals as well as to a lesser extent on sponges, mollusks, bryozoans, tunicates, foraminfera, algae, and detritus. It is relatively uncommon and usually secludes itself under overhanging corals.

Indo-pan-Pacific: E. Africa to Panama, n. to the Ryukyus, s. to Lord Howe and Easter Is.; throughout Micronesia.

Arothron nigropunctatus (Bloch &Schneider,1801)
Blackspotted puffer   Pl. 142B,C,D
(*A. citrinellus*)

SL: to ca. 27 cm (10.7 in); D 10-11; A 10-12; P 17-19.

This is the most common species of *Arothron* of outer reef flats and clear lagoon and seaward reefs, wherever there is an abundance of live corals. It feeds primarily on corals, usually *Acropora* tips, but also preys on crustaceans and mollusks. This species has three basic color phases, one of which is primarily yellow, like that of *A. meleagris*, but with larger and more widely scattered black spots.

Indo-Pacific: E. Africa to the Line Is., n. to the Ryukyus, s. to New South Wales and New Caledonia; throughout Micronesia; replaced by *A. diadematus* in the Red Sea.

Arothron stellatus (Bloch & Schneider, 1801)
Star puffer   Pl. 142E,F
(*A. alboreticulatus*; *A. aerostaticus*)

SL: to > 84 cm (33.0 in); D 10-12; A 10-11; P 17-19.

This is truly the giant among puffers, reaching a total length well in excess of a meter! It is a relativley uncommon inhabitant of patch reefs and coral slopes near sandy areas of clear lagoon and seaward reefs. Juveniles may occur on reef flats; adults are known from depths of 3 to 58 m. One specimen from Enewetak had fed entirely on the starfish *Linkia guildingi*.

Indo-Pacific: Red Sea to the Tuamotus, n. to s. Japan, s. to Lord Howe Is.; throughout Micronesia.

Subfamily Canthigasterinae (Sharpnose puffers or Tobies): characterized by an elongate pointed snout (1.3-1.8 in head), a single nostril on each side of the snout, and relatively small size (usually ≤11 cm).

Canthigaster amboinensis (Bleeker, 1865) Pl. 143A
Ambon sharpnose puffer
(*C. natalensis*)

SL: to 107 mm (4.2 in); D 10-(12); A 10-(11); P 16-(17).

This is Micronesia's largest and fastest-swimming *Canthigaster*. It occurs almost exclusively in the surge zone and upper submarine terrace of seaward reefs. Juveniles are highly secretive and remain in holes of the outer reef flat and reef margin. This species is usually solitary and covers a large area during its feeding forays. It feeds primarily on coralline red algae, and to a lesser extent on corals, filamentous green and red algae, and invertebrates including mollusks, brittle stars, tunicates, foraminiferans, and polychaetes.

Indo-pan-Pacific: E. Africa to the Galapagos Is., n. to s. Japan and the Hawaiian Is., s. to Queensland and the Society Is.; throughout Micronesia.

Canthigaster bennetti (Bleeker, 1854)   Pl. 143B
Bennett's sharpnose puffer
SL: to 75 mm (3.0 in); D 9-11(≤10); A 8-10(9); P 14-(15).

Bennett's sharpnose puffer occurs primarily in inner reef flats and sheltered lagoons, but may rarely occur to a depth of 10 m on seaward reefs. It feeds primarily on filamentous green algae and to a lesser extent on fleshy and coralline red algae, and a wide variety on benthic invertebrates.

Indo-Pacific: E. Africa to the Tuamotus, n. to s. Taiwan, s. to New South Wales; throughout Micronesia.

Canthigaster compressa (Procé, 1822)   Pl. 143C
Fingerprint sharpnose puffer
SL: to 87 mm (3.4 in); D 8-10(9); A 8-9(9); P 15-18.

This intricately patterned *Canthigaster* is a rare inhabitant of clear sand-bottomed channels and lagoons to a depth of 16 m. It is known from Guam on the basis of the photograph herein.

Indo-Australian: Philippines to the Solomon Is. (possibly to Fiji), n. to the Ryukyus, s. to Vanuatu; Belau and Guam in Micronesia.

Canthigaster coronata (Vaillant & Sauvage, 1875)
Crowned sharpnose puffer   Pl. 143D
(*C. cinctus*)

SL: to 103 mm (4.1 in); D 9-(10); A (9)-10; P 16-(17).

The crowned sharpnose puffer inhabits sand and rubble areas of clear seaward reefs at depths of 11 to at least 79 m. It is rare throughout Micronesia. It feeds on a wide variety of benthic organisms including mollusks, sponges, algae, polychaetes, sea and heart urchins, brittle stars, tunicates, crustaceans, foraminiferans, and bryozoans.

Indo-Pacific: Red Sea to the Hawaiian Is., n. to s. Japan, s. to New South Wales; throughout Micronesia; absent from French Polynesia.

Canthigaster epilampra (Jenkins, 1903)   Pl. 143E
SL: to 91 mm (3.6 in); D 10; A 9; P 16-18(17).

This colorful *Canthigaster* inhabits steep outer reef slopes at depths of 9 to over 36 m, but is rare in less than 20 m. It is not uncommon along dropoffs and in the vicinity of caves and is usually solitary or paired. It feeds on a wide variety of small benthic invertebrates, primarily molluscs, echinoderms, and brachiopods, and occasionally on filamentous algae.

Tropical w. Pacific: Christmas Is., Indian Ocean, to the Hawaiian and Society Is., n. to s. Taiwan, s. to the Loyalty Is., Tonga, and Rarotonga; throughout Micronesia; closely related to *rapaensis* from Rapa and *marquesensis* from the Marquesas.

Canthigaster janthinoptera (Bleeker, 1855)
(*C. jactator* Woods, 1966)   Pl. 143F

SL: to 62 mm (2.4 in); D (9)-10; A (9)-10; P 16-18(17).

This small secretive *Canthigaster* inhabits clear lagoon and seaward reefs at depths of 1 to 30 m. It is generally uncommon and prefers areas of considerable shelter in the form of holes in dead and living corals. It is solitary or paired and feeds on a wide variety of organisms, primarily fleshy and filamentous algae, sponges, and polychaetes, as well as smaller quantities of tunicates, crustaceans, echinoderms, and corals.

Indo-Pacific: E. Africa to the Line, Marquesan, and Oeno Is., n. to s. Japan, s. to Lord Howe Is.; throughout Micronesia; replaced by *jactator* in the Hawaiian Is. and *punctatissimus* in the tropical e. Pacific.

Canthigaster leoparda Lubbock & Allen, 1979
Leopard sharpnose puffer   Pl. 144A
SL: to 56 mm (2.2 in); D 8-9; A 9; P 16.
This beautiful little *Canthigaster* is a rarely encountered inhabitant of caves of steep dropoffs at depths of 30 to 50 m.
Indo-Australian: Christmas Is. (Indian Ocean), Philippines, Ambon, and Guam.

Canthigaster solandri (Richardson, 1844)
Spotted sharpnose puffer   Pl. 144B,C
SL: to 85 mm (3.3 in); D 8-10(9); A 8-10(9); P 15-18(17).
This is by far the most common and ubiquitous sharpnose puffer. It ranges from the inner intertidal reef flat to a depth of at least 36 m on lagoon and seaward reefs and occurs over relatively open barren areas as well as among corals or under ledges. In the Marianas and Marshalls, juveniles are abundant on reef flats and in sheltered channels and harbors, while adults are generally confined to subtidal lagoon and seaward reefs. Elsewhere in Micronesia, it as well as other species of *Canthigaster* are relatively uncommon. It is frequently encountered in pairs, and occasionally in small groups. Aggression occasionally occurs in which antagonists face-off and raise a prominent ridge of skin along the midline of the back and belly. This may culminate in biting. *C. solandri* feeds primarily on filamentous green and red algae and coralline red algae, and to a lesser extent on corals and benthic invertebrates including tunicates, mollusks, echinoderms, polychaetes, crustaceans, and bryozoans. The geographically distinct Indo-Australian *papua* color form occurs at Belau and throughout the Indo-Australian region.
Indo-Pacific: E. Africa to the Line, and Tuamotu Is., n. to the Ryukyus, s. to New Caledonia and Tonga; throughout Micronesia; strays to the Hawaiian Is.; the population from the Philippines, Indonesia, New Guinea, Queensland, and Belau differs in coloration (formerly *C. papua*); replaced by *C. margaritata* in the Red Sea.

Canthigaster valentini (Bleeker, 1853)   Pl. 144D
Valentinni's sharpnose puffer
SL: to 80 mm (3.1 in); D 9: A 9; P (16)-17.
This is perhaps the second most common *Canthigaster* throughout most of Micronesia. It occurs among coral heads and rocks of subtidal lagoon and seaward reefs to a depth of at least 55 m. It feeds primarily on filamentous green and red aglae and tunicates as well as on smaller amounts of corals, bryozoans, polychaetes, echinoderms, mollusks, and brown and coralline red algae. A recent study at the Great Barrier Reef has demonstrated that this species is haremic with males controlling a territory containing from one to 7 females. Males spawn at mid-morning, with a different female each day. The eggs are laid in a tuft of algae

chosen by the female. *C. valentini* is mimicked by the non-toxic filefish, *Paraluteres prionurus*.
Indo-Pacific: Red Sea to the Tuamotus, n. to s. Japan, s. to Lord Howe Is.; throughout Micronesia.

DIODONTIDAE (PORCUPINEFISHES)

Porcupinefishes are very similar to the puffers, differing primarily in having prominent spines over the head and body. They also have larger eyes, broader pectoral fins, lack a median suture on the dental plates, and have an inconspicuous lateral line. The spines, actually highly modified scales, are either three-rooted and rigid (burrfishes, *Chilomycterus* and *Cyclichthys*), two-rooted and movable (*Diodon*), or a combination of the two (*Lophodiodon* and *Dicotolichthys*). The spines of *Diodon* normally lie backwards against the body, but stand erect when the fish inflates itself. A large inflated *Diodon* is as hard and round as a basketball, and with 5 to 7 cm spines covering nearly its entire surface, is an impenetrable fortress capable of choking a large shark to death. The hard beak-like jaws are well-suited for crushing the hard shells of mollusks or crustaceans, or tests of sea urchins. Spawning has been observed in one species, *Diodon holacanthus*. It spawns at the surface, either at dawn or dusk, as pairs or by groups of males with a single female. Three species of *Diodon* are known from Micronesia. One (*Diodon eydouxii*) is entirely pelagic, and the others are pelagic as juveniles. Pectoral counts exclude the rudimentary upper ray which is usually imbedded in adults. (Lit.: Leis, 1977)

Diodon hystrix Linnaeus, 1758   Pl. 144E
Porcupinefish
SL: to ca. 79 cm (31.0 in), pelagic stage to 17 cm(6.8 in); 14-17(15-16); A 14-16(≥ 15); P 21-25(22-24); spines long; D and A rounded.
The porcupinefish inhabits lagoon and seaward reefs to a depth of at least 50 m. It is not particularly common, and during the day is generally found resting under ledges or hovering high in the water. At night, it forages for hard shelled invertebrates, primarily sea urchins, gastropods, and hermit crabs. Pelagic juveniles are preyed upon by mahimahi, tuna, and billfishes; adults are preyed upon by tiger sharks.
Circumtropical: n. to s. Japan, the Hawaiian Is., and s. California, s. to Lord Howe and Easter Is.

Diodon liturosus Shaw, 1804   Pl. 144F
Shortspine porcupinefish
SL: to ca. 55 cm (21.6 in), pelagic stage to 8 cm (3.1 in); D 14-16(≥ 15); A 14-16(≤ 15); P 21-25(22-24); spines short.
This blotched porcupinefish differs from *D. hystrix* by its somewhat shorter spines, particularly those on the top of the head, as well as by color. It also rests in caves or under ledges during the day and forages at night.
Indo-Pacific: E. Africa to the Society Is., n. to s. Japan, s. to New South Wales; Belau, Kapingamarangi, and Kwajalein in Micronesia.

Suggested Further Reading

A complete bibliography is given on p. 282. Most of the works listed there are technical in nature, out of print, or can only be found in a good university library. A few of the more important popular and scientific works that are broad in scope, reasonably up-to-date, and, in most cases, still obtainable, are listed below. Books are shown in boldface.

Coral reefs

Reader's Digest Book of the Great Barrier Reef. F. H. Talbot (sci. consult.) and R. C. Steene (maj. photog.), 1984. Reader's Digest, Sydney, 384 p., 800+ col. pl.

Identification of Indo-Pacific fishes: regional works

Hawaiian Reef Fishes. J. E. Randall, 1985. Harrowood, Newton Square, PA, 79 p. + 177 col. pl.
Fishes of the Japan Archipelago. H. Masuda et. al., 1984. Tokai Univ. Press, Tokyo, 437 p +370 pls with 3,700 color ill.
Red Sea Reef Fishes. J. E. Randall, 1983. IMMEL, London, 192 p., 465 col. pl.
Smith's Sea Fishes. M. M. Smith and P. C. Heemstra, eds. 1986. Macmillan South Africa, Johanesburg, 1,047 p.+ 144 pl. with over 2,000 col. ill.
Reef fishes of the Indian Ocean. (Pacific marine fishes book 10). G.R. Allen and R. C. Steene, 1987. T.F.H., New Jersey, 240 p.
Trawled Fishes of southern Indonesia and northwestern Australia. T. Gloerfelt-Tarp and P. J. Kailola, 1984.

Systematic works on Indo-Pacific fishes

Sharks of Polynesia. R. H. Johnson, 1978. Les Éditions du Pacifique, Papeete, 170 p.
Sharks of Arabia. J. E. Randall, 1986. IMMEL, London.
Indo-Pacific Pipefishes. C. E. Dawson, 1985. Gulf Coast Res. Lab., Ocean Springs, MS, 230 p.
Butterfly and Angelfishes of the World, vol. 1: Australia. R. C. Steene, 1978. A.H. and A.W. Reed, Sydney, 144 p.
Butterfly and Angelfishes of the World, vol. 2 (remainder of species not incl. in v. 1). G. R. Allen, 1979. Wiley Interscience, 352 p.
Butterflyfishes of the World. W. E. Burgess, 1978. T.F.H., New Jersey, 832 p.
Anemonefishes. G. R. Allen, 1972. T.F.H., New Jersey, 288 p.

Damselfishes of the South Seas. G. R. Allen, 1975. T.F.H., New Jersey, 240 p.

Biogeography

Pacific plate biogeography, with special reference to shorefishes. V. G. Springer, 1982. Smithson. Contr. Zool., 376, iii+182 p.

Biology and behavior of reef fishes

Words of the Lagoon. R. E. Johannes, 1981. Univ. Calif. Press, Berkeley, 320 p.
Ecological relationships of the fish fauna on coral reefs of the Marshall Islands. R. W. Hiatt and D. W. Strasburg, 1960. Ecol. Monogr. 30(1): 65-127.
Feeding relationships of teleostean fishes on coral reefs in Kona, Hawaii. E. S. Hobson, 1974. Fishery Bull. 72(4): 915-1031.
Activity of Hawaiian reef fishes during the evening and morning transitions between daylight and darkness. E. S. Hobson, 1972. Fishery Bull. 70: 714-740.
Examples of mimicry and protective resemblance in tropical marine fishes. J. E. and H. A. Randall, 1960. Bull. Mar. Sci. Gulf Caribb. 10(4): 444-480.
New cases of mimicry in marine fishes. B. C. Russell et al., 1976. J. Zool., London, 180: 407-423.
The ecology of fishes on coral reefs. P. F. Sale, 1980. Ann. Rev. Oceanog. Mar. Biol., 18: 367-421.
Reproduction in Reef Fishes. R. E. Thresher. 1984. T.F.H., New Jersey, 399 p.

Dangerous marine life

Poisonous and Venomous Marine Animals of the World. B. W. Halstead, 1978. U.S. Govt. Printing Office.
A survey of ciguatera at Enewetak and Bikini, Marshall Islands, with notes on the systematics and food habits of ciguatoxic fishes. J. E. Randall, 1980. Fishery Bull. 78(2): 201-249.

Fishing

Fishing on Guam, Guide to the Coastal Resources of Guam: Vol. 3. S. S. Amesbury et al., 1986. Univ. Guam Press, Guam, 110 p.
Words of the Lagoon. R. E. Johannes, 1981. Univ. Calif. Press, Berkeley, 320 p.

Indo-Pacific Fishes:

A journal devoted solely to the revision of genera and higher categories of Indo-Pacific Fishes. Each issue features excellent color photographs and range maps for most species. The journal is highly recommended for anyone with an interest in fishes. It is available from the Bishop Museum Press, P.O. Box 19000-A, Honolulu, HI 96817-0916 (checks payable to Bishop Museum Press). A standing order with a 20% discount is available by subscription. The following have been published and are still available:

Price	No.	Title, author, etc.
$6.90	1	Revision of the gobiid genus *Stonogobiops*. D.F. Hoese and J. E. Randall, 1982. 18p, 9 col. figs.
$7.25	2	Revision of the Indo-Pacific labrid fish genus *Suezichthys*, with descriptions of four new species. B. C. Russell, 1985. 21 p, 11 col. figs.
$8.75	3	A review of the pomacentrid fishes of the genus *Stegastes* from the Indo-Pacific, with descriptions of two new species. G. R. Allen and A. R. Emery, 1985. 31 p, 24 col. figs.
$11.00	4	Revision of the gobiid fish genus *Istigobius*. E. O. Murdy and D. F. Hoese, 1985. 41p, 14 col. figs.
$9.00	5	A revision of the Indo-Pacific parrotfish genera *Calotomus* and *Leptoscarus* (Scaridae: Sparisomatinae). R. W. Bruce and J. E. Randall, 1985. 32 p, 10 col. figs.
$7.25	6	Revision of the Indo-Pacific apogonid fish genus *Pseudamia*, with descriptions of three new species. J. E. Randall, E. A. Lachner, and T. H. Fraser, 1985. 23 p, 4 col. figs.
$11.75	7	Revision of the Indo-Pacific dartfishes, genus *Ptereleotris* (Perciformes: Gobioidei). J. E. Randall and D. F. Hoese, 1985. 36 p, 23 col. figs.
$14.50	8	A revision of the Odacidae, a temperate Australian-New Zealand labroid fish family. M. F. Gomon and J. R. Paxton, 57 p, 26 col. figs.
$8.80	9	Revision and vicariance biogeography of the subfamily Congrogadinae (Pisces: Perciformes: Pseudochromidae). R. Winterbottom, 1985. 34 p, 6 col. figs.
$6.00	10	A review of the gobiid fish genera *Exyrias* and *Macrodondogobius*, with description of a new species of *Exyrias*. E. O. Murdy, 1985. 14 p, 6 col. figs.
$19.50	11	Review of the snappers of the genus *Lutjanus* (Pisces: Lutjanidae) from the Indo-Pacific, with the description of a new species. G. R. Allen and F. H. Talbot,1985. 87 p, 80 col. figs.
$9.80	12	Review of the monacanthid fish genus *Pervagor*, with descriptions of two new species. J. B. Hutchins, 1986. 32 p, 16 col. figs.
$12.00	13	Revision of the groupers of the Indo-Pacific genus *Plectropomus* (Perciformes: Serranidae). J. E. Randall and D. F. Hoese, 1986. 31 p, 28 col. figs.
$7.00	14	Revision of the Indo-Pacific lutjanid genus *Pinjalo*. J. E. Randall, G. R. Allen, and W. D. Anderson, 1987. 17 p, 3 col. figs.
$16.00	15	Revision of the Indo-Pacific fish family Caesionidae (Lutjanoidea), with descriptions of five new species. K. E. Carpenter, 1987. 56 p, 38 col. figs.
$11.50	16	Review of the Indo-Pacific fishes of the serranid genus *Liopropoma*, with descriptions of seven new species. J. E. Randall and L. Taylor, 1988. 47 p, 17 color figs.

Checklist of Micronesian Inshore and Epipelagic Fishes

The following list includes all inshore and epipelagic fish species known to occur at depths of 200 m (660 ft) or less within the fishery conservation zones of Guam and the former Trust Territory of the Pacific Islands. Native freshwater species are included because their larval phases are marine. Mesopelagic species that migrate to the surface at night are not included. The list is arranged in approximate phylogenetic order following Nelson (1984). Genera and species are listed alphabetically within their respective families or subfamilies. Undoubtedly many gaps still exist, particularly in the Carolines. It is expected that nearly all species known in the Marshalls or Marianas that also range to the west or south of Micronesia will eventually turn up in the Carolines, and that perhaps 100 or more additional species may be expected to occur in Belau. Many additional species may already be represented among some 10,000 lots of fishes housed at the California Academy of Sciences, most of which remain to be systematically examined.

Key to symbols and locations:

Caroline Is.: B = Belau; Y = Yap; If = Ifaluk; T = Truk; Po = Pohnpei; Kp = Kapingamarangi; K = Kosrae
Mariana Is.: sM = s. Marianas (Guam to Saipan); nM = n. Marianas (Anatahan to Maug)
Marshall Is.: M = Marshall Is.; W = Wake Is.

x = specimen collected	x?, s?, l? = identification needs confirmation	dp = 60-≥200 m
s = sight record	? = literature record of doubtful validity	pel = pelagic
p = photographic record	u = unid. species in genus or family	fw = fresh water as adults
l = accepted pre-1953 literature record	E = endemic	est = strictly estuarine and/
pc = personal communication	so. = in s. Marshalls, not in n. Marshalls	or fresh water

Taxa	B	Y	If	T	Po	Kp	K	sM	nM	M	W
Class CHONDRICHTHYES											
Order ORECTOLOBIFORMES											
RHINIODONTIDAE (WHALE SHARK)											
Rhiniodon typus (Rüppell) pel	p				s(pc)						
ORECTOLOBIDAE (NURSE, ZEBRA and CARPET SHARKS)											
Nebrius concolor (Lesson)	x	x	x	x	pc	x		x	s	x	
Stegastoma varium (Seba)	x	s									
Order CARCHARHINIFORMES											
HEMIGALEIDAE											
Triaenodon obesus (Rüppell)	x	x		x	x	x	x	x	l/s	x	s
CARCHARHINIDAE (REQUIEM SHARKS)											
Carcharhinus albimarginatus (Rüppell)	l			x	pc			x		x	
C. amblyrhynchos (Bleeker)	x	s		x	x	x	x	x	l/s	x	p
C. falciformis (Bibron) pel	l							x		x	
C. galapagensis (Snodgrass & Heller)								x		x	
C. limbatus (Valenciennes)										x	
C. longimanus (Poey) pel	l							s		x	
C. melanopterus (Quoy & Gaimard)	x	s	x		pc	x	s	x	s	x	s
Galeocerdo cuvier (Peron & Lesueur)	l				pc			x		x	
Negaprion acutidens (Rüppell)	l									x	
Rhizoprionodon oligolinx Springer	?										
SPHYRNIDAE (HAMMERHEAD SHARKS)											
Sphyrna lewini (Griffith & Smith)					x	x					
S. mokorran (Rüppell)	p										
Order LAMNIFORMES											
LAMNIDAE (MACKEREL SHARKS)											
Carcharodon carcharias (Linnaeus) dp pel							x				
ALOPIIDAE (THRESHER SHARKS)											
Alopias pelagicus Nakamura pel				x							
Order RAJIFORMES											
RHINOBATIDAE (GUITARFISHES)											
Rhinchobatus djiddensis (Forsskål)	u				x						
Order MYLIOBATIFORMES											
DASYATIDIDAE (STINGRAYS)											
Dasyatis kuhlii (Müller & Henle)	u			u	s?	x				s?	
Hymantura uarnak (Forsskål)	l	x		x							
Taeniura melanospilos Bleeker					pc		s	p	p	x	
Urogymnus asperrimus (Bloch & Schneider)										x	
MYLIOBATIDAE (EAGLE RAYS)											
Aetobatis narinari (Euphrasen)	l				pc		x			x	s
MOBULIDAE (MANTA RAYS)											
Manta alfredi (Kreft)	s				pc		s	p		x	s
Class OSTEICHTHYES											
Order ANGUILLIFORMES											
ANGUILLIDAE (FRESHWATER EELS)											
Anguilla bicolor McClelland fw	u			u	x						
A. marmorata Quoy & Gaimard fw	x			x	x						
MURAENIDAE (MORAY EELS)											
Anarchias allardicei Jordan & Seale			x	x			x			x	
A. cantonensis (Schultz)			x	x	x					x	
A. seychellensis Smith							x			x	

Taxa	B	Y	If	T	Po	Kp	K	sM	nM	M	W
Channomuraena vittata Richardson	x										
Echidna leucotaenia Schultz		x			x		x			x	
E. nebulosa (Ahl)		x			x	x	x	s	x	s	x
E. polyzona (Richardson)		x			x		x				
E. sp. (for *unicolor*)		x					x				
Enchelycore bayeri (Schultz)		x		x	x		x				
E. bikiniensis (Schultz)		x					x			x	
E. schismatorhynchus (Bleeker)		x					x				
Enchelynassa canina (Quoy & Gaimard)		x			x		x				
Gymnomuraena zebra (Shaw)		x		x	x		x			x	
Gymnothorax berndti Snyder dp	x						x				
G. buroensis (Bleeker)		x			x		x		x	x	x
G. elegans Bliss dp							x				
G. enigmaticus McCosker & Randall	x				x		x			x	
G. fimbriatus (Bennett)		x		x	x		x				
G. flavimarginatus (Rüppell)	p	x			x	x	s	x	x	x	x
G. fuscomaculatus (Schultz)		x		x	x		x				
G. gracilicaudus Jenkins		x			x		x				
G. hepaticus (Rüppell)		x					x				
G. javanicus (Bleeker)	p	x	s	s	x	s	x			x	p
G. margaritophorus Bleeker		x		x	x		x			x	
G. marshallensis (Schultz)		x					x			x	x
G. melatremus Schultz		x		x	x		x				
G. meleagris (Shaw & Nodder)	l	x			x	x	x			s	x
G. monochrous Bleeker										x	
G. monostigmus (Regan)		x			x		x				
G. neglectus (Tanaka) dp							x				
G. nudivomer (Playfair) dp in region							s (aq. spec.)				
G. pindae Smith		x		x	x		x			x	
G. polyuranodon (Bleeker) fw	x										
G. richardsoni (Bleeker)	l	x			x		x		x		
G. rueppelliae (McClelland)	x	x			x		x			x	
G. undulatus (Lacepède)	l	x			x	x	x	x		x	
G. zonipectus Seale	x	p	x		x	x		x		x	
Rhinomuraena quaesita Garman										s	x
Sideria picta (Ahl)	l	x			x	x	x	x	x	x	x
S. prosopeion (Bleeker)		x								x	
Strophiodon brummeri (Bleeker)							x				
Thyrsoidea macrura (Bleeker)	l?						x				
Uropterygius concolor Rüppell				x	x		x			x	
U. fijiensis Fowler & Bean		x									
U. fuscoguttatus Schultz				x	x		x				
U. goslinei McCosker & Randall	x			x							
U. kamar McCosker & Randall	x									p so.	
U. macrocephalus (Bleeker)		x					x			x	
U. marmoratus (Lacepède)		x			x		x			x	
U. micropterus (Bleeker)							x				
U. polyspilus (Regan)				x	x						
U. supraforatus (Regan)		x			x		x				x
U. xanthopterus Bleeker		x			x	x				x	
U. (Scuticaria) tigrinus (Lesson)							x				
CHLOPSIDAE (FALSE MORAYS)											

Taxa	B	Y	If	T	Po	Kp	K	sM	nM	M	W
Kaupichthys atronasus Schultz				x						x	x
K. brachychirus Schultz				x	x						x
K. hyoproroides (Strömann)			x	x	x	x			x		
CONGRIDAE (CONGER and GARDEN EELS)											
Subfamily Bathymyrinae											
Ariosoma scheelei (Strömman, 1896)										x	
Subfamily Congrinae											
Conger cinereus cinereus Rüppell	l		x	x	x		x			x	
?Parioconger kapingamaragiensis Rofen					x						
Poeciloconger fasciatus Günther										x	
Subfamily Heterocongrinae											
Gorgasia sp.							s			x	
Heteroconger hassi (Klausewitz & Eible-Eibesfeldt)	x						x			x	
MORINGUIDAE (SPAGHETTI EELS)-males pelagic; juvs & females on mud or sand											
Moringua ferruginea Bliss		u		x	u		x			x	
M. javanica (Kaup)	l			x			x			x	
M. microchir Bleeker				x			x			x	
MURAENESOCIDAE (PIKE EELS)											
Muraenesox cinereus (Forsskål) dp					x						
OPHICHTHIDAE (SNAKE EELS)											
Subfamily Myrophinae											
Muraenichthys gymnotus Bleeker			u?(as *M. gymnopterus*)							x	
M. laticaudata (Ogilby)			x	x		x				x	
M. macropterus Bleeker	l						x			x	
M. schultzi Bleeker			x	x	x					x	
M. sibogae Weber & deBeaufort										x so.	
Myrophis uropterus (Temminck & Schlegel)				x	x					x	
Schismorhynchus labialis (Seale)	x			x						x	
Schultzidia johnstonensis (Schultz & Wds)	x			x			x			x	
S. retropinnis (Fowler)				x	x					x	
Subfamily Ophichthinae											
Apterichtus klazingai (Weber)										x	
Brachysomophis sauropsis Schultz							x			x	
Caecula polyophthalmus (Bleeker)							x				
Callechelys marmorata (Bleeker)	l				x		x			x	
C. melanotaenia Bleeker			x		x		x			x	
Cirricaecula johnsoni Schultz										x	
Elapsopsis versicolor (Richardson)	l										
Evipes percinctus McCosker	x										
Ichthyapus vulturis (Weber & deBeaufort)	x										
Leiuranus semicinctus (Lay & Bènnett)	l		x	x	x		x			x	
Myrichthys bleekeri Gosline										x	
M. colubrinus (Boddaert)	l		x	x	x	s	x			x	
M. maculosus (Cuvier)			x	x	x	x	x			x	
Ophichthus cephalazona (Bleeker)	l				x						
Ophichthus n. sp.?										x	
Pheanomonas cooperae Palmer	x										
Phyllophichthus xenodontus Gosline			x	x	x					x	
Order ELOPIFORMES											
MEGALOPIDAE (TARPONS)											
Megalops cyprinoides (Broussonet)	l	p		pc			x				
ALBULIDAE (BONEFISHES)											
Albula glossodonta (Forsskål)	l						x			x	
Order GONORHYNCHIFORMES											
CHANIDAE (MILKFISH)											
Chanos chanos (Forsskål)	l	p		pc	x		x			x	p
Order SILURIFORMES											
PLOTOSIDAE (EEL CATFISHES)											
Plotosus lineatus (Thunberg)	x	p									
Order CLUPEIFORMES											
ENGRAULIDIDAE (ANCHOVIES)											
Thryssa baelama (Forsskål)	l	p					x				
Stolephorus punctifer (Fowler) pel											
S. heterolobus (Rüppell)	l						x	x			
S. devisi (Whitley)			l	l	l						
S. insularis Hardenberg		l	l	l							
S. indicus (VanHasselt)	l		l		x · x						
S. pacificus Baldwin			x		x						
CLUPEIDAE (HERRINGS, SPRATS, and SARDINES)											
Subfamily Dussumierinae											
Dussumieria elopsoides Bleeker										x	
Dussumieria sp. B	l	l	l	l		l	x				
Spratelloides delicatulus (Bennett)	l		x	l	x	x		x		x	
S. gracilis (Schlegel)	l		x							x	
Subfamily Clupeinae											
Amblygaster clupeoides (Bleeker)	l			l							
A. sirm (Walbaum)	l	l		l	l	x	l			l	
Herklotsichthys quadrimaculatus (Rüppell)	x		l	l	l					x	
Order AULOPIFORMES											
SYNODONTIDAE (LIZARDFISHES)											
Saurida gracilis (Quoy & Gaimard)	s		x	s	x	x	x	x		x	
S. nebulosa Valenciennes	x	x					x				
Synodus binotatus Schultz	x		x	x	x				x	l?	x
S. englemanni Schultz	x		x	x	x	x	s	x		x	
S. jaculum Russell & Cressey	x			x	x	p					

Taxa	B	Y	If	T	Po	Kp	K	sM	nM	M	W
S. variegatus (Lacepède)	x		x		x	x			x	l?	x
Order GADIFORMES											
BREGMACEROTIDAE											
Bregmaceros nectabanus Whitley pel							x			x	
Order OPHIDIIFORMES											
OPHIDIIDAE (CUSK EELS)											
Brotula multibarbata Temminck & Schlegel			x		x		x		x	x	
B. townsendi Fowler					x?						x
BYTHITIDAE (LIVEBEARING BROTULAS)											
Brosmophyciops pautzkei Schultz					x?			x			
Dinematichthys iluocoetenoides Bleeker			x		x?	x		x	x	x	
Microbrotula sp.			x								
CARAPODIDAE (PEARLFISHES)											
Carapus homei (Richardson)	l			x			x			x	
C. mourlani (Petit)			x			x	x	x			
C. parvipinnis (Kaup)	l			x			x				
Encheliophis gracilis (Bleeker)	l		x				x			x	
E. vermicularis Müller	x						x				
Onuxodon margaritifer (Rendahl)				x							
Order GOBIESOCIFORMES											
GOBIESOCIDAE (CLINGFISHES)											
Lepadichthys caritus Briggs	x										
L. minor Briggs							x				
Liobranchia stria Briggs							x			x	
Order BATRACHOIDIFORMES											
ANTENNARIIDAE (FROGFISHES)											
Antennarius analis (Gosline)	x	x								x	
A. biocellatus	x										
A. coccineus (Lesson)	x	x		x	x		x			x	
A. commersonii (Latreille)	l?						s				
A. dorehensis Bleeker			x		x		x				
A. nummifer (Cuvier)	l						x			x	
A. maculatus (Desjardins)							p				
A. pictus (Shaw & Nodder)			x				x			x	
A. randalli Allen										x	
A. rosaceus (Smith & Radcliffe)										x	
Antennatus tuberosus (Cuvier)			x		x	x				x	
Histrio histrio (Linnaeus)				s		x				x	
Order ATHERINIFORMES											
ATHERINIDAE (SILVERSIDES)											
Atherion elymus Jordan & Starks			x		x		x			x	
Atherinomorus duodecimalis (Cuvier&Valenciennes) l		l									
A. endrachtensis (Quoy & Gaimard)						l					
?A. insularum whitei (Schultz) =*lacunosus*?						x					
A. lacunosus (Schneider)	x	l		l	l		l	x			
Hypoatherina barnesi Schultz			x		x	x					
H. ovalaua (Herre)	l		x	l	l	x	l	x			
H. cylindrica				l							
Stenatherina panatela (Jordan & Richard.)	x	also "Carolines"									
ISONIDAE (KEELED SILVERSIDES)											
Iso hawaiiensis Gosline										x	
Order CYPRINODONTIFORMES											
BELONIDAE (NEEDLEFISHES)											
Ablennes hians (Valenciennes) pel							x			x	
Platybelone argalus platyura (Bennett)	s		x		x		x	x	s	x	
Strongylura incisa (Valenciennes)	l		x		x	s	x			x	
S. leiura leiura (Bleeker)	l			x							
Tylosurus crocodilis crocodilis (Lesueur)	s				x	s	x	s	x		
HEMIRHAMPHIDAE (HALFBEAKS)											
Euleptorhamphus viridis (VanHasselt) pel							x			x	
Hemiramphus archipelagicus Coll. & Par.)							x	x			
H. far (Forsskål)	x										
Hemiramphus lutkei (Collette)				x							
Hyporhamphus acutus acutus (Günther)					x		x			x	
Hyporhamphus affinis (Günther)			x		x		x			x	
Hyporhamphus dussumieri (Valenciennes)			x		x		x			x	
Oxyporhamphus m. micropterus (Val.)pel							x			x	
Zenarchopterus dispar Valenciennes	l		(as *denkeri*) ?pc	x							
EXOCOETIDAE (FLYINGFISHES)											
Cheilopogon spilonopterus (Bleeker) pel							x			x	
C. spilopterus (Valenciennes) pel							x				
C. unicolor (Valenciennes) pel							x			x	
Cypselurus angusticeps Nich. & Bred. pel							x			x	
C. poecilopterus (Valenciennes) pel							x	l			
C. speculiger (Valenciennes) pel							x				
Exocoetus volitans Linnaeus pel	l									l?	x
Parexocoetus b. brachypterus (Rich.) pel							x	x			
P. m. mento (Valenciennes) pel	l				x		x			x	
Prognichthys albimaculatus (Fowler) pel							x				
P. sealei Abe pel							x				
Order BERYCIFORMES											
ANAMOLOPIDAE (FLASHLIGHTFISHES)											
Anamolops katoptron Bleeker					x (Oroluks)		x				
Photoblepheron palpebratus (Boddaert)						likely-?				x	
HOLOCENTRIDAE (SOLDIERFISHES and SQUIRRELFISHES)											

Taxa	B	Y	If	T	Po	Kp	K	sM	nM	M	W
Subfamily Myripristinae											
Myripristis adustus Bleeker	x	p	x		x	x	p	x		x	
M. amaenus (Castlenau)	p		x		x	s	x	x	x		
M. berndti Jordan & Evermann	p	p	x		x		x	x	x	p	
M. chryseres Jordan & Evermann					x						
M. hexagona (Lacepède)	p										
M. kuntee Cuvier	p	p	x		x	x		x	x	x	
M. murdjan (Forsskål)	p				x	x	x	x	x	s?	x p?
M. pralinia Cuvier			x		x	x	x	x	x		x
M. violacea Bleeker	p	p	x	s	x	x	x	s	x		x
M. vittata Cuvier	p				x		x			x	
M. woodsi Greenfield			x		x	x		x		x	
Ostichthys kaianus (Günther) dp							x				
Plectrypops lima (Valenciennes)			x		x		x	x	x		
Subfamily Holocentrinae											
Neoniphon argenteus (Valenciennes)	x	p	x		x	x	x	x		x	
N. aurolineatus (Liénard, 1839)					x						
N. opercularis (Valenciennes)	s	p	x	s	x	x	x	x		x	
N. sammara (Forsskål)	x	p	x	s	x	x	x	x	x	l	x
Sargocentron caudimaculatum (Rüppell)	p	s		s	x	x	s	x	s	x	
S. diadema (Lacepède)	ls	p	x	s	x	x		x	s	x	
S. dorsomaculatum (Shimizu & Yamakawa)			x	x							
S. ittodai (Jordan & Fowler)	x		x								
S. melanospilos (Bleeker)	s							x			
S. microstoma (Günther)	s		x		x	x	x	x	s	x	
S. praslin (Lacepède) (as *rubrum*)-l			x		x		x	x		x so.	
S. punctatissimum (Cuvier)			x		x	x		x	s	x	
S. spiniferum (Forsskål)	x	p	x	s	x	x	x	x	s	x	p
S. tiere (Cuvier)	l	p	x		x	x	x	x	x	x	p
S. tieroides (Bleeker)	x	x	x		x		x	x		x	
S. violaceum (Bleeker)	p		x		x	x	s			x so.	
Order SYNGNATHIFORMES											
AULOSTOMIDAE (TRUMPETFISHES)											
Aulostomus chinensis (Linnaeus)	ls	p	x	s		x	s	x	l	x	
FISTULARIIDAE (CORNETFISHES)											
Fistularia commersoni Rüppell	ls	s	x	s		x	s	x	l	x	
CENTRISCIDAE (SHRIMPFISHES)											
Aeoliscus strigatus (Günther)	x			p	x						
SOLENOSTOMIDAE (GHOST PIPEFISHES)											
Solenostomus paradoxus (Pallas)					x	x				x	
SYNGNATHIDAE (PIPEFISHES and SEAHORSES)											
Subfamily Hippocampinae											
Hippocampus hystrix Kaup							x				
H. kuda Bleeker	l				pc						
Subfamily Syngnathinae											
Bhanotia nuda Dawson	x										
Bulbonaricus brauni (Dawson & Allen)	x										
Choeroichthys brachysoma (Bleeker)	x					x					
C. sculptus (Günther)	x				x		x		x		
Corythoichthys flavofasciatus (Rüppell)	x	x	x	p		x	x	x		x	x
C. haematopterus (Bleeker)	x	x									
C. intestinalis (Ramsay)	x	x	x	x	x	x	x	x	x		x
C. nigripectus Herald		x					x			x	
C. ocellatus Herald	x										
C. polynotatus Dawson	x										
C. schultzi Herald	x									x	
Cosmocampus banneri (Herald & Randall)										x	
C. darrosanus (Dawson & Randall)					x						
C. maxweberi (Whitley)										x	
Doryramphus e. excisus Kaup	x	x	xUlithix			x		x	x	x	
D. jansii (Herald & Randall)	x		s								
D. n. negrosensis Herre	x	x									
D. (Dunkerocampus) dactyliophorus (Bl.)	x		Ulithi	x		x		x			
Halicampus brocki (Herald)							x		x		x
H. dunckeri (Chabanaud)	x			x							
H. mataafae (Jordan & Seale)	x							x		x	
H. nitidus (Günther)	x										
Hippichthys cyanospilus (Bleeker) fw		x									
H. spicifer (Rüppell) fw	l		x		x						
Micrognathus andersonii (Bleeker)	x	x		x			x				
M. brevirostris pygmaeus Fritzsche	x										
Microphis (Coelonotus) leiaspis (Blk.)fw	x										
M. (Lophocampus) brevidorsalis (deB.)fw	x										
M. (L.) retzii (Bleeker) fw				x							
M. (Oostethus) b. brachyurus (Bleeker)fw	x	x			x						
M. (O.) manadensis (Bleeker) fw	x										
Minyichthys myersi (Herald & Randall)					x						
Phoxocampus diacanthus (Schultz)	x	x			x		x				
Syngnathoides biaculeatus (Bloch)	x				x		x			x so.	
Trachyramphus bicoarctata (Bleeker)					x						
Order PEGASIFORMES											
PEGASIDAE (DRAGONFISHES)											
Eurypegasus draconis (Linnaeus)				pc		x		x so.			
Order SCORPAENIFORMES											
DACTYLOPTERIDAE (HELMET GURNARDS)											
Dactyloptena orientalis (Cuvier)	l			pc		x					

Taxa	B	Y	If	T	Po	Kp	K	sM	nM	M	W
D. petersoni (Nyström) dp							x				
PLATYCEPHALIDAE (FLATHEADS)											
Cymbacephalus beauforti (Knapp)	x	x									
Platycephalus arenicola (Schultz)					x			x		x	
P. chiltonae (Schultz)							x			x	
P. longiceps Cuvier (after Matsuura)	x?										
P. otaitensis (Bleeker)					x					x	
Sorsogona welanderi (Schultz)										x	
?Onigocia macrolepis (Bleeker)			x?								
?Inegocia sp.			x?		x?						
CARACANTHIDAE (ORBICULATE VELVETFISHES)											
Caracanthus maculatus (Gray)					x		x?	x	x	x	
C. unipinna (Gray)	x				x			x	x	x	
TETRAROGIDAE (WASPFISHES)											
Tetraroge barbata (Cuvier)	x										
APLOACTINIDAE (VELVETFISHES)											
Cocotropis n. sp.										x	
SCORPAENIDAE (SCORPIONFISHES)											
Subfamily Scorpaeninae											
Parascorpaena mcadamsi (Fowler)	x-(as *oglinus*)									x	
P. mossambica (Peters)	x		x?		x		x			x so.	
Pontinus macrocephalus (Sauvage) dp		u/p					x				
P. sp. cf. *nigerimum* Eschmeyer dp							x				
Rhinopias frondosa (Günther)					x (Condor Rf-s. of Pohnpei)						
Scorpaenodes hirsutus (Smith)					x					x	
S. kelloggi (Jenkins)					x			x		x	
S. minor (Smith)					x		x			x	
S. parvipinnis (Garrett)			x		x	x				x	
S. varipinis Smith					x						
S. guamensis (Quoy & Gaimard)	x		x		x		x	x	x		x
Scorpaenopsis diabolus (Cuvier)	l	p	x		x	x		x	x	s	x
S. macrochir Ogilby	x	p			x						x
S. fowleri (Pietschmann)					x		x			x	
S. oxycephala (Bleeker)	x		x?		x?		x			x	
S. papuensis (Cuvier)	x										
Scorpaenopsis n. sp.	x				"Carolines"					x	
Sebastapistes cyanostigma (Bleeker)	x		x		x		x	x	x	x	
S. galactacma Jenkins					x					x	
S. mauritiana (Cuvier)					x					x	
S. strongia (Cuvier)	l		x		x		x	x	x		x
Taenianotus triacanthus Lacepède	l		x		x			x	s	x	
Subfamily Synanceiinae											
Synanceia verrucosa Bloch & Schneider	x	x	x		x		x	x	x		x
Subfamily Choridactylinae											
Inimicus didactylus (Pallas)	x										
Subfamily Pteroinae											
Dendrochirus biocellatus (Fowler)					x		x			x	
D. brachypterus (Cuvier)					x		x				
D. zebra (Cuvier)	x									x	
Pterois antennata (Bloch)	s				x	x	s	x	x	x	x p
P. radiata Cuvier	x				x		x	x		x	
P. volitans (Linnaeus)	p	p	x	p	x			x	x	x	s x
Order PERCIFORMES											
SERRANIDAE (FAIRY BASSLETS and GROUPERS)											
Subfamily Anthiinae											
Holanthias borbonius (Valenciennes) dp							x				
H. katayamai Randall, Maugé, & Plessis dp							x				
Luzonichthys waitei (Fowler)	p									x so.	
L. whitleyi Smith	p?										
Plectranthias fourmanoiri Randall							x			x	
P. kamii Randall dp							x			x	
P. longimanus (Weber)				Ulithi						x	
P. nanus Randall	x			Ulithi						x	
P. winniensis (Tyler)										x	
Plectranthias n. sp. dp							x				
Pseudanthias cooperi (Regan)	p						x			x	
P. pleurotaenia (Bleeker)	p						x			x	
P. randalli (Lubbock & Allen)	p						x			x so.	
P. ventralis ventralis (Randall)								p		x	
Pseudanthias sp.							x				
Pseudanthias spp. (4, all dp)										p(4)	
P. (Franzia) huchtii (Bleeker)	p										
P. (F.) squammipinnis (Peters)	p										
P. (Mirolabrichthys)											
bartlettorum (Randall & Lubbock)	x							p		x so.	
P. (M.) bicolor (Randall)								p		x	
P. (M.) dispar Herre	p						x			.x so.	
P. (M.) lori (Lubbock & Randall)	x										
P. (M.) pascalus (Jordan & Tanaka)	x	x			x	p	x	s	x	p	
P. (M.) smithvanizi (Randall & Lubbock)	x									x so.	
P. (M.) tuka Herre & Montalban	x										
Serranocirrhitus latus Watanabe	x										
Subfamily Epinephelinae											
Aethaloperca rogaa (Forsskål)	lp				pc	x		s	x		
Anyperodon leucogrammicus (Val.)	lp	x			x				x		
Cephalopholis analis (Valenciennes) dp							x				

Taxa	B	Y	If	T	Po	Kp	K	sM	nM	M	W
C. argus (Schneider)	lp	s	x		x	x	p	x	x	x	p
C. boenack (Bloch, 1790)	p										
C. igarashiensis Katayama dp				x			x	pc			
C. leopardus (Lacepède)	s		x		x	x	s	x	x	x	
C. miniata (Forsskål)	lp				x	x	x		x		
C. polleni (Bleeker)	p					x					
C. sexmaculata (Rüppell)	lp	p				s	x		x		
C. sonnerati (Valenciennes)	l	p	x				x		x		
C. spiloparaea (Valenciennes)	x	p				x	x		x		
C. urodeta (Bloch & Schneider)	xp	s	x	s	x	x	s	x	s	x	
Cromileptes altivelis (Valenciennes)	l						x				
Gracila albomarginata (Fowler & Bean)	p	p				x	x		x		
Epinephelus caeruleopunctatus (Bloch)	x				x	x?	x			x so.	
E. chlorostigma (Valenciennes)	x	s				pc					
E. cyanopodus (Richardson)	l	Mortlocks-x		x					x		
E. fasciatus (Forsskål)	l	p	x		pc			x	s	x	p
E. fuscoguttatus (Forsskål)	lp				x		x		x		
E. miliaris Valenciennes	l	p									
E. hexagonatus (Schneider)	l	p	x	pc	x	s	x	s	x	p	
E. macrospilos (Bleeker)	lp	p	x		x		x		x		
E. maculatus (Bloch)		p		pc			x	pc	x		
E. malabaricus (Schneider)	s										
E. melanostigma Schultz	s		x		x				x		
E. merra Bloch	xp	s	x	s	x	x	x	s	x		
E. microdon (Bleeker)	lp		x	x	x	s	x	s	x	p	
E. morrhua (Valenciennes) dp		p				pc	s	s			
E. ongus (Bloch)					x?				x		
E. retouti Bleeker dp in region	x				pc						
E. septemfasciatus (Thünberg) dp						x	s				
E. socialis (Günther)							x	x			
E. spilotoceps Schultz			x	x	x	s			x		
E. tauvina (Forsskål)	l		x		pc		x		x		
E. (Promicrops) lanceolatus (Bloch)	lp				pc		x		x		
Plectropomus areolatus (Rüppell)	x	x	s		x		x		x		
P. laevis (Lacepède, 1801)	x						x	s	x		
P. leopardus (Lacepède)	x	s?		x +Mortlocks							
P. oligacanthus Bleeker	l		p		x				x so.		
Saloptia powelli Smith dp		p					x				
Variola albimarginata Baissac							x				
V. louti (Forsskål)	l	s	x	s	x		pc	x	s	x	
Uncertain status:											
Liopropoma lunulatum (Guichenot) dp					x						
L. mitratum Lubbock & Randall	x	x	x								
L. multilineatum Randall & Taylor	x										
L. pallidum (Fowler)						x	x	x			
L. susumi (Jordan & Seale)		x		x					x		
L. tonstrinum Randall & Taylor	x			x		x			x		
GRAMMISTIDAE (SOAPFISHES)											
Belonoperca chaubanaudi Fowler & Bean	x			x					x		
Grammistes sexlineatus (Thünberg)	x	x	x	x	p	x		x			
Grammistops ocellatus Schultz				x					x		
Pogonoperca punctata (Valenciennes)						x			p so.		
Pseudogramma bilineatus (Schultz)			x	x	x		x				
P. polyacantha (Bleeker) ·			x	x	x		x				
Pseudogramma n. sp.							x				
CALLANTHIIDAE											
Grammatonotus sp. 1 dp							x				
Grammatonotus sp. 2 dp							x				
PLESIOPIDAE (PRETTYFINS; LONGFINS)											
Calloplesiops altivelis (Steindachner)	x		s	x		x			x so.		
Plesiops caeruleolineatus Rüppell	x		x	x	x		x		x		
P. corallicola Bleeker	x		x		x	s	x		x		
PSEUDOCHROMIDAE (DOTTYBACKS)											
Pseudochromis cyanotaenia Bleeker	x		x	x	x		x		x		
P. fuscus Müller & Troschel	p	l	x		x	x	s?				
P. marshallensis Schultz					p	s			x		
P. melanotaenia Bleeker	x		x								
P. polynemus Fowler	s										
P. porphyreus Lubbock & Goldman	x				s	(60 m) s?					
Pseudoplesiops revellei Schultz					x		x		x		
Pseudoplesiops rosae Schultz			x				x		x		
Pseudoplesiops typus Bleeker									x		
Pseudoplesiops sp. 1					x		x				
ACANTHOCLINIDAE (SPINY BASSLETTS)											
Acathoplesiops hiatti Schultz									x		
CIRRHITIDAE (HAWKFISHES)											
Amblycirrhitus bimacula (Jenkins)			x		x		x	s	x		
Cirrhitichthys falco Randall	s				x		x	s			
C. oxycephalus (Bleeker)	p	(as aprinus)-	x?	x	x		x so.				
Cirrhitus pinnulatus (Bloch & Schneider)	x		x	x	x	s	x	x			
Isocirrhitus sexfasciatus (Schultz)							x				
Neocirrhitus armatus Castlenau					p	x	s		p		
Oxycirrhitus typus Bleeker					s	s			x so.		
Paracirrhites arcatus (Cuvier)	xp		x	x	s	x	s	x	p		
P. forsteri (Schneider)	lp		x	x	x	x	s	x	p		
P. hemistictus (Günther)			x		x	s	x	s	x	p	

Taxa	B	Y	If	T	Po	Kp	K	sM	nM	M	W
AMBASSIDAE (GLASSIES)											
Ambassis buruensis Bleeeker fw	l			x			x				
A. interrupta (Bleeker) fw	l										
APOGONIDAE (CARDINALFISHES)											
Subfamily Apogoninae											
Apogon coccineus Rüppell	x		x		x	x		x	s	x	
A. doryssa (Jordan & Seale)						x		x			
A. (Jaydia) ellioti (Day)									x so.		
A. (Nectamia) amboinensis Bleeker	x			p	pc?						
A. (N.) angustaus (Smith & Radcliffe)	x	x			x	x	x	s			
A. (N.) bandanensis Bleeker			x		x						
A. (N.) compressus (McCulluch)	p										
A. (N.) cyanosoma Bleeker			x		x		x		x		
A. (N.) dispar Fraser & Randall	x										
A. (N.) fuscus (Quoy & Gaimard)	s		x		x	x		x			
A. (N.) guamensis Valenciennes	x		x		x	x	s	x	x		
A. (N.) lateralis Valenciennes	l	s?			x		x				
A. (N.) mydrus Jordan & Starks							x				
A. (N.) nigrofasciatus Lachner	x		x		x	x	s	x	x		
A. (N.) novemfasciatus Cuvier	x		x	s	x	x	x	x	x		
A. (N.) sangiensis Bleeker	x	x									
A. (N.) sp. cf. semilineatus Schlegel	p										
A. (N.) taeniophorus Regan			x				x	s	x		
A. (Pristiapogon) exostigma (Jord. & St.)	x	x	x		x	x	x	x		x	x
A. (P.) fraenatus Valenciennes	x	x	x			x		x	s		
A. (P.) kallopterus Bleeker	x	x	x		x	x	s	x	s	x	x
A. (P.) taeniopterus Bennett	Ulithi+	x		x			x		x		
A. (Pristicon) melas Bleeker	x										
A. (P.) trimaculatus (Cuvier)	l	s	x		x	x		x			
A. (Zapogon) evermanni Jordan & Snyder									x		
A. (Zoramia) fragilis Smith	x	x			l	x	l		x so.		
A. (Z.) leptacanthus Bleeker	x	x	x	s	x	x	x	x	x		
A. (Z.) gilberti (Jordan & Seale)	x	x		x?							
A. (Z.) perlitus Fraser & Lachner	x										
Apogonichthys ocellatus (Weber)	x		x		x	x		x			
A. perdix (Bleeker)	x					x		x so.			
Archamia biguttata Lachner	x						x				
A. fucata (Cantor)	p	l		p	x	x	p	x		x	
A. zosterophora (Bleeker)	xp	sl					x				
Foa brachygramma (Jenkins)							x				
Foa sp.									x so.		
Fowleria aurita (Valenciennes)					x?						
F. isostigma (Jordan & Seale)			x	x		x		x			
F. marmorata (Alleyne & MacLeay)			x	x			x		x		
F. variegata (Valenciennes)			x		x						
Cheilodipterus isostigma Schultz	x		x		x		x				
C. lineatus (Lacepède)	x				x?		x				
C. macrodon (Lacepède)	p		x	s	x	x	s	x			
C. quinquelineata (Cuvier)	x	s	x	s	x	x	s	x			
C. truncatus (Linnaeus)						x		x			
Rhabdamia cypselurus Weber	l		l		l	x	l		x		
R. gracilis (Bleeker)						x		x			
Siphamia fistulosa (Weber)							x				
S. fuscolineata Lachner									x		
S. versicolor (Smith & Radcliffe)				Carolines			x				
Sphaeramia nematoptera (Bleeker)	x	s		x							
S. orbicularis (Cuvier)	x	s		x	x		s	x			
Subfamily Pseudaminae											
Gymnapogon philippinus (Herre)					x						
G. urospilotus Lachner			x		x	x		x	x		
Pseudamia amblyuroptera (Bleeker)	x	x	x		x			x			
P. gelatinosa Smith	x		x	x	x	x	x				
P. hayashii Randall, Lachner, & Fraser	x		x?		x		x				
P. zonata Randall, Lachner & Fraser	s										
Pseudamiops gracilicauda (Lachner)							x		x		
THERAPONIDAE (TIGERFISHES)											
Terapon jarbua (Forsskål)	l										
KUHLIIDAE (FLAGTAILS)											
Kuhlia marginata (Cuvier)	l	as salelea-	x?				s	s	x		
K. mugil (Forster)	x		x		x		x	s	x		
K. rupestris (Lacepède) fw	l	p		x		x	pc				
PRIACANTHIDAE (BIGEYES; GLASSEYES)											
Heteropriacanthus cruentatus (Lacepède)		p	x				x	pc	x		
Priacanthus hamrur (Forsskål)	p						x		x		
MALACANTHIDAE (SAND TILEFISHES)											
Hoplolatilus cuniculus Randall & Dooley							x				
H. fronticinctus (Günther)	x										
H. starcki Randall & Dooley	x		x				s	x	x		
Malacanthus brevirostris Guichenot	x		x		x			x	x		
M. latovittatus (Lacepède)	x		x				x		x		
ECHENEIDAE (REMORAS)											
Echeneis naucrates Linnaeus	l								x		
Phtheirichthys lineatus (Menzies) pel							x				
Remora remora (Linnaeus)	l				x		x		x		
Rhombochirus osteochir (Cuvier) pel							x				
CARANGIDAE (JACKS; TREVALLYS)											

Taxa	B	Y	If	T	Po	Kp	K	sM	nM	M	W
Tribe Carangini											
Alectis ciliaris (Bloch)	l	p					s		x		x
A. indicus (Rüppell)	s										
Atule mate (Cuvier)	l									x	
Carangoides caeruleopinnatus (Rüppell)dp							x				
C. dinema Bleeker	p										
C. fulvoguttatus (Forsskål)	l		l				s				
C. ferdau (Forsskål)	p						s	s			x
C. orthogrammus Joardan & Gilbert	lp				x	p	x				x
C. plagiotaenia (Bleeker)	p						x			x so.	
C. talamparoides Bleeker dp							x				
Caranx lugubris Poey	lp	p			pc		p	x	s	x	p
C. ignobilis (Forsskål)	l				pc		x	pc	x		
C. papuensis Alleyne & MacLeay	x	p									
C. melampygus (Cuvier)	x	p	x	s	pc	x	p	x	s	x	p
C. sexfasciatus Quoy & Gaimard	x	p	x	s	pc	x	s	pc	x		p
Decapterus macarellus (Cuvier) pel							x				
D. macrosoma Bleeker pel	l		l				s				
D. maruadsi (Temminck & Schlegel) pel							p			x	
D. russelli (Rüppell) pel	l										
Gnathanodon speciosus (Forsskål)	l				pc	x	x	x			
Selar boops (Valenciennes)	l		l								
S. crumenophthalmus (Bloch)	l	p	x	l	l		ls	x	x	x	
Ulua mndibularis (MacLeay)	l										
Uraspis helvolus (Forster) dp	l	p?					x				
Tribe Naucratini											
Elagatis bipinnulatus (Quoy & Gaimard)	x	p					x			x	
Naucrates ductor (Linnaeus) pel							x				
Scomberoides lysan (Forsskål)	l	s					s	x	pc	x	p
Seriola dumerili (Risso) dp					pc	xp	s				
S. rivoliana Valenciennes	l	p							xp	pc	p
Tribe Trachinotini											
Trachinotus bailloni (Lacepède)	s		x					x	pc	x	
T. blochii (Lacepède)	l						s	x		x	
CORYPHAENIDAE (DOLPHINFISHES)											
Coryphaena equiselis Linnaeus, 1758 pel							x				
Coryphaena hippurus Linnaeus, 1758 pel	l	pc			pc		x	pc	x		
LEIOGNATHIDAE (PONYFISHES; SLIPMOUTHS)											
Gazza achlamys Jordan & Starks				x			x				
Gazza minuta (Bloch)	l	p		l			l				
Leiognathus bindus (Valenciennes)	l	l		l			l				
Leiognathus elongatus (Günther)	l										
Leiognathus equulus (Forsskål)	l	p		x			ls	x			
Leiognathus smithursti Ramsay & Ogilby	p						l				
Leiognathus stercorarius Evermann & Seale	p							x			
Secutor ruconius (Hamilton-Buchanan)	p			l							
EMMELICHTHYIDAE											
Emmelichthys karnellai Heemstra & Randall dp							x				
Erythrocles scintillans (Jordan & Thompson)dp							x				
LOBOTIDAE (TRIPLEFINS)											
Lobotes surinamensis (Bloch) pel							x				
GERREIDAE (MOJARRAS)											
Gerres abbreviatus Bleeker	l	p									
G. argyreus (Schneider)			x				x	s	x		x
G. filamentosus Cuvier			p								
G. oblongus Cuvier	l		x				x				
G. oyena (Forsskål)	l		x								
G. punctatus Cuvier	l?										
SILLAGINIDAE (WHITINGS)											
Sillago sihama (Forsskål)	l?										
LUTJANIDAE (SNAPPERS)											
Subfamily Etelinae											
Aphareus furca (Lacepède)	l	p	x	s	pc		p	x	s	x	
A. rutilans Cuvier dp	l				pc			x	s		
Aprion virescens Valenciennes	l	p			pc			x	s	x	
Etelis carbunculus Cuvier dp	l	pc			pc			pc	x	x	
E. coruscans Valenciennes dp		p			pc			pc	x	x	
Paracaesio sordidus Abe & Shinohara dp								x	x		
P. xanthurus (Bleeker) dp								x	x		
Pristipomoides amoenus Snyder dp								x	x		
P. auricilla (Jordan, Evermann, & Tanaka) dp		p			pc			x	x		
P. filamentosus (Valenciennes) dp		p						x	x		
P. flavipinnis Shinohara dp					pc			x	x		
P. seiboldi (Bleeker) dp								x	x		
P. zonatus (Valenciennes) dp	l	p			pc			x	x		
Randallichthys filamentosus (Fourmanoir) dp							x				
Subfamily Paradicichthyinae											
Symphorichthys spilurus Günther	ls										
Subfamily Lutjaninae											
Macolor macularis Fowler, 1931	x						p				
M. niger (Forsskål)	lp	s	s				p	x	s	x	
Lutjanus argentimaculatus (Forsskål)	x	x	x					s	x		
L. bohar (Forsskål)	lp	s	x	x	x		p	x	s	x	
L. biguttatus (Valenciennes)	p					x					
L. decussatus (Cuvier)	p										
L. ehrenbergi (Peters)	x	s?	x	x							
L. fulvus (Schneider)	x	s	x	x	x	x	x	x	s	x	p
L. gibbus (Forsskål)	x	p			x		s	x	s	x	
L. kasmira (Forsskål)	x	s	x		x	x	x	x	x	x'	
L. malabaricus (Schneider)	lp					pc					
L. monostigmus (Valenciennes)	x	p	p		x		s	x	s	x	
L. rivulatus (Cuvier)	x								s?		
L. semicinctus Quoy & Gaimard		s			p	x	x	p			x so.
L. vitta (Quoy & Gaimard)	l						x			x	
SYMPHYSANODONTIDAE											
Symphysanodon typus (Bleeker) dp	l					x					
CAESIONIDAE (FUSILIERS)											
Subfamily Caesioninae											
Caesio caerulaurea Lacepède	x	s	x	s	x	x	x	s	x		
C. cuning (Bloch)	x										
C. lunaris Cuvier	p		x								
C. teres Seale	p	s	x	s			p	x	s		
Pterocaesio lativittata Carpenter	p										
P. marri Schultz		s					s	x		x	x
P. tile (Cuvier)	x		x			x	x	x	s		
P. pisang (Bleeker)	p					x					
P. trilineata Carpenter	p					x					
Subfamily Gymnocaesioninae											
Gymnocaesio gymnopterus (Bleeker)									x		
HAEMULIDAE (SWEETLIPS; GRUNTS; JAVELINFISHES)											
Subfamily Plectorhinchinae											
Diagramma pictum (Thünberg)	l										
Plectorhinchus albovittatus (Rüppell)										x	
P. celebecus (Bleeker)	l										
P. chaetodonoides (Lacepède)	x	p									
P. gaterinoides (Smith)	lp	p				pc?s					
P. gibbosus (Lacepède)						x	p		s	x	
P. goldmanni (Bleeker)	lp				p		s				
P. obscurus (Günther)	ls										p so.
P. orientalis (Bloch)	lp	p				pc?s	x	s			
P. picus (Cuvier)							x	s	x		
Subfamily Pomadasyinae											
Pomadasys kaakan (Cuvier)	l										
NEMIPTERIDAE (THREADFIN BREAMS and SPINECHEEKS)											
Subfamily Nemipterinae											
Nemipterus hexadon (Cuvier)	l?										
N. peronii (Quoy & Gaimard)	l?										
N. tolu (Cuvier)	l?										
Subfamily Scolopsinae											
Scolopsis bilineatus (Bloch)	p	s				pc					
S. ciliatus (Lacepède)	s	p									
S. lineatus Quoy & Gaimard	s	p	x			x	x	x	pc	x	
S. margaritifer (Cuvier)	p										
S. monogramma (Kühl & VanHasselt)	l										
?S. taeniopterus (Cuvier)	l?										
S. trilineatus Kner	p	p									
?S. xenochrous Günther		s?									
Subfamily Pentapodinae											
Pentapodus caninus (Cuvier)	p										x
P. macrurus (Bleeker)						pc?				x	
LETHRINIDAE (EMPERORS)											
Gnathodentex aurolineatus (Lacepède)	lp	p	x	s	x	x	s	x	s	x	
Gymnocranius griseus (Schlegel)		p								x	x?so.
G. japonicus Akazaki										p	x
G. lethrinoides (Bleeker)										x	
?G. microdon (Bleeker)										x?	
Lethrinus amboinensis Bleeker									s?	x	
L. elongatus Valenciennes	l		x					s	x		
L. harak (Forsskål)	x	p					p	x		x	
L. hypselopterus Bleeker	p		x								
L. kallopterus Bleeker	l							s	x		
L. lentjan Lacepède	x										
L. mahsenoides Valenciennes	l					x?					
?L. microdon Valenciennes	l?					x?	s?				
L. nematacanthus Bleeker								x			
L. ornatus Valenciennes								s			
L. semicinctus Valenciennes					p	x?	x?	x			
L. ramak (Forsskål)	x							x		x	p
L. rubrioperculatus Sato		p							s?	x	
L. xanthocheilus (Klunzinger)	x	p						s		x	
Monotaxis grandoculus (Forsskål)	lp	p	x	s			x	s	x	x	p
Wattsia mossambicus (Smith) dp								x			
MULLIDAE (GOATFISHES)											
Mulloides flavolineatus (Lacepède)	x	p	x	s	x		x	x	s	x	
M. vanicolensis (Valenciennes)	l	p	x	s			x	s	x	x	
M. pflugeri (Steindachner)								x			x so.
Parupeneus barberinoides (Bleeker)	x	p									
P. barberinus (Lacepède)	x	p	x	s	x	x	x	x	s	x	p
P. bifasciatus (Lacepède)	x		x			x	p	x	s	x	
P. ciliatus (Lacepède)								x			
P. cyclostomus (Lacepède)	l	p	x	s	s	x	x	x	s	x	p
P. heptacanthus (Lacepède)									x	x	

Taxa	B	Y	If	T	Po	Kp	K	sM	nM	M	W
P. indicus (Shaw)	l	p			x		s				
P. multifasciatus (Quoy & Gaimard)	x	p	x	s	x	x	s	x	s	x	p
P. pleurostigma (Bennett)		s	x	s		x		x	s	x	
Upeneus taeniopterus Cuvier			Carolines				x			x so.	
U. tragula Richardson	x										
U. vittatus (Forsskål)	x	p			x		s	x			
PEMPHERIDAE (SWEEPERS)											
Parapriacanthus ransonneti (Steindachner)	p			p						x	
Pempheris oualensis Cuvier	l		p	x	s	x		x	x	s	x
TOXOTIDAE (ARCHERFISHES)											
Toxotes jaculator (Shaw) fw, est	x	s									
KYPHOSIDAE (RUDDERFISHES; SEA CHUBS)											
Kyphosus bigibbus Lacepède							s		p	p	
Kyphosus cinerascens (Forsskål)	s-	p		s			x	x	s	x	p?
Kyphosus vaigiensis (Quoy & Gaimard)	x	p	Ulithi				s	x	s?	x so.	
OPLEGNATHIDAE (KNIFEJAWS)											
Oplegnathus punctatus (Temminck & Schlegel)									s(pc;Pagan)		
EPHIPPIDAE (BATFISHES; SPADEFISHES)											
Platax orbicularis (Forsskål)	x	s			p	pc	s	p	x		x
P. pinnatus (Linnaeus)	p										
P. tiera (Forsskål)	p	p									
MONODACTYLIDAE (MONOS)											
Monodactylus argenteus (Linnaeus)	l								x		
?*M. sebae* Lacepède	l			x?							
SCATOPHAGIDAE (SCATS)											
Scatophagus argus (Linnaeus)	l	p			x						
CHAETODONTIDAE (BUTTERFLYFISHES)											
Chaetodon auriga Forsskå	x	s	x	s	x	x	x	x	s	x	p
C. barronessa Cuvier	x	s									
C. bennetti Cuvier	x	s	x	s	pc	x	s	x	s	x	
C. burgessi Allen & Starck	x			x							
C. citrinellus Cuvier	x	p	x	s	x	x	x	x	s	x	
C. ephippium Cuvier	x	p	x	s	x	x	s	x	s	x	p
C. flavocoronatus Myers										x	
C. kleinii Bloch	p	s	x	s	x	x		s		x	
C. lineolatus Cuvier	s	s			pc			x	s	x	
C. lunula (Lacepède)	s	p	x	s	pc	x	s	x	s	x	p
C. melannotus Bloch	x	p	s		x		x	x			
C. mertensii Cuvier	x	s	x		pc		s	x	s	x	
C. meyeri Schneider	x	p			x	x				x so.	
C. modestus Temminck & Schlegel dp										x	
C. ocellicaudus Cuvier	x										
C. octofasciatus Bloch	x										
C. ornatissimus Solander	x	p	x		pc	x	s	x	s	x	p
C. oxycephalus Bleeker	x										
C. punctatofasciatus Cuvier	x	s	x	s	x		s	x	s	x	p
C. quadrimaculatus Gray							x	s	x	p	
C. rafflesii Bennett	x	p	x		pc	x	p			x	
C. reticulatus Cuvier	x	p	x		x	x	s	x	s	x	p
C. semeion Bleeker	x	s	x	s	?	x		s		x	
C. speculum (Kuhl & Van Hasselt)	x	s									
C. tinkeri Schultz										x	
C. trifascialis (Quoy & Gaimard)	x	p		s	x	x	s	x	pc	x	
C. trifasciatus Park	x	p	x	s	x	x	s	x	pc	x	
C. ulietensis Cuvier	l	p	x	s	pc	x	s	x	pc	x	p
C. unimaculatus Bloch	l	s	x		x	x	s	x		x	
C. vagabundus Linnaeus	x	p	x	s	x	x	x	x			
Coradion chrysozonus (Cuvier)	x										
Forcipiger flavissimus Jordan & McGregor	x	s			x		x	x	s	x	
F. longirostris (Broussonet)	s	x?		x	x?		x	s	x	p	
Hemitaurichthys polylepis (Bleeker)	x	x	x		pc		x	s	x		
H. thompsoni Fowler	x										p
Heniochus acuminatus (Linnaeus)	x	s		x						x	p?
H. chrysostomus Cuvier	x	x	x		x	x	p	x	s	x	
?*H. diphreutes* Jordan dp in region?								s?			
Heniochus monoceros Cuvier	x	x			pc		x	x			
Heniochus singularis Smith & Radcliffe	s	x					s	x			
Heniochus varius (Cuvier)	x	p			x	x				x so.	
POMACANTHIDAE (ANGELFISHES)											
Subfmily Holocanthinae											
Apolemichthys griffisi (Carlson & Taylor)					p						
A. trimaculatus (Lacepède)	s	x			x						
A. xanthopunctatus Burgess				x							
Centropyge bicolor (Bloch)	lp	s	x			x	p	s	x		
C. bispinosus (Günther)	lp		x		x		x				
C. colini Smith-Vaniz & Randall	x					x					
C. flavicauda Fraser-Brunner	x									s	
C. flavissimus (Cuvier)				x	x	x	x	s	x	p	
C. heraldi Woods & Schultz			x		pc		s	x	pc	x	
C. loriculus (Günther)	x				x	x	p	x		x	p
C. multicolor Randall & Wass					x		s	x			
C. multifasciatus (Smith & Radcliffe)	x				s		x		x		
C. nigriocellus Woods & Schultz							x (Tinian)				
C. nox (Bleeker)	s					x					
C. shepardi Randall & Yasuda								x	x		
C. tibicen (Cuvier)					p	s	x				

Taxa	B	Y	If	T	Po	Kp	K	sM	nM	M	W
C. vrolicki (Bleeker)	p		s	x	s	x	x	xp	x		x
Genicanthus bellus Randall								x		x	s
G. melanospilos (Bleeker)	x										
G. watanabei (Yasuda & Tominaga)									x		p
Pygoplites diacanthus (Boddaert)	x	p	x		x	x	x	x	x	s	x
Subfamily Pomacanthinae											
Chaetodontoplus mesoleucus (Bloch)	p										
Pomacanthus imperator (Bloch)	lp	s						x	s	x	
P. semicirculatus (Cuvier)	s										
P. (Euxiphipops) navarchus (Cuvier)	lp	x									
P. (E.) sexstriatus (Kuhl & Van Hasselt)	lp	p									
P. (E.) xanthometopon (Bleeker)	lp	p			p		s				
POMACENTRIDAE (DAMSELFISHES)											
Subfamily Amphiprioninae											
Amphirion chrysopterus Cuvier	x		x		x	x	p	x	s	x	
A. clarkii (Bennett)	x		x	s				x	s		
A. melanopus Bleeker	x	s	x		x		s	x		x	
A. peridaeraion Bleeker	x	s			x	x	s	x	s	x	
A. tricinctus Schultz & Welander											xE
Subfamily Chrominae											
Chromis acares Randall & Swerdloff	s				x		p	x	s	x	p
C. agilis Smith	s				x	x	s	x	s	x	p
C. alpha Randall, 1987	x					x		s	x		x
C. amboinensis (Bleeker)	x				x		p	x		x	
C. analis (Cuvier)	x							x		x	
C. atripectoralis Welander & Schultz	x	p		s	x					x	
C. atripes Fowler & Bean	x									p so.	
C. caudalis Randall, 1987	x										
C. delta Randall, 1987	x										
C. elerae Fowler & Bean								s	x	x so.	
C. lepidolepis Bleeker	x	s		x		x	p	x		x	
C. lineata Fowler & Bean	x										
C. margaritifer Fowler	x	s		x		x	x	s	x		
C. retrofasciata Weber	x										
C. ternatensis (Bleeker)	x			x	s	x		x	s	x	x
C. vanderbilti (Fowler)							p	x	s	x so.	
C. viridis (Cuvier)	x		s	x		x	x	x	x	s	x
C. weberi Fowler & Bean	x									x	
C. xanthochir (Bleeker)	x										
C. xanthura (Bleeker)	x			s	x			x	x		
Dascyllus aruanus (Linnaeus)	x		x	s	x	x	x	x	s	x	
D. melanurus Bleeker	x	s		x							
D. reticulatus (Richardson)	x	s		x	s	x		x	s	x	
D. trimaculatus (Rüppell)	x	s		x	s	x	x		s	x	
Subfamily Lepidozyginae											
Lepidozygus tapienosoma (Bleeker)	x						p	x	x	x	
Subfamily Pomacentrinae											
Abudefduf lorenzi Hensley & Allen	x										
A. notatus (Day)	p										
A. saxatilis (Linnaeus)	x	s		x				x	s	x	x
A. septemfasciatus (Cuvier)	x	s		x	s		x		s	x	x
A. sexfasciatus (Lacepède)	x	p		s		x		s	x	s	x
A. sordidus (Forsskål)	x	s		x		s		x		s	x
Amblyglyphidodon aureus (Cuvier)	x				x	x	x	x			
A. curacao (Bloch)	x	p			s	x	x	x	x		
A. leucogaster (Bleeker)	x	s			x		s			x	
A. ternatensis (Bleeker)	x	s									
Cheiloprion labiatus (Day)	x-										
Chrysiptera biocellata (Quoy & Gaimard)	x	s			x	x	x	x		x	
C. caeruleolineata (Allen)								p		x so.	
C. cyanea (Quoy & Gaimard)	x	s									
C. glauca (Cuvier)	x		x		x	x	s	x		x	
C. leucopoma (Lesson)	x	p	x	s		x	s	x	s	x	
C. oxycephala (Bleeker)	x										
C. rex (Snyder)	x										
C. talboti (Allen)	p										
C. traceyi (Woods & Schultz)	x		x	s	x	x	x	x		x	
C. unimaculata (Cuvier)	x										
Dischistodus chrysopoecilus (Schl. & Mül.)	x	s									
D. melanotus (Bleeker)	x	p									
D. perspicillatus (Cuvier)	x	p									
Hemiglyphidodon plagiometopon (Blkr)	x	x									
Neopomacentrus nemurus (Bleeker)	x	s									
N. taeniurus (Bleeker) fw	x										
N. violascens (Bleeker)									i		
Paraglyphidodon melas (Cuvier)	x	p									
P. nigroris (Cuvier)	x	p									
Plectroglyphidodon dickii (Liénard)	x	s	x	s	x	x	x	s	x	s	x	p
P. imparipennis (Vaillant & Sauvage)	x	s		x	s	x	x				
P. johnstonianus Fowler & Ball	x	s		x	s		x	s	x	p	
P. lacrymatus (Quoy & Gaimard)	x	s		x	s	x	s	x	s	x	
P. leucozona (Bleeker)	x	s		x	s	p		s	x	s	x
P. phoenixensis (Schultz)				x		x	x	x	x		
Pomacentrus amboinensis Bleeker	x	s		x		x	x	x	x		
Pomacentrus arenarius Allen	x										
P. bankanensis Bleeker	x	s									

Taxa	B	Y	If	T	Po	Kp	K	sM	nM	M	W
P. brachialis (Cuvier)				s	x						x
P. burroughi Fowler	x										
P. chrysurus Cuvier	x										
P. coelestis Jordan & Starks	x	s			x						x
P. emarginatus Cuvier	x										
P. grammorhynchus Fowler	x			p	x						
P. moluccensis Bleeker	x	s									
P. nigromanus Weber	x										
P. pavo (Bloch)	x	s	x	p	x	x	x				x
P. philippinus Evermann & Seale	s			s	x		x				
P. reidi Fowler & Bean	x										
P. simsiang Bleeker	x										
P. vaiuli Jordan & Seale	x	s	x	s	x	x				x	s x
Pomacentrus sp. 2	x										
Pomachromis exilis (Allen & Emery)				x							x
P. guamensis Allen & Larson								xE	sE		
Stegastes albifasciatus (Schlegel & Müller)	x	s	x			x	s			x	x
S. fasciolatus (Ogilby)	x		x	x	x	x	x	s		x	x
S. lividus (Bloch & Schneider)	x	p	x	s	x		p	x			x
S. nigricans (Lacepède)	x	s	x	s	x	x	x	x			x
LABRIDAE (WRASSES)											
Subfamily Bodianinae											
Bodianus anthioides (Bennett)	s					s	s	x		x	
B. axillaris (Bennett)	s	p		x		x	x	s			x
B. bimaculatus Allen	x										
B. diana (Lacepède)	p										p so.
B. loxozonus (Snyder)							x				x
B. mesothorax (Schneider)	p				x	s					
B. tanyokidus Gomon & Madden dp							x				
Choerodon anchorago (Bloch)	x	s						s?(as *azurio*)			
Polylepion russelli (Gomon & Randall) dp							x				
Subfamily Pseudodacinae											
Pseudodax moluccanus (Valenciennes)	x					s	p	s			x
Subfamily Cheilininae											
Cheilinus arenatus Valenciennes	x						x				x
C. bimaculatus Valenciennes					pc			s			x
C. celebecus Bleeker	p	p	x		x	x					x
C. chlorourus (Bloch)		p		s						x	p
C. digrammus (Lacepède)	p			p	p		p	x			x
C. fasciatus (Bloch)	ls	p	x	s	x	x	s				x
C. orientalis Günther	p					x		so.	x		
C. oxycephalus Bleeker	s		x	s	x		x	s			x
C. trilobatus Lacepède	ls	p		s	x		x	s		x	p
C. undulatus Rüppell	ls	s		s			s	x		x	p
C. unifasciatus Streets	s		x			x	s	x		s	x
Epibulus insidiator (Pallas)	x	p	x	s	x	x	x			x	p
Epibulus n. sp.	x										
Wetmorella albofasciata Schultz & Marshall				x							x
W. nigropinnata (Seale)	x	x	x	x	x	x	x				x
Xiphocheilus sp.	l										
Cymolutes praetextatus (Quoy & Gaimard)	x?(as *lecluse*)						x				x
C. torquatus (Valenciennes)											x
Novaculichthys macrolepidotus (Bloch)							x				
N. taeniourus (Lacepède)	ls	p	x		x	x	s	x			x
Xyrichtys aneitensis (Günther)				u (as *niveilatus?*)	x		x				x
X. celebecus (Bleeker)											x
X. pavo Valenciennes	(as *dea*) x						x				x
X. n. sp. A (of Masuda et al., 1984) dp							x (Tinian)				
"Cirrhilabriod" genera:											
Cirrhilabrus cyanopleura (Bleeker)	p			s?							
C. exquisitus Smith	p										p so.
Cirrhilabrus n. sp.1	p?				p	x					x
Cirrhilabrus n. sp. 2											x
Paracheilinus n. sp.1											x
Paracheilinus n. sp. 2											x
Pseudocheilinops ataenia Schultz	p										
Pseudocheilinus evanidus Jord. & Everm.	p		x		x			x			x so.
P. hexataenia (Bleeker)	s	s	x		x	x	s	x			x
P. octotaenia Jenkins	p					x		x			
P. tetrataenia Schultz	s					s	x				x
Pseudocheilinus n. sp.								s			x
Pterogogus cryptus Randall	x		x				x				x
P. guttatus (Fowler & Bean)	x										
Subfamily Corinae											
Anampses caeruleopunctatus Rüppell	x	s					x	s		x	p
A. geographicus Valenciennes	l				l						
A. melanurus Bleeker	s										x so.
A. meleagrides Valenciennes	s		x				x			x	
A. twisti Bleeker	s	s	x				s			x	x
Cheilio inermis (Forsskål)	x	p	x			x	s	x			x
Coris aygula Lacepède	lp	s					x	s		x	x
C. gaimardi (Quoy & Gaimard)	lp	s	x		x	x	x	x		s	x
C. variegata (Rüppell)	p			s		x					x
Gomphosus varius Lacepède	ls	p	x	s	x	x	x	x		s	p
Halichoeres biocellatus Schultz					x			x		s	x p
H. chloropterus (Bloch)	p										

Taxa	B	Y	If	T	Po	Kp	K	sM	nM	M	W
H. chrysus Randall	p										x
H. hartzfeldii (Bleeker)								x		x	
H. hortulanus (Lacepède)	x	s	x	s	x	x	x	x		s	x
H. margaritaceus (Valenciennes)	s	s	x	s	x	x	s	x		s	x
H. marginatus Rüppell	p	s			x	s	x	x		s	x
H. melanurus (Bleeker)	p			p	x	x	s				
H. melasmapomus Randall	x							s			x
H. prosopeion (Bleeker)	x										
H. richmondi Fowler & Bean	p			x	x	?					x so.
H. scapularis (Bennett)	s										
H. trimaculatus (Quoy & Gaimard)	s	p	x		x	x	x	x		s	x
Halichoeres n. sp.?	p										
Hemigymnus fasciatus (Bloch)	ls	s	x			x	x	x		x	p
H. melapterus (Bloch)	ls	p	s			x	x	x		s	x
Hologymnosus annulatus (Lacepède)	s							x		s	p so.
Hologymnosus doliatus (Lacepède)	s		Ulithi							x	
Macropharyngodon meleagris (Val.)	x	s	x	s	x			x		s	x
M. negrosensis Herre	x										x
Pseudocoris yamashiroi (Schmidt)	p										x
Pseudojuloides atavai Randall & Randall								p			
P. cerasinus (Snyder)								s			x
Stethojulis bandanensis (Bleeker)	ls	s	x	s	x	x	s	x		s	x p
S. strigiventor (Bennett)	s				x		s	x	s?	x	
S. trilineata (Bloch & Schneider)	l				x		x	l?			
Thalassoma amblycephalum (Bleeker)	p			x	s	x	x	x		s	x
T. hardwickii (Bennett)	p	p	x		x	x	s	x			x
T. janseni (Bleeker)	p		x	p				p			
T. lunare (Linnaeus)	p	s					s				x so.
T. lutescens (Lay & Bennett)	s	s	x				s	x		s	x
T. purpureum (Forrskål)	ls			x			x	s		x	x
T. quinquevittatum (Lay & Bennett)	s	s	x		x	x	s	x		s	x
T. trilobatum (Lacepède)	ls		x			x?	x	s		x	
Subfamily Labrichthyinae ?("Labrichthyiform")											
Diproctacanthus xanthurus (Bleeker)	x										
Labrichthys unilineatus (Guichenot)	x	p		p	x	x	s	x			
Labroides bicolor Fowler & Bean	s	s	x	s	x	x	x	s		x	
L. dimidiatus (Valenciennes)	x	s	x	s	x	x	x	s		x	
L. pectoralis Randall & Springer	x		x?			p	p	x		x	p
Labropsis alleni Randall	x										x
L. micronesica Randall	x		x					x		s	x
L. xanthonota Randall				x				x		s	x
SCARIDAE (PARROTFISHES)											
Subfamily Sparisomatinae											
Calotomus carolinus (Valenciennes)	s	p	x		x	x	x	x		s	x
C. spinidens (Quoy & Gaimard)	l				x					x	x
Leptoscarus vaigiensis (Quoy & Gaimard)	x	p						x			
Subfamily Scarinae											
Bolbometopon muricatum (Valenciennes)	x	s				s	p	s			p
Cetoscarus bicolor (Rüppell)	x	s	x	s			x	s		x	
Hipposcarus longiceps (Valenciennes)	ls	p	x			x	s	x			
Scarus altipinnis (Steindachner)	ls	s				x	s	x			
S. atropectoralis Schultz	p										x
S. bleekeri (deBeaufort)	p		x		x						x
S. bowersi (Snyder)	x										
S. chameleon Choat & Randall	p										x
S. dimidiatus Bleeker	x	p			x	x	s				x so.
S. festivus Valenciennes	p	p					p				x
S. flavipectoralis Schultz					Carolines						x
S. forsteni (Bleeker)	lp	x				s	x	s	p		p
S. frenatus Lacepède	lp			x			x	s	x		p
S. frontalis Valenciennes							x	s	x		p
S. ghobban Forsskål	s	p		s	x			s			x
S. gibbus Rüppell	lp	p	p		x	s	x	s		x	p
S. globiceps Valenciennes	lp	p		x	s	x					x
S. javanicus Bleeker	p										
S. niger Forsskål	x		x				s				p
S. oviceps Valenciennes	s	p				s	x	s		p	p
S. prasiognathos Valenciennes	lp										
S. psittacus Forsskål	s	p	x			x	s	x			
S. pyrrhurus (Jordan & Seale)	x										
S. quoyi Valenciennes	x										
S. rivulatus Valenciennes	p	p				s		x			
S. rubroviolaceus (Bleeker)	lp						x	s		x	
S. schlegeli (Bleeker)	x	p	x	s			x			pc	x
S. sordidus Forsskål	ls	p	x		x	x	s	x			x
S. spinus Kner	p	p		x			x				x
Scarus n. sp. 1 (Randall & Myers)								x			
MUGILIDAE (MULLETS)											
Chaenomugil leuciscus (Günther)			x					x		x	
Crenimugil crenilabis (Forsskål)	l	p	x					x		pc	x
Liza ceramensis Bleeker	l										
L. melinoptera (Valenciennes)	l										
L. vaigiensis (Quoy & Gaimard)	l	p	x				x			x	x
Oedalechilus labiosus (Valenciennes)	l		x								x
Valamugil engeli (Bleeker)			x					x		pc	x
V. seheli (Forsskål)	l									x	

Taxa	B	Y	If	T	Po	Kp	K	sM	nM	M	W
SPHYRAENIDAE (BARRACUDAS)											
Sphyraena acutipinnis Day			x		x		x			x	
S. barracuda (Walbaum)		p			x	x	pc			x	p
S. forsteri Cuvier	p	p	x		x		x				
S. genie Klunzinger	p	p			p		x				
S. novaehollandiae Günther					p						
S. obtusata Cuvier				x	x						
POLYNEMIDAE (THREADFINS)											
Polydactylus sexfilis (Valenciennes)	l		x		x		x				
PINGUIPEDIDAE (SANDPERCHES)											
Parapercis clathrata Ogilby			x		x		x				
P. cylindrica (Bloch)	p										
P. millipunctata (Günther)		s	x	s	x	x	x				
P. xanthozona (Bleeker)	x										
TRICHONOTIDAE (SAND-DIVERS)											
Trichonotus n. sp.									p	x	
CREEDIIDAE (SANDBURROWERS)											
Chalixodytes tauensis Schultz							x			x	
Limnichthys donaldsoni Schultz										x	
URANOSCOPIDAE (STARGAZERS)											
Uranoscopus sp. (2 spp.?)					x						
TRIPTERYGIIDAE (TRIPLEFINS)											
Enneapterygius hemimelas (Kner & Steindachner)										x	
E. minutus (Günther)										x	
E. nanus (Schultz)							x			x	
Helcogramma capitata Rosenblatt	x	x		x	x		x			x	
H. chica Rosenblatt					x		x			x	
H. hudsoni (Jordan & Seale)										x	
Norfolkia brachylepis (Schultz)							x			x	
BLENNIIDAE (BLENNIES)											
Tribe Salariini											
Alticus saliens (Lacepède)							x	x			
Atrosalarius fuscus holomelas (Günther)	x			x						x	
Cirripectes castaneus (Valenciennes)	x	x	x		x						
C. fuscoguttatus Strasburg & Schultz	x	x	x								
C. perustus Smith	xpc	xpc	xpc								
C. polyzona (Bleeker)	x	x	x?		x	x?	x	x	x	x	
C. quagga Fowler & Ball	x	x	x		x		x				
C. stigmaticus Strasburg & Schultz	x	x	x	x	x						
C. variolosus (Valenciennes)	x	x	x	x	x	x	s		x	x	
Ecsenius bicolor (Day)	x				s	x	x	s		x	
E. opsifrontalis Chapman & Schultz	p	Ulithi			x	x	s			x	x
E. stellifer Springer	x										
E. yaeyamaensis (Aoyagi)	x	x	x		s?						
Entomacrodus caudofasciatus (Regan)	x				x					x	
E. cymatobiotus Schultz & Chapman			x								
E. decussatus (Bleeker)			x		x		x			x	
E. niuafoouensis (Fowler)							x			x	
E. sealei Bryan & Herre			x		x		x			x	
E. stellifer stellifer Jordan & Snyder							x				
E. striatus (Quoy & Gaimard)			x	x			x	x		x	
E. thalassinus (Jordan & Seale)			x	x	x		x				
Exalias brevis (Kner)	l		x	x	x		x			x	
Glyptoparus delicatulus Smith			x								
G. jugularis (Klunzinger)			x								
Istiblennius chrysospilos (Bleeker)			x				x	x		x	
I. cyanostigma (Bleeker)				x	x						
I. edentulus (Bloch & Schneider)	x	x	x		x		x			x	
I. gibbifrons rodenbaughi Schultz & Chapman	x		x		x	p	x			x	
I. lineatus (Valenciennes)	x	x			x		x			x	
I. periophthalmus (Valenciennes)	l	x			x		x			x	
Litobranchus fowleri (Herre)	x										
Nannosalarias nativitatis (Regan)					x						
Prealticus amboinensis (Bleeker)							x				
P. natalis (Regan)							x	x?			
Prealticus sp.											p so.
Rhabdoblennius rhabdotrachelus (Fowler & Ball)	x		x	x	x					x	
R. snowi (Fowler)		x			x	x	x			x	
Salarias fasciatus (Bloch)	x		x	x	x	x				x	
Salarias guttatus Valenciennes	p				x						
Salarias luctuosus Whitley	p?										
Stanulus seychellensis Smith			x+Ulithi	x	x		x				
Tribe Omobranchini											
Enchelyurus kraussi (Klunzinger)							x				
Omobranchus rotundiceps obliquus (Gar.)	x	x	x				x				
Omox biporos Springer	x		x								
Parenchelyurus hepburni (Snyder)			x				x				
Tribe Nemophini											
Aspidontus dussumieri (Valenciennes)	x						x				
A. taeniatus taeniatus Quoy & Gaimard	x		x		x	x	x	x			
Meiacanthus anema (Günther)		x?									
M. atrodorsalis atrodorsalis (Günther)	x	x	x	s	x	x				x	
M. ditrema Smith-Vaniz	x										
M. grammistes (Valenciennes)	x	x									
Petroscirtes breviceps (Valenciennes)	x	x									
P. mitratus Rüppell	x				x	x				x	

Taxa	B	Y	If	T	Po	Kp	K	sM	nM	M	W
P. thepasi	x	x									
P. variabilis Cantor	x										
P. xestus Jordan & Seale	x	Carolines					x			x	
Plagiotremus l. laudandus (Whitley)	x						x			x	
P. rhynorhynchus (Bleeker)	x				s		x		s	x	p
P. tapienosoma (Bleeker)	x	s	x	s	x	x	x	s	x	x	x
Xiphasia matsubarai Okada & Suzuki dp										x	x
SCHINDLERIIDAE											
Schindleria praematurus (Schindler) pel											x
CALLIONYMIDAE (DRAGONETS)											
Anaora tentaculata Gray	x	x					x				
Callionymus enneactis Bleeker	x	x									
C. delicatulus Smith	x										
C. simplicicornis Valenciennes					x	x			x		x
Diplogrammus goramensis (Bleeker)	x			x+Ulithi			x			x	x
Synchiropus circularis Fricke							xE				
S. laddi Schultz	x									x	
S. morrisoni Schultz				Ant	x				p	x	
S. ocellatus (Pallas)						x				p so.	
S. splendidus (Herre)	x				x						
Synchiropus sp. (Rota)									pE		
ELEOTRIDIDAE (SLEEPERS; GUDGEONS)											
Butis amboinensis (Bleeker) fw	l				x						
Calumia godeffroyi (Günther)					x		x				
Eleotris fusca (Bloch & Schneider) fw	l	p	x		x		x			x	
Ophieleotris aporos (Bleeker) fw	x				x		x			x	
Ophiocara porocephala (Valenciennes) fw	x				x	x					
Oxyeleotris lineolatus (Steindachner) fw							x				
XENISTHMIDAE (WRIGGLERS)											
Allomicrodesmis dorotheae Schultz											x
Xenisthmus polyzonatus (Klunzinger)									x		
Xenisthmus spp.(≥1)							x			x	
MICRODESMIDAE (WORMFISHES and DARTFISHES)											
Subfamily Microdesminae											
Gunnellichthys monostigma Smith										x	x
G. pleurotaenia Bleeker						x				x	x
G. viridescens Dawson		x					x				x
Paragunnellichthys seychellensis Dawson	x						x				
Subfamily Pteleotrinae											
Nemateleotris decora Randall & Allen	x										
N. helfrichi Randall & Allen							x			x	
N. magnifica Fowler	x	s				x		s	x	pc	x
Parioglossus formosus (Smith)	x										
P. lineatus Rennis & Hoese	x										
P. nudus Rennis & Hoese	x										
P. palustris (Herre)	x										
P. rainfordi McCulluch	x					x					
P. raoi (Herre)						x					
P. taeniatus Regan	x										
P. verticalis Rennis & Hoese						x					
Ptereleotris evides (Jordan & Hubbs)	x	s	x	s	x	x	x	x	x	s	x
P. hanae (Jordan & Snyder)										x	
P. heteroptera (Bleeker)						x	x		x	x	x
P. lineopinnis (Fowler) dp										x	
P. microlepis Bleeker	s						x		x	s	x
P. zebra (Fowler)	s								x	s	x
GOBIIDAE (GOBIES)											
Fossorial species, prawn-associated:											
Amblyeleotris fasciata (Herre)									x	x	x
A. fontaseni (Bleeker)	p										
A. guttata (Fowler)						x				x	
A. periophthalma (Bleeker)	p					x	x				
A. steinitzi (Klausewitz)									x	x	
A. randalli Hoese & Steene	x										
A. wheeleri (Pulonin & Lubbock)											x
Cryptocentroides insignis (Seale)	l					x					
Cryptocentrus caruleomaculatus (Herre)	x	x									
C. cinctus (Herre)	p	p									
C. koumansi (Whitley)	u						p	x			
C. octafasciatus Regan							x				
C. singapurensis (Herre)	x										
C. strigilliceps (Jordan & Seale)						x			x	x	
Cryptocentrus sp. A	x										
Ctenogobiops aurocingulus (Herre)		x				x				x	
C. feroculus Lubbock & Pulonin						x				x	
C. pomastictus Lubbock & Pulonin	s?						x			u	p?
C. tangararoai Lubbock & Pulonin							x				
Lotilia graciliosa Klausewitz	p									p	x
Mahidolia mystacina (Valenciennes)	(as*Waitea* sp.)- x?					p					
Vanderhorstia ambanoro (Fourmanior)										p	x
V. ornatissima Smith		x				x		x		x	
Fossorial species, non-prawn-associated:											
Amblygobius decussatus (Bleeker)	x				x		x	x?			x
A. hectori (Smith)	p					x	x				
A. nocturnus (Herre)						x			x		
A. phalaena (Valenciennes)						x	x	s	x	x	x

Taxa	B	Y	If	T	Po	Kp	K	sM	nM	M	W
A. rainfordi (Whitley)	pl			p							x
Oplopomops diacanthus (Schultz, 1943)				x							x
Oplopomus oplopomus (Valenciennes)	l		x	x	x			x			x
Signigobius biocellatus Hoese & Allen	x										
Silhouettea sp.											x
Valenciennea muralis (Valenciennes)	x										
V. puellaris (Tomiyama)							x				x
V. sexguttatus (Valenciennes)				x	x	x					x
V. strigatus (Brousonet)	x	p	x				x	s	x	s	x
Valenciennea spp. (≥1)	x										x
Non-fossorial species:											
Acentrogobius bonti est	u			x							
Asterropteryx ensiferus (Bleeker)											x
A. semipunctatus Rüppell	x						x	s	x		x
Austrolethops wardi Whitley			x								
Awaous grammepomus (Bleeker) fw	x										
A. guamensis (Valenciennes) fw							x				
Bathygobius cocosensis (Bleeker)							x			x	
B. cotticeps (Steindachner)							x				
B. fuscus fuscus (Rüppell)	l		x		x		x			s?	x
Bryaninops amplus Larson	x						x				
B. erythrops (Jordan & Seale)			e.Carolines								
B. natans Larson				x			x				
B. ridens Smith			Ulithi	x							
B. youngei (Davis & Cohen)	x										
Cabillus tongarevae (Fowler)											x
Callogobius bauchotae Goren											x
C. centrolepis Weber											x
C. hasselti (Bleeker)	x			x							x
C. maculipinnis (Fowler)	l						x				x
C. okinawae (Snyder)											x
C. plumatus (Smith)							x				
C. sclateri (Steindachner)	l			x?			x				x
Callogobius sp. (≥1)			x								x
Cristagobius sp.			x								
Eviota afelei Jordan & Seale							x				x
E. albolineata Jewett & Lachner	x		Carolines								
E. bifasciata Lachner & Karnella	x										
E. cometa Jewett & Lachner				x							
E. distigma Jordan & Seale		x	x	x			x			x	
E. fasciola Karnella & Lachner	x		x Ulithi	x	x?		x	x	x		
E. herrei Jordan & Seale	x										
E. infulata (Smith)				x	x						
E. lachdebrerei Giltay	x			x	x		x				
E. latifasciata Jewett & Lachner				x	x						
E. melasma Lachner & Karnella	x		x								
E. nebulosa Smith	x						x			x	
E. pellucidus Larson			x				x				
E. prasina (Klunzinger)	x										
E. prasites Jordan & Seale		x									
E. punctulata Jewett & Lachner	x			x	x						
E. queenslandica Whitley	x	x									
E. saipanensis Fowler							x				
E. sebreei Jordan & Seale	x		xUlithi								x
E. sigillata Jewett & Lachner	x			x	x						
E. smaragdus Jordan & Seale							x	s	x		
E. sparsa Jewett & Lachner	x										
E. storthynx (Rofen)	x	x									
E. zonura Jordan & Seale	x		x Ulithi	x			x	s	x		
Eviota spp. (≥1)								u	u	u	
Exyrias belissimus (Smith)	x						x	x			
E. puntang (Bleeker)							x				
Fusigobius longispinus Goren							x				u?
F. neophytus (Günther)	s		x	x			x	s	x		
Fusigobius sp. 1							x				u?
Gladiogobius ensifera (Bleeker)	l										
Glossogobius biocellatus (Val.) est			x								
G. celebius (Valenciennes) fw	x			x							
G. guirus fw				x							
Gnatholepis anjerensis (Bleeker)		x		x			x				x
G. scapulostigma Herre							x				x
Gnatholepis sp.										p	
Gobiodon albofasciatus Sawada & Arai	p										
G. citrinus (Rüppell)		s	x	s			x				x
G. erythrospilus Bleeker		x		x							x
G. okinawae Sawada, Arai, & Abe	p										
G. quinquestrigatus (Valenciennes)							x				x
G. rivulatus (Rüppell)	ls	x	x	x			x				x
Gobiopsis bravoi (Herre)	x	x		x							
Heteroeleotris sp.		x		x							x
Istigobius decoratus (Herre)										p	x
I. ornatus (Rüppell)	l			x	x						x
I. rigilius (Herre)											x
I. spence (Smith)				x							
Kelloggella cardinalis Jordan & Seale	x										
K. quindecimfasciata (Fowler)											x

Taxa	B	Y	If	T	Po	Kp	K	sM	nM	M	W
Macrodontogobius wilburi Herre	x		x								x
Mugilogobius tagala Herre est							x				
M. villa Herre est	u?						x				
Opua nephodes E. K. Jordan											x
Oxyurichthys microlepis (Bleeker) est				x							
O. guibei Smith est							x				
O. ophthalmonema (Bleeker) est							x				
O. papuensis (Valenciennes) est					x		x				
O. tentacularis est					x						
Padanka sp. fw	u?										
Palutris pruinosa (Jordan & Seale) est	u?										x
P. reticularis Smith est				x							
Paragobiodon echinocephalus (Rüppell)	l	x					x	x	x		x
P. lacunicolus (Kendall & Goldsborough)						x	x		x		x
P. melanosomus (Bleeker)		x		x			x				x
P. modestus (Regan, 1908)											x
P. xanthosomus (Bleeker)											x
Periophthalmus gracilis Eggert	x										
P. koelreuteri (Pallas)	x						x	x	x		
Pleurosicya bilobatus (Koumans)	x		x				x			x	
P. muscarum (Jordan & Seale)								x		x	
Priolepis cinta (Regan)						x	x				
P. farcimen (Jordan & Evermann)											x
P. inhaca (Smith)									x		
P. semidoliatus (Valenciennes)							x		x		
Pseudogobius javanicus (Bleeker) fw	x										
Redigobius bikolanus (Herre) fw	x						x				
R. horiae (Herre) fw	xE										
R. sapangus (Herre) fw	x		x								
Sicyopus leprurus Sakai & Nakamura fw							x				
S. zosterophorum (Bleeker) fw	x										
Sicyopus spp. (≥1) fw	x		x								
Sicyopterus macrostetholepis (Bleeker) fw							x				
S. micrurus (Bleeker) fw	x										
Sicyopterus sp. (2) fw	x										
Stenogobius genivittatus (Valenciennes) fw	x	Carolines									
Stenogobius sp. fw			x								
Stiphodon elegans (Steindachner) fw	x		x				x		x		
Stiphodon spp. (≥1) fw			x								
Taenioides limicola Smith est							x				
Trimma caesiura Jordan & Seale		x					x		x		x
T. eviotops Schultz	p?						x			x	x
T. naudei Smith								x	x	x	
T. okinawae (Aoyagi)											x
T. tevegae Cohen & Davis	p								p		
T. taylori Lobel									p?		
Trimma n. sp.	p										
Trimma spp. (≥ 7 spp.)						x	x		x	x	x-6spp
KRAEMERIIDAE (SAND-DARTS)											
Kraemeria bryani Schultz											x
K. cunicularia (Rofen) fw	x										
K. samoensis Steindachner										x	x
ACANTHURIDAE (SURGEONFISHES and UNICORNFISHES)											
Subfamily Acanthurinae (Surgeonfishes)											
Acanthurus achilles Shaw		x			x			x	s	x	p
A. bariene (Lesson)	p										
A. blochii Valenciennes	l	s			x		s	x	s		x
A. chronixis Randall							x?	xE			
A. dussumieri Valenciennes								x	s		
A. guttatus (Bloch & Schneider)	x	p	x				x	x	s	x	p
A. leucocheilus Herre	p										
A. leucopareius (Jenkins)								x	x		x
A. lineatus (Linnaeus)	x	p	x	s	x	x	x	x	x	s	x
A. maculiceps (Ahl)	p	p	x							p	
A. mata Cuvier										?	x
A. nigricans (Linnaeus)	x	s	x	s			x	s	x		
A. nigricauda Dunker & Mohr	x	p	x		x	x	s	x	s	x	x
A. nigrofuscus (Forsskål)	l	s	x	s	x	s	x	s	x	s	x
A. nigroris Valenciennes	x	s	x	s			x	x	s	x	
A. olivaceus Bloch & Schneider	x	s	x	s			x	s	x	s	p
A. pyroferus Kittlitz	lp	p	x			x		x	s	x	
A. thompsoni (Fowler)	p					x	s	x	s	x	x
A. triostegus triostegus (Linnaeus)	x	x	x	s	x	x	x	x	x	s	x p
A. xanthopterus Valenciennes	l	p	x	s	x		s	x	s	x	
Ctenochaetus binotatus Randall	x		x				x		x	x	
C. hawaiiensis Randall							x	x	x		
C. marginatus (Valenciennes)			Mortlocks-x		x	x				p so.	
C. striatus (Quoy & Gaimard)	x	x	x	s	x	x	x	x	s	x	
C. strigosus (Bennett)				x			x		x	x	
C. tominiensis Randall	s										
Paracanthurus hepatus (Linnaeus)	lp						x	s	x		
Zebrasoma flavescens (Bennett)	x	s					x	s	x	p	
Z. scopas (Cuvier)	l		x	s	x	x	s	x			
Z. veliferum (Bloch)	x	s	x	s	x	x	s	x	p		
Subfamily Nasinae (Unicornfishes)											
Naso annulatus (Quoy & Gaimard)	p	s					x	s	x		

Taxa	B	Y	lf	T	Po	Kp	K	sM	nM	M	W
N. brachycentron (Valenciennes)	l						x				
N. brevirostris (Valenciennes)	lp					s	x	s		x	
N. hexacanthus (Bleeker)	lp		x		x			x	x		x
N. lituratus (Bloch & Schneider)	x	x	x	s	x	x	x	s	x	s	x p
N. lopezi Herre	x									s?	
N. tuberosus Lacepède	lp	s					x	s	s		
N. unicornis (Forsskål)	l	p	x		x	x	s	x	s	x	
N. vlamingii (Valenciennes)	lp	p	x	s	x	x	x	x		x	
ZANCLIDAE (MOORISH IDOL)											
Zanclus cornutus (Linnaeus)	x	p		s			x	s	x	p	
SIGANIDAE (RABBITFISHES; SPINEFOOTS)											
Siganus argenteus (Quoy & Gaimard)	x	s	x	s		x	s	x		x	
S. canaliculatus (Park)	x	p									
S. corallinus Valenciennes	x										
S. doliatus Cuvier	x	x		s	x		s				
S. fuscescens (Houttuyn)	x			x							
S. guttatus (Bloch)	s	s?									
S. lineatus (Valenciennes)	x	p									
S. oramin (Schneider)	x										
S. puellus (Schlegel)	x	p		s	x	x	s			x so.	
S. punctatus (Schneider)	x	x	x		x?	x	s	x		x	
S. punctatissimus Fowler & Bean	p										
S. spinus (Linnaeus)	l	p		s			s	x			
S. vermiculatus (Valenciennes)	s						x				
S. (Lo) vulpinus (Schlegel and Müller)	x	p			x					x	
Siganus sp.					p						
SCOMBRIDAE (TUNAS and MACKERELS)											
Acanthocybium solandri (Cuvier) pel	x				x	x	x	s		x	
Auxis thazard (Lacepède) pel							x				
Euthynnus affinis (Cantor) pel	x						x	s		x	
Grammatorcynus bilineatus (Rüppell)	ls			p	x			x		x	
Gymnosarda unicolor (Rüppell)	lp	p		x		x?	s	x	pc	x	
Katsuwonus pelamis (Linnaeus) pel	x	x	x	x	x	x	x	x	x	x	x
Rastrelliger brachysoma (Bleeker)	l										
R. kanagurta (Cuvier)	ls										
Scomber japonicus Houttuyn pel	l										
Scomberomorus commerson (Lacepède)	lp										
Thunnus alalunga (Gmelin) dp pel						p					
T. albacares (Bonnaterre) pel	x	x	x	x	x	x	x	x		p	x x
Thunnus obesus (Lowe) dp pel (Longline catches)											
ISTIOPHORIDAE (MARLINS)											
Istiophorus platypterus (Shaw & Nodder) pel	l					p					
Makaira indica (Cuvier) pel	u					x					
Makaira nigricans Lacepède pel						p					
Tetrapterus angustirostris Tanaka pel						x					
NOMEIDAE											
Psenes cyanophrys Cuvier pel							x		u		
Order **PLEURONECTIFORMES**											
BOTHIDAE (LEFTEYE FLOUNDERS)											
Asterorhombus intermedius (Bleeker)							u		x		
Bothus mancus (Brousonet)	x	p	x		x	x		x		x	
B. pantherinus (Rüppell)	l		x			x	s	x	s?	x	
Engyprosopon sp. dp						x					
PLEURONECTIDAE (RIGHTEYE FLOUNDERS)											
Samariscus triocellatus Woods					x				x		
SOLEIDAE (SOLES)											
Aseraggodes melanostictus (Peters)	(as *dubius*) x?			x			x				
A. smithi Woods							x				
A. whitakeri Woods							x				
Pardachirus pavoninus (Lacepède)	x										
Soleichthys heterohinos (Bleeker)				x			x		x		
Order **TETRAODONTIFORMES**											
BALISTIDAE (TRIGGERFISHES)											
Abalistes stellatus (Lacepède)	l										
Balistapus undulatus (Mungo Park)	x	s	x	s	x	x	x	s	x	s	x
Balistoides conspicillum (Bloch & Schn.)	x		x				x	pc	x		
B. viridescens (Bloch & Schneider)	x	p				s	x	s		x	
Canthidermis maculatus (Bloch) pel	x						x	pc	x		
Melichthys niger (Bloch)	s		p		x		s	x	s	x	p
M. vidua (Solander)	p	x	x		x		s	x	s	x	p
Odonus niger (Rüppell)	s		p	x		x	s	x	s	x	
Pseudobalistes flavimarginatus (Rüppell)	x	s	x			x	x	p	x		x
P. fuscus (Bloch & Schneider)							x			x	
Rhinecanthus aculeatus (Linnaeus)	x	x	x		x	x	x	x	pc	x	p
R. rectangulus (Bloch & Schneider)	p	p	x		x	x		x	s	x	
R. verrucosa (Linnaeus)	p	x		s		x					
Sufflamen bursa (Bloch & Schneider)	lp	s	x			s	x	s		x	
S. chrysoptera (Bloch & Schneider)	s	x	x	s	x	x	s	x	s	x	
S. freanatus (Latreille)		p	x			x		x	s	x	
Xanthichthys auromarginatus (Bennett)	s						x	u	x		
X. careuleolineatus Randall, Matsuura, & Zama dp							x		s		
X. mento (Jordan & Gilbert)										p	
Xenobalistes tumidipectoris Matsuura dp						x					
MONACANTHIDAE (FILEFISHES; LEATHERJACKETS)											
Acreichthys tomentosus (Linnaeus)	x										
Aluterus monoceros (Linnaeus)						x					

Taxa	B	Y	lf	T	Po	Kp	K	sM	nM	M	W
A. scriptus (Osbeck)	lp	s					x			x	
Amanses scopas (Cuvier)	x	s			x		x	s	s	x	
Brachaluteres taylori Woods											x
Cantherhines dumerilii (Hollard)	x	s	x		x	x	s	x	s	x	
C. fronticinctus (Playfair & Günther)							s		p so.		
C. pardalis (Rüppell)	ls	p	x			x		x	s	x	
Oxymonacanthus longirostris (Bl. & Sch.)	x	s.			s	x		x	s	x	
Paraluteres prionurus (Bleeker)	x		x	s	x			x	pc	x	
Paramonacanthus cryptodon (Bleeker) prob dp as adults											x
P. japonicus (Tilesius) prob dp as adults											x
Pervagor alternans (Ogilby)											x
P. aspricaudus (Hollard)											x
P. janthinosoma (Bleeker)	x		x		u	u		x			
P. melanocephalus (Bleeker)	x										x
P. nigrolineatus (Herre)	x										
OSTRACIIDAE (TRUNKFISHES; BOXFISHES)											
Lactoria cornuta (Linnaeus)	x					x					
L. diaphana (Bloch & Schneider) pel	l					x					
L. fornasini (Bianconi)						x			x		
Ostracion cubicus Linnaeus	x	s	x	s		x		x		x	
O. meleagris Shaw	p	s	x			x	s	x	s	x	
O. solorensis Bleeker	x										
Rhynchostracion nasus (Bloch)	x										
?R. rhynorhynchus (Bleeker)	s?										
TRIODONTIDAE (TRIPPLETOOTH PUFFERS)											
Triodon macropterus Lesson dp pel							x				
TETRAODONTIDAE (PUFFERS)											
Amblyrhinchotus honckenii (Bloch)										x so.	
Arothron hispidus (Linnaeus)	x		p (as *reticulatus*) x?			s	x			x	p
A. manilensis (Procé)	x	x				s	x			x	
A. mappa (Lesson)	x						x			x so.	
A. meleagris (Lacepède)			x				x		x	s	x
A. nigropunctatus (Bloch & Schneider)	x	x	x			x		x	s	x	
A. stellatus (Bloch & Schneider)	x			p	x					x	
Canthigaster amboinensis (Bleeker)			x				x		x	s	x
C. bennetti (Bleeker)	x			s	x	x		x	s	p	
C. compressa (Procé)	x						p				
C. coronata (Vaillant & Sauvage)			x				x		x	x	p so.
C. epilampra (Jenkins)	x						x			x so.	
C. janthinoptera (Bleeker)	x		x		x	x		x	s	x	
C. leoparda Lubbock & Allen	x										
C. solandri (Richardson)	x		s		x	s	x			x	
C. valentini (Bleeker)	x	s	s			s	x	pc		p so.	
Lagocephalus lagocephalus (Linnaeus) pel	l										
Lagocephalus sceleratus (Gmelin) pel	l										
DIODONTIDAE (PORCUPINEFISHES)											
Diodon eydouxii Brisout de Barneville pel											
D. hystrix Linnaeus	x		x				x	s	x		x
D. liturosus Shaw	x	p				x				p so.	

Bibliography

Abe, T. 1939. A list of the fishes of the Palao Islands. Palao Trop. Biol. Stn. Stud., 1: 523-583.

Allen, G. R. 1972a. Anemonefishes, their classification and biology. T.F.H. Publ., Neptune, NJ, 288 p.

____. 1972b. Observations on a commensal relationship between *Siphamia fuscolineata* (Apogonidae) and the crown-of-thorns starfish, *Acanthaster planci*. Copeia 1972(3): 595-597.

____. 1973. *Bodianus bimaculatus*, a new species of wrasse (Pisces: Labridae) from the Palau Archipelago. Proc. Biol. Soc. Wash. 86(32): 385-390.

____. 1975a. The biology and taxonomy of the cardinalfish *Sphaeramia orbicularis* (Pisces; Apogonidae). J. Roy. Soc. West. Aust. 58(3): 86-92.

____. 1975b. Damselfishes of the south seas. T. F. H. Publ., Neptune, NJ, 240 p.

____. 1978. The status of *Abudefduf sexfasciatus* (Lacepède), a pomacentrid fish from the Indo-west Pacific. Copeia 1978(2): 328-330.

____. 1979. Butterfly and Angelfishes of the World, Vol. 2. Wiley Interscience, New York, 352 p.

Allen, G. R. and N. J. Cross. 1983. A new species and two new records of squirrelfishes (Holocentridae) from the eastern Indian Ocean and Australia. Rev. Fr. Aquar. 10(1): 5-8.

Allen, G. R. and A. R. Emery. 1985. A review of the pomacentrid fishes of the genus *Stegastes* from the Indo-Pacific, with descriptions of two new species. Indo-Pacific Fishes no. 3, 31 p., 3 col. pls.

Allen, G. R., D. F. Hoese, J. R. Paxton, J. E. Randall, B. C. Russell, W. A. Stark II, F. H. Talbot, and G. P. Whitley. 1976. Annotated checklist of the fishes of Lord Howe Island. Rec. Aust. Mus. 301(51): 365-454.

Allen, G. R., and R. H. Kuiter. 1978. *Heniochus diphreutes* Jordan, a valid species of butterflyfish (Chaetodontidae) from the Indo-west-Pacific. Jr. R. Soc. West. Australia 61(1): 11-18.

Allen, G. R. and H. K. Larson. 1975. *Pomachromis guamensis*, a new species of damselfish (Pomacentridae) from the Mariana Islands. Micronesica 11(1): 123-126.

Allen, G. R. and H. K. Larson. 1975. *Pomachromis guamensis*, a new species of damselfish (Pomacentridae) from the Mariana Islands. Micronesica 11(1): 123-126.

Allen, G. R., and J. E. Randall. 1977. Review of the sharpnose pufferfishes (subfamily Canthigasterinae) of the Indo-Pacific. Rec. Aust. Mus. 30(17): 475-517.

Allen, G. R., and B. C. Russell. 1986. Fishes. *in* P. F. Berry (Ed.) Faunal surveys of the Rowley Shoals, Scott Reef and Seringapatam Reef North-western Australia. Rec. West. Aust. Mus. Suppl. no. 25: 75-103.

Allen, G. R., and W. A. Starck II. 1973a. Notes on the ecology, zoogeography, and coloration of the gobiesocid clingfishes, *Lepadichthys caritus* Briggs and *Diademichthys lineatus* (Sauvage). Proc. Linn. Soc. New South Wales 97: 95-97.

____. 1973b. A new species of butterflyfish (Chaetodontidae) from the Palau Islands. Trop. Fish Hob. March 1973: 17-28.

____. 1982. The anthiid fishes of the Great Barrier Reef, Australia, with the description of a new species. Rev. Fr. Aquariol. 9(2): 47-56.

Allen, G. R., and R. Steene. 1979. The fishes of Christmas Island, Indian Ocean. Aust. Nat. Parks and Wildlife Service, Special Publ. no. 2, v+81 p.

____. 1988. Ref fishes of the Indian Ocean. (Pacific marine fishes book 10). T.F.H., Publ., Neptune, NJ, 240 p.

Allen, G. R. and F. H. Talbot. 1985. Review of the snappers of the genus *Lutjanus* (Pisces: Lutjanidae) from the Indo-Pacific, with the description of a new species. Indo-Pacific Fishes no. 11, 87 p., 10 col. pl.

Amesbury, S. A. 1978. Distributional analysis of the fishes on the reefs of Yap. *in* R. T. Tsuda (Ed.). Marine biological survey of Yap lagoon. Univ. Guam Mar. Lab. Tech. Rep. no. 45: 87-131.

Amesbury, S. A., M. W. Colgan, R. F. Myers, R. K. Kropp, and F. A. Cushing. 1981. Biological monitoring study of airport runway expansion site Moen, Truk, eastern Caroline Islands pt. B. construction phase. Univ. Guam Mar. Lab. Tech. Rep. 74, 125 p.

Amesbury, S. A., D. R. Lassuy, R. F. Myers, and V. Tindzik. 1979. A survey of fish resources of Saipan Lagoon. Univ. Guam Tech. Rep. no. 52, 58p.

Amesbury, S. A., J. A. Marsh, R. H. Randall, and J. O. Stojkovich. 1977. Limited current and underwater biological survey of proposed Truk tuna fishery complex, Dublon Is., Truk. Univ. Guam Mar. Lab. Tech. Rep. 36, 49 p.

Amesbury, S. A., and R. F. Myers. 1982. Guide to the coastal resources of Guam, vol. 1: The Fishes. Univ. Guam Press, 141 p.

Bagnis. R., P. Mazellier, J. Bennett, and E. Christian. 1972. Fishes of Polynesia. Les Éditions du Pacifique, Papeete, 368 p.

Baldwin, W. J. 1983. *Stolephorus pacificus*, a new species of tropical anchovy (Engraulidae) from the western Pacific Ocean. Micronesica 19(1-2): 151-156.

Bauchot, M. L., M. Desoutter, Guézé, and J. E. Randall. 1985. Catalogue critique des types de poissons du Muséum National d'Histoire Naturelle (Suite) (Famille des Mullidae). Bull. Mus. Natl. Hist. Nat., Paris, sér. 4, sect. A, 7(2), suppl.: 1-25.

Bauchot, M. L., M. Desoutter, and J. E. Randall. 1984. Catalogue critique des types de poissons du Muséum National d'Histoire Naturelle (Suite) (Famille des Serranidae). Bull. Mus. Natl. Hist. Nat., Paris, sér. 4, sect. A, 6(3), suppl.: 3-82.

Bell, L. J. and P. L. Colin. 1986. Mass spawning of *Caesio teres* (Pisces: Caesionidae) at Enewetak Atoll, Marshall Islands. Env. Biol. Fishes 15(1): 69-74.

Berry, F. H., Smith-Vaniz, W. F., and J. B. Moberly. 1983. Identification of trevallys or crevalles (genus *Caranx*) of the Indian and Pacific Oceans. Intl. Game Fish Assoc., Ft. Lauderdale, 4p.

Böhlke, J. E. and J. E, Randall. 1981. Four new garden eels (Congridae: Heteroncongrinae) of the Pacific and Indian Oceans. Bull. Mar. Sci. 31(2): 366-382.

Briggs, J. C. 1955. A monograph of the clingfishes (order Xenopterygii). Stanford Ichthy. Bull. 6: 1-224.

Bright, G. R., and J. A. June. 1981. Freshwater fishes of Palau, Caroline Islands. Micronesica 17(1/2): 107-111.

Bruce, R. W., and J. E. Randall. 1985. Revision of the Indo-Pacific parrotfish genera *Calotomus* and *Leptoscarus*. Indo-Pacific Fishes no. 5, 32 p., 3 col. pls.

Bryan, P. G. 1973. Three new shark records from Guam, Mariana Islands. Micronesica 9(1): 159-160.

Burgess, W. E. 1973. *Apolemichthys xanthopunctatus*, a new species of angelfish (family Pomacanthidae) from the Pacific Ocean. Trop. Fish Hob. Aug. 1973: 55-89.

____. 1978. Butterflyfishes of the world. A monograph of the family Chaetodontidae. T. F. H. Publ., Neptune City, NJ. 832 p.

Burgess, W. E. and H. R. Axelrod. 1975. Pacific Marine Fishes. Book 6, Fishes of Melanesia. T.F.H. Publ., Neptune City, NJ. pp. 1383-1654, 479 col. figs.

Burgess, W. E. and H. R. Axelrod. 1975. Pacific Marine Fishes. Book 7, Fishes of The Great Barrier Reef. T.F.H. Publ., Neptune City, NJ pp. 1655-1925, 412 col. figs.

Cantwell, G. E. 1964. A revision of the genus *Parapercis*, family Mugiloididae. Pac. Sci. 18(3): 239-280.

Carlson, B. 1985. The mating system of the spotted coral blenny, *Exallias brevis*. (abstract for Proc. Second Int. Conf. on Indo-Pacific Fishes, Tokyo)

Carpenter, K. 1987. Revision of the Indo-Pacific fish family Caesionidae (Lutjanoidea), with descriptions of five new species. Indo-Pacific Fishes no.15, 56p.

Castle, P. H. J. 1968. The congrid eels of the western Indian Ocean and the Red Sea. Ichth. Bull. Rhodes Univ. 33: 658-726.

Chave, E. H. and D. B. Eckert. 1974. Ecological aspects of the distributions of fishes at Fanning Island. Pac. Sci. 28: 297-317.

Choat, J. H. and J. E. Randall. 1986. A review of the parrotfishes (family Scaridae) of the Great Barrier Reef of Australia with description of a new species. Rec. Aust. Mus. 38: 175-228.

Clark, E. 1979. Red Sea fishes of the family Tripterygiidae with descriptions of eight new species. Israel J. Zool. 28: 65-113.

Clark, E. and A. George. 1979. Toxic soles, *Pardachirus marmoratus* from the Red sea and *P. pavoninus* from Japan, with notes on other species. Env. Biol. Fish. 4(2): 103-123.

Cohen, D. M., and W. P. Davis. 1969. Vertical orientation in a new gobioid fish. Pac. Sci. 23(3): 317-324.

Coleman, N. 1981. Australian Sea Fishes North of 30ºS. Doubleday, Sydney and Aukland. 279 p., 223 col. figs.

Coleman, N. 1980. Australian Sea Fishes South of 30ºS. Doubleday, Sydney and Aukland. 302 p., 279 col. figs.

Colin, P. L. 1976. Filter feeding and predation on the eggs of *Thalassoma* sp. by the scombrid fish *Rastrelliger kanagurta*. Copeia 1976(3): 596-597.

Colin, P. L., D. M. Devaney, L. Hillis-Colinvaux, T. H. Suchanek, and J. T. Harrison, III. 1986. Geology and biological zonation of the reef slope, 50-360 m depth at Enewetak Atoll, Marshall Islands. Bull. Mar. Sci. 38(1):111-128.

Collette, B.B. 1974. Geographic variation in the central Pacific halfbeak, *Hyporhamphus acutus* (Günther). Pac. Sci. 28(2): 111-122.

____. 1983. Recognition of two species of double-lined mackerels (*Grammatorcynus*: Scombridae). Proc. Biol. Soc. Wash. 96(4): 715-718.

Collette, B. B., and C. E. Nauen. 1983. FAO species catalogue. Vol. 2 Scombrids of the World. FAO Fish. Synop., (125) vol. 2: 137p.

Collette, B. B., and N. V. Parin. 1978. Five new species of halfbeaks (Hemiramphidae) from the Indo-West-Pacific. Proc. Biol. Soc. Wash. 91(3): 731-747.

Collette, B. B., and F. H. Talbot. 1972. Activity patterns of coral reef fishes with emphasis on nocturnal-diurnal changeover. *In* B. B. Collette and S. A. Earle (Eds.). Results of the Tektite program: Ecology of Coral Reef Fishes. Sci. Bull. (14), Nat. Hist. Mus. Los Angeles.

Compagno, L. J. V. 1984. FAO species catalogue. Vol. 4 Sharks of the World. FAO Fish. Synop., (125) vol. 4, pts. 1-2, 655 p.

Conde, B. and D. Terver. 1983. *Malacanthus latovittatus*. Rev. Fr. Aquariol. 2/83: 261-264.

Cressey, R. 1981. Revision of the Indo-Pacific fishes of the genus *Synodus* (Pisces: Synodontidae). Smithson. Contr. Zool. 342: 53 p.

Cuvier, G., and Valenciennes, A. 1828-1849. Histoire naturelle des poissons. Levrault, Paris. 22 vols.

Dawson, C. E. 1973. Indo-Pacific distribution of microdesmid fishes (Gobioidea). J. Mar. Biol. Ass. India, 15(1): 318-322.

____. 1975. Notes on Indo-Pacific pipefishes (Pisces: Syngnathidae) with description of two new species. Proc. Biol. Soc. Wash. 88(25): 263-280.

____. 1976. Review of the Indo-Pacific pipefish genus *Choerichthys* (Pisces: Syngnathidae) with description of two new species. Proc. Biol. Soc. Wash. 89(3): 39-66.

____. 1977a. Review of the pipefish genus *Corythoichthys* with description of three new species. Copeia 1977 (2): 295-338.

____. 1978. Review of the Indo-Pacific pipefish genus *Bhanotia*, with description of *B. nuda* n. sp. Proc. Biol. Soc. Wash. 91(2): 392-407.

____. 1981. Review of the Indo-Pacific pipefish genus *Doryrhamphus* Kaup (Pisces: Syngnathidae), with descriptions of a new species and a new subspecies. Ichty. Bull. J.L.B. Smith Inst. Ichth. no. 44, 27 p.

____. 1982. Review of the genus *Micrognathus* Dunker (Pisces: Syngnathidae), with description of *M. natans*, n. sp. Proc. Biol. Soc. Wash. 95(4): 657-687.

____. 1984. Review of the Indo-Pacific pipefish genus *Trachyrhamphus* (Syngnathidae). Micronesica (1982)18: 163-191.

____. 1985. Indo-Pacific pipefishes (Red Sea to Americas). Gulf Coast Res. Lab., Ocean Springs, MS, vi+230 p.

deBeaufort, L.F. 1940. The fishes of the Indo-Australian Archipelago. 8. Leiden: E.J. Brill. 508 p.

deBeaufort, L.F. and J. C. Briggs. 1962. The fishes of the Indo-Australian Archipelago. 11. Leiden: E.J. Brill. 481 p.

deBeaufort, L.F. and W. M. Chapman. 1951. The fishes of the Indo-Australian Archipelago. 9. Leiden: E.J. Brill. 484 p.

Donaldson, T. J. 1984. Mobbing behavior by *Stegastes albifasciatus* (Pomacentridae), a territorial mosaic damselfish. Japan. J. Ichthy. 31(3): 345-348.

Dor, M. 1984. Checklist of the Fishes of the Red Sea. CLOFRES Israel Acad. Sci. Human. xxv+437p.

Dunlap P. V. and M. J. McFall-Ngai. 1984. *Leiognathus elongatus* (Perciformes: Leiognathidae): two distinct species based on morphological and light organ characters. Copeia 1984(4).

Eschmeyer, W. N., Y. Hirosaki, and T. Abe. 1973. Two new species of the scorpionfish genus *Rhinopias*, with comments on related genera and species. Proc. Calif. Acad. Sci., ser.4, 39(16): 285-310.

Eschmeyer, W. N. and K. Rama Rao. 1973. Two new stonefishes (Pisces: Scorpaenidae) from the Indo-west Pacific, with a synopsis of the subfamily Synanceiinae. Proc. Calif. Acad. Sci., ser.4, 39(18): 337-382.

Eschmeyer, W. N., K. Rama Rao, and L. E. Hallacher. 1979. Fishes of the scorpionfish subfamily Choridactylinae from the western Pacific and the Indian Ocean. Proc. Calif. Acad. Sci., ser.4, 41(20): 475-500.

Eschmeyer, W. N. and J. E. Randall. 1975. The scorpaenid fishes of the Hawaiian Islands, including new species and new records (Pisces: Scorpaenidae). Proc. Calif. Acad. Sci., ser.4, 40(11): 265-334.

Fisher, W. and D. J. P. Whitehead (Eds). 1974. FAO species identification sheets for fishery purposes. Eastern Indian Ocean and Western Central Pacific. 4 vols. Rome: FAO.

Fitch, J. E. and S. J. Crooke. 1984. Revision of eastern Pacific catalufas (Pisces: Priacanthidae) with description of a new genus and discussion of the fossil record. Proc. Calif. Acad. Sci. 43(19): 301-315.

Fourmanoir, P. and P. Laboute. 1976. Poissons de Nouvelle Calédonie et des Nouvelles Hébrides. Les Éditions du Pacifique, Papeete. 376 p., 848 col. figs.

Fourmanoir, P., J. M. Griessinger, and Y. Plessis. 1974. Faune ichthyologique des Gambier. Cahiers du Pacifique no. 18 Tome II: 543-559.

Fowler, H. W. 1925. Fishes of Guam, Hawaii, Samoa, and Tahiti. Bull. B. P. Bishop Mus. 22: 1-38.

____. 1928. The fishes of Oceania. Mem. B. P. Bishop Mus. 10, 540 p.

____. 1931a. The fishes of Oceania, Suppl. 1. Mem. B. P. Bishop Mus. 11: 313-381.

____. 1931b. Contribution to the biology of the fishes of the the Philippines Archipelago and adjacent regions. The fishes of the families Pseudochromidae, Lobotidae, Pempheridae, Priacanthidae, Lutjanidae, Pomadasyidae, and Teraponidae collected by the United States Bureau of Fisheries steamer "Albatross", cheifly in the Philippine seas and adjacent waters. Bull. U. S. Nat. Mus. 100, 11: xi+388 p.

____. 1934. The fishes of Oceania, Suppl. 2. Mem. B. P. Bishop Mus. 11: 375-455.

____. 1936. Contribution to the biology of the fishes of the Philippines Archipelago and adjacent regions. The fishes of the families Banjosidae, Lethrinidae, Sparidae, Girellidae, Kyphosidae, Oplegnathidae, Gerridae, Mullidae, Emmelichthyidae, Sciaenidae, Sillaginidae, Arripidae, and Enoplosidae collected by the United States Bureau of Fisheries steamer "Albatross", cheifly in the Philippine seas and adjacent waters. Bull. U. S. Nat. Mus. 100, 12: 465 p.

____. 1945. Fishes from Saipan Island, Micronesia. Proc. Acad. Nat. Sci. Philadelphia 97: 59-74.

____. 1949. The fishes of Oceania, Suppl. 3. Mem. B. P. Bishop Mus. 12: 37-186.

____. 1959. Fishes of Fiji. Govt. of Fiji, Suva. 670 p., 243+3 suppl. text figs.

Fowler, H. W., and B. A. Bean. 1928. The fishes of the families Pomacentridae, Labridae and Calliodontidae, collected by the United States Bureau of Fisheries steamer "Albatross", chiefly in Philippine seas and adjacent waters. Bull. U. S. Nat. Mus. 100(7): 1-525.

____. 1929. Contribution to the biology of the the Philippines Archipelago and adjacent regions. The fishes of the series Capriformes, Ephipiformes, and Squamipennes, collected by the United States Bureau of Fisheries steamer "Albatross", chiefly in Philippine seas and adjacent waters. Bull. U. S. Nat. Mus. 100, 8: xi+352.

____. 1930. Contribution to the biology of the the Philippines Archipelago and adjacent regions. The fishes of the families Amiidae, Chandidae, Duleidae, and Serranidae, collected by the United States Bureau of Fisheries steamer "Albatross", chiefly in the Philippine Islands and adjacent seas. Bull. U. S. Nat. Mus. 100, 10: ix+334, 27 figs.

Fraser, T. H. 1972. Comparative osteology of the shallow water cardinalfishes [Perciformes: Apogonidae] with reference to the systematics and evolution of the family. Ichth. Bull. J.L.B. Smith Inst. Ichth., Rhodes Univ., Grahamstown, no. 34, 105 p.

Fraser, T. H. and E. A. Lachner. 1985. A revision of the cardinalfish subgenera *Pristiapogon* and *Zoramia* (genus *Apogon*) of the Indo-Pacific Region (Teleostei: Apogonidae). Smithson. Contr. Zool. no. 412.

Fraser, T. H. and J. E. Randall. 1976. Two new Indo-west Pacific cardinalfishes of the genus *Apogon*. Proc. Biol. Soc. Washington 88(47): 503-508.

Fricke, R. 1982. New species of *Callionymus*, with a revision of the *variegatus*-group of that genus (Teleostei: Callionymidae). J. Nat. Hist. 1982(16): 127-146.

____. 1983. Revision of the Indo-Pacific genera and species of the dragonet family Callionymidae (Teleostei). Braunschweig: J. Cramer. 774p.

____. 1984. A new species of the dragonet genus *Synchiropus* from the Mariana Islands (Teleostei: Callionymidae). Estrato dagli Annali del Museo Civico di Storia Naturale di Genova LXXXV: 67-72.

Fritzche, R. 1976. A revision of the cornetfish genus *Fistularia* (Fistulariidae), with description of intrageneric relationships and zoogeography. Bull. Mar. Sci. 26(2): 196-204.

Garrick, J. A. F. 1982. Sharks of the genus *Carcharhinus*. NOAA Techn. Rep. NMFS Circ. no. 445: 1-194.

Gladfelter , W. B., J. C. Ogden, and E. H. Gladfelter. 1980. Similarity and diversity among coral reef fish communities: a comparison between tropical western Atlantic (Virgin Islands) and tropical central Pacific (Marshall Islands) patch reefs. Ecology 61: 1156-1168.

Gloerfelt-Tarp, T., and P. J. Kailola. 1984. Trawled fishes of southern Indonesia and northwestern Australia. Australian Development Assistsance Bureau, Australia; Directorate General of Fisheries, Indionesia; German Agency for Technical Cooperation, Federal Republic of Germany. xvi+407 p., 3pls., 564 figs.

Goldman, B. and F. H. Talbot. 1976. Aspects of the ecology of coral reef fishes. in O. A. Jones and R. Endean (Eds). Biology and Geolgy of Coral Reefs, Vol. 3: Biology 2: 125-154.

Goren, M. 1978. A new gobiid genus and seven new species from Sinai coasts (Pisces: Gobiidae). Senkenberg. Biol. 59(3/4): 191-203.

____. 1979a. The Gobiinae of the Red Sea (Pisces: Gobiidae). Senkenberg. Biol. 60(1/2): 13-64.

____. 1979b. *Callogobius bauchotae* new species from Marshall Island (Gobiidae, Pisces). Cybium, sér. 3, 1979 (7): 41-44.

Greenfield, D. W. 1974. A revision of the squirrelfish genus *Myripristis* Cuvier (Pisces: Holocentridae). Sci. Bull. Nat. Hist. Mus. Los Angel. Cty. 19: 1-54.

Grovhoug, J. G. and R. S. Henderson. 1976. Distribution of fishes at Canton Atoll *in* S. V. Smith and R. S. Henderson (Eds.). An environmental survey of Canton Atoll lagoon. Naval Undersea Research and Development Center, San Diego: 99-157.

Guichenot, A. 1847. Description de deux nouvelles especes de Cossyphes. Revue Zoologique 282-284.

Hadley-Hansen, P. E. 1986. Revision of the tripterygiid fish genus *Helcogramma*, including descriptions of four new species. Bull. Mar. Sci. 38(2): 313-354.

Halstead, B. W. 1967. Poisonous and Venemous Marine Animals of the World. Vol. 2, xxxi+1070 p., 203 pls., 194 figs. U. S. Govt. Printing Office, Washington, D. C.

Hara, S., H. Kohno, and Y. Taki. 1986. Spawning behavior and early life history of the rabbitfish, *Siganus guttatus*, in the laboratory. Aquaculture 59: 273-285.

Harmelin-Vivien, M. L. and C. Bouchon. 1976. Feeding behavior of some carnivourous fishes (Serranidae and Scorpaenidae) from Tulear (Madagascar). Mar. Biol. 37: 329-340.

Harry, R. R. 1953. Ichthyological field data of Raoroia Atoll, Tuamotu Archipelago. Atoll Res. Bult., *no.* 18:1-190, 7 figs.

Helfman, G. S. and J. E. Randall. 1973. Palauan fish names. Pac. Sci. 23(2): 136-153.

Hensley, D. A. and G. R. Allen. 1977. A new species of *Abudefduf* (Pisces: Pomacentridae) from the Indo-Australian Archipelago. Rec. West. Aust. Mus. 6(1): 107-118.

Herald, E. S., and J. E. Randall. 1972. Five new Indo-Pacific pipefishes. Proc. Calif. Acad. Sci., ser. 4, 39(11): 121-140.

Herre, A. W. 1927. Philippine surgeonfishes and moorish idols. 1927. Philipp. J. Sci. 34(4): 403-478.

____. 1935. A check list of the fishes of the Pelew Islands. J. Pan-Pacific Res. Inst., 10: 163-166.

____. 1936. Fishes of the Crane Pacific Expedition. Field Mus. Nat. Hist., Zool. Ser., Pub. 353: 1-472, 50 figs.

____. 1953a. Check-list of Philippines fishes. U. S. Fish and Wildl. Serv. Res. Rep. 20: 977 p.

____. 1953b. The tropical Pacific Eleotridae with vomerine teeth with descriptions of two new genera and two new species from the Marshall Islands. Phil. J. Sci. 82: 189-192.

Herre, A. W. and H. R. Montalban. 1927. The Philippine butterflyfishes and their allies. Philipp. J. Sci. 34(1): 1-113.

____. 1928a. Philippine sparoid and rudderfishes. Philipp. J. Sci. 33(4): 397-441.

____. 1928b. The Philippine siganids. Philipp. J. Sci. 35(2): 151-185.

Hiatt, R. W. and D. W. Strasburg. 1960. Ecological relationships of the fish fauna on coral reefs of the Marshall Islands. Ecol. Monogr. 30(1): 65-127.

Hobson, E. S. 1972. Activity of Hawaiian reef fishes during the evening and morning transitions between daylight and darkness. Fishery Bull. , 70: 715-740.

____. 1974. Feeding relationships of teleostean fishes on coral reefs in Kona, Hawaii. Fishery Bull. 72(4): 915-1031.

Hoese, D. F. 1975. A revision of the gobiid fish genus *Kellogella*. Rec. Aust. Mus. 29(17): 473-484.

____. 1984. Gobioidei: Relationships. *in* H. G. Moser, et al. (Eds.) Ontogeny and Systematics of Fishes. American Society of Ichthyologists and Herpetologists, Spec. Publ. no. 1: 588-590.

Hoese, D. F. and G. R. Allen. 1977. *Signigobius biocellatus*, a new genus and species of sand-dwelling coral reef gobiid fish from the western tropical Pacific. Japan. J. Ichthy. 23(4): 199-207.

Hoese, D. F. and R. Steene. 1978. *Amblyeleotris randalli*, a new species of gobiid fish living in association with alpheid shrimps. Rec. West. Aust. Mus. 6(4): 379-389.

Hutchins, J. B. 1986. Review of the monacanthid fish genus *Pervagor*, with descriptions of two new species. Indo-Pacific Fishes no. 12: 35 p., II col. pls.

Hutchins, J. B. and J. E. Randall. 1982. *Cantherhines longicaudus*, a new filefish from Oceania, with a review of the species of the *C. fronticinctus* complex. Pacif. Sci. 36(2): 175-185.

Hutchins, J. B. and R. Swainston. 1985. Revision of the monacanthid fish genus *Brachaluteres*. Rec. West. Aust. Mus. 12(1): 57-78.

Ikehara, I. I., H. T. Kami, and R. K. Sakamoto. 1970. Exploratory fishing survey of the inshore fisheries resources of Guam. Proc. 2nd CSK Symp., Tokyo: 425-437.

Jewett, S. L., and E. A. Lachner. 1983. Seven new species of the Indo-Pacific genus

Eviota (Pisces: Gobiidae). Proc. Biol. Soc. Wash. 96(4): 780-806.

Johannes, R. E. 1981. Words of the Lagoon. Univ. Calif. Press. Berkeley, Calif. 320 p.

Johnson, G. D. 1980. The limits and relationships of the Lutjanidae abd associated families. Bull. Scripps Inst. Oceanog. 24: 1-114.

Johnson, R. H. 1978. Sharks of Polynesia. Les Éditions du Pacifique, Papeete. 170 p., numerous col. figs.

Jones, G. 1985. Revision of the Australian species of the fish family Leiognathidae. Aust. J. Mar. Freshw. Res., 36: 559-613.

Jones, R. S. 1968. Ecological relationships in Hawaiian and Johnston Island Acanthuridae (Surgeonfishes). Micronesica 4(2): 309-361.

Jones, R. S., and J. A. Chase. 1975. Community structure and distribution of fishes in an enclosed high island lagoon in Guam. Micronesica 11(1): 127-148.

Jordan, D. S. and B. W. Evermann. 1903. The Aquatic Resources of the Hawaiian Islands. Part I. The Shore Fishes. U.S. Bur. Fisheries Bull. for 1903. Vol. 23: xxvii+574 p. 73 col. pls., 65 pls., 229 figs.

Jordan, D. S., and A. Seale. 1905. The fishes of Samoa. Bull. U. S. Bureau of Fisheries 25: 173-488.

Kami, H. T. 1971. Check-list of Guam fishes, Suppl. I. Micronesica 7(1-2): 215-228.

____. 1975. Check-list of Guam fishes, Suppl. II. Micronesica 11(2): 115-121.

Kami, H. T., I. I. Ikehara, and F. P. DeLeon. 1968. Check-list of Guam fishes. Micronesica 4(1): 95-131.

Kanazawa, R. H. 1958. A revision of the eels of the genus *Conger* with descriptions of four new species. Proc. U. S. Nat. Mus. 108(3400): 219-267.

Karnella, S. J., and E. A. Lachner. 1981. Three new species of the *Eviota epiphanes* group having vertical trunk bars (Pisces: Gobiidae). Proc. Biol. Soc. Wash. 94(2): 264-275.

Kishimoto, H., K. Amaoka, H. Kohno, and T. Hamaguchi. 1987. A revision of the black-and-white snappers, genus *Macolor*(Perciformes: Lutjanidae). Japan. J. Ichthy. 34(2): 146-156.

Klausewitz, W. 1982. List der in den maledivischen Gewässern gesammelten Fische. *in* I. Eibl-Eibesfeldt. Die Malediven: Paradies im Indischen Ozean (in German), 305-307.

Knapp, L. W. 1973: *Platycephalus beauforti*, a new species of flathead (Pisces: Platycephalidae) from the western Pacific. Proc. Biol. Soc. Wash. 86(10): 117-126.

Kobayashi, D. R. 1986. Social organization of the spotted sharpnose puffer, *Canthigaster punctatissima* (Tetraodontidae). Env. Biol. Fishes 15(2): 141-145.

Koumans, F. P. 1953. The Fishes of the Indo-Australian Archipelago. 10. Gobioidea. Leiden: E. J. Brill. 423 p.

Kuiter, R. H. and J. E. Randall. 1981. Three look-alike Indo-Pacific labrid fishes, *Halichoeres margaritaceus*, *H. nebulosus* and *H. miniatus*. Revue Fr. Aquariol. 8(1): 13-18.

Kyushin, K., K. Amaoka, K. Nakaya, and H. Ida. 1977. Fishes of the Indian Ocean. Hiroshige Ehara, Tokyo. 392 p.

Kyushin, K., K. Amaoka, K. Nakaya, H. Ida, Y. Tanino, and T. Senta. 1982. Fishes of the South China Sea. Japan Marine Fishery Resource Research Center, Tokyo. 333p., 291 col. figs.

Lachner, E. A., and S. J. Karnella. 1980. Fishes of the Indo-Pacific genus *Eviota* with descriptions of eight new species (Teleostei: Gobiidae). Smithson. Contr. Zool. 315: 1-127.

Lachner, E. A., and J. F. McKinney. 1978. A revision of the Indo-Pacific fish genus *Gobiopsis* with descriptions of four new species (Pisces: Gobiidae). Smithson. Cont. Zool. 262: 1-52.

Larson, H. K. 1976. A new species of *Eviota* with discussion of the nominal genera *Eviota* and *Eviotops*. Copeia 1976(3): 498-502.

____. 1983. Notes on the biology of the goby *Kellogella cardinalis* (Jordan & Seale). Micronesica 19(1-2): 157-164.

____. 1985. A revision of the gobiid genus *Bryaninops* (Pisces), with a description of six new species. The Beagle, Occas. Pap. N. Ter. Mus. Arts and Sci. 2(1): 57-93.

Larson, H. K., and D. F. Hoese. 1980a. The species of the Indo-West Pacific genus *Calumia* (Pisces: Eleotridae). Proc. Linn. Soc. N. S. W., 104(1): 17-20.

____. 1980b. Fishes of the Indian Ocean: A. Systematical section, XXIII Gobiidae. "Meteor" Forsch.-Ergebnisse Reihe D, no. 32: 33-43.

Lassuy, D. R. 1979. Oceanographic conditions in the vicinity of Cabras Island and Glass Breakwater for the potential development of ocean thermal energy conversion on Guam. Univ. Guam Mar. Lab. Tech. Rep. no. 53, 30 p.

____. 1980. Effects of "farming" behavior by *Eupomacentrus lividus* and *Hemiglyphidodon plagiometopon* on algal community structure. Bull. Mar. Sci. 30: 304-312.

Lee, S. 1985. Fishes of the family Haemulidae (Teleostei: Percoidei) of Taiwan. Bull. Inst. Zool., Acad. Sinica 24(2): 257-272.

____. 1986. Fishes of the family Nemipteridae (Teleostei: Percoidei) of Taiwan. Bull. Inst. Zool., Acad. Sinica 25(2): 161-175.

Leis, J. M. 1978. Systematics and zoogeography of the porcupinefishes (*Diodon*, Diodontidae, Tetraodontiformes), with comments on egg and larval development. Fish. Bull. 76(3): 535-567.

Lewis, A. D., B. R. Smith, and C. P. Ellway. 1983. A guide to the common tuna baitfishes of the South Pacific Commission Area. SPC Handbook no. 23, iv+81 p.

Lobel, P. S. 1979. Description of a new Hawaiian gobiid fish of the genus *Trimma*. Breviora 456: 13.

____. 1981. *Bodianus prognathus* (Labridae, Pisces), a new longnose hogfish from the central Pacific. Pac. Sci. 35(4): 45-50.

Losey, G. S. 1972. Predation protection in the poison-fang blenny *Meicanthus atrodorsalis* and its mimics, *Ecsenius bicolor* and *Runula laudandus* (Blenniidae). Pac. Sci. 26(2): 129-139.

____. 1975. *Meicanthus atrodorsalis*: field evidence of predation protection. Copeia 1975(3): 574-576.

Lubbock, R., and G. R. Allen. 1978. A distinctive new *Anthias* (Teleostei: Serranidae)

from the western Pacific. Rec. West. Aust. Mus. 6(2): 259-268.

____. 1979. *Canthigaster leoparda* a new sharpnose pufferfish (Teleostei: Tetraodontidae) from the central indo-Pacific. Rev. Fr. Aquariol. 6: 87-90.

Lubbock, R., and N. V. C. Polunin. 1977. Notes on the Indo-West Pacific genus *Ctenogobiops* (Teleostei:Gobiidae), with descriptions of three new species. Revue Suisse Zool. 84(2): 505-514.

Major, P. F. 1973. Scale feeding behavior of the leatherjacket, *Scomberoides lysan* and two species of the genus *Oligoplites* (Pisces: Carangidae). Copeia 1973: 151-154.

Marliave, J. B. 1985. Color polymorphism in sibling *Amphiprion*: is the reef-fish lottery rigged? Env. Biol. Fish. 12(1): 63-68.

Masuda, H., K. Amaoka, C. Araga, T. Uyeno, and T. Yoshino. Eds. 1984. The Fishes of the Japanese Archipelago. Tokai Univ. Press, Tokyo. xxii+437 p., 370 pls.

Matsuura, K. 1980. A revision of Japanese Balistoid fishes: I. Family Balistidae. Bull. Natn. Sci. Mus. (Tokyo), Ser. A (Zool.), 6(1): 27-69.

____. 1981. *Xenobalistes tumidipectoris*, a new genus and species of triggerfish (Tetraodontiformes, Balistidae) from the Marianas Islands. Bull. Natn. Sci. Mus., Tokyo, Ser. A, 7(4): 191-200.

____. 1982. A list of fishes collected in the Palau and Yap Islands. Proc. Japan. Soc. Syst. Zool. no. 23: 82-89.

Matsuura, K., and T. Shimizu. 1982. The squirrelfish genus *Adioryx*, a junior synonym of *Sargocentron*. Japan. J. Ichthyol. 29(1): 93-94.

Matsuura, K. and M. Toda. 1981. First records of two pufferfishes, *Arothron mappa* and *A. reticularis*, from Japan. Japan. J. Ichthy. 28(1): 91-93.

Mauge, L. A. 1967. Contribution préliminaire à l'inventaire ichtyologique de la région de Tuléar. Rec. Trav. Sta. Mar. Endoume, (fasc. hors sér.) Suppl. 7: 101-132.

Mauge, L. A. and R. Bauchot. 1984. Les genres et sous-genres de Chaetodontidés étudiés par une méthode d'analyse numérique. Bull. Mus. Natn. Hist. Nat., Paris, sér. 4 (2): 453-485.

McCosker, J. E. 1972. Two new genera and two new species of western Pacific snake-eels (Apodes: Ophichthidae). Proc. Calif. Acad. Sci. ser. 4, 39(10): 111-120.

____. 1977a. The osteology, classification, and relationships of the eel family Ophichthidae. Proc. Calif. Acad. Sci. ser. 4, 41(1): 423p., 45 figs.

____. 1977b. Fright posture of the plesiopid fish *Calloplesiops altivelis*: an example of Batesian Mimicry. Science 197(4301): 400-401.

____. 1978. Synonymy and distribution of *Calloplesiops* (Pisces: Plesiopidae). Copeia 1978(4): 707-710.

____. 1979. The snake eels (Pisces: Ophichthidae) of the Hawaiian Islands, with the descriprions of two new species. Proc. Calif. Acad. Sci. ser. 4, 42(2): 57-67.

McCosker, J. E., K. Hatooka, K. Sasaki, and J. T. Moyer. 1984. Japanese moray eels of the genus *Uropterygius*. Japan. J. Ichthyol. 31(3): 261-267.

McCosker, J. E., and J. E. Randall. 1977. Three new species of Indo-Pacific moray eels (Pisces: Muraenidae). Proc. Calif. Acad. Sci. ser. 4, 41(3): 161-168.

____. 1982. Synonymies of Indian Ocean eels, with the description of *Gymnothorax enigmaticus*, a moray previously known as *G. ruppeli*. Proc. Calif. Acad. Sci. 43(2): 17-24.

McCosker, J. E., and R. H. Rosenblatt. 1975. The moray eels (Pisces:Muraenidae) of the Galapagos Islands, with new records and synonymies of extralimital species. Proc. Calif. Acad. Sci. ser. 4, 40(13):417-427.

____. 1987. Notes on the biology, taxonomy, and distribution of flashlightfishes (Beryciformes: Anamolopidae). Japan. J. Ichthy. 34(2): 157-164.

McKay, R. J. 1985. A revison of the fishes of the family Sillaginidae. Mem. Queensland Mus. 22(1): 1-73.

McKinney, J. F. and E. A. Lachner. 1984. *Callogobius crassus*, a new fish from the Indo-Pacific region (Teleostei: Gobiidae). Proc. Biol. Soc. Wash. 97(3): 627-631.

Mees, G. F. 1962. A preliminary revision of the Belonidae. Zool. Verhandelingen, no. 54: 1-96.

Morgans, J. F. C. 1982. Serranid fishes of Tanzania and Kenya. J. L. B. Smith Inst. Ichthy., Ichthy. Bull. no. 46: 1-44.

Moyer, J. T. 1981. Interspecific spawning of the pigmy angelfishes *Centropyge shepardi* and *C. bispinosus* at Guam. Micronesica 17(1-2): 119-124.

Moyer, J. T. and M. Sano. 1985. First record of the lizardfish *Synodus jaculum* from Japan. Japan. J. Ichthyol. 32(1): 90-92.

Munro, I. S. R. 1967. The fishes of New Guinea. Dept. Agric., Stock, and Fisheries, Pt. Moresby. xxxvii+651 p., 6 col. pls., 78 pls., 23 text figs.

Murdy, E. O. 1985. A review of the gobiid fish genera *Exyrias* and *Macrodontogobius*, with description of a new species of *Exyrias*. Indo-Pacific Fishes no. 10: 14 p., II col. pls.

Murdy, E. O. and D. F. Hoese. 1985. Revision of the gobiid fish genus *Istigobius*. Indo-Pacific Fishes no. 4: 41 p., III col. pls.

Myers, R. F. 1979. Fishes *in* L. G. Eldredge et al. Marine environmental survey of Okat, Kosrae. Univ. Guam Mar. Lab. Tech, Rep. no. 63, 101p.

____. 1980a. First record of the angelfish, *Cetropyge colini* (Pomacanthidae), from Guam, Mariana Islands. Japan. J. Ichthyol. 26(4): 361-363.

____. 1980b. *Chaetodon flavocoronatus*, a new species of butterflyfish (Chaetodontidae) from Guam, Mariana Islands. Micronesica 16(2): 297-303.

____. 1988. An annotated checklist of the fishes of the Mariana Islands. Micronesica 21(1-2).

Myers, R. F., and J. W. Shepard. 1980. New records of fishes from Guam, with notes on the ichthyofauna of the southern Marianas. Micronesica 16(2): 304-347.

Nalbant, T. T. 1986. Studies on Chaetodont fishes. III. Redescription of the genus *Roaops* Maugé & Bauchot, 1984, and some problems on the phylogeny and evolution of butterflyfishes (Pisces, Chaetodontidae). Trav. Mus. Hist. nat. Gr. Antipa, 28: 163-184.

Nelson, J. S. 1984. Fishes of the world. 2nd. ed. John Wiley and Sons, New York,523 p.

Nelson, J. S. and J. E. Randall. 1985. *Crystallodytes pauciradiatus* (Perciformes), a new creediid fish species from Easter Island. Proc. Biol. Soc. Wash. 98(2): 403-410.

Parin, N. V. 1967. Review of marine needlefishes of the west Pacific and Indian

Oceans. Trudy Okeanol. Inst. 84: 3-83. (In Russian; NMFS translation no. 68).

Parin, N. V., B. B. Collette, and Y. N. Scherbachev. 1980. Preliminary review of the marine halfbeaks (Hemiramphidae, Beloniformes) of the tropical Indo-West Pacific. Trans. P. P. Shirshov Inst. Ocean. 97: 7-173.

Pietsch, T. W. and D. B. Grobecker. 1987. Frogfishes of the world. Systematics, zoogeography, and behavioral ecology. Stanford, xxiv+420 p.

Polunin, N. V. C. and R. Lubbock. 1977. Prawn-associated gobies (Teleostei: Gobiidae) from the Seychelles, western Indian Ocean: systematics and ecology. J. Zool., Lond. 183: 63-101.

Popper, D. and L. Fishelson. 1973. Ecology and behavior of *Anthias squamipinnis* (Peters, 1855) (Anthiidae, Teleostei) in the coral habitat of Eilat (Red Sea). J. Exp. Zool., 184: 409-424.

Quoy, J. R. C., and J. P. Gaimard. 1824-1825 Voyage autour du monde, entrepris par ordre du roi, execute sur les corvettes de "S. M. l'Uranie" et at "Physicienne", pendant les annees 1817-1820: Zoologie, Poissons.

____. 1834. Voyage de decouvertes de "l'Astrolabe", execute par ordre du roi, pendant les annees 1826-1829, sons le commandement de M. G. Dumont d'Urville. Poissons, Paris: 647-720.

Randall, H. A. and G. R. Allen. 1977. A revision of the damselfish genus *Dascyllus* (Pomacentridae) with the description of a new species. Rec. Aust. Mus. 31(9): 349-385.

Randall, J. E. 1955a. A revision of the surgeon fish genus *Ctenochaetus*, family Acanthuridae, with descriptions of five new species. Zoologica, N. Y., 40: 149-168.

____. 1955b. A revision of the surgeon fish genera *Zebrasoma* and *Paracanthurus*. Pac. Sci., 9(4): 396-412.

____. 1955c. Fishes of the Gilbert Islands. Atoll Res. Bull. 47, xi+243 p.

____. 1956a. A revision of the surgeon fish genus *Acanthurus*. Pac. Sci. 10(2): 159-235.

____. 1956b. *Acanthurus rackliffei*, a possible hybrid surgeonfish (*A. achilles* x *A. glaucopareius*) from the Phoenix Islands. Copeia 1956: 21-25.

____. 1960. A new species of *Acanthurus* from the Caroline Islands, with notes on the systematics of other Indo-Pacific surgeonfishes. Pac. Sci. 14(3): 266-279.

____. 1963a. Review of the hawkfishes (family Cirrhitidae). Proc. U. S. Nat. Mus. 114(3472): 389-451.

____. 1963b. Notes on the systematics of parrotfishes (Scaridae), with emphasis on sexual dichromatism. Copeia 1963(2): 225-237.

____. 1964a. A revision of the filefish genera *Amanses* and *Cantherhines*. Copeia 1964(2): 332-361.

____. 1964b. Notes on the groupers of Tahiti, with a description of a new serranid fish genus. Pac. Sci. 18: 281-296.

____. 1972a. A revision of the labrid fish genus *Anampses*. Micronesica 8(1-2): 151-190.

____. 1972b. The Hawaiian trunkfishes of the genus *Ostracion*. Copeia 1972(4): 756-768.

____. 1973. Tahitian fish names and a preliminary check-list of the fishes of the Society Islands. Occ. Pap. B. P. Bishop Mus. 24(11): 167-214.

____. 1974a. Notes and color illustrations of labrid fishes of the genus *Anampses*. UO. Japan. Soc. of Ichthy. Tokyo 21:10-16, pls. I-II.

____. 1974b. The status of the goatfishes (Mullidae) described by Forsskål. Copeia 1974(1): 275-277.

____. 1975. A revision of the Indo-Pacific angelfish genus *Genicanthus*, with descriptions of three new species. Bull. Mar. Sci. 25(3): 393-421.

____. 1976. A review of the Hawaiian lbrid fishes of the genus Coris. UO. Japan. Soc. of Ichthy. Tokyo 26: 1-10, pls. I-IV.

____. 1977. A contribution to the biology of the whitetip reef shark (*Triaenodon obesus*). Pac. Sci. 31(2): 143-164.

____. 1978. A revision of the Indo-Pacific labrid fish genus *Macropharyngodon*, with descriptions of five new species. Bull. Mar. Sci. 28(4): 742-770.

____. 1979. A review of the serranid fish genus *Anthias* of the Hawaiian Islands, with descriptions of two new species. Cont. Sci. Nat. Hist. Mus. Los Ang. Cty. 302, 13 p.

____. 1980a. Revision of the fish genus *Plectranthus* (Serranidae: Anthiinae) with descriptions of 13 new species. Micronesica 16: 101-187.

____. 1980b. New records of fishes from the Hawaiian Islands. Pac. Sci. 34(3): 211-232.

____. 1980c. Two new Indo-Pacific labrid fishes of the genus *Halichoeres*, with notes on other species of the genus. Pac. Sci. 34(4): 415-432.

____. 1980d. A survey of ciguatera at Enewetak and Bikini, Marshall Islands, with notes on the systematics and food habits of ciguatoxic fishes. Fishery Bull. 78(2): 201-249.

____. 1981a. Revision of the labrid fish genus *Labropsis* with descriptions of five new species. Micronesica 17(1-2): 125-155.

____. 1981b. Two new species and six new records of labrid fishes from the Red Sea. Senkenberg. Marit. 13(1/3): 79-109.

____. 1981c. A review of the Indo-Pacific Sand Tilefish genus *Hoplolatilus* (Perciformes: Malacanthidae). Freshw. Mar. Aquar. 4(12): 39-46.

____. 1981d. *Luzonichthys earlei* a new species of anthiine fish from the Hawaiian Islands. Freshw. Mar. Aq. 4(9): 13-18.

____. 1981e. A revision of the labrid fish genus *Pseudojuloides*, with descriptions of five new species. Pac. Sci. 35(1): 51-74,

____. 1982. A review of the labrid fish genus *Hologymnosus*. Rev. Fr. Aquariol 9: 13-21.

____. 1983a. Revision of the Indo-Pacific labrid fish genus *Wetmorella*. Copeia 1983(4): 875-883.

____. 1983b. Red Sea Reef Fishes. IMMEL, London. 192 p., 465 col. figs.

____. 1985a. On the validity of the tetraodontid fish *Arothron manilensis* (Procé). Japan. J. Ichthyol. 32(3): 347-354.

____. 1985b. Fishes, *in* B. Delesalle, R. Galzin, and B. Salvat (Eds.). Fifth Intl. Coral Reef Congress, Tahiti, 27 May-1 June, 1985. Vol. 1:"French Polynesian Coral Reefs:379-520.

____. 1985c. Guide to Hawaiian Reef Fishes. Harrowood, Newton Square, PA. 79 p., 177 col. pls.

____. 1986a. 106 new records of fishes from the Marshall Islands. Bull. Mar. Sci. 38(1): 170-252.

____. 1987a A preliminary synopsis of the groupers (Perciformes: Serranidae: Epinephelinae) of the Indo-Pacific region. pp. 89-188 *in* J. J. Polovina and S. Ralston, eds. Tropical snappers and groupers: biology and fishery management. Westview Press, Boulder Colorado., x+659 p.

____. 1987b Three nomenclatural changes in Indo-Pacific surgeonfishes (Acanthuridae). Pac. Sci. 41(1-4): 54-61

Randall, J. E., and G. R. Allen. 1973. A revision of the gobiid fish genus *Nemateleotris*, with description of two new species. Quart. J. Taiwan Mus. 26(3-4): 347-467.

Randall, J. E., G. R. Allen, Burhanuddin, M. Hutomo, and O. K. Sumadhiharga. 1976. Preliminary list of fishes collected during the Rumphius Expedition II. Oseanologi di Indonesia. no. 6: 45-67.

Randall, J. E., G. R. Allen, and R. C. Steene. 1977. Five probable hybrid butterflyfishes of the genus *Chaetodon* from the central and western Pacific. Rec. West. Aust. Mus., 6(1): 3-26.

Randall, J. E., M. L. Bauchot, and M. Desoutter. 1985. *Chromis viridis* (Cuvier), the correct name for the Indo-Pacific damselfish previously known as *C. caerulea* (Cuvier, 1830). Cybium 9(4): 411-413.

Randall, J. E., and A. Ben-Tuvia. 1983. A review of the groupers (Pisces: Serranidae: Epinephelinae) of the Red Sea, with description of a new species of *Cephalopholis*. Bull. Mar. Sci. 33(2): 373-342.

Randall, J. E. and V. E. Brock. 1960. Observations on the ecology of epinepheline and lutjanid fishes of the Society Islands with emphasis on food habits. Trans. Amer. Fish. Soc. 89(1): 9-16.

Randall, J. E., and R. W. Bruce. 1983. The parrotfishes of the subfamily Scarinae of the western Indian Ocean, with descriptions of three new species. Ichth. Bull. J. L. B. Smith Inst. Ichth. no. 47, 39 p.

Randall, J. E., and J. H. Choat. 1980. Two new parrotfishes of the genus *Scarus* from the Central and South Pacific, with further examples of sexual dichromatism. Zool. J. Linn. Soc. 70: 383-419.

Randall, J. E., and J. K. Dooley. 1974. Revision of the Indo-Pacific branchiostegid fish genus *Hoplolatilus*, with description of two new species. Copeia 1974(2): 457-471.

Randall, J. E., and A. Edwards. 1984. A new labrid fish of the genus *Thalassoma* from the Pitcairn Group, with a review of related Indo-Pacific species. J. Aquaric. & Aquat. Sci. IV(2): 13-32.

Randall, J. E. and A. C. Egana. 1984. Native names of Easter Island fishes, with comments on the origin of the Rapanui people. Occas. Pap. B. B. Bishop Mus. 25 (12): 1-16.

Randall, J. E., and P. Gueze. 1981. The holocentrid fishes of the genus *Myripristis* of the Red Sea with clarification of the *murdjan* and *hexagonus* complexes. Nat. Hist. Mus. Los Ang. Cty. Sci. Contr. 334, 16 p.

Randall, J. E., and P. C. Heemstra. 1986. *Epinephelus truncatus* Katayama, a junior synonym of the Indo-Pacific serranid fish *Epinephelus retouti* Bleeker. Japan. J. Ichthyol. 33(1): 51-56.

Randall, J. E., and G. S. Helfman. 1972. *Diproctacanthus xanthurus*, a cleaner wrasse from the Palau Islands, with notes on other cleaning fishes. Trop. Fish Hob., July 1972: 87-95.

Randall, J. E., and D. F. Hoese. 1985. Revision of the Indo-Pacific dartfishes, genus *Ptereleotris* (Perciformes: Gobioidei). Indo-Pacific Fishes no. 7: 36 p., IV col. pls.

____. 1986. Revision of the groupers of the Indo-Pacific genus *Plectropomus* (Perciformes: Serranidae). Indo-Pacific Fishes 13, 31p.

Randall, J. E., H. Ida and J. T. Moyer. 1981. A review of the damselfish genus *Chromis* from Japan and Taiwan, with description of a new species. Japan. J. Ichthyol. 28(3): 203-242.

Randall, J. E. and W. Klausewitz. 1973. A review of the triggerfish genus *Melichthys*, with a description of a new species from the Indian Ocean. Senkenberg. Biol. 54(1/3): 57-69.

Randall, J. E., and E. A. Lachner. 1986. The status of the Indo-west Pacific cardinalfishes *Apogon aroubiensis* and *A. nigrofasciatus*. Proc. Biol. Soc. Wash. 99(1): 110-120.

Randall, J. E., E. A. Lachner, and T. H. Fraser. 1985. A revision of the Indo-Pacific fish genus *Pseudamia*, with descriptions of three new species. Indo-Pacific Fishes no. 6, 23p.

Randall, J. E., P. S. Lobel, and E. H. Chave. 1985. Annotated checklist of the fishes of Johnston Island. Pac. Sci. 39(1):24-80.

Randall, J. E., and R. Lubbock. 1981. A revision of the serranid fishes of the subgenus *Mirolabrichthys* (Anthiinae: *Anthias*), with descriptions of five new species. Cont. Sci. Nat. Hist. Mus. Los Ang. Cty. 333, 27 p.

____. 1982. A new Indo-Pacific dartfish of the genus *Ptereleotris* (Perciformes: Gobiidae). Rev. Fr. Aquariol. 9(2): 41-46.

Randall, J. E., L. A. Mauge, and Y. B. Plessis. 1979. Two new anthiine fishes of the genus *Holanthias* from the southern and western Pacific. Japan J. Ichthyol. 26(1): 15-25.

Randall, J. E., K. Matsuura and A. Zama. 1978. A revision of the triggerfish genus *Xanthichthys*, with a description of a new species. Bull. Mar. Sci. 28(4): 688-706.

Randall, J. E. and J. E. McCosker. 1975. The Eels of Easter Island with a description of a new moray. Cont. Sci. Nat. Hist. Mus. Los Ang. Cty. 264, 32 p.

____. 1982. Two new serranid fishes of the genus *Anthias* from the central Pacific. J. Aquaric. II(3): 59-69.

Randall, J. E., S. M. Mead, and A. P. L. Sanders. 1978. Food habits of the giant humphead wrasse, *Cheilinus undulatus* (Labridae). Env. Biol. Fishes 3(2): 235-238.

Randall, J. E. and G. Nelson. 1979. *Scarus japanensis*, *S. quoyi* and *S. iserti* - valid names for parrotfishes presently known as *S. capistratoides, S. blochii,* and *S. croicensis.* Copeia 1979(2): 206-212.

Randall, J. E. and R. F. G. Ormond. 1978. On the Red Sea parrotfishes of Forsskal, *Scarus psittacus* and *Scarus ferrugineus.* Zool. J. Linn. Soc. 63:239-248.

Randall, J. E., and H. A. Randall. 1960. Examples of mimicry and protective resemblance in tropical marine fishes. Bull. Mar. Sci. Guf. Carib. 10(4): 444-480.

_____. 1981. A revision of the labrid fish genus *Pseudojuloides,* with descriptions of five new species. Pac. Sci. 35(1): 51-74.

_____. 1987. Annotated checklist of the fishes of Enewetak Atoll and other Marshall Islands. *in* Devaney, D. M., E. S Reese, B. L. Burch, and P. Helfrich, eds. The natural history of Enewetak Atoll. v. II. Biogeography and systematics. Dept. Energy, Office Sci. Tech. Inf. pp. 289-324.

Randall, J. E., T. Shimizu, and T. Yamakawa. 1982. A revision of the holocentrid fish genus *Ostichthys,* with description of four new species and a related new genus. Japan. J. Ichthyol. 29(1):1-26.

Randall, J. E. and Y. H. Sinoto. 1978. Rapan fish names. Occ. Pap. B. P. Bishop Mus. 24(15): 291-306.

Randall, J. E. and M. M. Smith. 1982. A review of the labrid fishes of the genus *Halichoeres* of the western Indian Ocean, with descriptions of six new species. Ichthy. Bull. Rhodes Univ. J. L. B. Smith Inst. 45: 1-24.

Randall, J. E., M. M. Smith, and K. Aida. 1980. Notes on the classification and distribution of the Indo-Pacific soapfish, *Belonoperca chabanaudi* (Perciformes: Grammistidae). J. L. B. Smith Inst. Ichthyol. Spec. Pub. no. 21, 8 p.

Randall, J. E. and V. G. Springer. 1973. The monotypic Indo-Pacific labrid fish genera *Labrichthys* and *Diproctacanthus* with description of a new related genus, *Larabicus.* Proc. Biol. Soc. Wash., 86(23): 279-298.

_____. 1975. *Labroides pectoralis,* a new species of labrid fish from the tropical western Pacific. UO, Japan. Soc. of Ichthy. Tokyo, 25: 4-11, pl.I.

Randall, J. E. and R. C. Steene. 1983. *Rhinecanthus lunula* a new species of triggerfish from the South Pacific. Freshw. Mar. Aq. 6(7): 45-51.

Randall, J. E. and S. N. Swerdloff. 1973. A review of the damselfish genus *Chromis* from the Hawaiian Islands, with descriptions of three new species. Pac. Sci. 27(4): 327-349.

Randall, J. E. and L. Taylor. 1988. Review of the Indo-Pacific fishes of the serranid genus *Liopropoma,* with descriptions of seven new species. Indo-Pacific Fishes no. 13, 47 p.

Randall, J. E. and R. C. Wass, 1974. Two new pomacanthid fishes of the genus *Centropyge* from Oceania. Japan. J. Ichthyol. 21(3): 137-144.

Randall, J. E. and P. J. P. Whitehead. 1985. *Epinephelus cyanopodus* (Richardson), a senior synonym of *E. hoedtii* (Bleeker), and comparison with the related *E. flavocaeruleus* (Lacepède). Cybium 1985, 9(1): 29-39.

Randall, J. E. and R. Yasuda. 1979. *Centropyge shepardi,* a new angelfish from the Mariana and Ogasawara Islands. Japan. J. Ichthy. 26(1): 55-61.

Randall, R. H. and R. F. Myers. 1983. Guide to the coastal resources of Guam, vol. 2: The Corals. Univ. Guam Press, 128 p.

Rehder, H. A. and J. E. Randall. 1975. Ducie Atoll: Its history, physiography and biota. Atoll Res. Bull: no. 183, 55p., 29 figs.

Rennis, D. S. and D. F. Hoese. 1985. A review of the genus *Parioglossus,* with descriptions of six new species (Pisces: Gobioidei). Rec. Aust. Mus. 36: 169-201.

Robertson, D. R. 1983. On the spawning behavior and spawning cycles of eight surgeonfishes (Acanthuridae) from the Indo-Pacific. Env. Biol. Fishes 9: 193-223.

Robertson, D. R., N. V. C. Polunin, and K. Leighton. 1979. The behavioral ecology of the Indian ocean surgeonfishes (*Acanthurus lineatus, A. leucosternon* and *Zebrasoma scopas*): their feeding strategies, and social and mating systems. Env. Biol. Fishes, 4: 125-170.

Robertson, D. R., R. Reinboth, and R. W. Bruce. 1982. Gonochorism, protogynous sex-change and spawning in three sparisomatinine parrotfishes from the western Indian Ocean. Bull. Mar. Sci. 32(4): 868-879.

Rofen, R. R. 1961. Identifications of fish collections from Kapingamaringi, Eastern Caroline Ids., Ifaluk, Western Caroline Islands, Raroia, Tuamotu Archipelago. Biol. Invest. in the Pacific area, Pac. Sci. Board, Nat. Acad. Sci-Nat. Res. Counc. 117 p. (unpublished report)

Rosenblatt, R. H., J. E. McCosker, and I. Rubinof. 1972. Indo-west Pacific fishes from the Gulf of Chiriqui, Panama. Contr. Sci. Nat. Hist. Mus. Los Angel. Cty. no. 234, 18 p.

Russell, B. C. 1983. Annotated checklist of the coral reef fishes in the Capricorn-Bunker Group, Great Barrier Reef, Australia. Great Barrier Reef Marine Park Authority, Queensland, 184 p., 49 col. figs.

Russell, B. C., G. R. Allen, and H. R. Steene. 1976. New cases of mimicry in marine fishes. J. Zool., London 180: 407-423.

Sale, P. F. 1974. Mechanisms for co-existence in a guild of territorial fishes at Heron Island. Proc. 2nd Intl. Coral Reef Symp. , 1: 193-206.

_____. 1980. The ecology of fishes on coral reefs. Ann. Rev. Oceanog. Mar. Biol., 18: 367-421.

Sano, M., M. Shimizu, and Y. Nose. 1984. Food habits of Teleostean reef fishes in Okinawa Island, southern Japan. Univ. Mus., Univ. Tokyo Bull. no. 25, v+128 p.

Sato, T. 1978. A synopsis of the sparoid fish genus *Lethrinus,* with description of a new species. Univ. Mus. Univ. Tokyo Bull. no. 15, 70 p.

Schroeder, R. E. 1980. Philippine Shore Fishes of the Western Sulu Sea. Bureau Fisheris and Aquatic Resources; National Media Production Center, Manila. xvi+266p., 611 col. figs., 1 text fig.

Schultz, E. T. 1986. *Pterois volitans* and *Pterois miles*: two valid species. Copeia 1986(3): 686-690.

Schultz, L. P. 1943. Fishes of the Phoenix and Samoan Islands collected in 1939 during the expedition of the U.S.S. "Bushnell." Bull. U. S. Nat. Mus. 180: x, 1-316.

_____. 1969. The taxonomic status of the controversial genera and species of parrot-fishes with a descriptive list (family Scaridae).Smithson.Contr.Zool.no.17: v+49 p.

Schultz, L. P., W. M. Chapman, E. A. Lachner, and L. P. Woods. 1960. Fishes of the Marshall and Marianas Islands. Bull. U. S. Nat. Mus. 202, 2: vii+438 p., pls. 74-123, figs. 91-132.

Schultz, L. P., E. S. Herald, E. A. Lachner, A. D. Welander, and L. P. Woods. 1953. Fishes of the Marshall and Marianas Islands. Bull. U. S. Nat. Mus. 202, 1: xxxii+685 p., 74 pls., 90 figs.

Schultz, L. P., L. P. Woods, and E. A. Lachner. 1966. Fishes of the Marshall and Marianas Islands. Bull. U. S. Nat. Mus. 202, 3: vii+176 p., pls. 124-148, figs. 133-156.

Seale, A. 1901. Report of a mission to Guam, Part II. Fishes. Occ. Pap. B. P. Bishop Mus. 1(3): 61-128.

Shaklee, J. E. and C. S. Tamaru. 1981. Biochemical and morphological evolution of Hawaiian bonefishes (*Albula*). Syst. Zool. 30(2): 125-146.

Shao, K. and J. P. Chen. 1987. Fishes of the family Platycephalidae (Teleostei: Platycephaloidei) of Taiwan with descriptions of two new species. Bull. Inst. Zool. Acad. Sinica 26(1): 77-94.

Shao, K., J. Chen, and M. Jzeng. 1987. New records of gobiid fishes associated with snapping shrimps. J. Taiwan Mus. 40(1): 57-69.

Shepard, J. W. and K. A. Meyer. 1978. New records of labrid fishes from Japan. UO (29): 31-40.

Shepard, J. W., and J. T. Moyer. 1980. Annotated checklist of the fishes of Miyake-Jima, Japan. I. Pomacentridae, Chaetodontidae, and Pomacanthidae. Publ. Seto Mar. Biol. Lab. 25(1/4): 227-241, 2 pls.

Shepard, J. W., and R. F. Myers. 1982. A preliminary checklist of the fishes of Guam and the southern Mariana Islands. *In* A working list of the marine organisms from Guam. Univ. Guam Mar. Lab. Tech. Rep. no. 70: 60-88.

Shimizu, T and T. Yamakawa. 1979. Review of the squirrelfishes (subfamily Holocentrinae: Order Beryciformes) of Japan, with a description of a new species. Japan. J. Ichthy. 26(2): 109-147.

Smith, C. L. 1964a. Some pearlfishes from Guam with notes on their ecology. Pac. Sci. 18(1):34-40.

_____. 1964b. *Teanioides limicola,* a new goby from Guam. Micronesica 1(12): 145-150.

Smith, C. L. and J. C. Tyler. 1972. Space resource sharing in a coral reef fish community. Bull. Nat. Hist. Mus. Los Angel. Cty. 14: 125-170.

Smith, J. L. B. 1957a. The fishes of the family Scorpaenidae of the western Indian Ocean. pt. 1 The subfamily Scorpaeninae. Ichth. Bull. Rhodes Univ. 5: 75-88.

_____. 1958. The fishes of the family Eleotridae in the western Indian Ocean. Ichth. Bull. Rhodes Univ. 11: 137-163.

_____. 1959. Gobioid fishes of the families Gobiidae, Periophthalmidae, Trypauchen-idae, Taenioididae, and Kraemeriidae of the western Indian Ocean. Ichth. Bull. Rhodes Univ. 13: 185-225.

_____. 1960. Coral fishes of the family Pomacentridae from the western Indian Ocean and Red Sea. Ichth. Bull. Rhodes Univ. 19: 317-349.

_____. 1961. Fishes of the family Apogonidae of the western Indian Ocean and the Red Sea. Ichth. Bull. Rhodes Univ. 22: 373-419.

_____. 1962a. The moray eels of the western Indian Ocean and the Red Sea. Ichth. Bull. Rhodes Univ. 23: 421-444.

_____. 1962b. Sand-dwelling eels of the western Indian Ocean and the Red Sea. Ichth. Bull. Rhodes Univ. 24: 447-466.

_____. 1962c. Fishes of the family Gaterinidae of the western Indian Ocean and Red Sea, with a resume of known Indo-Pacific species. Ichth. Bull. Rhodes Univ. 25: 469-502.

_____. 1966. Fishes of the subfamily Nasinae with a synopsis of the Prionurinae. Ichth. Bull. Rhodes Univ. 32: 635-682.

Smith, J. L. B. and M. M. Smith. 1963. The Fishes of the Seychelles. Rhodes Univ., Grahamstown. 215 p., 42 col., 56 b & w pls.

Smith, M. M., and P. C, Heemstra (Eds.). 1986. Smith's Sea Fishes. Macmillan South Africa, Johannesburg., 1047 p., 144 pl.

Smith-Vaniz, W. F. 1976. The sabre-toothed blennies, tribe Nemophini (Pisces: Blenniidae). Acad. Nat. Sci. Philad. Monograph 19, 196 p.

_____. 1987. The sabre-toothed blennies, tribe Nemophini (Pisces: Blenniidae): an update. Proc. Acad. Nat. Sci. Philad. 139: 1-52.

Smith-Vaniz, W. F., M. L. Bauchot, and M. Desoutter. 1979. Catalogue critique des types de poissons du Museum national d'Histoire naturelle (Familles des Carangidae et des Nematistiidae). Bull. Mus. Natn. Hist. Nat., Paris, 4e ser. 1, 1979, sect. A, no. 2: 18-66.

Smith-Vaniz, W. F. and J. E. Randall. 1974. Two new species of angelfishes (*Centropyge*) from the Cocos-Keeling Islands. Proc. Acad. Nat. Sci. Phila. 126(8): 105-113.

Smith-Vaniz, W. F. and V. G. Springer. 1971. Synopsis of the tribe Salariini, with description of five new genera and three new species (Pisces: Blenniidae). Smithsonian Cont. Zool. 73: 1-72.

Springer, V. G. 1967. Revision of the circumtropical shore-fish genus *Entomacrodus* (Blenniidae: Salariinae). Proc. U. S. Natl. Mus. 122(3582): 1-150.

_____. 1968. The Indo-Pacific blenniid fish genus *Stanulus,* with description of a new species from the Great Barrier Reef (Blenniidae; Blenniinae; Salariini). Proc. Biol. Soc. Wash. 81: 111-122.

_____. 1971. Revision of the fish genus *Ecsenius* (Blenniidae, Blenniinae; Salariini). Smithson. Contr. Zool., 72:1-74.

_____. 1972a. Additions to revisions of the blenniid fish genera *Ecsenius* and *Entomacrodus,* with descriptions of three new species of *Ecsenius.* Smithson. Contr. Zool., 134: iii, 1-13.

_____. 1972b. Synopsis of the Tribe Omobranchini with descriptions of three new genera and two new species (Pisces: Blenniidae). Smithson. Contr. Zool. 130: 1-31.

_____. 1981. Notes on blenniid fishes of the tribe Omobranchini, with descriptions of two new species. Proc. Biol. Soc. Wash. 94(3): 699-707.

____. 1982. Pacific plate biogeography, with special reference to shorefishes. Smithson. Contr. Zool., 376: iii, 1-182.

____. 1983. *Tyson belos*, new genus and species of western Pacific fish (Gobiidae, Xenisthminae), with discussions of gobioid osteology and classification. Smithson. Cont. Zool. 390: 1-40.

____. 1985. *Oman ypsilon*, a new genus and species of blenniid fish from the Indian ocean. Proc. Biol. Soc. Wash. 98(1): 90-97.

____. 1988. The Indo-Pacific blenniid fish genus *Ecsenius*. Smithson. Cont. Zool. 465: 1-134+14 pls.

Springer, V. G. and M. F. Gomon. 1975. Revision of the blenniid fish genus *Omobranchus* with descriptions of three new species and notes on other species of the tribe Omobranchini. Smithson. Contr. Zool. 177: 1-135.

Springer, V. G., Burhanuddin, and M. F. Gomon. 1974. List of fishes collected during Rumphius Expedition I. Oseanologi di Indonesia. no. 1: 39-45.

Springer, V. G., C. L. Smith, and T. H. Fraser. 1977. *Anisochromis straussi*, new species of protogynous hermaphroditic fish and synonymy of Anisochromidae, Pseudoplesiopidae and Pseudochromidae. Smithson. Contr. Zool. 252: 1-15.

Steene, R. C. 1978. Butterfly and Angelfishes of the World. Vol.1: Australia. Sydney: A.H. and A. W. Reed, 144 p.

Strasburg, D. W. 1967. *Gunnellichthys monostigma* and *Ecsenius bicolor*, new fish records from the Marshall Islands. Copeia 1967(4): 839-840.

Strasburg, D. W., E. C. Jones, and R. T. Iversen. 1968. Use of a small submarine for biological and oceanographic rersearch. J. du Conseil 31(3): 410-426.

Sunobe, T., and K. Shimada. 1987. First record of the gobiid fish *Eviota fasciola* from Japan. Japan. J. Ichthy. 34(1): 96-99.

Talbot, F. (sci. cons.) and R. Steene (maj. photog.). 1984. Reader's Digest Book of the Great Barrier Reef. Reader's Digest, Sydney. 384 p., 800+col. pl.

Thresher, R. E. 1982. Courtship and spawning of the emperor angelfish *Pomacanthus imperator*, with comments on reproduction by other pomacanthid fishes. Mar. Biol. 70: 149-156.

____. 1984. Reproduction in Reef Fishes. T.F.H. Pub., Neptune City, NJ. 399 p.

Thresher, R. E. and P. L. Colin. 1986. Trophic structure, diversity and abundance of fishes of the deep reef (30-300 m) at Enewetak, Marshall Islands. Bull. Mar. Sci. 38(1): 253-272.

Tsuda, R. T., S. S. Amesbury, S. C. Moras, and P. P. Breman. 1975. Limited current and underwater biological survey at point Gabert wastewater outfall on Moen, Truk. Univ. Guam Mar. Lab. Tech. Rep. 20, 39 p.

Uda, M. 1971. Fishery Oceanographic studies of frontal eddies and transport associated with the Kuroshio system including the "subtropical countercurrent". *in* the Kuroshio: A symposium on the Japan Current. East-West Center Press, Honolulu, pp. 593-604.

Vermeij, G.J., E. A. Kay, and L. G. Eldredge. 1983. Molluscs of the northern Mariana Islands, with special reference to the selectivity of oceanic dispersal barriers. Micronesica 19(1-2): 27-55.

Vivien, M. L. 1975. Place of apogonid fish in the food webs of a Malagasy coral reef. Micronesica 11(2): 185-198.

Walker, M. H. 1978. Food and feeding habits of *Lethrinus chrysostomus* Richardson (Pisces: Perciformes) and other Lethrinids on the Great Barrier Reef. Aust. J. Mar. and Freshw. Res. 29(5): 623-630.

Waples, R. S. 1982. A biochemical and morphological review of the lizardfish genus *Saurida* in Hawaii, with the description of a new species. Pac. Sci. 35(3): 217-235.

Wass, R. C. 1984. An annotated checklist of the fishes of Samoa. NOAA Tech. Rep. NMFS SSRF no. 781, v+43 p.

Weber, M. and L. F. deBeaufort. 1913. The Fishes of the Indo-Australian Archipelago, 2. Leiden: E.J. Brill. 404p.

____. 1916. The Fishes of the Indo-Australian Archipelago, 3. Leiden: E.J. Brill. 455p.

____. 1922. The Fishes of the Indo-Australian Archipelago, 4. Leiden: E.J. Brill. 410p.

____. 1929. The Fishes of the Indo-Australian Archipelago, 5. Leiden: E.J. Brill. 458p.

____. 1931. The Fishes of the Indo-Australian Archipelago, 6. Leiden: E.J. Brill. 448p.

____. 1936. The Fishes of the Indo-Australian Archipelago, 7. Leiden: E.J. Brill. 607p.

Whitley, G. P. 1940. Illustrations of some Australian fishes. Aust. Zool. 9: 397-428.

Williams, J. T. 1984. Synopsis and phylogenetic analysis of the pearlfish subfamily Carapinae (Pisces: Carapidae). Bull. Mar. Sci. 34(3): 386-397.

____. 1985. *Cirripectes imitator*, a new species of western Pacific blenniid fish. Proc. Biol. Soc. Wash. 98(2): 533-538.

____. in press. Revision of the Indo-Pacific blenniid fish genus *Cirripectes*. Indo-Pacific Fishes.

Winterbottom, R. 1984. A review of the gobiid fish genus *Trimma* from the Chagos Archipelago, central Indian Ocean, with the description of seven new species. Can. J. Zool. 62: 695-715.

Witzell, W. N. 1981. Predation on juvenile green sea turtles, *Chelonia mydas*, by a grouper, *Promicrops lanceolatus* (Pisces; Serranidae) in the Kingdom of Tonga, South Pacific. Bull. Mar. Sci. 31(4): 935-936.

Wongratana, T. 1975. *Soleichthys siammakuti* n. sp., a rare sole from the Gulf of Thailand. Senkenberg. Biol. 56(1/3): 21-29.

Woodland, D. J. 1983. Zoogeography of the Siganidae (Pisces): an interpretation of distribution and richness patterns. Bull. Mar. Sci. 33(3): 713-717.

____. 1986. Wallace's Line and the distribution of marine inshore fishes. Proc. Second Int. Conf. on Indo-Pacific Fishes, Tokyo, 453-460.

Woodland, D. J. and G. R. Allen. 1977. *Siganus trispilos*, a new species of Siganidae from the eastern Indian ocean. Copeia 1977(4): 617-620.

Woodland, D. J. and J. E. Randall. 1979. *Siganus puelloides*, a new species of rabbitfish from the Indian Ocean. Copeia 1979(3): 390-393.

Woods, L. P. 1955. Western Atlantic species of the genus *Holocentrus*. Fieldiana Zool. 37: 91-119.

Whitehead, P. J. P., and W. Ivantsoff. 1983. *Atherina lacunosa* and the fishes described by J. R. Forster. Japan. J. Icthyol. 29(4): 355-364.

Yasuda, F. and A. Zama. 1975. Notes on the two rare chaetodontid fishes, *Parachaetodon ocellatus* and *Coradion chrysozonus*, from the Ogasawara Islands. J. Tokyo Univ. Fisheries 62(1): 33-38.

Young, P. C., and R. B. Martin. 1982. Evidence of protogynous hermaphroditism in some lethrinid fishes. J. Fish Biol. 21: 475-484.

____. 1985. Sex ratios and hermaphroditism in nemipterid fish from northern Australia. J. Fish Biol. 26(3): 273-287.

Yoshino, T. 1982. Damselfishes of the genus *Dischistodus* found in the Ryukyu Islands. Bull. College Sci. Univ. Ryuk., no. 33: 69-74.

Yoshino, T. and S. Nishijima. 1981. A list of fishes found around Sesoko Island, Okinawa. Seseko Mar. Sci. Lab. Tech. Rep. no. 8, 87 p.

Yoshino, T. and H. Senou. 1983. A review of the gobiid fishes of the genus *Ctenogobiops* from Japan. Galaxea, 2: 1-13.

Zama, A and K. Fujita. 1977. An annotated checklist of fishes from the Ogasawara Islands. J. Tokyo Univ. Fish. 63(2): 87-138.

Zama, A and F. Yasuda. 1979. An annotated list of fishes from the Ogasawara Islands-Suppl. I, with zoogeographical notes on the fish fauna. J. Tokyo Univ. Fish. 65(2): 139-163.

Index of Scientific Names

Valid names of species and genera occurring in Micronesia are in **bold** type. In cases where the first species listed in a genus is invalid, only the generic portion of its name is in bold type. Color plates are indicated in bold type, text pages are indicated in plain type. Names of subfamilies, families, and higher categories are in capital letters.

Index of Common Names

Text entries are in plain type, color plates are in **bold** type.

The Author

Robert F. Myers was born in Leesburg, Virginia in 1953. As the son of a Defense Department linguist, he spent most of his childhood overseas where he developed an intense interest in the terrestrial and aquatic animals of each post. His first two years of high school were spent in Hong Kong, living a few blocks from the beach at Repulse Bay where he took up skin diving and kept his first marine aquarium. The next three years were spent in northern Virginia where his fascination with the ocean grew, nurtured by marine aquaria and the growing popular literature on diving and marine science. After a year of college, he transferred to the University of Hawaii where he began studying coral reef fishes in their own environment, took up underwater photography, and became actively involved in local dive clubs, graduating in 1975 with a BA in zoology. As an undergraduate, he surveyed populations of fishes around Oahu, collected moray eels and sharks at Johnston Island, and assisted in the collection of potentially toxic fishes at Enewetak Atoll. In 1977 he moved to Guam to pursue graduate studies at the University of Guam Marine Laboratory. There he divided his time between studies, underwater photography, and employment before earning an MS in biology in 1984.

The relatively poorly known waters of Micronesia offered new horizons in photography and faunal studies, leading to the discovery of hundreds of new locality records and several new species. Since moving to Guam he has written or collaborated on numerous scientific papers and technical reports as well as the first two books in the series "The Coastal Resources of Guam" which covered fishes and corals. His photographs have appeared in many additional scientific and popular magazines and books.

In 1981 he founded Coral Graphics and met his future wife, Kathy, also an accomplished diver and photographer. Since 1982 he has worked full-time as a fisheries biologist for the Government of Guam.

100°   120°   140°   160°

Korea

Japan

China

Izu
Islands

Ryukyu
Islands

Bonin
(Ogasawara)
Islands

Marcus
Is.

Yaeyama
Islands

Taiwan

20°

Wake
Is.

South

China

Sea

Philippines

Mariana
Islands

Saipan

Guam

Andaman
Islands

Gulf of
Thailand

Yap

Belau

Pohnpei

Kwajalein

Truk

Nicobar
Islands

Caroline   Islands

Kosrae

Singapore

Celebes
(Sulawesi)

0°

Nauru

Borneo

Sumatra

Moluccas

New
Guinea

New
Britain

Solomon
Islands

Santa
Isl

Java

New
Caledonia

Bali

Timor

Arufura

Great

Coral Sea

Christmas
Is.

Sea

Cocos-
Keeling Is.

Scott
Reef

Barrier

Reef

Loyalt
Is

Rowley
Shoals

20°

Northwest
Cape

Australia

No

Shark
Bay

Lord Howe
Is.

100°   120°   140°   160°

Central and W